# Devon Bird Atlas
## 2007–2013

# Devon Bird Atlas
## 2007–2013

**Edited by Stella Beavan & Mike Lock**

Published by Devon Birds
info@devonbirds.org
www.devonbirds.org

Registered Charity 228966

---

First published January 2016

ISBN 978-0-9556028-9-4

Design and image editing by Tim Davis, DJEnvironmental
www.djenvironmental.com
info@djenvironmental.com

Maps produced by Mike Hounsome using DMAP software © Dr Alan Morton

Printed by Page Bros, Norwich

The publisher gratefully acknowledges the permission granted by the British Trust for Ornithology to utilize data submitted to them via the national Atlas website www.bto.org/volunteer-surveys/birdatlas.

---

The paper used for this book has been certified as coming from well-managed forests and other controlled sources according to the rules of the Forest Stewardship Council.

---

Recommended citation:
Beavan, S.D. & Lock, J.M. (eds). 2016. *Devon Bird Atlas 2007–2013*. Devon Birds, Cornworthy, Devon.

Cover artwork by Mike Langman
Back cover photos: Buzzard (Mark Darlaston), Dipper (Dave Scott), Pied Flycatcher (Steve Hatch)

Frontispiece: The Exe Estuary at the end of the Exeter Canal (Jeremy Barker)
Inset: Avocet (Richard Hargreaves)
Endpapers: Avocets at Bowling Green Marsh (Neil Bygrave)

# Contents

*Photo: (Skylark) Barry Bowden*

# Map of Devon

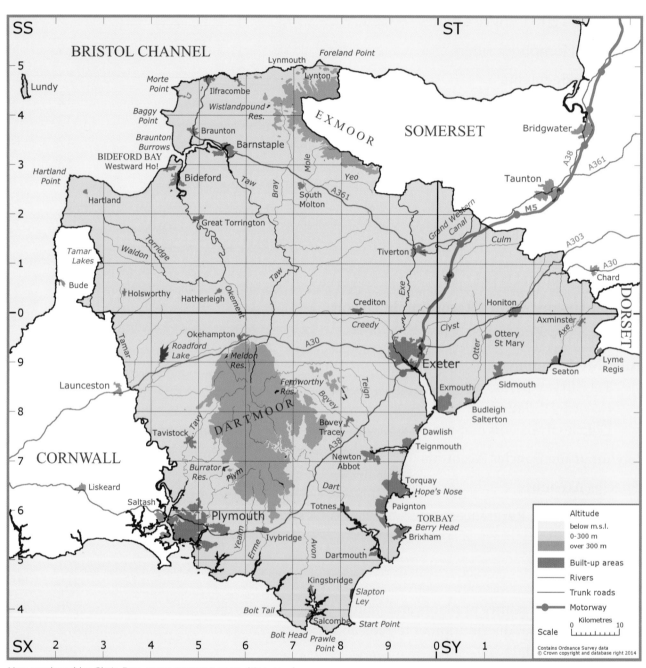

*Map produced by Chris Dee, www.garganeyconsulting.co.uk*

*Photo: (Cuckoo) Steve Hatch*

# Foreword

By HRH Prince Charles

CLARENCE HOUSE

There is no doubt that the county of Devon has a particular magic all of its own. It is rightly famed for its deep lanes, high hedge banks, oak woods, lush pastures, flower-rich meadows, wild moorland, beautiful beaches and rocky bays. The second largest county in England, Devon has an almost unrivalled range of different habitats that offer homes to a wide diversity of wildlife, including some of our rarest and most charismatic birds.

The new *Devon Bird Atlas* documents all the species that breed or winter in the county. It is an impressive publication; the product of tens of thousands of hours of fieldwork by hundreds of volunteers. Every inch of the county has been visited, in Winter and in the breeding season, and every record has been analysed and documented. You hold in your hands the Domesday Book of birds in Devon at the start of the twenty-first century.

The story it has to tell is a mixed one. Thirty years ago, there were no Little Egrets in Devon; now this elegant white heron is a fairly common sight along our coastlines. Other birds that have fared well include Goosander, now found along many of our upland rivers, Siskin, Dartford Warbler and Nightjar. Good conservation work, in partnership with local farmers in South Devon, has also reversed the decline of the Cirl Bunting, a bird that was heading towards extinction in England.

Many of our farmland birds have fared much less well. The plight of the Cuckoo is becoming more widely known. This iconic species has all but disappeared from most lowland areas; fortunately, in Devon it has found a stronghold on Dartmoor. The hope is that this herald of Spring will be able to re-colonise old haunts once the reasons for its decline are identified and addressed. Other species are in even greater trouble. The hauntingly evocative cry of the Curlew is tragically rarely heard; Golden Plover no longer breed in the county; Lapwing and Turtle Dove look doomed to follow.

I believe we still have the chance to reverse these declines. To do that we need two things: strong partnerships and reliable evidence. Since 2005, the Duchy of Cornwall has worked closely with Dartmoor National Park Authority, the R.S.P.B. and Natural England to operate the Dartmoor Wader Project. The Project has monitored the breeding success of key wader species, particularly Curlew and Lapwing. The results have proved fascinating, and demonstrated the importance of correct habitat and targetted predator control. The Project has implemented habitat improvements with the assistance of both Duchy tenants and local landowners. Crows have been controlled to increase hatch rates and subsequent chick survival.

The partnerships, such as the Dartmoor Wader Project, are being forged by conservationists, scientists, farmers, landowners and passionate individuals. The evidence that is needed for positive conservation measures to work is here in this book.

We owe it to future generations to do all we can to conserve not just the beauty of Devon, but its biodiversity too. Without its birds, and particularly the rarer and more vulnerable species that are so prone to predation, this jewel of a county will lose much of what makes it special.

I can only commend the work of the Devon Birds Association, its members and volunteers, for their vision in producing this new Atlas. I hope that it is the foundation upon which we can build a more balanced home, one in which people and Nature can live together and flourish in harmony with one another.

# Preface

THE CAPACITY of the ornithological community of Devon to rise to the challenge of producing the results described in this fascinating Atlas has to be admired. At 6,707 sq km , Devon is one of the largest of English counties. However its human population – and its ornithologists – are not spread evenly; they are mostly in the south and there are large areas, especially in the north-west as well as Dartmoor and Exmoor where few people live and which require special efforts to cover. Yet every one of Devon's 1,858 tetrads (blocks of 2x2 = 4 sq km) was the subject of an intensive bird survey during 2007–2013, not just in one season but in both summer and winter. This is a huge achievement and something of which Devon's ornithologists can be proud. The team that led this effort deserve special praise, particularly those who coordinated the fieldwork – the late Mark Blacksell, the late John Woodland, John Twyford and Stella Beavan – and those who conceived and edited this stunning book – Stella Beavan and Mike Lock. Now, we not only have detailed knowledge of the current distribution of Devon's breeding birds and can compare that with the results of the earlier *Devon Tetrad Atlas 1977–1985*, but for the first time we know how our birds are distributed in winter.

The Devon Atlas Project was born out of the British Trust for Ornithology's *Bird Atlas 2007–2011* Project, the methods for which did not require complete coverage of all of Devon's 1,858 tetrads. Therefore the Devon Birds Society decided to carry on and complete coverage of all tetrads over an additional two years and also to extend seasonal coverage to the whole year. Those were courageous decisions, first because complete coverage would entail a huge amount of additional work, second because proper analysis and writing-up would require an enormous amount of expert input and third because the final publication, this book, would require substantial funding.

A major purpose of atlases such as this is to provide an accurate assessment of the status of our birds over a particular period of years so that future change can be measured and conservation priorities decided. So it is only when a second atlas project is completed that this aim can be fulfilled and the effort that went into the first atlas fully justified. Therefore, as the organizer of the Devon Tetrad Atlas Project 1977–1985, I am absolutely delighted to see the results of this second Atlas in relation to breeding distribution, particularly in the way that they show how the status of Devon's breeding birds has changed over the past thirty years. What struck me most when I first saw the maps is that the majority of species, 84 (about 60%), have a substantially different distribution now to the one they had thirty years ago. We are getting used to the idea that our countryside is changing; even so, 60% of species having substantially different distributions seems a lot and emphasizes the dynamic nature of our bird populations.

The other really striking and worrying aspect is that, of the 84 species whose breeding populations have shown substantial change, three times as many have contracted ranges (61) than have expanded ranges (23). I find it really quite shocking that species that thirty years ago were familiar and common throughout Devon with almost ubiquitous distributions, such as Cuckoo, Skylark, Yellowhammer and Starling, are now missing from large parts of the county and not easy to find even where they still occur. Even more desperate is the plight of Lapwings and Grey Partridges for which the reduction in the number of occupied tetrads exceeds 90%. The reasons for these losses vary but a large proportion can be attributed to modern agricultural practices which for many species have reduced the availability of food, such as invertebrates and weed seeds, and have led to a loss of breeding sites for others.

A very few of the species for which breeding range has apparently contracted may have been under-recorded in the second Atlas because of different methodology compared with the first Atlas. This is explained in both the book's introductory material and also in those species accounts where it is relevant. Generally, however, this is a minor issue which in no way detracts from the value of the results or the reality of the widespread distribution declines that have been recorded.

It is vital that the publication of this Atlas is followed by urgent consideration of the conservation issues that it highlights. In all cases of breeding population decline, research into causes is essential where they have not already been determined. In some cases, the problem may not lie in Devon but at migration stopover sites or winter quarters elsewhere, but in many others it is Devon's problem and we do not fully understand it; this particularly applies to such sedentary species as Marsh Tit, Willow Tit, Little Owl and Lesser Spotted Woodpecker.

The problems of bird population decline cannot all be addressed at the same time; therefore there should be prioritization. For example, if the present trend continues we will lose Curlew as a Devon breeding species within the next few years. If we do, there will no longer be any Curlews that have an attachment to Devon and it will be very difficult to get them back because recolonization will depend on the settlement of young birds from other (probably still dwindling) populations. Therefore everything possible should be done to prevent Curlew going extinct as a breeding species in Devon and that must be a top priority. In contrast, a species that has suffered a more than 90% decline, Grey Partridge, would in all probability be much easier to reintroduce because it is sedentary and its requirements – farmland with headlands untreated with insecticides or herbicides and weedy stubble in winter – are well known. Therefore it is perhaps not such a high priority.

The changes in agricultural practices that have such a negative impact on bird populations were already taking place at the time of the 1977–1985 *Devon Tetrad Atlas*, in fact the 1970s and 1980s were probably the time of the greatest change. It was happening everywhere: hedges were being grubbed out, plastic land drains were being laid to drain damp ground and everything was being sprayed. In fact I have vivid memories of seeing all this going on while filling in gaps in the coverage of the first Atlas in the Culm Measures area of north-west Devon in the early 1980s. At that time I could still find breeding Grasshopper Warblers and Curlews there but the drainage of their nesting areas (damp vegetated valley bottoms and elevated moorlands respectively) was in full swing. I also remember trying to find Yellowhammers in 1984 near Halwill Junction in SS40 and being very puzzled as to why they were apparently absent (the gap can be seen in the 1977–1985 map on page 422 and is a lot bigger in the 2007–2013 map). That time must have been the beginning of the period over which the Yellowhammer population lost ground all over the county.

Changes in agricultural practices are certainly the reason why many of our breeding birds have declined, but it is manifestly unfair and wrong to blame the farmers. The farmers have been governed and manipulated and incentivized by successive governments and the European Union; they work in a very competitive environment in which margins are low, especially at the time of writing in the dairy industry. However, there are mechanisms – agri-environment schemes – that allow farmers to be paid by government to manage their land in a way that is nature-friendly. Clearly more of these are needed, but they will only be put into effect if we – who know what is going on – present the data we have collected and batter the politicians and bureaucrats into submission. Therefore, ultimately, if we lose our breeding birds it is as much our fault as everyone else involved.

But it is not all doom and gloom; several breeding bird populations have increased – and not just the species, such as Herring Gull and Canada Goose, that some of us do not like so much. Devon has been colonized by a wonderful duck, Goosander, and a fantastic big, powerful bird of prey, Goshawk. Siskins, Dartford Warblers, Little and Great Crested Grebes, Cetti's Warblers, Nightjars and Crossbills have all expanded their ranges, and on Lundy Puffin and Manx Shearwater populations have recovered, thanks to the eradication of rats. Let us rejoice!

**Willow Warbler – in Devon
concentrated more in the north
and west of the county.**

*Photo: Barry Bowden*

*Previous page: (Bar-tailed Godwit) Roy Churchill & (Black-tailed Godwits) Neil Bygrave*

This Atlas has much more than the maps that enable us to compare breeding distributions over thirty years and I especially welcome those that show how abundances vary across the county in both summer and winter. Although the value of these will only be fully realized when they are repeated in 20–30 years time, they reveal many patterns that are not apparent from the simple distribution maps. One real eye-opener for me was to compare the summer abundance maps of the closely-related Chiffchaff and Willow Warbler. During 1977–1985, both species had virtually ubiquitous distributions, so presumably their rather different habitats were available in almost every tetrad. During 2007–2013, the distribution of Chiffchaffs had hardly changed, but Willow Warblers were much thinner in the south. However, the summer abundance maps show how the two species relate to one another in the county in much more detail. The Chiffchaff population is concentrated in the south and east of the county; Willow Warblers in the north and west.

Although for many resident species the winter abundance maps are similar to those for summer, there are several that show subtle but significant differences. Skylark is a particularly interesting case. Despite the breeding population decline, there are still many Skylarks in Devon in both summer and winter. We know little about their migration and it is possible that summer and winter populations comprise largely different birds. But the abundance maps show how the main breeding areas of Dartmoor and Exmoor are largely deserted in winter when the population becomes concentrated in the low-lying parts of the county, especially along the south coast.

The main interest of the winter abundance maps is surely their detailed portrayal, for the first time, of the distribution of our inland winter visitors. They show patterns I would not have predicted: Bramblings mainly in the south, Redwings and Fieldfares with similarly widespread distributions, but avoiding coastal areas and the moors, Starlings mainly in the north and west.

Finally I have nothing but admiration and congratulations to the team, headed by Stella Beavan and Mike Lock, who conceived this splendid book and put it together. The layout, by Tim Davis, is efficient and attractive; the texts are concise but tell us what we need to be told; and the photographs – all of them – are stunning!

**Humphrey Sitters**
Beer, Devon
September 2015

# Acknowledgements

THIS ATLAS could not have been produced without the countless hours of effort given freely by over a thousand volunteers. Inevitably we may not have named everyone who took part; their contribution is in no way diminished by their omission.

We would like to thank Humphrey Sitters, as the architect of the first ever Atlas that detailed the breeding birds of Devon, for kindly agreeing to write the preface to this Atlas. We also extend our thanks to the Duchy of Cornwall and His Royal Highness Prince Charles for financial support and His Royal Highness in particular for authoring the foreword to the Atlas. Devon County Council made a major funding contribution to the preparation and production of the Atlas. Their generosity has also enabled the provision and distribution of copies of the *Devon Bird Atlas* to the county libraries, secondary schools, further education colleges and universities within their area.

## GENERATION OF FIELD DATA

This has been undertaken by everyone contributing records to Devon Birds and to the British Trust for Ornithology (BTO) *Bird Atlas 2007–11* for the county of Devon, both Timed Tetrad Visits (TTVs) and roving records. All those who contributed records are listed in Appendix 1.

Records submitted to the following BTO surveys are also included: BirdTrack, Breeding Bird Survey, Garden Bird Watch, Heronries Census, Nest Record Scheme, Waterways Breeding Bird Survey, Wetland Bird Survey and Ringing Scheme.

RSPB Datasets and JNCC Seabird Data were also used to prepare the Atlas maps.

Breeding records from the Barn Owl Trust were included in the original *Bird Atlas 2007–11* and those records are also included in this Atlas.

Lastly, we wish to thank all volunteer observers who have submitted a record, either directly or indirectly, to Devon Birds (previously Devon Bird Watching & Preservation Society), thus contributing to the million plus observations on which this Atlas is based.

## ORGANIZATION

Organization of the TTV coverage of the whole of Devon was a mammoth task. For this, the county was split into three areas: South, organized by Julia Harris, North by Paul Madgett and East by Roger Little. The first two named had to deal with the largest areas and should be especially thanked.

Our immense thanks go to the BTO for keeping their atlas data capture system open for a further two years, until 2013, without which the data management would have been almost impossible.

John Woodland as the BTO Regional Representative started the atlas process with the assistance of Mark Blacksell, but unfortunately Mark passed away in January 2008 and John in December of the same year. After an interregnum, during which Dawn Balmer of the BTO managed the allocation of tetrads, John Twyford took over for just over a year, with Stella Beavan as his deputy. Stella, who then became, and remains, the BTO Regional Representative, bore the brunt of the workload and made sure all tetrads were allocated to observers and regularly updated on the BTO system.

At county level special thanks go to Julia Harris, Assistant Recorder and Data Manager, who handled all records submitted directly to Devon Birds, and to Mike Hounsome for manipulating databases into one manageable set of data. Mike subsequently generated all the Atlas maps, an easy statement to write but a very time-consuming and detailed exercise.

Peter Robinson as record validator worked constantly to ensure the veracity of all the observers' records, assisted by Mark Darlaston who validated all the Schedule 1 raptors.

The Devon Birds Records Committee (DBRC) is thanked for their work to ensure that rarities were identified accurately.

## PREPARATION

The species accounts – which form the main body of the text – were written by numerous authors. Each is identified on the pages on which 'their' species appear. We are extremely grateful for the important contribution each has made to the Atlas.

**Juvenile Pochards at Sherpa Marsh, Taw/Torridge Estuary, July 2012.**

*Photo: Rob Jutsum*
*Photo: (Grey Heron) Neil Bygrave*

The Devon Birds Atlas Group was preceded by the BTO Steering Group. Members of the latter, not mentioned elsewhere, were Penny Avent, Jeremy Hatch, Neil Trout and Mike Tyler.

The Atlas Committee, which provided a strong backbone to the whole process, was formed in 2009 and continued until late in 2015. Membership of the committee changed over time to draw on the skills needed to achieve the tasks necessary to produce the Atlas. Stella Beavan again shouldered much of the work and she, together with all of the committee members, are equally thanked for their time and effort over several years, in some cases almost a decade.

The committee members and their main responsibilities:

- ❏ Stella Beavan – joint editor, chair, author liaison and project manager
- ❏ Mark Darlaston – raptor record validator
- ❏ Tim Davis – proof-reading, Atlas design, typesetting, image-editing and production
- ❏ George Harris – Atlas Committee secretary (and chair of Devon Birds)
- ❏ Julia Harris – South Devon TTV coordinator, Assistant Devon Birds recorder and Data Manager
- ❏ Mike Hounsome – data management and manipulation, statistical analysis, map production, species account review and Devon Atlas webmaster
- ❏ Mike Langman – art editor
- ❏ Roger Little – fundraiser, East Devon TTV coordinator, financial advisor and Devon Birds treasurer
- ❏ Mike Lock – joint editor, liaison with printers and Devon Birds Publications Committee chair
- ❏ Paul Madgett – North Devon TTV coordinator
- ❏ Peter Robinson – records validator and species account reviewer
- ❏ Paul Stubbs (deceased) – early South Devon TTV coordinator
- ❏ Steve Waite – Devon Birds recorder

We thank all the photographers who kindly provided the photographs that help to make the Atlas visually spectacular. Each is identified on the pages on which their photographs appear. We are especially grateful to Nature Photographers Limited, in the guise of Paul Sterry and Rob Read, for providing photographs of species where none were available or suitable from Devon-based photographers.

Tim Jones spent very many days reading and commenting on the texts and is thanked for his diligence.

David Price provided the digital versions of the maps presented in the *Devon Tetrad Atlas 1977–85* and without his help in many ways the presentation of those maps in this Atlas would not have been possible.

Tony John is thanked for preparing the bibliography, James Diamond for providing an impartial overview of the accounts, Chris Dee of Garganey Consulting for providing a new colour map of Devon and Mike Langman for the wonderful painting of the Dipper which features on the cover.

## FUNDING

A tremendous response was received from Devon Birds' members and branches, ringing groups, organizations and individuals when asked to sponsor specific species. We are very grateful for their donations. All are acknowledged on the appropriate species account pages.

In addition to those organizations previously mentioned, Natural England made a significant financial contribution to support the Atlas for which we are extremely grateful.

Contributions were received from the following charitable trusts which we would like to thank: Manydown Charitable Trust, Norman Family Trust, John Spedan Lewis Foundation and Uplands Charitable Trust.

We also received species sponsorship from our three patrons, Clinton Estates, Glendinning and Michelmore Hughes, to whom we extend our sincere thanks for their continuing support of Devon Birds.

**Devon Birds Atlas Group**

# The Devon Environment

## A GEOLOGICAL SUMMARY

Why is Devon so good for birds? An underlying reason is that it is the most geologically diverse county in England. All major rock-types are represented – igneous (granite intrusions, lava flows, dykes); metamorphic (slates, schists, quartzites, hornfels) and sedimentary (sandstones, shales, limestones). These rocks formed during all the major geological periods from the Devonian to the Quaternary (from around 400 million years ago (mya)) to the present. This complexity has given rise to a diverse landscape with a wide altitudinal range.

Devon is the only English county with substantial lengths of coastline facing north, south, east and west – plus a sizeable island (Lundy). Thus Devon's position in the path of prevailing south-westerly winds from the Atlantic, along with the varied relief and altitudinal range, produces significant climatic variations from one part of the county to another.

The underlying rock-types reacting with these other factors have produced a range of soils and vegetation, variously exploited by humans. The resulting habitats are thus diverse, providing niches favouring different species of birds.

Ultimately all the above are the result of Devon's long geological history. A summary here may help explain our present variety.

Turning the clock back around 400 million years would show us a world unrecognizable today. What is now 'Devon' was then far south of the equator – and much of the county's geology is explicable in terms of its very gradual progress northward across the globe. Our oldest rocks, seen today at the surface in both North and South Devon, are mainly sediments – tough sandstones, mud-rocks (mudstones and shales, now mainly metamorphosed into slates) and limestones – laid down in tropical seas offshore from major landmasses to north and south. North of what is now Devon, huge deltas were building out from a northern landmass (which now forms parts of present-day Wales and eastern North America – no Atlantic Ocean at this stage). The muds and sands of these ancient deltas are now exposed, as slates, mudstones and sandstones, on and around Exmoor. The southern part of our present county was then under water, and these warm waters were clear enough at times for limey reefs and muds to accumulate which became the limestone cliffs of Torbay and Berry Head. All these

rocks are now placed in the Devonian period of geological time (Devon is the only English county with a geological period named after it, recognized worldwide).

Deposition of muds and sands, plus some lime-rich and silica-rich layers, continued into the ensuing Carboniferous period (roughly 360–300 mya). Devon was now in equatorial climes. A large part of these deposits have been termed the 'Culm Measures' in Devon, and their outcrop now occupies much of central Devon – there are a few thin seams of coal ('culm') within these, especially in the vicinity of Bideford. Associated with this sediment accumulation was some volcanic activity, more especially in what is now the south of the county.

While these Devonian and Carboniferous sediments and volcanic rocks were accumulating, the Rheic Ocean was also gradually closing and tectonic plate movements starting to crush some of the muds and sands. Pressures were greatest in the south, and the rocks now seen in the Start Point–Bolt Head area

**The limestone cliffs of Berry Head.**

*Photo: Mike Langman*
*Photo: (Peregrine) Barry Bowden*

were so strongly heated and crushed that the muds and volcanics metamorphosed into schists – crystalline rocks with an aligned texture. Elsewhere muds became slates, sands became sandstones and quartzites, and everywhere they were folded and faulted, with uplift on a grand scale towards the end of Carboniferous times. This folding is often not evident in our present landscape, but is still vividly displayed in some cliffs, especially on the Hartland coast of north-west Devon. The tilted and folded layers often erode into ledges on the cliffs, providing nesting sites for seabirds and Peregrines.

This phase resulted in a dramatic change in geography, with an east–west mountain chain (Variscan), including all of what is now Devon, replacing the former shallow seas and deeper ocean. The present-day east–west 'grain' of much of Devon, especially the north coast and Exmoor, is inherited from these ancient structural trends. Heat-flow at depth was great enough to partially melt some of the

**The characteristic vegetation of the East Devon Pebblebed Heaths.**

*Photo: David Glaves*

rocks, forming a semi-liquid granitic magma, which was intruded upwards. We see this today as the granite mass of Dartmoor, which is connected below the surface to other now-exposed parts in Cornwall such as Bodmin Moor, St Austell, Land's End and the granite masses of the Isles of Scilly. Fluids within this magma permeated the granite as it cooled and contracted, as well as escaping into the surrounding rocks, producing mineral veins, while in places the components of the granite (alumino-silicate minerals called feldspars) were altered to kaolin-rich materials (china clay). Later erosion exposing this granite intrusion has left us with the dramatic upland landscape of Dartmoor, with poor acid soils and much peat formation – and breeding sites for birds such as Curlew.

Around the same time (just under 300 mya) all the former continental blocks were joining up to form one huge block, 'Pangea', with 'Devon' now far from the sea. Further northward movement had brought the county into latitudes now occupied by the Sahara and other deserts. Rapid erosion of the newly formed mountains, initially accompanied by much volcanic activity, caused periodic flash-flooding leading to flanking scree and wadi deposits, finer materials being carried further by water and wind to form desert dunes and salt-lake deposits. This

continued throughout Permian and Triassic times (roughly 300–200 mya), the resultant deposits often being known as 'New Red Sandstone' (as distinct from the 'Old Red Sandstone' of South Wales and the Welsh Borders, of Devonian age). These rocks appear today in the Torbay area and south-east Devon, and northwards to Tiverton, with an east–west narrow outcrop past Crediton – the red colour of the breccias (literally 'broken' rock), conglomerates, sandstones and mudstones being due to oxidation of the iron content, and bringing about the term 'Red Devon'. This, so beloved of tourist brochures, gives rise to generally well-drained soils, now mainly in arable cultivation. There is thus a contrast with those parts of Devon underlain by the less permeable Devonian and Carboniferous rocks, where grassland is a major land use. The Pebblebed Heaths of East Devon are underlain by ancient river gravels and sands of the Triassic; their high permeability and low fertility led to historic land-use practices, such as regular burning and grazing, producing their characteristic vegetation, and colonization by species such as Dartford Warbler.

Throughout the Permo-Triassic, the Variscan mountains continued to be eroded, with 'un-roofing' of the Dartmoor granite, such that by the start of the succeeding Jurassic period (roughly 200–145 mya) 'Devon' was an area of low relief, and rising sea levels started to submerge the landscape. Pangea was now beginning to break up into the continental blocks more recognizable today. Clays and limey muds were the main deposits, seen today in south-east Devon though on the coast only at Seven Rock Point, immediately west of Lyme Regis. The 'Jurassic Coast' is a misleading name for the part of this coastline which is in Devon since, from just east of Exmouth to the county boundary, just west of Lyme Regis, the Cretaceous rocks lie directly on the Triassic ones, the Jurassic sediments having been eroded locally before the first Cretaceous beds were laid down. During Cretaceous times (145–65 mya) the seas probably eventually extended across the whole of our area, depositing mainly sands at first, followed by lime in deeper but clear waters – with Chalk being the result. Today this is found on land only in south-east Devon, where it is most readily seen at Beer Cliffs, but also occurs offshore west of Lundy and under the English Channel.

Sub-aerial and shoreline erosion during Jurassic and Cretaceous times gradually 'trimmed off' the last remnants of the Variscan mountains, so that the Chalk sediment would have overlain an essentially flat surface cut across the older, often tightly folded, earlier rocks.

The break-up of Pangea had now proceeded far enough to start separating the British part of 'proto-Europe' from North America. This break-up was caused by deep-seated mantle plumes rising and doming the continental blocks, causing these to rift apart in the same manner as in East Africa and the Red Sea today. Devon has its own small-scale 'rift valleys', formed along the line of the Sticklepath Fault, a great tear in our local crust, running roughly north-west from the Bovey Tracey area through north-east Dartmoor (the granite boundary is here displaced a mile or so laterally), along the Petrockstowe Basin, into Bideford/Barnstaple Bay near Peppercombe, and passing just east of Lundy,

**The Sticklepath Fault zone near Chagford – a great tear in Devon's crust.**

*Photo: Mike Russell*

with an even larger, though totally submerged, sedimentary basin being associated with it there. The emplacement of the Lundy granite dates from this general period, around 50 mya, subsequent erosion and sea-level changes having left it forming most of the present island.

This regional uplift caused the cover of Chalk (and in the more easterly parts also the underlying Jurassic and Permo-Triassic sediments) to be tilted generally eastwards and gradually eroded. For example, the Chalk that formerly extended across Haldon was removed completely, leaving just a layer of the flints (nodular silica concretions) which it had contained as evidence of the Chalk's earlier extent. Across East Devon a landscape of flat-topped ridges, capped with Cretaceous Greensand – a sandy layer, often calcareous, with layers and nodules of chert (similar to flint), but only rarely 'green' – or with clay-with-flints that is the residue of eroded Chalk, developed. Small areas of Chalk and Greensand sea-cliffs remain from Branscombe eastwards, and are just hard enough to provide nesting sites for a few Fulmars, gulls and Cormorants. The uplift left the more ancient Carboniferous and Devonian rocks, and the granite of Dartmoor, exposed to erosion once more, from early Tertiary times to the present. Sub-tropical weathering of the granite (Devon still being in more southerly latitudes than at present) added to the existing kaolinization of the feldspar component,

and this easily eroded material was washed into the 'rift-valleys' referred to above. Mining and quarrying of these resultant ball-clay deposits in the Bovey Tracey area, along with the in-situ china clay workings on south-east Dartmoor, have given us a number of water-filled depressions, now significantly adding to our standing waterbody inventory, to the great benefit of waterbirds. The recent conversion of old clay workings at Meeth into a Devon Wildlife Trust reserve with large lakes is one example.

This re-exposure of the sub-Chalk erosion surface, lowered somewhat by continued erosion, may be the underlying reason for the essentially flat plateau surface over much of North and Mid Devon, and parts of the south, dissected by often steep-sided valleys 'etched out' by weathering and river erosion of the weaker parts of the underlying strata and their joint and fault patterns. These steep valley sides are frequently wooded and comprise a significant proportion of our total woodland, thus affecting the distribution of many bird species.

In the far north of the county, down-faulting of the area now comprising the Bristol Channel, with relative uplift of the ancient rocks to the south, has produced a landscape with the highest ground close to the north coast of Exmoor and Hartland. One result is that the highest sea-cliffs in England are on the Exmoor coast. Short but steeply graded streams

flow down to this Bristol Channel coast, but rivers such as the Exe and Tamar, with sources just to the south of this watershed, flow to the English Channel. The courses of the Torridge and Taw seem to have a more complex history; in the case of the Torridge partly relating to the 'rift valley' referred to above.

During the last two million years or so the planet has been subjected to periods of intense cold, interspersed with warmer conditions, a succession of glacial and interglacials, the present being merely the latest of these interglacials. Although the evidence for actual glacial ice invading Devon is limited and still disputed in its extent, there is no doubt that the 'Ice Ages' (Quaternary to geologists), with their great climatic and sea-level fluctuations, dramatically changed the details of our landscape.

Constant freeze-thaw and deep-seated permafrost caused surface soils and loose material to move down-slope, even on shallow angles. In the uplands, especially Dartmoor, these processes acted upon already partly rotted bedrock, removal of the loose material leaving behind the cores of relatively unaltered rock which we know as tors – present in

small numbers in places such as Lynton's Valley of Rocks (sandstone and slate), as well as the numerous examples on Dartmoor (granite). These tors and the surrounding boulder fields and clitter (frost-shattered rocks) moved down-slope and provide nest sites for species such as Wheatear, while the use of the hard bedrock as stone walls adds to this avian resource.

This down-slope movement tended everywhere to infill the valleys and bury the earlier cliff-lines, resulting in a smooth convex-concave profile to both our uplands and much of our coastline – though the lower concave sections, being composed of loose materials, have often eroded away as sea levels rose again, wave action trimming the coasts and rivers starting to remove some of the infill of their valleys.

The river valleys have a complex recent geological history, the following pattern of events repeating itself many times during the Quaternary. As sea level fell during the cold phases of the Quaternary, so the rivers (when not frozen solid) flowed over newly exposed coastal plains, and their valleys gradually became eroded down to the new low sea level. Inland from our present coast this meant that the

**The sheltered waters and shorelines of
the Exe Estuary.**

*Photo: Jeremy Barker*

valleys became deeply incised into the plateau, while on our present coast the floors of these valleys were cut well below our present sea level. Thus when sea level rose again with the warming climate, the lower sections of the river courses flooded, giving rise to our deep and lengthy estuaries (rias). In the north only the Rivers Taw and Torridge display such features, but the coastline of the south and to a lesser extent the south-east of Devon is extremely indented by these rias; for example on the Rivers Exe, Teign, Plym and Tamar. Their sheltered waters and shorelines are popular 'winter resorts' for many wildfowl and waders.

In later prehistoric and historic times, felling of the primeval forests and ploughing of the hinterland has resulted in increased erosion once more, with substantial infill of the upper reaches of these estuaries, giving sizeable areas of saltmarsh and freshwater marsh, with their characteristic avifauna.

The loose infills of the valleys have been reworked many times by their rivers, resulting in a complex series of sandy and gravelly terraces. Bank erosion producing river-cliffs can provide nesting opportunities for Kingfishers and Sand Martins – though the rapid rises in water levels consequent on heavy rainfall on the relatively impermeable rocks of the catchment areas of many rivers can cause periodic loss of such nests and colonies.

On the coast, the most recent phases of erosion and deposition have trimmed our cliffs, with long-shore drift of loose materials blocking some smaller estuaries with sand and shingle bars, leaving lagoons behind them – for example Slapton Ley. Other estuaries have sand/shingle spits partly blocking them, often with sand-dune development behind sandy beaches, and marsh development behind these, for example Dawlish Warren, Northam Pebble Ridge, Braunton Burrows. Many of our best birding sites are in such locations.

*Text: Paul Madgett*

## DEVON'S WEATHER

Devon is a large county with two coasts – one facing the Bristol Channel and the other facing the English Channel – and a great variety of topography, so it is difficult to summarize the weather for the whole county; for example the differences between Dartmoor, the South Hams and the East Devon heaths are considerable. The Meteorological Office divides the country into regions and Devon falls within the 'England SW and S Wales Region' such that average figures for this region could act as a proxy for weather over the whole of Devon.

The weather graphs (Figures 1–6) were produced from figures for the England SW and S Wales Region on the Met Office website (see Appendix 5, *Climate data, 2007–2013*). As well as showing the absolute values (Figures 1, 3 & 5), these graphs show the deviation from the average values for the period 1961–1990 (Figures 2, 4 & 6). The *Devon Tetrad Atlas 1988* covered the period 1977 to 1985 with most records collected between 1978 and 1983. This

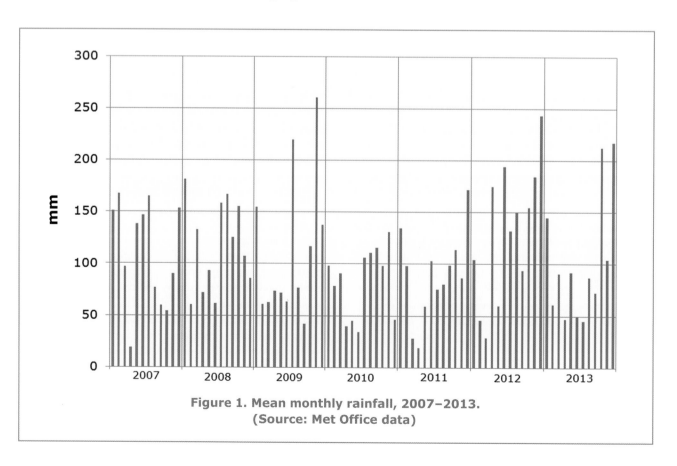

**Figure 1. Mean monthly rainfall, 2007–2013.**
**(Source: Met Office data)**

conveniently falls towards the end of the Meteorological Office 1961–1990 period, so we can cautiously use these deviation graphs to compare the weather between the two Atlas surveys.

Devon, lying as it does on the western side of Britain, has an oceanic climate with relatively cool summers and warm winters. It is exposed to the prevailing westerly winds, and the interaction between these and the high ground of Dartmoor and Exmoor determines the variations in climate across the county. Winds from the west are usually moisture-laden and as they are forced upwards by the rising ground they release this moisture as rain. The seas surrounding Devon are also, on average, the warmest in Britain over the year and this means that coastal areas are generally mild, and also milder than the interior of what is a large county. However, the general mildness of the county's climate can be rudely interrupted on occasion when easterly winds from the continent of Europe bring cold dry air and clear skies, leading to low temperatures by day and night.

Rainfall in Devon varies greatly across the county. Parts of East Devon, particularly close to sea level along the Exe Estuary, receive less than 800 mm of rain, while Princetown, lying at 435 metres above sea level (masl), averages over 2,000 mm. Much of the county receives between 800 and 1,200 mm annually. Seasonal distribution does not show any well-marked pattern, although in recent years there has been a tendency towards dry springs (March–April) and wet Octobers (Figure 1).

Summers remain fickle and droughts are rarely of any great length; in ten years of recording at Musbury (East Devon) there has been no month without rain (J M Lock, pers. obs.). Much of the rain comes as spells lasting two to six hours as fronts pass from the west, but at times, particularly in summer, heavy downpours can occur in which 25 mm or more of rain falls in a short time. Another feature is the occurrence of cloudy mild drizzly days when the county lies in the warm sector of a slow-moving depression. Cloud base at these times may be very low, down to 100 m or less, so that the moors and lower hills are shrouded in mist. Hail is uncommon but may be violent when it occurs; a storm at Ottery St Mary in the early hours of 30 October 2008 deposited about 200 mm of rain, largely as hail, in two hours and produced drifts up to 1.2 m deep (Grahame *et al.* 2009). Figure 2 shows that most of the months in 2010, 2011 and 2013 were drier than average, while there was a particularly wet summer in 2012.

Snow is fairly uncommon at or close to sea level in Devon, but falls on average on 15–20 days a year on the higher parts of the moors. Heavy falls, such as those in 1947 and 1963, may block roads and isolate moorland farms and communities, as well as providing a ready source of carrion for Ravens, Buzzards and Magpies. Near the coast, however, such falls as do occur are generally short-lived and thaw rapidly.

The temperature in Devon is moderated by the surrounding seas. Because the sea cools slowly, the

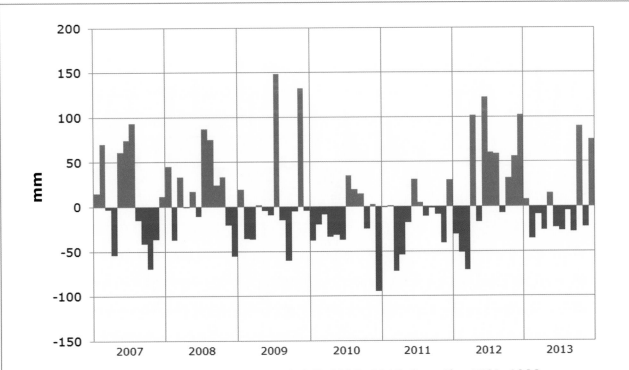

**Figure 2. Deviation of mean monthly rainfall, 2007–2013, from the 1961–1990 average. (Source: Met Office data)**

coldest Devon month is often February, while elsewhere in England it is usually January that is coldest. Likewise, in summer the hottest weather, usually in July, gives lower maximum temperatures than further east in southern England. The strong winds and maritime climate also mean that the fall in temperature with altitude is not as great as one might expect; the mean annual temperature at Princetown is 8.8°C, while at Torquay, on the south coast, it is 11.0°C. Using a normal lapse rate of 1°C

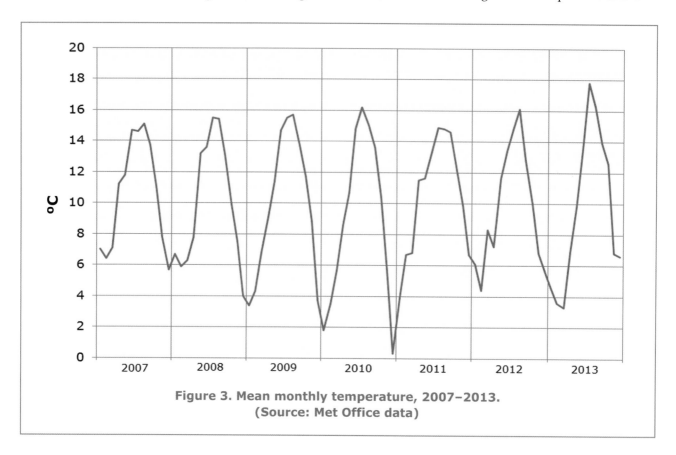

Figure 3. Mean monthly temperature, 2007–2013.
(Source: Met Office data)

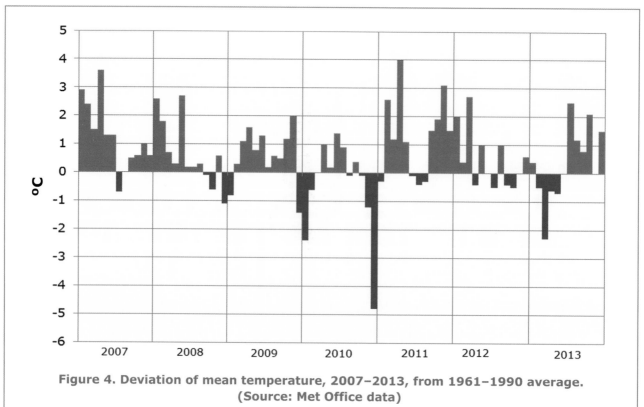

Figure 4. Deviation of mean temperature, 2007–2013, from 1961–1990 average.
(Source: Met Office data)

per 100 m, one might expect the annual mean at Princetown (435 masl) to be about 6.7°C. The proximity of the sea means that the coasts, particularly the south coast, are relatively warm, and this is accentuated by the many deep valleys which provide shelter. Figure 3 shows that there were particularly cold winters in 2009/10, 2010/11 and 2012/13 and particularly warm winters in 2007/08 and 2011/12. Figure 4 shows that the Atlas period was generally warmer than average.

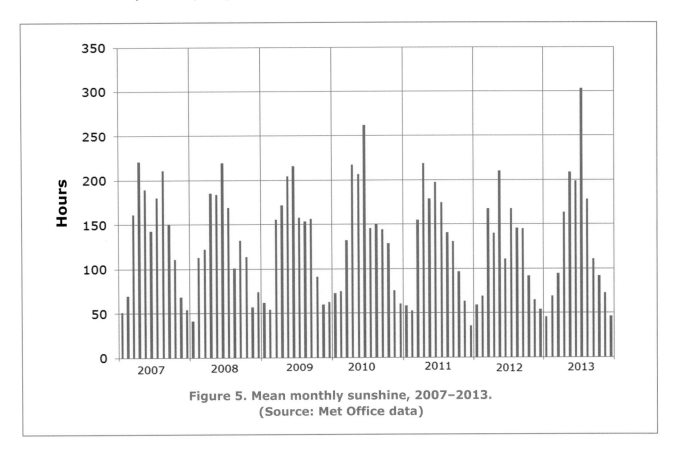

Figure 5. Mean monthly sunshine, 2007–2013.
(Source: Met Office data)

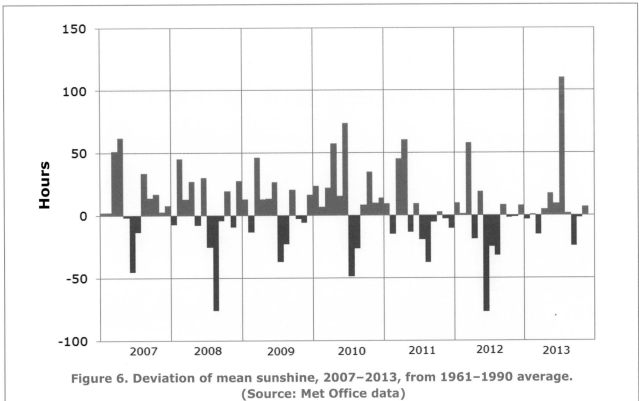

Figure 6. Deviation of mean sunshine, 2007–2013, from 1961–1990 average.
(Source: Met Office data)

## Weather during the Atlas period

The most significant weather events during the Atlas period were the cold spells of January–February 2009, December 2009 to February 2010, and December 2010. A summary for each year follows. The monthly average rainfall, temperature and sunshine hours are shown in Figures 1–6 on the previous pages, where they are compared with the 1961–1990 averages.

Atlas recording began on 1 November 2007. Both November and December temperatures were close to average, although there was a cold spell in mid-November. Early December was rainy and windy but settled conditions returned with cold easterly winds, to be replaced by duller, warmer and wetter weather late in the month.

2008 was a wet year. Late winter and spring were mild with average rainfall. After a dry June, July and August were both very wet. An average September gave way to a wet October but a somewhat drier and cooler spell in November and December. December was cooler than average, giving some indication of the cold to come.

2009 was a very mixed year. An unwise interpretation of the Met Office's prediction of a warmer than average summer as a 'barbecue summer' led to much disappointment when the summer months were changeable and often wet, and with around average temperatures. Spring and autumn were dry and November was stormy, but the striking features of the year were the cold spells in early January, early February and on and off through December.

2010 was a generally cool and dry year. January saw great cold with significant snowfall, and this continued through February and into the first half of March. Summer was changeable with good spells of warm sunny weather, and these continued into October. By mid-November cold had set in and December was the coldest for 100 years, with snow and frost widespread.

2011 was a changeable year without great extremes. The cold of December 2010 continued into the first week of January but then gave way to milder weather followed by a warm dry March and April. After an average summer, the first few days of October were exceptionally warm. November and December were very changeable with short cold spells lasting for a day or two but nothing to match the previous winter.

2012 began with a very dry spell, January, February and March all being dry and warm; it was the warmest spring on record in southern England. April, however, was cool and wet with repeated depressions sweeping in from the south-west. After a relatively warm and sunny May, both June and July were wet, with exceptional rainfall and flooding in East Devon in early July. August was also wet, but September and October were mild with near-average rainfall. November and December were both very wet with much river flooding and strong winds. In spite of the dry start, rainfall for the year was well above average.

The first half of 2013 had one main feature – a cold dry spring. Cold east winds dominated February and March and continued until early April. May, June and July were all similar in that the early part of each was warm and settled and the latter part wet and often windy. Atlas recording finished at the end of July, the dramatic storms of the late autumn falling outside the recording period.

*Text: J M Lock & Mike Hounsome*

## NATURAL AREAS

Natural England (2014) has divided Great Britain into a number of Natural Areas which share various natural features but which do not follow political or natural boundaries. These natural areas cover both the land and coastal waters, with coasts being dealt with both under the local land-based areas and also under the relevant coastal waters area. Here coasts will be dealt with under the coastal waters areas. The Devon Natural Areas, some of which extend outside the county, are described below.

### Marine Natural Areas – coastal waters

#### Lyme Bay

Lyme Bay extends from Portland Bill in the east to Start Point in the west. It is an area of shallow sea in which fish are abundant. It is an important feeding ground for seabirds including Balearic Shearwaters. Between the Devon border, just west of Lyme Regis, and Axmouth is the Undercliffs National Nature Reserve. Here land-slipping has produced a wooded coast with soft cliffs and pebble beaches, but also

with some inland chalk cliffs produced by the slippage of the land to seaward. The cliffs support a few pairs of Fulmars as well as Peregrines and Ravens. The dense ash woodland has many woodland birds and is the last place where Nightingales nested in Devon. The Axe Estuary is small but holds wintering waders and duck and is one of the few remaining places in Devon where Redshank breed. Recent habitat creation has brought, among other things, nesting Oystercatchers. Between Axmouth and Branscombe, cliffs, largely of Chalk and Greensand, are home to Fulmars and Cormorants as well as to numerous Jackdaws and a pair or two of Ravens. The wind-pruned scrub on the cliff slopes is favoured by newly arrived migrants.

From Branscombe to Teignmouth the coast is formed mainly of red cliffs of mudstones, sandstones and coarser sediments. Over most of their length these are too unstable to provide nesting sites, but in the west the rock becomes harder and more markedly layered and supports a colony of Kittiwakes at Straight Point, and Cormorants and Shags in the Dawlish area. The Otter Estuary is small but its waters and associated wet meadows provide good birding sites. The Exe Estuary is much larger,

**Snow on Dartmoor.**

*Photo: Mike Langman*

25

with wide expanses of mud and sand at low water, and has large wintering populations of waders, ducks and geese; Black-tailed and Bar-tailed Godwits, Avocets and Dark-bellied Brent Geese have nationally important wintering populations here. The sandy promontory of Dawlish Warren partially closes the estuary mouth and is much used as a high-tide roost, as is Bowling Green Marsh Reserve at Topsham near the head of the estuary. Both sites are very well watched and provide many records of Devon rarities. The Teign Estuary also has extensive mudflats at low water but holds many fewer birds than the Exe.

Beyond Teignmouth we soon arrive at the hard limestones of Torbay. The sea stacks of Ore Stone and Thatcher Rock hold colonies of gulls, Cormorants, Shags and Guillemots, and the cliffs at Berry Head have the largest colony of Guillemots on the Devon mainland. Between Berry Head and the Dart Estuary the cliffs are largely of shale, with 'head' (loose deposits resulting from freezing and thawing in periglacial times) at the top. The Dart Estuary itself is extensive and holds good wintering bird populations; it is also Devon's main breeding site for Egyptian Geese. The shale cliffs continue to the eastern end of Slapton Sands. Here a bar of sand and shingle has built up across the mouth of the Gara river and impounded a large freshwater lake, Slapton Ley. The eastern part of this is almost

entirely covered by reeds but the western part has both large areas of open water and fringing beds of reeds and bulrush. The reeds are extensive and hard to survey, but it seems reasonably certain that Bitterns have bred here in recent times and that Marsh Harriers have prospected. There are large populations of Reed and Sedge Warblers, with Cetti's Warblers in the fringing scrub. Great Crested Grebes have their largest Devon population here, and Gadwall also breed. In the winter many species of ducks and grebes can be found, particularly when rough weather drives them off the sea. Migrating hirundines roost in the reedbeds and feed over the open water. Pied and White Wagtails roost here in numbers on autumn migration and have been extensively studied.

The shale cliffs continue westwards beyond Torcross, interrupted by another coastal lake, Beesands Ley, which holds similar but smaller populations of the birds that are found at Slapton. The coast then becomes more rugged as the shales are replaced by the harder schists of Start Point, but cliff-nesting birds are few.

### Start Point to Plymouth

From Start Point westwards to Prawle Point the coast is rocky but the cliffs are not particularly high and are covered at the top with a thick layer of 'head'. The sheltered valleys make this a good area for arriving migrants in spring. Beyond Portlemouth lies the opening of the Kingsbridge Estuary, a classic drowned river valley extending seven kilometres inland and with several branches. Extensive areas of mud at low tide provide good sheltered habitat for waders and duck in the winter (Waterhouse 2014).

West of the Kingsbridge Estuary lies the craggy coast extending from Bolt Head to Bolt Tail. Although the cliffs are high, they do not form ledges and there are few or no breeding seabirds. The downs and fields behind the coast between Soar and Bolberry are a fruitful area for migrants in spring and autumn. At Bolt Tail the coast turns north–south with low cliffs and some sand dunes between Hope Cove and Bantham, at the mouth of the Avon. Two small streams in valleys at South Huish and South Milton are intermittently dammed by sea-deposited sand or gravel, producing marshes and reedbeds; high seas or heavy rainfall may lead to the barriers breaching and the fresh water draining to the sea, or to the marshes being flooded with salt water (Tucker 2007). Bantham, with its broad sandy beach, lies at the mouth of the Avon, whose estuary, while long, is quite narrow and does not support large numbers of wintering birds, although it is not without interest for the birdwatcher. Burgh Island at the mouth of the Avon has some breeding Shags and Herring Gulls on its cliffs.

Beyond Bantham the coast runs east–west, with low cliffs topped, like those further east, with 'head'. The narrow estuaries of the Erme and the Yealm break through; like the Avon, they are relatively narrow and neither supports large numbers of wintering ducks or waders, although migrating Ospreys pass through both estuaries in spring. The banks of these estuaries are lined with ancient oak woodlands. The Yealm opens into Wembury Bay, whose rocky shoreline provides winter habitat for waders and gulls. The coast then turns northwards and becomes the eastern shore of Plymouth Sound. The entrance to the Sound is partially blocked by the Plymouth Breakwater. The Plym Estuary lies on the east side of Plymouth Sound, which then narrows into the Tamar Estuary which carries water from both the River Tavy to the east and the River Tamar to the west, the latter forming the county boundary with Cornwall. The Plym Estuary supports important numbers of wintering waders, including Avocets.

**Prawle Point in the distance, seen from Start Point.**

*Photo: Mike Langman*

### The North Coast

This natural area extends from the Cornish border between Morwenstow and Hardisworthy to the Somerset border at Glenthorne, east of Foreland Point. The tidal range here is very large so that extensive areas of foreshore can be exposed at low water, providing feeding areas for shorebirds. From Morwenstow the coast runs northwards to Hartland Point. Although the cliffs here are high, they do not have suitable breeding ledges and breeding auks are scarce or absent, although both Ravens and Peregrines manage to breed. Hartland Point is, however, a noted seawatching site, with substantial numbers of divers seen during the winter and significant shearwater movements in summer and early autumn.

The coast then turns eastwards, with low cliffs and the occasional cove such as that at Clovelly, until the mouth of the Taw/Torridge Estuary is reached at Appledore. The Torridge flowing from the south, and the Taw, coming from the south-east, join at Crow Point and provide a large area of mud- and sand-flats that support large numbers of waders and some duck and geese during the winter. A large area of sand dunes, Braunton Burrows (which supports breeding Shelduck and small numbers of wintering raptors) has developed to the north of the estuary mouth. The beaches here formerly had breeding Ringed Plover but ease of access and greatly increased numbers of free-roaming dogs mean these are now at best intermittent breeders. On the seaward side of Braunton Burrows lies the extensive beach of Saunton Sands which supports good numbers of Sanderling in the winter months. To the north lie the headlands of Baggy Point and Morte Point, which are separated by Morte Bay. At Bull Point the coast then turns to run east–west and the whole of the north coast from here to Foreland Point is backed by rocky cliffs, often of considerable height. In a few places these cliffs are the stronghold of breeding auks. Numbers, particularly of Razorbills, are very difficult to estimate because of the inaccessibility of the coast, but there may well be between 500 and 1,000 pairs of Razorbills and between 1,000 and 1,500 pairs of Guillemots. A small Kittiwake colony persists to the west of Wringapeak, near Woody Bay. The tops of the cliffs are occupied by moorland, on Great and Little Hangman, Holdstone Down and Trentishoe Down, which supports breeding Stonechats and plenty of Meadow Pipits and Skylarks. The steep slopes between Woody Bay and Lee Bay carry 'hanging' sessile oakwoods, with important populations of Redstarts, Pied Flycatchers and Wood Warblers. There are also a number of short fast-flowing streams draining north to this Exmoor coast, which have good numbers of Grey Wagtails and Dippers.

The island of Lundy lies some 18 kilometres north-north-west of Hartland Point. It is mainly granite, with some metamorphosed sedimentary

Photo: Jeremy Barker

rocks at the southern end. Its undulating plateau is covered by a mosaic of heather moorland, extensively grazed grassland and more intensively managed pasture. There are several small bodies of fresh water, while the relatively sheltered east-facing combes support small copses of deciduous trees. Lundy is well watched in spring and autumn and many records of rarities come from there. Breeding seabirds are abundant on the rugged west-facing cliffs, with Fulmars, Shags, Razorbills and Guillemots all common and showing signs of recent increases, while Kittiwakes are in long-term decline. Puffins and Manx Shearwaters were virtually extinct as successful breeders until a concerted rat eradication campaign in 2002–2004, with the island being declared rat-free in 2006. Both species are now showing increases in breeding numbers, with a particularly rapid growth in the shearwater colony, and Storm Petrels were first proved to breed in 2014. Other ground-nesting species such as Water Rails and Wheatears also appear to be benefiting from the absence of rats.

**Saunton Sands and the Marram Grass-covered sand dunes of Braunton Burrows.**

*Photo: Jeremy Barker*

**Much of Exmoor within Devon is dominated by improved and semi-improved grassland.**

*Photo: Roy Churchill*

### Terrestrial Natural Areas

#### Exmoor and the Quantocks

This Natural Area includes all of North Devon north of a line from the Taw Estuary through South Molton. Only a small part – about one third of Exmoor – lies within Devon. The remainder, including the Brendon Hills and Quantock Hills, is in Somerset. Unlike Dartmoor, Exmoor does not have a granite core, but is underlain by sedimentary rocks mainly of Devonian age: gritstones, sandstones and slates. These only form tors in a few places, such as the Valley of Rocks west of Lynton. There is little 'clitter' in the Dartmoor sense, but there are extensive areas of valley-side scree in places such as Valley of Rocks, Heddon Valley, Sherrycombe, the East Lyn Valley and Caddow Combe. On its north side Exmoor is bounded by the sea, with steep slopes and cliffs. There is some heather-covered moorland and also areas of acid grassland. Bogs are not as extensive as on Dartmoor. The underlying sedimentary rocks weather to produce more fertile soils than does the Dartmoor granite, so improvement and cultivation

**Hoaroak Water, one of the numerous water courses that flow to the North Devon coast.**

*Photo: Margaret Phillips*

extend further onto the moor than on Dartmoor, such that much of Exmoor within Devon is dominated by improved and semi-improved grassland, and there is little really wild country. The valleys and coastal slopes are often occupied by oak woodlands which provide breeding habitat for Redstarts, Wood Warblers and Pied Flycatchers.

Exmoor supports many of the same moorland birds as does Dartmoor, but Red Grouse are now almost certainly extinct, with few if any records since 2010; they were introduced, as on Dartmoor. Black Grouse, however, hung on longer on Exmoor than on Dartmoor but they are now extinct. Golden Plover and Dunlin, which seem to need large areas of bog, are absent from Exmoor. Ring Ouzels last nested there in 2006. The absence of tors and associated short grassland means that Wheatears are scarcer than on Dartmoor, but they do breed in stone walls, for example on Brendon Common and adjacent areas, while Whinchats, which prefer the border between open moorland and woodland or scrub, are commoner on Exmoor. Curlew formerly nested on Exmoor but no longer do so, and Merlin now only occasionally breeds there.

The major rivers of Exmoor, the Exe and its tributary the Barle, both drain southwards. Several short rivers, such as the East and West Lyn, and numerous streams flow to the north coast. The major Exmoor reservoir, Wimbleball Lake, lies in Somerset, but the smaller Wistlandpound Reservoir is in

Devon, at the western edge of the moor, attracting small numbers of wintering and passage waterbirds.

### The Culm

This natural area occupies most of northern Devon. It is developed on the Culm Measures, which are Carboniferous sediments, mainly shales and sandstones, that weather to produce heavy acid soils. The vegetation that develops over this is acid species-rich grassland which, traditionally, was grazed in summer after the taking of a hay crop, and left largely ungrazed in winter because it was too wet. This is now often referred to as 'Culm Grassland', or 'Rhôs Pasture'. Such grasslands formerly supported breeding Curlew but the remaining areas are now small and probably therefore unsuitable. Snipe still breed, however. The grasslands and associated hedges still provide habitat for Stonechats and Tree Pipits, as well as hunting grounds for Barn Owls and, in winter, small numbers of Short-eared Owls, Merlins and Hen Harriers. Patches of wet woodland support most of Devon's surviving Willow Tits, and scrubby margins and tall grass patches are good for Grasshopper Warblers. Most of the grasslands have now been drained and improved for agriculture, and unimproved Culm Grassland is virtually confined to nature reserves. Other areas have been drained, ploughed and resown with species-poor ryegrass mixtures which are regularly cut for silage during the summer; some maize is also grown. Hedges, which were formerly very abundant, have over time been cleared and levelled, but there remains a network of hedges that provide nesting sites for many farmland bird species, as well as corridors for movement. These negative impacts have been partly remedied by the efforts of Devon Wildlife Trust, which has acquired several areas of Culm Grassland that they are restoring and managing sustainably, as well as working on connecting the scattered remaining patches.

Other habitats within the Culm Natural Area include cliff-top grasslands which are found along much of the north coast, particularly the Hartland peninsula. Here some areas of grassland have been lost to afforestation to form Hartland Forest, although a side-effect of this has been the creation of Nightjar habitat in young plantations.

## Dartmoor

Dartmoor sits as a great lump in the western centre of Devon. It is underlain by a huge mass of granite injected about 300 million years ago into the base of mountains created by a continental collision. The granite baked the surrounding rocks, hardening and altering them and injecting mineralized veins. Subsequent weathering has removed the mountains to leave the granite dome the shape of which, it is believed, more or less reflects the original shape of the underground magma mass. Over much of the area the granite is covered by peat or sandy weathering products but on the tops of hills the granite is often exposed to form the tors that are such a feature of Dartmoor. On the south-western corner of the moor the granite has been altered by a combination of steam from the magma and subsequent weathering to produce deposits of china clay, which are mined in large pits on Lee Moor. Dartmoor can be divided into northern and southern

**The exposed granite of Longaford Tor, Dartmoor.**

*Photo: Mike Russell*

portions along a line running eastwards from Tavistock through Two Bridges and then south-eastwards to Ashburton. The altitude of the moor means that it intercepts rain-bearing westerly winds, and both the northern and southern moorland heights receive 2,000 mm of rain or more every year; lowland Devon receives 1,000 mm or less annually.

The most widespread vegetation of the high moor is blanket bog which occupies the two major plateau areas of northern and southern Dartmoor. Blanket bog has Cotton Grass, Purple Moor Grass, Deergrass and species of *Sphagnum* moss as the dominants. It is perpetually wet and overlies peat which may be several metres deep. Small pools can be found on the bog surface and here and there straight banks show where the peat has been cut for fuel in the past. Birds of the blanket bog are few: Dunlin, Snipe and sometimes Teal on the pools. On better-drained slopes blanket bog is replaced by moorland which may be dominated either by grasses – mainly Sheep's Fescue and Mat Grass often accompanied by small amounts of the yellow-flowered Tormentil, the white Heath Bedstraw and the pink Lousewort – or dwarf shrubs such as Ling and Western Gorse. Red Grouse, introduced at the beginning of the last century, favour areas of their main food plant, Ling. On some undergrazed slopes Purple Moor Grass may become dominant, and on lower, well-drained slopes Bracken can take over and form a dense sward that excludes most other species. Some slopes are covered in boulders ('clitter') which sheep cannot enter and here Whortleberry forms dwarf thickets; on the open moor it is grazed heavily by sheep and rarely exceeds a few centimetres in height. In places gorse forms thickets which are a favourite nesting place for Linnets. The drier heaths and grasslands are used by Stonechats, Whinchats, Wheatears, Meadow Pipits and Skylarks, among others. The first two, together with Cuckoos, need some larger trees or shrubs to provide look-outs and song-posts.

River valleys are many; the rivers are generally fast-flowing and clear and Dippers and Grey Wagtails occur along them. The gravelly banks were formerly favoured by Common Sandpipers but this species is now extremely rare on Dartmoor. The lower stretches of the rivers, particularly where they flow through woodland, are favoured by Goosanders (but which roost on the reservoirs) and, here and there, by a flourishing feral population of Mandarin Ducks.

The natural woodlands of Dartmoor are mainly of Sessile Oak with occasional Rowans over a dense moss-dominated ground layer. If grazing is absent or light, then Whortleberry and Great Wood-rush may form dense stands, but both are highly palatable to sheep and easily eliminated or confined to the tops of boulders which sheep cannot reach. The main woodlands are in the steep-sided valleys in which the rivers flow off the moor and which are home to some of Dartmoor's most iconic birds: Wood Warbler, Redstart and Pied Flycatcher, the last much encouraged by nestbox provision. A few small upland woodlands occupy the sides of river valleys higher on the moor. Of these, Wistman's Wood is the most famous; the other two, Piles Copse and Black Tor Beare, are less well known.

Conifer plantations form the largest woodlands on Dartmoor, with those at Bellever, Soussons, Fernworthy and Burrator being the largest. These hold various species that have moved in; Coal Tits and Goldcrests are common but Redpolls, Siskins and Crossbills have also colonized the plantations and some are abundant in places.

Dartmoor has no natural areas of freshwater of any size, but reservoirs have been built on the Avon above South Brent, at Burrator, Fernworthy, Venford and Meldon. These reservoirs hold populations of Brown Trout which provide food for Goosanders that both feed and (in greater numbers) roost there.

Dartmoor is grazed by sheep, cattle and ponies belonging to commoners exercising their commoners' rights. All animals range freely, although most remain close to their home areas. Areas of the moor are burned ('swaling') in the early spring to improve grazing, particularly of Purple Moor Grass, which sheds its leaves in the winter to produce a thatch of dead material. Burning also reduces shrub and tree regeneration on the moor. Bracken is completely underground at the time of burning and does not appear to be affected.

Dartmoor is a favourite recreation area for walkers and riders, and in some areas – and at times such as the Ten Tors Challenge in May – disturbance is considerable. Dogs allowed to run freely during the breeding season cannot help the breeding success of ground-nesting species. Much of the northern part of the moor is used as a training area by the military, and this gives some relief from walkers whose movements are restricted when training and live firing are in progress.

**The dense sward of Purple Moor Grass at Muddilake, looking towards Holne Ridge, central Dartmoor.**

Photo: Mike Russell

**The mix of farmland and urban areas around Torbay.**

*Photo: Mike Langman*

## South Devon

The South Devon Natural Area is a landscape of rolling hills separated by river valleys. It is bounded in the east by the Teign Valley and extends north to the edges of Dartmoor and westwards to the Tamar Valley up to Tavistock. The area is underlain by folded Devonian shales and slates, with isolated patches of limestone, particularly around Torbay and Plymouth, with smaller patches at Buckfastleigh and around Newton Abbot. At Berry Head and Hope's Nose these form cliffs and sea stacks that are home to nesting seabirds, while the upper parts of the cliffs and the limestone grasslands are home to several rare plant species. The built-up areas of Torbay and Plymouth provide habitats for Collared Doves and other urban species, and berry-bearing shrubs around the car parks of large stores are often used by Waxwings during invasions. Roofs and chimney-stacks are much used by breeding gulls, mainly Herring Gulls but also a few Lesser and Great Black-backed Gulls. Harbours such as that at Brixham provide shelter for seabirds in rough weather as well as a source of food from fish discards and offal.

Much of the area is used for intensive agriculture, with much dairying, raising of beef cattle and sheep grazing, but also with some cereal crops on the higher and more level ground. Fields are generally small and separated by Devon banks which may have a hedge on top. Narrow sunken lanes with flower-rich banks often separate areas of fields. Some areas of coastal grassland remain relatively unimproved and are grazed extensively by cattle.

The river valleys are often steep-sided and covered with oak woodlands. The *Devon Tetrad Atlas*

*1977–85* included a few records of species such as Pied Flycatcher and Wood Warbler from these, but there are few recent records, perhaps because these areas are often difficult of access. Woodcock are frequent in these woods in winter. The rivers themselves have Dippers, Grey Wagtails and Kingfishers.

The coastal strip has already been dealt with in the Lyme Bay section above. Heathlands occur here and there along the coast and on a few of the higher hills, as well as in the Bovey Basin on the eastern boundary of the area, where flooded claypits also provide the only areas of open water away from the coastal leys.

## Devon Redlands

The Devon Redlands, underlain mainly by Permo-Triassic sands, silts and clays, are fertile, easily cultivated and mainly under arable crops. The oxidized iron in the soils gives them the red colour so characteristic of 'Red Devon'. They occupy much of the lower catchment of the River Exe, underlie the city of Exeter, and also much of the catchment of the River Otter.

However, local areas of more recent sediments – Cretaceous on the Haldon Ridge and late Triassic under the East Devon Pebblebed Heaths – are very free-draining and infertile and support internationally

**Yellowhammer – relatively common in the arable farmland of the Blackdowns.**

*Photo: Gray Clements*

important areas of lowland heath dominated by Ling with Bell Heather in drier sites and Cross-leaved Heath in wetter places. Gorse and Western Gorse form scrubby thickets favoured by Dartford Warblers, with Stonechats on the open heath. In the past these heathlands were maintained free from trees by a combination of grazing, burning and turf-cutting, and modern management attempts to replicate these processes.

The mature woodlands of the Haldon Ridge and the natural updraughts produced by the steep escarpment provide good raptor habitat. Honey-buzzards used the area in the past but last bred here more than 20 years ago. Plantations here and on the Pebblebed Heaths are managed on a long-term rotation and provide Nightjars with nesting sites after felling and in the young regrowth stages.

The estuaries of the Teign, Exe and Otter have been mentioned under the Lyme Bay maritime Natural Area above. All support saltmarsh and have areas of mud and sand exposed by low tides which provide important feeding areas for wintering waders, ducks and geese. The sand dunes at Dawlish Warren and Exmouth support good dune vegetation and provide shelter for arriving and departing migrants.

The agricultural areas are mainly occupied by arable cultivation and support farmland and hedgerow birds. The eroding vertical banks of the lowland rivers provide nesting sites for Sand Martins and Kingfishers, although these areas are vulnerable to summer floods.

### The Blackdowns

The Blackdowns Natural Area occupies much of East Devon, including the catchments of the Culm, Axe and Otter. It extends into Somerset in the north and into Dorset in the east, while its western boundary lies a few kilometres to the west of the Otter Valley.

Much of the area is underlain by Cretaceous age Upper Greensand or Chalk (or the clay-with-flints residue of Chalk weathering) separated by valleys eroded into the underlying Jurassic and Triassic clays and mudstones.

A patchwork of small farms covers much of the area; grazing of sheep and cattle is the mainstay of agriculture. The exception is the coastal strip between Seaton and Lyme Regis where Chalk uplands support intensive arable farming, mainly of barley and oil-seed rape.

Heathland was formerly widespread on the tops of the ridges, and fragments remain at the Stockland Turbaries and elsewhere. Patterns of neatly rectangular fields show where heathland was converted to agriculture in the 1800s and 1900s, contrasting with the smaller irregular fields in the valleys.

The heathlands formerly supported birds now rare or extinct in the county. Pulman (1875) claimed that Black Grouse (known in Devon as 'Heath Poults') "packed" on Trinity Hill near Axminster in the first quarter of the 19th Century, and D'Urban & Mathew (1892) believed that they were still present in the Blackdowns. Curlew are now on the brink of extinction in the Blackdowns, while Pied Flycatchers and Redstarts bred in oak woodlands there until the late 1990s and may still do so irregularly. Plantations on former heathland have Nightjars in clearings, as well as breeding Siskins and visiting Crossbills. Bullfinches are abundant in the many hedges of the farmland. In the coastal arable strip, Skylarks, Yellowhammers and Whitethroats are relatively common.

## *Man-made factors*

### Agriculture

Devon is an agricultural county. Much of the land is, however, too wet and/or hilly for regular arable cropping, and livestock production, both dairying and for meat, is dominant over much of the county. Grass is the main crop.

The uplands of Dartmoor and Exmoor are grazed by sheep, cattle and ponies, although declining demand has led to a reduction in the last. The management of these uplands has been dictated largely by the grazing needs of the commoners and there is much dispute about 'correct' stocking levels. Burning ('swaling') in early spring is a widespread practice which, if properly carried out in small patches, could lead to habitat diversity. However, the fires often spread across large areas, creating uniformity rather than diversity. They also destroy large numbers of invertebrates – potential bird food – if they are lit too late in the season or if they burn down into the peaty soil, as they may do in very dry conditions.

Much of the lowlands are managed for livestock. Dairying is widespread. The wetness of the climate does, however, mean that cattle must be kept off the land during the winter to avoid undue damage to the grassland from trampling ('poaching'). In the past a degree of trampling and poaching was tolerated as the cattle strip-grazed crops of winter fodder such as kale, which provided excellent shelter for many bird species. Nowadays, however, large quantities of winter fodder must be saved during the summer as hay crops no longer produce enough, and the making of silage is now the main means of conserving grass for the winter, not least because it requires a shorter period of dry weather than haymaking. Fields are cut for silage up to four times in a summer, leaving no time in which ground-nesting birds can raise a brood. To maintain high productivity, large amounts of nitrogenous fertilizers are added, and run-off of these can cause eutrophication of waterbodies and adjacent land. Fertilized and frequently cut grass out-competes other plants and, in any case, most grassland now consists of drained and regularly ploughed and reseeded leys that are poor in biodiversity and structural diversity and which provide few habitat niches for birds. To supplement the feed available from grass, fodder crops, particularly maize, are widely planted. Maize requires high nutrient inputs, and weed control within it is almost complete. Some bird species shelter in the crop and Swallows and wagtails may roost there, but the lack of food makes

it an unsuitable habitat. Although some maize seeds may remain after harvest, these are too large for most bird species. In a few places a catch-crop such as stubble turnips are planted after the autumn harvest to provide late winter fodder, usually for sheep, and these offer useful bird habitat.

The trend in dairying is for cattle to spend more time indoors and less in the fields. In East Devon (and probably elsewhere) some farms now keep their dairy cattle indoors throughout the year, with robot milking leading to higher yields that offset the high costs of setting up the systems. Such systems mean that yet more forage must be saved and leave little incentive to retain traditional grazed pastures. The future for birds in such systems is bleak.

### Mitigation and stewardship schemes

The well-documented decline in the numbers of farmland birds has led to the introduction of various schemes that give farmers incentives to carry out wildlife-friendly working. These are controlled by the Department for Environment, Food and Rural Affairs (DEFRA) and are known as Stewardship Schemes. These schemes are administered by Natural England. In essence, farmers are paid a sum that compensates them for not taking the cheapest option and for carrying out actions that maintain and enhance the wildlife and landscape value of their holdings. The schemes are divided into Entry Level (ELS), a basic level in which all farms can participate, and Higher Level (HLS), which is competitive and directed at habitats at greatest risk. There are also schemes for organic farmers (Organic ELS) and upland farmers (Upland ELS).

The long list of options available often have very detailed prescriptions which may deter some farmers from participating. Some of the treatments most relevant to farmland birds include:

- ❏ leaving stubbles over winter
- ❏ leaving field margins unsown and/or untreated with insecticides and herbicides
- ❏ leaving bare patches in arable fields ('Skylark plots')
- ❏ cutting hedges and cleaning ditches in rotation rather than all at once
- ❏ providing winter feed through game cover crops or through feeders
- ❏ fencing small upland woods to exclude sheep and encourage the ground vegetation, and
- ❏ the creation of bands of tall grass ('beetle banks') across arable fields.

**Leaving winter stubbles – an option with considerable benefits for farmland birds.**

*Photo: Mike Russell*

Many of these schemes arise from long-term research on Grey Partridge by the Game and Wildlife Conservation Trust (formerly the Game Conservancy Trust) (e.g. Potts 2012). While 60% of farmers are in Entry Level Schemes, uptake of the less popular treatments is very low (e.g. Skylark plots – less than 2%). While these schemes probably have had some effect on farmland bird numbers, they are most effective when carefully used by farmers and conservation organizations in partnership. The Cirl Bunting recovery scheme in South Devon, run by the RSPB, shows how such a scheme can work. Of course, much of Devon's agricultural land is devoted to the growing of feed for cattle, while most of the available agri-environmental schemes are geared to arable land. The options for hedge and ditch management, however, apply equally to land used for fodder production.

### Forestry

Forestry has changed a good deal in recent years. The tax incentives for extensive planting have largely been lost and little new planting now takes place other than post-felling. Many of the conifer plantations established in the years after World War II are now reaching harvesting age. Where conifer plantations were sited on former heathland, there are incentives under Higher Level Stewardship to allow regeneration of heathland, and this has benefited Nightjars among other species. More broadleaf trees are now planted, both as plantations and as blocks, corridors or edges in and around conifers. This should improve these plantations as bird habitat, adding species to the Goldcrests, Coal Tits, Siskins, Chaffinches and Woodpigeons that use conifer plantations.

However, there are threats to some plantation species. The fungus-like pathogen *Phytophthora ramorum* – first discovered in California in the mid-1990s and known in North America as 'sudden oak death' (even though only American species of oak are susceptible) – has caused considerable damage to larch plantations and a good deal of precautionary felling of larch has taken place since 2009 in many parts of Devon. Ash die-back, caused by a fungus, is a threat hanging over many small plantations and hedgerow trees, as well as to the natural Ash woods in the county, such as those within the Axmouth-Lyme Regis NNR. As of March 2015 the Forestry Commission had confirmed one 'wider environment' outbreak in Devon (i.e. an outbreak affecting established trees rather than those in a nursery or recent plantation) near Tiverton. Of course, tree death may have its beneficial side-effects for birds: Lesser Spotted Woodpeckers thrived – albeit temporarily – after the great die-off of English Elm trees from Dutch Elm Disease. Will the same happen if and when the countryside is full of dead Ash trees?

*Text: J M Lock*

# DEVON HABITAT TYPES

## Woodlands

Devon supports many kinds of woodland (Figures 7 & 8), some planted, some natural, although all have been managed to some degree in the past. Oak woodlands of two kinds are widespread. First there are the Sessile Oak-dominated woodlands that occupy the slopes of the river valleys around Dartmoor and Exmoor. The amount of undergrowth in these woodlands depends very much on the degree of grazing; heavily grazed woods may have little but a carpet of moss beneath the trees. Where grazing is sparse or absent there can be a dense field layer, often of Bilberry, as at Yarner Wood. These woods are home to some of Devon's most attractive birds – Pied Flycatcher, Redstart and Wood Warbler among them.

Lowland oakwoods dominated by Pedunculate Oak tend to be found in smaller patches, scattered through the Devon lowlands, often in places such as steep slopes which were difficult to clear and cultivate. They often have a shrubby understorey in which Hazel is often common, as is Holly. These woodlands would probably have been managed as coppice in the past, with the underwood being cut at ten- to fifteen-year intervals, and the large trees being felled at much longer intervals when the need for them arose. Such woodlands hold large populations of Blue Tits and Great Tits, as well as tree specialists such as Treecreepers, Nuthatches and Great Spotted Woodpeckers. Corvids roost in them and sometimes nest there, as do Woodpigeons. Robins and Wrens are common in the understorey.

Ash is probably commonest in the eastern part of the county where there are more calcareous soils. Pure ashwoods are found in the Axmouth-Lyme Regis National Nature Reserve but are otherwise rare. These woodlands, as well as hedgerow Ashes, are now threatened by Ash Dieback, which will probably kill the majority of Devon's Ash trees within the next 20 years. The dying trees may provide a brief bonanza for woodpeckers (as happened after the ravages of Dutch Elm Disease in the 1960s) but their loss will leave a major gap in the county's woodland estate.

Alder grows along lowland rivers throughout the county and also forms strips of woodland along spring lines. The ground beneath is often very wet and may bear large tussocks of Greater Tussock-sedge. Alders produce seed in small cones that hang

**Beech trees – a prominent feature of the Devon landscape – in Abbeyford Woods, near Okehampton.**

*Photo: Mike Russell*

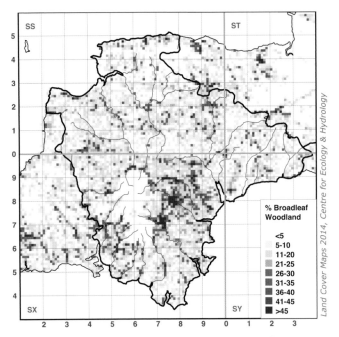

**Figure 7. Percentage of broadleaf woodland in Devon.**

*Land Cover Maps 2014, Centre for Ecology & Hydrology*

on the tree through the winter and provide food for roaming flocks of Goldfinches, Siskins and Redpolls.

Willows, like Alder, grow along rivers but the smaller species also form low woodlands in wet valleys and hollows, often near the coast but also inland. These coastal scrubby woodlands provide food and shelter for incoming migrants. Inland, particularly in North Devon, they are the main habitat of Willow Tits.

Beech is a very widely planted tree in Devon, and Rackham (2006) did not consider it native to the county, although there are prehistoric records of subfossil material. Ivimey-Cook (1984) considered it to be "probably introduced". Whatever its true status, it has been extensively planted both for forestry and as a hedgerow tree and is now a prominent feature of the landscape in many parts of the county. If management ceases, beech hedges become linear woods. Beech has also been planted, or has naturally regenerated from planted stock, to form almost pure woodlands in places, often on the acid soils of the surroundings of Dartmoor. Beech casts a heavy shade and has a dense network of roots close to the surface, so that beechwoods often lack much of a woody understorey, and may have little in the way of herbaceous ground flora either. Wood Warblers find such places to their liking, however.

Plantations of conifers are found mainly on and around Dartmoor, as well as on the acid ridge tops of East Devon and elsewhere, many of them occupying former heathland. The main planted species are Scots Pine, Corsican Pine and hybrid Larch, with some Sitka Spruce and Douglas Fir, as well as small-scale plantings of, among others, Western Red-cedar and Western Hemlock-spruce. There may be a dense

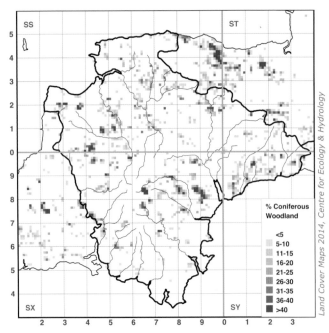

Figure 8. Percentage of coniferous woodland in Devon.

*Land Cover Maps 2014, Centre for Ecology & Hydrology*

% Coniferous
Woodland

<5
5-10
11-15
16-20
21-25
26-30
31-35
36-40
>40

### Thickets and scrub

Thicket and scrub are essentially dwarf woodlands, although the dominant species are usually not the same as those in woodland. In other words they are not just young woodland. Thickets may be successional stages, becoming woodland if left alone, or they may be climax vegetation in their own right.

Scrub dominated by Hawthorn and often interlaced with Bramble is found on many sites – road and rail margins, woodland edges, abandoned agricultural land and derelict industrial sites among them. Hawthorn scrub can produce a good crop of berries that provide winter feeding for thrushes. The dense thorny shrubs also provide roosting and nesting sites for thrushes, finches and pigeons.

Gorse forms thickets on heathlands, on the lower slopes of Dartmoor and Exmoor and along coasts. These provide nesting sites and year-round cover for Dartford Warblers and are important nesting sites for Linnets, Yellowhammers and Reed Buntings (Marshall *et al.* 2014). A distinctive thicket type is found on exposed coastal cliff-slopes, such as at Beer Head in East Devon. Here a mixture of Blackthorn, Hawthorn, Elder and other species forms a dense level-topped thicket. Any shoots that project much above the rest are usually burned off by salt-laden winds during gales. The birds of these cliff thickets seem, perhaps not surprisingly, to have been little studied. Wrens and Dunnocks seem to be abundant, Linnets breed here, and the thickets provide a first refuge for arriving migrants.

mixed undergrowth in the early stages of plantations and this can provide shelter for a wide range of species, particularly Willow Warblers. Once the canopy has closed, usually after 10–15 years, the dense shade excludes virtually all other plants. Conifer plantations are popular with Coal Tits and Goldcrests and provide nesting sites for Woodpigeons and Goshawks. After felling, the cleared areas are attractive to Nightjars and sometimes Tree Pipits.

## Hedges

Devon has a greater length of hedges than any other English county, and parts of the Blackdown Hills have the greatest density of hedges in Britain. Most Devon hedges incorporate an earth bank, often stone-faced, which adds to the range of habitats that they provide. (In fact a 'Devon hedge' may, by definition, consist of a bank only, without any trees or shrubs). There is often also a ditch beside the hedge. A high proportion of Devon's hedges are ancient, with a wide variety of woody species within them. Hedges provide food and shelter for birds, and also act as corridors along which birds (and other animals) can move from one area of woodland or scrub to another.

Traditionally, hedges were managed either by laying or coppicing. Both techniques aimed at producing a stock-proof barrier and both produced firewood as a by-product. The interval between managements was at least two years and usually much longer; coppicing would take place at longer intervals than laying. Both these methods produced tall hedges with plenty of old growth on which flowers and fruits were produced, providing food for birds and other animals in the autumn and winter.

Devon has suffered less than many counties from hedge removal, but changes in management have been huge. Nowadays most hedges are flailed annually to a constant height, and the sides are also trimmed ('faced up') annually. There is therefore little berry- and fruit-bearing growth, and such fruit as there may be is often destroyed by flailing in late summer. Annually flailed hedges thus offer much less food for birds (and mammals such as Dormice) than unflailed ones. Nesting birds are to a large extent protected because hedge cutting on farms is not permitted between 1 March and (since 2015) 31 August if the farmer is to receive his basic acreage payment. Purely practical reasons such as accessibility to farm vehicles mean that the vast majority of flailing takes place before November because after that the ground is often too wet.

There is little doubt that changes in hedge management, and in particular a change to cutting at two- to three-yearly intervals, such as is proscribed in some agri-environmental schemes, could greatly help our farmland birds.

**Broadleaf and coniferous woodland against a backdrop of hedgerow-lined fields near Arlington, North Devon.**

*Photo: Roy Churchill*

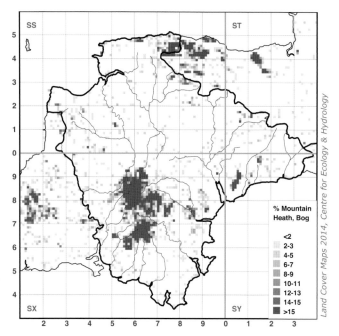

Figure 9. Percentage of mountain, heath and bog in Devon.

*Land Cover Maps 2014, Centre for Ecology & Hydrology*

## Heathlands

Heathlands are dominated by dwarf shrubs, mainly in the heather family, Ericaceae. In Devon they are found mainly on Dartmoor, Exmoor and East Devon (Figure 9). The common factor in the occurrence of heathland is the extreme acidity and nutrient-poverty of the soil which has discouraged clearance and improvement for agriculture.

On the lowland Pebblebed Heaths of East Devon, developed over the pebbly sandy sediments of Triassic age, the commonest dwarf shrub is Heather, with Bell Heather in drier sites and Cross-leaved Heath in the wetter ones. Western Gorse is common in drier sites, as is the common Gorse. The latter forms thickets that provide excellent cover for nesting birds of many species. In the past these lowland heaths were maintained by a combination of grazing, burning and turf cutting. Now some grazing, accidental burning and tree and scrub clearance maintain them in their open state. These heathlands are the stronghold of Dartford Warblers in Devon but also hold Tree Pipits, Nightjars and Stonechats.

Heathland was formerly much more widespread in East Devon on the flat hilltops underlain by Greensand and clay-with-flints. Only small fragments remain at, for instance, Fire Beacon Hill and Mutters Moor near Sidmouth, and Trinity Hill near Axminster where Pulman, writing in 1875, mentioned Black Grouse ('Heath Poults') "packing" in the first years of the 19th century. According to D'Urban & Mathew (1892) Black Grouse were still present in the second half of the 19th century in various places in the Blackdown Hills, where, again, fragments of heathland remain to this day.

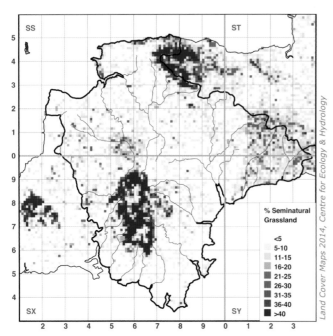

**Figure 10. Percentage of seminatural grassland in Devon.**

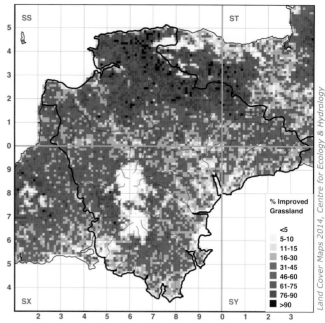

**Figure 11. Percentage of improved grassland in Devon.**

Nowadays Tree Pipits, Stonechats and Nightjars are the special birds of these sites.

The upland heaths of Dartmoor and Exmoor are still extensively grazed by sheep, cattle and ponies and, mainly on Exmoor, by Red Deer. Heather tends to be commonest on the drier eastern side of Dartmoor, with grass heath more widespread in the west. The highest parts have extensive areas of blanket bog with Cotton Grass, Purple Moor-grass and *Sphagnum* mosses. Dunlin still breed in these wet areas, as well as, until a few years ago, Golden Plover. The open moorland supports high populations of Skylarks and Meadow Pipits, with Wheatears in areas of short grass. Red Grouse, introduced early in the 20th century, are scattered over the moors wherever their food plant, Ling, occurs. The heathlands of Exmoor are basically similar but have almost certainly lost Red Grouse as a breeding species in the last ten years; Dunlin and Golden Plover have, as far as is known, never bred on Exmoor. The moors there may not be high enough for these species which are (or were) confined to the highest parts of Dartmoor.

### Grasslands

Grasslands (Figures 10 & 11) are often divided into 'permanent' and 'temporary'. The division between the two depends on one's point of view. At present, agricultural bureaucrats call anything more than six years old 'permanent', whereas a botanist or plant ecologist would look for areas unploughed or unseeded for 50 years or more when seeking species-rich 'permanent' grasslands.

Raised stocking rates and the consequent need for increased grassland productivity mean that most lowland farmed grasslands are treated as 'short-term leys'. They are ploughed and sown with productive strains of rye-grass such as Perennial Rye-grass, Italian Rye-grass and their hybrids. Once established, this is cut three to five times every summer for three to five years, usually for silage or haylage, and then ploughed again and reseeded. Often maize is planted for a year or two before reseeding with grass. The pressure for increased productivity also means that fertilizer inputs, particularly of nitrogen, are now much greater, favouring coarser and more productive grass species, even if the grassland has not been reseeded.

All this is in contrast to the more traditional methods of management in which a hay crop would be taken in June–August and the aftermath then grazed until the autumn. The vagaries of our summer weather mean that haymaking is too uncertain and too labour-intensive for the modern livestock farmer, and yields are too low.

The effects of these changes on farmland birds are twofold. Firstly, most permanent grasslands have structure, particularly if not intensively managed. Ungrazed clumps and tussocks provide cover for ground-nesting birds. Secondly, frequent summer cutting means that species such as Lapwing do not have a long enough window of opportunity between cuts in which to breed successfully. Of course, some

**Farmland near Whiddon Down – Devon still retains extensive areas of cultivated fields.**

*Photo: Mike Russell*

species benefit from frequent cutting. Species such as corvids that forage in short grass flock into recently cut fields, as do gulls.

Much of lowland Devon is now occupied by intensively managed short-term grasslands. The main areas of permanent grassland are to be found around the fringes of Dartmoor and Exmoor, as well as in a strip along the north and south coasts. Here rough grasslands, mainly made up of fescues and bents, often with clumps of Gorse and other shrubs, are grazed at low intensity by cattle and sheep. On the south coast Cirl Buntings thrive in this habitat, and around the moorland fringes Yellowhammers, Linnets, Tree Pipits and Chaffinches find good habitat here.

### Arable land

Devon is not noted for its arable land but there are still extensive areas of cultivated fields. Often these are on a small scale, with much of the wheat and barley grown being used for livestock feed, often on the farm, but there are also more extensive areas in the east and north of the county, and in the South Hams, where cultivation is on a larger scale. In the South West as a whole, the area under wheat was close to 180,000 ha in 2010–2012, falling to 140,000 ha in 2013 after the very wet autumn of 2012 prevented much autumn sowing. The balance between spring-sown and autumn-sown barley also showed the effects of the 2012 autumn; the ratio in 2012 was 41,000 ha autumn-sown to 70,000 ha spring sown, and in 2013, 32,000 ha autumn-sown to 127,000 ha spring-sown, with spring barley taking up some of the space that would have been under wheat. A crop that has become more prominent in recent years, and particularly since its use in biofuel production began, is oil-seed rape. The area of oil-seed rape in the South West was 65,000 ha in 2012 and 64,000 ha in 2013. All oil-seed rape is autumn-sown, if possible in August, contributing to the early ploughing of cereal stubbles (see below).

Until the 1960s much of the area under cereals lay fallow under stubble through the winter, providing a valuable source of spilled grain and weed seeds for overwintering birds of many species. Since then there has been a steady move from spring sowing to autumn sowing, so that stubbles no longer remain over winter and this source of winter food has been lost.

Almost all arable crops, apart from those under organic cultivation regimes, are treated with both herbicides and pesticides. The long-continued use of herbicides now means that weedy fields are a rare

sight and close inspection of most cereal fields shows that they are virtually weed-free. Even the margins are often treated by hand with a total weed-killer such as glyphosate. Insecticides are also widely used; many species which feed on seeds when adult require protein-rich insect food for their growing young, and insects in crops have declined not only through direct killing by pesticides but also through the lack of broad-leaved weed food plants (Potts 2012).

Sitters (1988) remarked on the great increase in nitrogen fertilizer application between 1962 (44 kg per ha per year) and 1982 (132 kg per ha per year). The increase has continued but at a much slower rate, with the 2012 figure being 144 kg per ha per year. The price of nitrogenous fertilizers has increased substantially, and machinery is now capable of applying it with much greater precision – both factors tending to limit its use. Nevertheless, heavy nitrogen and phosphate applications over the years have encouraged the growth of tall rank plants such as Common Nettle and Hogweed, and tall grasses such as Cock's-foot and False Oat-grass. Communities of such species now occupy many roadsides and field margins.

Maize is now widely grown as a fodder crop. Seed is sown in late April or May on heavily fertilized and deeply cultivated ground. A single herbicide treatment may be possible before the crop becomes too tall. Growth is rapid and by August the crop is usually two metres or more tall, casting a dense shade and thus virtually weed-free. In September or early October it is harvested with a forage harvester which cuts the whole plant into small chippings which are then made into silage for winter feed. It is hard to know how much use birds make of the crop as it is all but impossible to view birds within it. Blackbirds have been seen leaving a crop as it was being harvested (J M Lock, pers. obs.) and Swallows may roost in it (Elphick 2011). Some maize stubbles remain over winter, but the maize grains are too large to be useful as food to anything smaller than a Woodpigeon, and weed seeds are almost absent.

Other arable crops such as potatoes and swedes are grown to a small extent. As bird habitats they are probably limited in value, although weed control in these crops is more difficult so that weed seed populations may be higher.

### Freshwater bodies

Devon has very few natural areas of open fresh water (Figure 12). The largest natural freshwater body is Slapton Ley which, like its close neighbour Beesands Ley, is a lagoon separated from the sea by a shingle bar. South Milton Ley is similar but has little open water. These South Devon leys are surrounded by a fringe of Common Reed and/or Reedmace. They are shallow and there is a good deal of submerged vegetation. Slapton Ley is the main site in Devon for Great Crested Grebes and Gadwall,

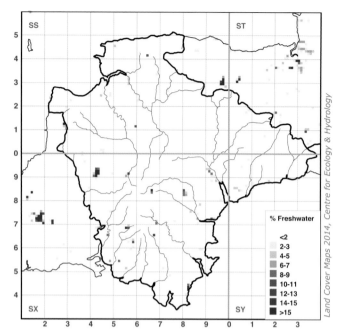

**Figure 12. Percentage of freshwater bodies in Devon.**

and there are probably more Coots here than anywhere else in the county. Numbers of Coots and various ducks are much augmented by migrants in winter, and species that normally live at sea may move onto the Ley in rough weather. The reed fringe holds Reed and Sedge Warblers, and Cetti's Warblers use the scrubby drier fringes of the reeds. The extensive reedbeds around the Ley have in the past provided breeding sites for transient Bitterns, Savi's Warblers and, possibly, Marsh Harriers, although none of these has established itself as a breeding species.

Devon's reservoirs are mainly on the uplands of Dartmoor – Avon Dam, Venford (Holne), Burrator, Fernworthy, Meldon and Kennick. Wistlandpound is the only large one on Devon Exmoor; there is also a small one (Swincombe) at Challacombe. The waters that they hold are generally acid and nutrient-poor, and there is little submerged vegetation. Fish, mainly trout, are not very abundant, although some stocking takes place at Fernworthy and Kennick. Small numbers of Cormorants feed on most, if not all, of Devon's reservoirs, while Goosanders use the reservoirs mainly for roosting, as do gulls.

The only large lowland reservoir in Devon is Roadford which, at 300 ha, almost doubles the area of open fresh water in the county. It is large enough and its water is rich enough to produce plenty of food for birds. Duck of various types, including diving ducks and sawbills, use it intermittently in the winter. There are substantial gull roosts and Black-headed Gulls have attempted to nest.

Industrial working has produced new open waters in several parts of the county. On the eastern flank of Dartmoor, china-clay workings have left pits that have filled with water. Claypits in the Bovey

Basin have also filled with water and one of these, Stover Lake, is now a reserve that holds a wide range of species. Further north the former Meeth Quarry between Hatherleigh and Great Torrington has been taken over as a reserve by Devon Wildlife Trust, and its open waters are being colonized by, among other species, Great Crested and Little Grebes.

## Rivers

Devon is well endowed with rivers. Most have their sources on Dartmoor or Exmoor but some of the East Devon rivers rise in the Blackdown Hills. The upper reaches of the moorland rivers are generally fast-flowing over a rocky or stony bed, with little submerged vegetation apart from mosses and liverworts. These upper reaches are the habitat of Grey Wagtails and Dippers. Common Sandpipers formerly nested along the gravelly stretches but are now rare or absent. Fish, if present, are small, usually the young stages of trout and Salmon.

The middle reaches of these rivers flow more gently, often in deep valleys through woodland. Slow-flowing pools alternate with swifter riffles, and the river bottom is often gravelly. Submerged plants are few, mostly mosses and liverworts, although a few submerged flowering plants, often Water-milfoil, may grow in sheltered spots. Trout and young Salmon are commoner here, and migrating Salmon may rest in the deeper pools. Dippers and Grey Wagtails are still present and are joined by Goosanders which feed here by day, and may breed, and by the introduced Mandarin Duck, which breeds in tree hollows in the woodland.

The lower reaches of Devon rivers have a much gentler gradient and usually flow slowly through farmland. Long slow-flowing stretches are separated by short riffles over gravel, and the river often spills over its banks at times of high flood, covering the adjacent farmland along the valley. Weirs often slow the flow further, though these are gradually being removed to ease the passage of migratory fish. Some lowland rivers have a lot of submerged vegetation, often species of Water-crowfoot, often with Canadian Waterweed, Horned Pondweed and various pondweeds. Trout and Salmon are usually present and may be joined by other species such as Eel and Dace. Mullet will, in summer, travel several kilometres upriver from the estuary, well beyond the influence of salt water. Grey Wagtails haunt these lower stretches but Dippers and Goosanders are usually absent. Mute Swans may graze the grass fields adjacent to the river and Mallard may be present particularly where people feed them; both species will breed along the river. Cormorants flight inland from the estuaries to feed and Grey Herons stalk the slow-flowing pools and shallows. The vertical earth banks provide nesting opportunities for Kingfishers and Sand Martins, though both are vulnerable to summer floods.

**Rising in the Blackdown Hills, the River Otter flows through East Devon to the English Channel at Lyme Bay.**

*Photo: Dave Smallshire*

### Estuaries

Devon is particularly well supplied with estuaries. The reasons for this are explained in the geological introduction but, in brief, when the sea level was lower during the Ice Ages, the rivers cut down well below the current sea level. As the sea rose again, so these valleys were flooded and became filled with silts and clays. Nutrient-rich sediments are constantly brought down by the rivers so that the estuary muds become a rich habitat for marine invertebrates and these in turn provide rich feeding for birds, mainly waders, ducks and geese. In a few estuaries Eel-grass forms areas of tidally submerged 'grassland' which is grazed by geese. The rich invertebrate fauna also provides food for young fish, and for species such as Mullet, Bass and Flounder, estuaries are very important nursery areas. The young fish are of course an important food source for many birds, and the adults are preyed on by Cormorants and by passing Ospreys.

On the north coast the combined estuary of the Taw and Torridge is by far the largest. On the south coast, from east to west, are the estuaries of the Axe, Otter, Exe, Teign, Dart, Kingsbridge (which lacks a major inflowing river), Avon, Erme, Yealm, Plym and Tamar. All are, to varying degrees, important sites for birds. The Exe Estuary, because it is the largest, holds the highest numbers. It also produces the largest numbers of species and rarities, not least because it is comparatively well watched.

### The Sea

The seas around Devon are comparatively shallow and rich in species. The many rivers bring down mineral nutrients which enrich the sea, although much of the nutrient load must be trapped in the long estuaries. Other nutrient additions come – or came – from the numerous sewer outlets that

**The Taw Estuary near Barnstaple, combined with the Torridge Estuary the largest on Devon's north coast.**

*Photo: Roy Churchill*

**A Brixham trawler – the seas around Devon are comparatively shallow and fish are abundant along both coasts.**

*Photo: Mark Darlaston*

formerly discharged human waste untreated into the sea, providing productive sites for gull-watchers. However, most of these have now been replaced by onshore treatment of the sewage, although many of these may discharge into the sea in times of flood when their storage capacity is overwhelmed.

The sea in the Bristol Channel along the north coast of Devon is often turbid, probably because of the strong scouring effects of the very large tides on the fine sediments in this area, while on the south coast the sea is often much clearer. This has implications for bird species that rely on sight to catch their prey.

Fish are abundant along both coasts. Flatfish such as Plaice and Dab are common on sandy substrates. Larger species such as Turbot and Brill occur but only their young stages are likely to be taken by birds. In winter, Whiting are common and are joined by Cod, albeit in smaller numbers. In summer the main event is the arrival of Mackerel which move

inshore at this time, often in pursuit of European Sprats, the young of other fish and, increasingly as the seas become warmer, Anchovies. All these smaller species, particularly when driven to the surface by Mackerel and other predatory fish, are fed on by seabirds of all kinds, but particularly gulls, terns, Shags, Cormorants and shearwaters. Gannets feed mainly on the larger species – Mackerel, Pilchards and Herring. These larger fish may themselves be concentrated and driven to the surface by the various dolphin species that occur in Devon waters.

## Urban areas

Towns and villages (Figure 13) are often ignored or overlooked as a bird habitat. They do, of course, occupy land that could provide bird habitat, and an increasing population now means that there is pressure to expand many urban areas and to create new ones. Urban habitats do, however, support numerous bird species. Those of us who have done Timed Tetrad Visits for the Atlas will know well that one can walk through long lengths of country roads and footpaths, seeing only the odd Blackbird, Robin or Carrion Crow, and then coming to an old-established farmstead or hamlet and immediately struggling to record the House Sparrows, Swallows, Chaffinches, Jackdaws, Pied Wagtails and many more that frequent these settlements. Old untidy farms are also far richer in birds that neatly gentrified ones.

Towns themselves provide a home for Feral Pigeons – although improved hygiene and refuse collection have reduced the food available, as have campaigns to discourage feeding of pigeons. Peregrines are now a feature of many large towns and cities, feeding largely on Feral Pigeons, although recent studies (Dixon & Drewitt 2012) have shown that they take a wide range of species, including migrants passing over the city at night and illuminated from below by the street lighting. Swifts breed in towns, although tidying-up and weather- and bird-proofing of buildings have reduced their opportunities. In the last 50 years gulls, particularly Herring Gulls but also Lesser and Great Black-backed Gulls, have taken to breeding on inland buildings, and their vigorous defence of their young can bring clashes with householders and passers-by.

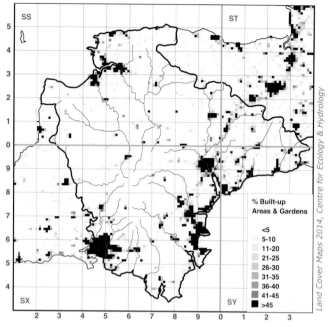

Figure 13. Percentage of built-up areas and gardens in Devon.

Land Cover Maps 2014, Centre for Ecology & Hydrology

Urban and suburban gardens are an excellent habitat for many bird species. Our national love of feeding 'our' garden birds is somewhat negated by an equally strong obsession with keeping dogs and cats, but in spite of this, populations of tits, finches, sparrows and thrushes are high in gardens. Sparrowhawks take advantage of the concentrations of small birds and regularly ambush bird tables. Woodland species such as Nuthatches and Great Spotted Woodpeckers supplement their diets from peanut and sunflower seed feeders, and Goldfinches, Siskins and, to a lesser but increasing extent, Lesser Redpolls come to take energy-rich oily Niger seeds. Robins have moved from accompanying Wild Boars in the forests of continental Europe to joining the gardener as he or she digs the vegetable plot.

**Chudleigh, at the end of the Teign Valley on the eastern edge of Dartmoor.**

*Photo: Dave Smallshire*

*Text: J M Lock*

# A Brief History of Bird Recording in Devon

Devon has been well supplied with accounts of its birds over the last 120 years; the following is a very short summary of their history which has been comprehensively covered by David Jenks (2004) in his *A History of Devonshire Ornithology*.

D'Urban & Mathew's *Birds of Devon* (1892) belongs very much to the 'What's hit's history; what's missed's mystery' era, but in its considerable detail gives us a picture of a time when Corncrakes rasped in every hayfield, Montagu's Harriers bred regularly and Cirl Buntings were common around both the north and south coasts. This book was followed by Dixon's *Bird-Life in a Southern County* (1899) which is a habitat-by-habitat account rather than an avifauna. There was then a long hiatus, broken by local accounts such as Loyd's *The Birds of South-east Devon* (1929) and *Bird Life in Devon* (Walmesey White 1931).

It was left to Robert Moore to fill the ever-widening gap. His *The Birds of Devon* (1969) is very much a compilation; rather strangely, the accounts of each species are almost the same length, with Skylark and Crested Lark – for which there is only one acceptable modern record – receiving almost equal amounts of text. However, it filled a gap and provided an essential up-to-date summary against which records could be judged.

Two local avifaunas appeared close together early this century. The first was Roger Smaldon's *The Birds of Dartmoor* (2005), closely followed by *The Birds of*

*Lundy* by Tim Davis and Tim Jones (2007). Both cover their area in great detail and are valuable resources much used in the present work. For the whole county, however, it was the turn of Michael Tyler to produce a new and up-to-date account of Devon's birds after a 50-year gap. *The Birds of Devon* (Tyler 2010) summarizes the taxonomic status of each species and their occurrence in the county, and gives notes on present distribution, status and abundance. He had the advantage of being able to draw on two invaluable sources, discussed below. His publication was the first to be extensively illustrated.

The first source on which Tyler was able to draw was Humphrey Sitters's pioneering *Tetrad Atlas of the Breeding Birds of Devon* (1988). The mapping of the distribution of living organisms by grid squares ('dot maps') had been pioneered by botanists in, for instance, Perring & Walters's *Atlas of the British Flora* (1962) and adopted later by ornithologists in the first *Atlas of Breeding Birds in Britain and Ireland* (Sharrock 1976). Early dot maps used 10 x 10-km squares (hectads) but soon the need for a finer scale encouraged workers to move to a tetrad (2 x 2-km) scale, which has become the standard for mapping of most living organisms in Britain, even though it involves surveying 25 times more squares than in the hectad system.

The Sitters Atlas was a brave venture. Fieldwork lasted for eight years (1977–1985). The author did a great deal of the survey work himself, but he also enlisted the help of a large number of volunteer observers, many of them members of the Devon Bird Watching & Preservation Society, but with some involvement of the wider public. Remarkably good coverage was achieved, and the resulting maps

provide a hugely valuable baseline with which the present survey can be compared.

The other valuable source upon which Tyler and the present survey were able to draw is the *Devon Bird Reports*, produced annually since 1927. These have grown from short papers produced as part of the *Transactions of the Devonshire Association* to the present *c.*200-page tomes that summarize the status of species in the county as well as listing records for the relevant year. Since 1990 the reports have been compiled from a computerized database of all records submitted to the County Recorder, and those databases are archived by Devon Birds and are available to researchers.

The need for a new atlas of the distribution of Devon's birds has been recognized for some time. Some earlier attempts came to nothing and it was probably the commencement of work for the BTO's *Bird Atlas 2007–11* (Balmer *et al.* 2013) that stimulated the start of work at county level. Even so, fieldwork for this *Devon Bird Atlas* began well after the start of work on the National Atlas and continued almost until publication of the latter.

The results differ from most of the recent plethora of county and tetrad atlases in that there is a baseline for comparison. This means that we have real comparative data from which to assess changes in Devon's birds over the last 30 years. Such comparisons can be complicated by differences in survey techniques and changing criteria for proving breeding. In spite of this, our new Atlas demonstrates some striking changes: the spread of Little Egret and Cetti's Warbler; the probable loss of Golden Plover as a breeding species; the decline of the Cuckoo and Ring Ouzel; and the spread of Herring Gulls from the coast to inland towns. This Atlas also differs from its predecessor in that in includes winter and summer records, and non-breeders as well as breeders. It also attempts to give an index of abundance of each species, based on the technique of Timed Tetrad Visits introduced for the latest National Atlas.

So what can be expected from the next atlas in 30–40 years time? Perhaps breeding Red Kites, Great White Egrets and Stone Curlews; possibly breeding Penduline Tits and Serins, as well as the loss of Ring Ouzel and Dunlin as breeding species. The era of climate change combined with increasing population, greater recreational pressure on the countryside and more intensive farming will make the coming years challenging ones for Devon's birds.

*Text: J M Lock*

**The Cuckoo has seen one of the largest declines of any bird in Devon over the last 30 years.**

*Photo: Steve Hatch*

# What has the Atlas achieved?

THIS ATLAS, like other county atlases, can make comparisons with the BTO breeding bird surveys at the 10-km square (hectad) level for 1968–72 (Sharrock 1976), 1988–91 (Gibbons *et al.* 1993) and 2007–11 (Balmer *et al.* 2013), and for wintering birds with the *Winter Atlas 1981–84* (Lack 1986). However, this Devon Atlas is unusual in that we have a basis for comparison at the tetrad level in the form of the 1977–85 *Devon Tetrad Atlas* (Sitters 1988); this covered breeding species only, while the present survey covered wintering ones as well.

The present Atlas was able to draw on work carried out for the BTO's 2007–2011 Atlas, but full-scale county fieldwork at the tetrad level did not start until 2008 and continued into 2013, well after the finish of the national survey. Sitters's survey was based on 84,201 individual registrations, with an average of 46 species recorded in each tetrad. There were 39,634 records of confirmed breeding (22 per tetrad), 33,313 of probable breeding (18 per tetrad) and 11,254 of possible breeding (6 per tetrad). The present survey was based on 1,124,863 records from various sources; of these, 525,797 were breeding records, slightly more than six times the number of breeding records used by Sitters. This survey recorded 160 species: 137 confirmed breeders, 8 probable and 15 possible, while a fourth category, 'present', included, for instance, summering non-breeders like Common Scoter.

So what changes have occurred? Twenty-three species had breeding records in significantly more tetrads. These include species such as Little Grebe, Cormorant, Canada Goose, Mandarin, Tufted Duck, Goosander, Goshawk, Lesser Black-backed Gull, Great Black-backed Gull, Herring Gull, Nightjar, Cetti's Warbler, Sedge Warbler, Raven, Common Crossbill and Lesser Redpoll. On the other hand, 60 species had breeding records in statistically fewer tetrads; these include Grey Heron, Kestrel, Grey Partridge, Lapwing, Curlew, Turtle Dove, Cuckoo, Swift, Skylark, Meadow Pipit, Grey Wagtail, Dipper, Ring Ouzel, Mistle Thrush, Whitethroat, Wood Warbler, Spotted Flycatcher, Jay, Starling, Linnet, Yellowhammer and Reed Bunting. Complete losses from the county – most of them on the brink at the time of the Sitters Atlas – include Golden Plover, Black Grouse, Common Tern, Nightingale and Corn Bunting. Among 11 species gained are Little Egret and Greylag Goose, the latter arising from naturalized birds. These are detailed on page 60.

What has caused these changes? There is discussion under the individual entries for each species, but a summary is merited here.

Some of the species that have increased appear to have found unoccupied niches. Little Egrets seem to complement Grey Herons, often sharing their breeding sites but taking much smaller prey; they have colonized Devon since the Sitters Atlas, first breeding in 2002. Little Grebes have benefited from new areas of open water, as have Tufted Ducks. Mandarin Ducks have found that there are no other river-dwelling herbivorous ducks. The larger gulls have moved away from breeding on coastal cliffs to artificial sites in towns and villages where they also benefit from our wasteful eating habits. Nightjars have exploited the cleared areas left when conifer plantations mature and are felled; they may suffer in future as new plantings grow up or are replaced by broadleaved trees. Dartford Warblers benefited from a series of mild winters but were cut back by those of 2009/10 and 2010/11; their population is cyclical, driven by hard winters which kill many individuals. Siskins have taken to garden feeders and to conifer plantations, so their increase can be attributed to a change in behaviour.

In the 'lost' list, the disappearance of Nightingales is part of a wider reduction in the species' British range; various reasons have been put forward for this (see Balmer *et al.* 2013). Hawfinches are such elusive and scarce birds that they are likely to have been missed by surveyors and may well still breed somewhere in the county. Tree Sparrows and Corn Buntings were always very scarce in Devon and their loss can probably be attributed to changes in agriculture: autumn ploughing of stubbles and regular flailing of hedges, for instance. Other species, such as Common Tern, Hoopoe and Serin, never had more than a very tenuous toehold in the county, and the last two may return if the climate warms.

The list of species that have declined is depressingly large. The possible reasons for the decline are discussed in the individual species accounts but some general patterns can be suggested. Firstly there is a group of farmland birds that includes Grey Partridge, Lapwing, Turtle Dove, Barn Owl and Skylark. These seem likely to have been affected by changes in agricultural practices: weed and insect control continued over many years leading to reduced food availability; autumn ploughing of stubbles so that weed seeds and spilled grain are not available during the winter months; and a change in grassland management from haymaking to silage harvesting, with several cuts at fairly short intervals throughout the summer, giving no time for ground-nesting species to raise a brood.

Another declining group is made up of woodland species such as Stock Dove, Tawny Owl, Lesser Spotted Woodpecker, Song Thrush, Wood Warbler, Spotted Flycatcher, Marsh Tit, Nuthatch and Treecreeper. The reasons for their decline are more difficult to pinpoint, but decreased woodland management, the thinning of undergrowth by high deer populations and increased disturbance through recreational use may all play a part.

Declining species that often nest in or on buildings include Stock Dove, Swift, House Martin, Pied Wagtail and Starling; all may well have suffered from a tidying up of buildings with the blocking of possible nest sites. House Sparrows, which also often breed in holes in buildings, suffer similarly but the decline in Devon shown by this survey is not statistically significant.

Another declining group is made up of species that make use of rough, often old, grassland for feeding; here we can include Kestrel, Barn Owl, Green Woodpecker, Meadow Pipit, Stonechat and Linnet. There has been a tendency towards improvement of areas of rough grassland through fertilizing and, often, ploughing and reseeding. This alters the plant species composition and also makes the habitat less suitable for small mammals – the principal food source for the predators.

Other farmland improvements may include the clearance of rough corners and small thickets and patches of scrub that formerly would have sheltered species such as Tawny Owl, Willow Warbler and Bullfinch.

Many of these changes appear to have been brought about by changes in farming practice and it is tempting to blame farmers for the losses of farmland birds. We should, however, rather be looking at the factors that drive farmers to strive for increased productivity. Farm prices are, at the time of writing, both low and volatile. The general population has become used to paying low prices for food while wasting between a third and a quarter of all that is bought. Loss-leader price-cutting by stores seeking to increase their market share has led to ridiculous states of affairs such as a litre of milk costing less than a litre of bottled water. In the long run we should be aiming to accept higher food prices – with the increase going to farmers – and to wasting less of what we buy. We should also be striving to increase the uptake of, and the amount of money available to, schemes such as Higher Level Stewardship and Countryside Stewardship that aim to improve the countryside as a habitat for birds and other wildlife. These schemes need to become more rigorous if they are to help permanently increase and sympathetically manage such habitats. A shining example of this in Devon is the success of the RSPB, supported by Devon Birds, in working with farmers in the South Hams to improve the habitat for Cirl Buntings. This has increased their population from 114 pairs in 1989 to 860 in 2009; there may well be over 1,000 pairs now. Only future surveys, whether of single species or on a grander scale such as carried out for this Atlas, will tell us.

*Text: J M Lock*

*Photo: Neil Bygrave (Great Tit, page 51)*

**Skylark – one of a group of farmland birds affected by changes in agricultural practice.**

*Photo: Paul Sterry/NPL*

# Atlas Methodology

## THE SURVEY PERIOD

Surveying for the British Trust for Ornithology's National Bird Atlas began on 1 November 2007 and continued until 31 July 2011.

The BTO based the survey on the now standard division of an Ordnance Survey 10-km square of the National Grid into twenty-five 2 x 2-km squares (tetrads). Each tetrad was designated with a letter of the alphabet, Tetrad A in the lower left-hand corner of the 10-km square and ending with Tetrad Z in the upper right-hand corner. The only letter of the alphabet not used was the letter O. (NB. In the 1977–85 *Devon Tetrad Atlas* the position of the letters was reversed, with Tetrad A at the upper left-hand corner of the 10-km square, ending with Tetrad Z at the lower right-hand corner.)

An online system designed by the BTO enabled tetrads to be allocated to volunteer surveyors by the Regional Organizer for each county and results to be entered directly by the surveyor. Two complementary field methods – Timed Tetrad Visits (TTVs) and Roving Records – were used, the first providing systematic data for assessing relative abundance and change, the second for collating basic distribution records.

TTVs were made to each tetrad, two in the breeding season (April–July) and two in the winter season (November–February). These required the surveyor to walk for one or two hours (each hour

Table 1. Criteria and codes used to define the categories of breeding for the BTO National Atlas and the Devon Bird Atlas.

| | | |
|---|---|---|
| **Non-breeder** | F | Flying over |
| | M | Migrant |
| | U | Summer visitor |
| **Possible breeder** | H | Observed in suitable nesting habitat |
| | S | Singing male* |
| **Probable breeder** | P | Pair in suitable nesting habitat |
| | T | Permanent territory (defended over at least one week) |
| | D | Courtship and display |
| | N | Visiting probable nest site |
| | A | Agitated behaviour |
| | I | Brood patch of incubating bird (bird in the hand) |
| | B | Nest building or excavating nest-hole |
| **Confirmed breeder** | DD | Distraction display or injury feigning |
| | UN | Used nest or eggshells found from this season |
| | FL | Recently fledged or downy young |
| | ON | Adults entering or leaving nest-site indicating occupied nest |
| | FF | Adult carrying faecal sac or food for young |
| | NE | Nest containing eggs |
| | NY | Nest with young seen or heard |

*In both of the two Devon Atlases the criteria used to determine confirmed, probable and possible breeding were the same, with the exception of 'Singing male' which was categorized as 'possible' for the 2007–13 survey but 'probable' in the 1977–85 survey.

recorded separately) along a route taking in the major habitats within a tetrad, recording all the birds seen or heard (but excluding young birds of the year during the breeding period). Observers had the option also to provide an estimate of population per species per tetrad. TTVs within individual tetrads had to be completed within the same breeding or wintering period.

The criteria and codes used to define the various categories of breeding are described in Table 1 on the previous page.

For the National Atlas, the BTO required completion of TTVs in a minimum of eight tetrads per 10-km square. The BTO had intimated that the National Atlas database could be used for collection of additional data by county ornithological organizations that wanted to carry out a full county survey at the tetrad level. Although the possibility of producing a Devon Bird Atlas was being discussed in 2009, it was not until 2010 that surveying for the county Atlas really began in earnest.

There were, however, several obstacles to be overcome. We were already nearly three years into the survey period; we had more than twice as much more work to carry out; and some of the work already carried out had not attempted to assess breeding status in every tetrad. We were further hampered by history because an earlier attempt to produce a second county tetrad Atlas had failed and some observers who had devoted time to that project were understandably reluctant to engage in a new one.

Despite these concerns, the Devon Birds Atlas Group decided that every tetrad in each 10-km square containing land within the county would be surveyed using the BTO Atlas method, and that an additional two years of fieldwork, up to 31 July 2013, would be carried out to achieve as near complete coverage as possible. Hence the area organizers responsible for recruiting the necessary surveyors and ensuring survey coverage in all tetrads set about their tasks.

*Text: Stella Beavan*
*Photo: Andrew Cunningham (Wood Warbler, page 53)*

## RECORD VALIDATION

The data used in the preparation of this *Devon Bird Atlas* were those in the database of the British Trust for Ornithology compiled for *Bird Atlas 2007–11*, together with additional data for the two years to summer 2013. In total these amounted to more than one million Devon records. However, analysis of these records down to tetrad level, rather than the BTO's 10-km square national level, meant that much more validation effort was needed. Nevertheless, the methodology of record validation was similar for both publications. Interestingly, the BTO's estimate

of an average 1% queried records per county meant that about 10,000 Devon records would have been queried during validation. An important factor in this whole process was the involvement of the wider public, some less skilled in identifying and recording birds than others.

Pre-analysis validation of observer data is a recognized and important step in the data-checking process and has been included for previous Britain and Ireland atlases. The primary purpose of validation is twofold: (a) to ensure an acceptable standard in the data submitted, e.g. by correcting data-entry errors or improving understanding of breeding codes, and (b) to address some of the more difficult issues, like apparent species misidentification. Thanks to the help and understanding of recorders, most data-entry errors were quickly and easily resolved, but if recorders failed to respond to queries, their records had to be discarded.

Many queries involved the use of inappropriate breeding codes. Obvious examples included failure to differentiate between birds seen entering a probable nest hole (code N for 'probable breeding') and birds entering a hole in circumstances indicative of an active nest (code ON for 'confirmed breeding'). In the latter case one would expect extra data, such as noticing that the birds were carrying food (e.g. woodpeckers) or to hear calling young (e.g. Jackdaws). Likewise, records of high tree-nesters such as Rook or Carrion Crow, shown as NE ('nest containing eggs'), were presumably based on apparently incubating birds, but were probably a guess and a simple 'ON' ('occupied nest') would have acceptably proved breeding.

Similarly, use of the FL ('recently fledged young') code has obvious dangers, as the next tetrad is never more than a kilometre away. For example, Mute Swans and other waterfowl often move several kilometres up or down stream from the nest site and may do so within a few days of hatching. Likewise, broods of recently fledged Starlings can soon move considerable distances, and there is an annual influx of recently fledged Black-headed Gulls to Devon in summer, though the species only bred once in the county in the whole survey period.

Such pedantry may seem unnecessary but ensuring the integrity of the data is of paramount importance, and errors or inconsistencies must be addressed wherever possible.

Species misidentification had two obvious origins: simple observer error or a real difficulty in separating similar species. Examples of the former might involve the separation of raptor species or offshore shearwaters. On the other hand, the separation of the redpolls, and Marsh and Willow Tits are more complex.

Most observers attributed any Devon redpoll records to Lesser Redpoll, avoiding any major identification issues and probably not introducing any serious distortion of the records. On the other hand, numerous recorders seemed unaware that Tree Sparrows are now apparently absent from Devon as a breeding species, occurring only as an extreme winter rarity. Similarly, reports of hybrid Carrion-Hooded Crows seem most unlikely since Hooded Crow is a rare passage migrant in Devon and occurred only in May 2012 during the entire Atlas period. Either these represented data-entry errors or involved crows showing aberrant plumage.

However, pride of place in the Devon ornithological confusion stakes goes to the two black-capped tits, Marsh Tit and Willow Tit. Willow Tit has suffered a catastrophic 82% decline in the UK for the years 1995–2011 (Risely *et al.* 2013) and is absent or near absent from Devon's three adjoining counties (Balmer *et al.* 2013). Of all species, these two perhaps underline one of the few difficulties in assessing the accuracy of records from unknown observers. While the Willow Tit data presented on pages 304–305 may overestimate both the species' current Devon range and the number of individuals involved, it does demonstrate a 76% decline since the 1977–85 *Devon Tetrad Atlas* – not very different from the overall picture reported by Risely *et al.* (2013), but both are greater than the 50% decline since 1988–1991 reported in *Bird Atlas 2007–2011*. It is clear that a species-specific survey is overdue and, largely because of what our survey revealed, this will commence in 2016.

*Text: Peter Robinson*

**Separating Willow Tit (above) from Marsh Tit – a challenge to the observer and for the validation of records.**

*Photos: Frank B Blackburn/NPL (top) & Andrew Cunningham*

## DATA ANALYSIS AND MAPPING

### Data collection

The data collection period for the National Atlas was from November 2007 to July 2011 but the BTO kindly allowed data for local atlases to be input after this period. For Devon the period was extended to the end of July 2013. The BTO online data input and validation system divided the data into three periods: Winter (November to February inclusive), Overlap (March and August to September) and Breeding (April to July but including breeding records from the other periods).

In January 2014, the BTO sent four comma-separated variable (CSV) files, two for 'Winter' and two for 'Breeding' (TTV and Roving Record for each period). Provisional maps were produced from these files but analysis showed that the Breeding files did not contain Nest Records for the period after the end of data collection for the National Atlas so these were requested and sent as a separate file in March 2014; this was merged with the existing Breeding (Roving) file. A further problem was discovered late in the mapping phase in that a significant number of records from the Overlap period were missing. These missing records were obtained from the BTO in September 2014 and merged with the Breeding (Roving) file. The data sets were thus complete by December 2014.

Examination of the complete data set revealed three more problems: (1) there were many thousands of duplicate records; (2) there were some extra commas in one of the fields; and (3) there were about 2,000 records that needed to be validated. The duplicate records were deleted (although they made no difference to the maps, they inflated the apparent number of records) and the spurious commas were replaced by spaces. The validator, Peter Robinson, checked the unvalidated records and the extra Overlap records were merged into the Devon databases.

Merging the additional data raised the question 'How do we define the Winter and Breeding mapping periods?' For the preliminary maps we had taken the two periods defined by the two sets of files initially sent by the BTO. The additional data forced us to reconsider what to do with records from the Overlap months. None of these questions arose with the TTV records because the Winter and Breeding TTV seasons were clearly defined as November to February and April to July respectively, so there were no TTV records in the Overlap period.

This problem is discussed on pages 34 and 36 of *Bird Atlas 2007–2011* where it is concluded that Winter is November to February for both Roving Records and TTVs, but that Breeding is not defined by months but by breeding activity, although the Breeding TTVs cover only April to July. Appendix 4 in the National Atlas shows, for a wide range of species, the months for which breeding records were to be included.

The Devon Birds Atlas Group decided that the Devon Atlas would cover the whole year, so in this Atlas 'Winter' is October to February inclusive and 'Breeding' is March to September inclusive with the addition of any acceptable breeding records outside this range. We thus had four data files: one each for Breeding and Winter TTVs and one each for Breeding and Winter 'other' records.

| Table 2. Sources of the *Devon Bird Atlas* records. | | |
|---|---|---|
| | **Records** | **Percent** |
| Timed Tetrad Visit | 310,825 | 27.632 |
| Roving | 308,939 | 27.465 |
| BTO BirdTrack | 270,224 | 24.023 |
| Devon Birds | 208,956 | 18.576 |
| BirdGuides | 10,665 | 0.948 |
| BTO Breeding Bird Survey | 8,011 | 0.712 |
| BTO Ringers | 3,416 | 0.304 |
| BTO Nest Record Scheme | 3,078 | 0.274 |
| BTO Wetland Bird Survey | 481 | 0.043 |
| BTO Heronries Census | 121 | 0.011 |
| RSPB Dataset | 83 | 0.007 |
| JNCC Seabird Data | 38 | 0.003 |
| BTO Garden Bird Watch | 19 | 0.002 |
| **Total** | **1,124,856** | **100.000** |

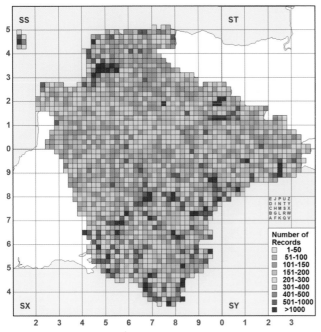

**Figure 14. Number of breeding-season records per tetrad.**

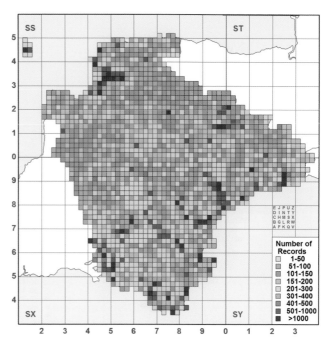

**Figure 15. Number of winter-season records per tetrad.**

## Sources of the records

Roving and TTV records were input using the BTO website, and records from the BTO's own surveys as well as from BirdTrack, Devon Birds and other sources were also incorporated (Table 2). These extra half-a-million records greatly enhanced the data set.

There were a total of 1,124,856 records, comprising 525,797 Breeding, 409,486 Winter, 99,835 Breeding TTV and 89,738 Winter TTV. Many of the non-TTV records were duplicates (i.e. the same birds being recorded by more than one person) but the amassing of more than 1.1 million records says much about the enthusiasm of more than 1,200 Devon volunteer recorders.

## Data manipulation

The four CSV files were initially manipulated using Microsoft Excel 2010. A computer program written in Power BASIC 6.03 then took each of these files to produce distribution files suitable for input into the mapping program DMAP 7.5 (© Alan Morton). A DMAP base map for Devon was produced by digitizing existing paper maps. Other programs were written to carry out statistical analyses, although some summaries were carried out using IBM SPSS 21 (Statistical Package for the Social Sciences).

## Coverage and effort

As well as producing distribution maps, the program produced files that DMAP could use to show the extent of coverage by the surveyors and the 'effort' put into surveying each tetrad. The coverage maps showed that every one of the 1,858 Devon tetrads

had been surveyed in both the breeding and winter periods. The 'effort' maps show the number of records submitted for each tetrad (Figures 14 & 15). These do not necessarily show the effort put into surveying because some tetrads have fewer birds present and available to record, but they do give an indication of the most intensively surveyed tetrads.

## Numbers of species and changes since the 1977–1985 survey

In total, 364 species were recorded in this survey – 306 in winter and 325 in the breeding season. There were 137 confirmed breeding species, eight probables and 15 possibles (= 160 species); the rest were just recorded as 'present' with no indication of breeding. Sitters (1988, Appendix 4) lists 147 breeding species occupying tetrads. There may be small differences in the recording methods and criteria for 'breeding' so it might not be possible to make direct comparisons, but it is safe to say there has been little change in the number of breeding species between the two surveys.

The number of species recorded in each tetrad in each season is shown in Figures 16 & 17 (overleaf). It is apparent that the pattern is the same for both seasons, with the estuaries having the most species and moorland having the least.

Most tetrads had between 30 and 49 species present in the breeding period but 33 tetrads had more than 109 species and 32 had between 90 and 109 species.

One of the reasons for producing this Atlas is to make comparisons between this 2007–2013 survey and Sitters's survey of 1977–1985. Where relevant in the species accounts in this Atlas there are tables that

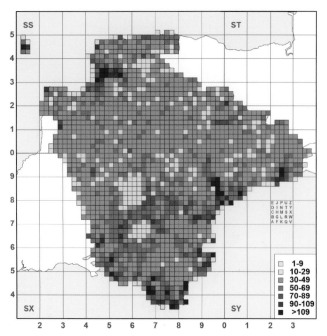

Figure 16. Number of species per tetrad
in the breeding period.

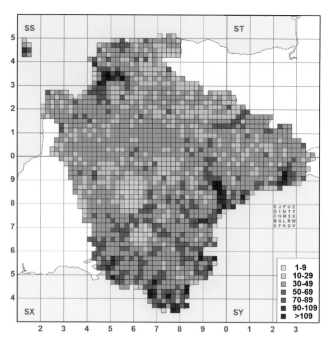

Figure 17. Number of species per tetrad
in the winter period.

make this comparison. The 1977–1985 survey covered 1,834 tetrads whereas the 2007–2013 survey covered 1,858. The increase is due to the addition of some tetrads that overlap adjacent counties as well as a few coastal ones that were not used in the previous survey because they consisted largely of offshore rocks or a few metres of headland (Figure 18).

The comparison between the number of occupied tetrads in the breeding season is shown for many species in a simple table in the species accounts. For example, Table 3 shows the number of tetrads occupied by Grasshopper Warblers at each level in each of the two surveys. Sitters (1988) did not have a 'Present' category but the 'Possible', 'Probable' and 'Confirmed' categories are comparable. This example shows that in the 1977–1985 survey 239 of the 1,834 tetrads surveyed had Grasshopper Warblers recorded as breeding (possible, probable or confirmed), whereas in the 2007–2013 survey 223 of the 1,858 tetrads surveyed had them recorded as breeding. A simple 2 x 2 contingency table analysis shows that these two proportions are not significantly different (P = 0.405), so we can say that there is no evidence of a change in the proportion of tetrads occupied during the breeding season by Grasshopper Warblers in Devon between the two surveys.

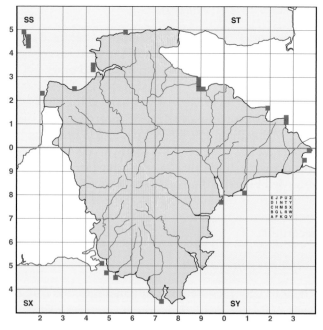

Figure 18. The 24 tetrads surveyed in
2007–13 but not in 1977–1985.

### Table 3. Comparison of the number of tetrads occupied by Grasshopper Warblers during the breeding period in 1977–1985 and in 2007–2013.

| Grasshopper Warbler | Present | | Possible | | Probable | | Confirmed | | Total | |
|---|---|---|---|---|---|---|---|---|---|---|
| | No. | % | No. | % | No. | % | No. | % | No. | % |
| 1977–1985 | – | – | 13 | 0.71 | 197 | 10.74 | 29 | 1.58 | 239 | 13.03 |
| 2007–2013 | 59 | 3.18 | 120 | 6.46 | 94 | 5.06 | 9 | 0.48 | 223 | 12.00 |
| Significance: The change is not significant (P =0.405) | | | | | | | | | | |

The statistical significance of the difference in the proportions of tetrads occupied between the two surveys is appended to the table using the following terminology:

❑ The change is not significant (P = 0.***)
   [i.e. the exact probability]
❑ The change is significant (P <0.05)
❑ The change is very significant (P <0.01)
❑ The change is highly significant (P <0.001)
❑ The change is extremely significant (P <0.0001)

The gains and losses of breeding birds between the 1977–1985 and the 2007–2013 surveys are shown in Table 4 (on page 60) and Figures 19 & 20. There are 52 species which show no change in the proportion of tetrads occupied and 23 species that show a significant increase. There are 11 new species and eight lost ones but the most worrying category is the 'Significantly fewer tetrads' where there are 60 species, many of which are what one might have thought of as common. Most of these species are still common but they are less widespread than they used to be.

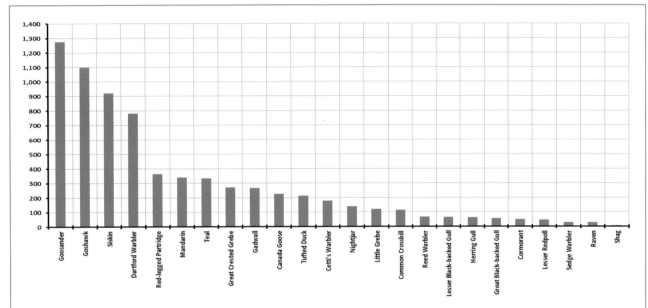

**Figure 19. Percentage increase in the number of tetrads occupied in the breeding season for all species where change is statistically significant.**

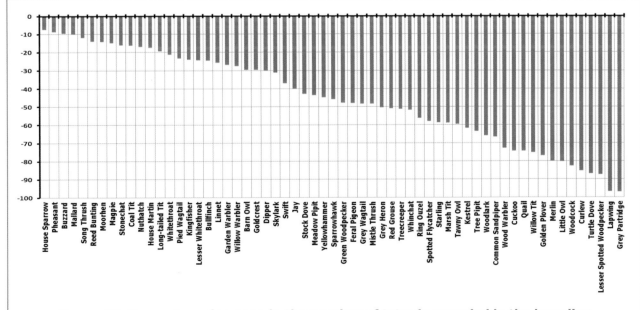

**Figure 20. Percentage decrease in the number of tetrads occupied in the breeding season for all species where the change is statistically significant.**

**Table 4. Significant changes (P <0.05) in the number of tetrads occupied by breeding birds between the 1975–1985 and the 2007–2013 surveys. Includes possible, probable and confirmed breeding categories.**

| | | | |
|---|---|---|---|
| **Gained** | Little Egret | Black Swan | Greylag Goose |
| | Egyptian Goose | Red-crested Pochard | Red-breasted Merganser |
| | Ruddy Duck | Little Ringed Plover | Black-headed Gull |
| | Red-backed Shrike | Common Rosefinch | |
| **Significantly more tetrads** | Little Grebe | Great Crested Grebe | Cormorant |
| | Canada Goose | Mandarin | Gadwall |
| | Teal | Tufted Duck | Goosander |
| | Goshawk | Red-legged Partridge | Lesser Black-backed Gull |
| | Herring Gull | Great Black-backed Gull | Nightjar |
| | Cetti's Warbler | Sedge Warbler | Reed Warbler |
| | Dartford Warbler | Raven | Siskin |
| | Common Crossbill | Lesser Redpoll | |
| **No Change** | Fulmar | Manx Shearwater | Shag |
| | Mute Swan | Shelduck | Garganey |
| | Shoveler | Pochard | Water Rail |
| | Corncrake | Coot | Oystercatcher |
| | Ringed Plover | Dunlin | Snipe |
| | Redshank | Kittiwake | Guillemot |
| | Razorbill | Puffin | Woodpigeon |
| | Collared Dove | Long-eared Owl | Great Spotted Woodpecker |
| | Sand Martin | Swallow | Rock Pipit |
| | Yellow Wagtail | Wren | Dunnock |
| | Robin | Redstart | Black Redstart |
| | Wheatear | Blackbird | Grasshopper Warbler |
| | Savi's Warbler | Blackcap | Chiffchaff |
| | Firecrest | Pied Flycatcher | Blue Tit |
| | Great Tit | Bearded Tit | Jackdaw |
| | Rook | Carrion Crow | House Sparrow |
| | Chaffinch | Greenfinch | Goldfinch |
| | Cirl Bunting | | |
| **Significantly fewer tetrads** | Grey Heron | Mallard | Sparrowhawk |
| | Buzzard | Merlin | Kestrel |
| | Red Grouse | Grey Partridge | Quail |
| | Pheasant | Moorhen | Golden Plover |
| | Lapwing | Woodcock | Curlew |
| | Common Sandpiper | Feral Pigeon | Stock Dove |
| | Turtle Dove | Cuckoo | Barn Owl |
| | Little Owl | Tawny Owl | Swift |
| | Kingfisher | Green Woodpecker | Lesser Spotted Woodpecker |
| | Woodlark | Skylark | House Martin |
| | Tree Pipit | Meadow Pipit | Grey Wagtail |
| | Pied Wagtail | Dipper | Whinchat |
| | Stonechat | Ring Ouzel | Song Thrush |
| | Mistle Thrush | Lesser Whitethroat | Whitethroat |
| | Garden Warbler | Wood Warbler | Willow Warbler |
| | Goldcrest | Spotted Flycatcher | Long-tailed Tit |
| | Marsh Tit | Willow Tit | Coal Tit |
| | Nuthatch | Treecreeper | Jay |
| | Magpie | Starling | Linnet |
| | Bullfinch | Yellowhammer | Reed Bunting |
| **Lost** | Black Grouse | Common Tern | Hoopoe |
| | Nightingale | Tree Sparrow | Serin |
| | Hawfinch | Corn Bunting | |

## Ubiquity

Species that occurred in 50% or more of tetrads in each of the two seasons are shown in Table 5. There are no surprises here, with 30 species common to both lists. These lists do not give any indication of the number of each species that are present in the tetrads, only their ubiquity. So, for example, while Carrion Crow is the most ubiquitous species in both the winter period and the breeding period (98% of tetrads in each season), it is almost certainly not the most numerous.

## Abundance

Which is the most abundant bird species in Devon? It is not possible to count all the birds in Devon but the number of records of each species might give an index of overall abundance. The 200 most recorded species in both the breeding and winter periods are shown in Table 6. These figures should be taken as indicative rather than definitive because, for example, counts of birds may be affected by the conspicuousness of each species, so that small and cryptic birds may be recorded less than they should be and *vice versa* for large and conspicuous ones.

## Altitudinal distribution

Data in visual form on the altitudinal distribution of tetrads and species in the breeding period are presented in Appendix 4 (pages 472–490).

## Map production

Maps were produced by DMAP as small Graphic Interchange Format (GIF) files for distribution to the Devon Birds Atlas Group and to the species account authors. These files are ideal for viewing on a computer screen and for emailing but they can show only 256 colours and are not scalable. For publication they were output as Encapsulated PostScript (EPS) files which are scalable and can show many thousands of colours. The mapping program DMAP blends colours using the three RGB colours (Red, Blue, Green) but the EPS files were output using the CMYK (Cyan, Magenta, Yellow, Black) colour model used in colour printing. This mismatch necessitated much experimentation with the colours so that the maps had the desired colours when reproduced in this Atlas.

*Text: Mike Hounsome*

### Table 5. Species which occur in 50% or more of tetrads in each season.

| Winter % | | | | | | |
|---|---|---|---|---|---|---|
| | Carrion Crow | 98 | Starling | 86 | Jay | 68 |
| | Blackbird | 95 | House Sparrow | 83 | Nuthatch | 67 |
| | Robin | 95 | Redwing | 83 | Bullfinch | 67 |
| | Chaffinch | 95 | Song Thrush | 81 | Goldcrest | 67 |
| | Woodpigeon | 93 | Pied Wagtail | 79 | Greenfinch | 66 |
| | Blue Tit | 93 | Rook | 79 | Herring Gull | 66 |
| | Buzzard | 92 | Pheasant | 78 | Goldfinch | 65 |
| | Great Tit | 92 | Raven | 78 | Meadow Pipit | 62 |
| | Wren | 92 | Coal Tit | 74 | Mistle Thrush | 60 |
| | Magpie | 91 | Fieldfare | 74 | Collared Dove | 56 |
| | Dunnock | 89 | Long-tailed Tit | 73 | | |
| | Jackdaw | 86 | G/S Woodpecker | 69 | | |
| **Summer %** | | | | | | |
| | Carrion Crow | 98 | Blackcap | 89 | Coal Tit | 65 |
| | Wren | 97 | Pheasant | 88 | Collared Dove | 63 |
| | Blackbird | 96 | House Sparrow | 88 | Goldcrest | 63 |
| | Chaffinch | 96 | Jackdaw | 87 | Long-tailed Tit | 62 |
| | Swallow | 96 | Song Thrush | 86 | Bullfinch | 61 |
| | Robin | 95 | Greenfinch | 83 | Whitethroat | 60 |
| | Woodpigeon | 95 | House Martin | 76 | Linnet | 60 |
| | Blue Tit | 94 | Rook | 75 | Herring Gull | 58 |
| | Buzzard | 93 | Pied Wagtail | 74 | Jay | 55 |
| | Chiffchaff | 93 | Willow Warbler | 74 | Swift | 53 |
| | Dunnock | 92 | G/S Woodpecker | 73 | Mallard | 50 |
| | Great Tit | 92 | Raven | 69 | Yellowhammer | 50 |
| | Goldfinch | 90 | Skylark | 67 | Mistle Thrush | 50 |
| | Magpie | 89 | Nuthatch | 67 | | |

## Table 6. The number of records of each of the 200 most recorded species.

| Species | Records | Species | Records | Species | Records |
|---|---|---|---|---|---|
| Blackbird | 33,089 | Reed Bunting | 4,523 | Green Sandpiper | 1,207 |
| Robin | 31,500 | Marsh Tit | 4,502 | Red-legged Partridge | 1,198 |
| Carrion Crow | 31,316 | Teal | 4,318 | Pied Flycatcher | 1,192 |
| Chaffinch | 30,487 | Redshank | 4,294 | Grasshopper Warbler | 1,183 |
| Blue Tit | 30,039 | Peregrine | 4,264 | Razorbill | 1,182 |
| Woodpigeon | 29,955 | Dunlin | 4,231 | Common Tern | 1,139 |
| Great Tit | 27,142 | Lesser Black-backed Gull | 3,884 | Common Crossbill | 1,068 |
| Wren | 26,717 | Dipper | 3,787 | Merlin | 1,057 |
| Dunnock | 24,961 | Feral Pigeon | 3,735 | Guillemot | 977 |
| Magpie | 24,421 | Kingfisher | 3,661 | Pochard | 956 |
| House Sparrow | 24,037 | Lapwing | 3,539 | Eider | 937 |
| Buzzard | 22,520 | Whimbrel | 3,284 | Arctic Skua | 930 |
| Jackdaw | 21,194 | Wigeon | 3,249 | Pintail | 906 |
| Goldfinch | 20,061 | Coot | 3,127 | Yellow Wagtail | 886 |
| Song Thrush | 19,189 | Turnstone | 3,085 | Hen Harrier | 856 |
| Pheasant | 18,358 | Tawny Owl | 3,063 | Osprey | 854 |
| Herring Gull | 18,356 | Shag | 2,966 | Goldeneye | 841 |
| Greenfinch | 18,232 | Great Crested Grebe | 2,960 | Avocet | 829 |
| Chiffchaff | 17,204 | Brent Goose | 2,933 | Purple Sandpiper | 828 |
| Swallow | 16,949 | Spotted Flycatcher | 2,926 | Black-necked Grebe | 827 |
| Pied Wagtail | 16,626 | Greenshank | 2,910 | Wood Warbler | 826 |
| Rook | 16,507 | Common Scoter | 2,882 | Great Skua | 797 |
| Starling | 15,563 | Gannet | 2,717 | Water Pipit | 753 |
| Blackcap | 14,285 | Cuckoo | 2,702 | Mandarin | 748 |
| Mallard | 14,098 | Rock Pipit | 2,692 | Velvet Scoter | 735 |
| Coal Tit | 13,670 | Garden Warbler | 2,664 | Greylag Goose | 734 |
| Raven | 13,544 | Mediterranean Gull | 2,655 | Ring Ouzel | 718 |
| Great Spotted Woodpecker | 13,408 | Ringed Plover | 2,555 | Spotted Redshank | 656 |
| Long-tailed Tit | 13,255 | Common Gull | 2,519 | Surf Scoter | 652 |
| Nuthatch | 12,624 | Golden Plover | 2,508 | Red Kite | 636 |
| Skylark | 12,528 | Sandwich Tern | 2,460 | Cattle Egret | 615 |
| Goldcrest | 11,998 | Black-tailed Godwit | 2,394 | Nightjar | 606 |
| Collared Dove | 11,642 | Redstart | 2,374 | Curlew Sandpiper | 531 |
| Bullfinch | 11,460 | Cirl Bunting | 2,325 | Little Owl | 526 |
| Meadow Pipit | 11,330 | Common Sandpiper | 2,292 | Pomarine Skua | 516 |
| Jay | 9,944 | Goosander | 2,225 | Lesser Whitethroat | 495 |
| Redwing | 9,761 | Black Redstart | 2,221 | Ruff | 491 |
| Linnet | 9,334 | Bar-tailed Godwit | 2,192 | Little Gull | 474 |
| Moorhen | 8,551 | Fulmar | 2,152 | Black-throated Diver | 457 |
| Willow Warbler | 8,547 | Brambling | 2,145 | Scaup | 457 |
| Black-headed Gull | 8,496 | Sanderling | 2,110 | Willow Tit | 451 |
| House Martin | 8,484 | Grey Plover | 2,088 | Little Ringed Plover | 432 |
| Mistle Thrush | 8,301 | Sand Martin | 2,047 | Lesser Spotted Woodpecker | 431 |
| Little Egret | 7,912 | Tufted Duck | 2,027 | Short-eared Owl | 426 |
| Stonechat | 7,504 | Barn Owl | 1,951 | Puffin | 423 |
| Grey Heron | 7,308 | Water Rail | 1,944 | Waxwing | 411 |
| Yellowhammer | 7,253 | Great Northern Diver | 1,920 | White Wagtail | 410 |
| Cormorant | 7,087 | Red-throated Diver | 1,898 | Jack Snipe | 406 |
| Canada Goose | 6,913 | Shoveler | 1,882 | Long-tailed Duck | 405 |
| Kestrel | 6,815 | Lesser Redpoll | 1,833 | Little Stint | 396 |
| Fieldfare | 6,700 | Red-breasted Merganser | 1,808 | Arctic Tern | 391 |
| Whitethroat | 6,577 | Sedge Warbler | 1,802 | Marsh Harrier | 368 |
| Siskin | 6,162 | Tree Pipit | 1,766 | Storm Petrel | 350 |
| Oystercatcher | 6,037 | Reed Warbler | 1,680 | Bittern | 345 |
| Stock Dove | 5,920 | Knot | 1,677 | Garganey | 340 |
| Grey Wagtail | 5,898 | Slavonian Grebe | 1,669 | Woodlark | 338 |
| Sparrowhawk | 5,868 | Kittiwake | 1,631 | Snow Bunting | 329 |
| Great Black-backed Gull | 5,862 | Woodcock | 1,518 | Black Swan | 327 |
| Mute Swan | 5,855 | Cettis Warbler | 1,477 | Sooty Shearwater | 319 |
| Wheatear | 5,803 | Manx Shearwater | 1,471 | Yellow-legged Gull | 312 |
| Green Woodpecker | 5,764 | Hobby | 1,466 | Egyptian Goose | 303 |
| Shelduck | 5,494 | Spoonbill | 1,423 | Wood Sandpiper | 302 |
| Swift | 5,387 | Firecrest | 1,398 | Little Tern | 275 |
| Curlew | 5,361 | Whinchat | 1,345 | Iceland Gull | 273 |
| Little Grebe | 5,034 | Gadwall | 1,289 | Red-crested Pochard | 268 |
| Treecreeper | 4,826 | Dartford Warbler | 1,269 | Yellow-browed Warbler | 260 |
| Snipe | 4,561 | Balearic Shearwater | 1,254 | | |

# Layout of the Species Accounts

THE MAIN section of accounts includes species on the British List which are recognized as regular in Devon as well as some 'Category D and E' species – those whose origin is doubtfully wild but which occur regularly in the county. Some of these, such as Egyptian Goose and Muscovy Duck, regularly breed in the wild and some will, undoubtedly, be included on the British List in due course.

In general, breeding species are allocated two pages and non-breeders one or less.

Wherever possible the order of species follows that of the current taxonomic order (BOU 2013) but there are occasional deviations for reasons of layout. The Devon list in Appendix 6 is in the current order.

Within the species accounts a few common abbreviations are used, either for terms or references, and these are fully explained in the Glossary in Appendix 7.

The United Kingdom's leading bird conservation organizations work together to review the status of the species that occur habitually in the UK, and to assign a 'conservation status' to each of them. All birds having a Red or Amber conservation status in the latest review (Eaton *et al.* 2015) are so indicated in their individual accounts, while the reasons for the listing are given in the Glossary (see page 501).

Wherever possible the species photographs have been taken by Devon photographers of birds within the county, but occasional recourse to other sources has been necessary.

### Interpretation of maps

There are five kinds of maps, although not all species will have all five:

#### 1) Breeding dot maps at tetrad resolution

These are the conventional breeding-season dot maps with the usual three kinds of red dots – indicating confirmed, probable or possible breeding – obtained from any breeding-season records that include a breeding code. There is a fourth kind of dot (small and pink) for tetrads where the species was recorded during the breeding period but which did not have a

breeding code. These will be mostly Atlas Roving Records as well as BirdTrack and Devon Birds records and are termed 'present'.

### 2) Breeding dots maps at 10-km resolution

These use the same data as the tetrad breeding dot maps but are plotted on a 10-km square basis. They can, however, include extra records that were recorded only at the 10-km level, resulting in 10-km dots occurring where there are no tetrad level dots. These maps are shown instead of the tetrad level maps for some of the most sensitive species for which the Devon Birds Atlas Group decided not to display localities to the exact tetrad level.

### 3) Breeding abundance maps

These show the maximum hourly TTV count in the breeding period (April to July) as coloured squares. They also include a 'present' category for birds recorded outside the TTVs (by Roving Records, BirdTrack, Devon Birds etc.), also taking in the months of March and August–September (see *Data collection*, page 56) if there has not been a TTV count for that species in that tetrad. It has not been possible to include counts for these extra records because the time period of the count is unknown; hence they are just 'present'.

### 4) Winter abundance maps

The same as 'Breeding abundance maps' but for the winter period (October to February).

### 5) Breeding dot maps 1977–1985

These are the conventional three sizes of breeding dot maps published in the *Devon Tetrad Atlas* for the 1977–1985 survey (Sitters 1988). They do not include a 'present' category but are otherwise comparable to the present breeding-period survey.

Each breeding species also has a table summarizing the comparison between the number of tetrads occupied in this survey and those occupied in the 1977–1985 survey. The tables also show the statistical significance of any change. This is explained in more detail under *Numbers of species and changes since the 1977–1985 survey*, page 57.

Following the main species accounts is a section covering species recorded only very occasionally during the Atlas period; this is divided into species on the British List (Categories A, B & C) and Category D & E species.

*Text: Stella Beavan & Mike Hounsome*
*Photos: Neil Bygrave (Wheatear) & Mike Langman (Turnstones)*
*Facing page: Blue Tit by Adrian Davey*

# SPECIES ACCOUNTS

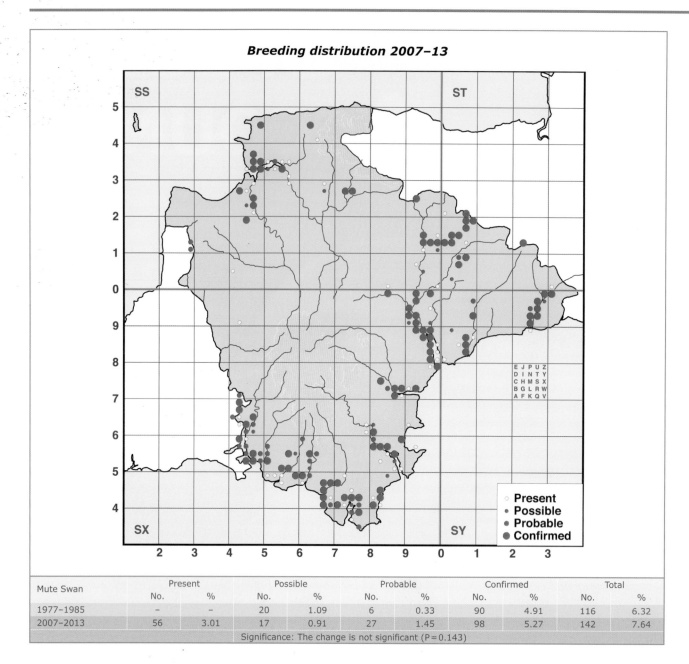

### Breeding distribution 2007–13

| Mute Swan | Present | | Possible | | Probable | | Confirmed | | Total | |
|---|---|---|---|---|---|---|---|---|---|---|
| | No. | % | No. | % | No. | % | No. | % | No. | % |
| 1977–1985 | – | – | 20 | 1.09 | 6 | 0.33 | 90 | 4.91 | 116 | 6.32 |
| 2007–2013 | 56 | 3.01 | 17 | 0.91 | 27 | 1.45 | 98 | 5.27 | 142 | 7.64 |
| Significance: The change is not significant (P = 0.143) | | | | | | | | | | |

### Breeding distribution 1977–85

### Breeding-period abundance 2007–13

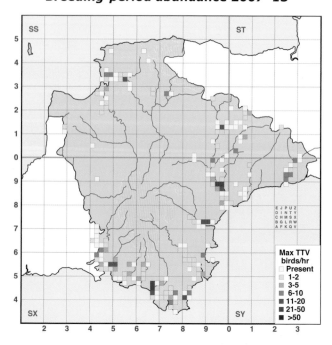

# Mute Swan

*Cygnus olor*

Amber listed

MUTE SWANS require extensive areas of open water for take-off and landing, together with relatively shallow, nutrient-rich waters with abundant submerged vegetation for feeding (though adjacent cereal and grass crops are also grazed). They are thus essentially restricted to Devon's estuaries, the wider reaches of larger rivers, canals and some lakes. This is reflected in both the breeding and winter maps, which show an almost complete absence from inland parts of the county. Densities are generally low throughout the year, with the exception of concentrations of non-breeding birds that build up in both summer and winter at a few favoured locations, such as the estuaries of the Avon, Axe, Plym and Tamar, the River Exe at Exeter and the River Taw at Newbridge, near Bishops Tawton.

Comparison with the previous Atlases suggests little apparent change at 10-km square level in overall breeding or wintering distribution. However, at tetrad level there is evidence of an expansion in the breeding population since the *Devon Tetrad Atlas 1977–85*, with an approximately 22% increase in the overall number of tetrads for which possible, probable or confirmed breeding was reported, and a 9% increase in the number of tetrads where breeding was confirmed.

There has been a particularly notable increase in the number of tetrads with evidence of possible, probable or confirmed breeding in parts of South and East Devon, whereas the number of such tetrads in North and West Devon appears to have fallen since 1977–85. The incidence of confirmed breeding along more inland parts of the River Taw appears to be noticeably lower, but whether this is due to differences in observer coverage between the two Atlases, or whether there has been a genuine decline – perhaps due to factors such as increased summer flooding, predation or changes in management of bankside vegetation – is unclear.

Nationally the Mute Swan population rose significantly during the 1980s and 1990s, probably, at least in part, in response to the ban on the use of lead in fishing weights, formerly a cause of high mortality due to poisoning after ingestion by swans (Rowell & Spray 2004). This change is most likely reflected in the increases indicated for Devon.

*Text: Tim Jones & Tim Davis / Photo: Neil Bygrave*

Balmer *et al.* 2013: 158; Sitters 1988: 58; Tyler 2010: 45

### Winter-period abundance 2007–13

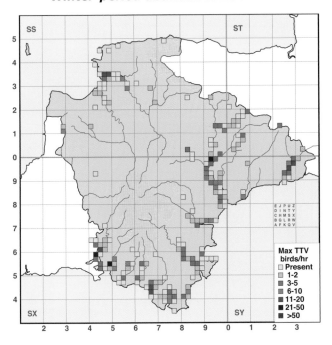

Max TTV birds/hr
- ☐ Present
- 1-2
- 3-5
- 6-10
- 11-20
- 21-50
- >50

# Black Swan
## *Cygnus atratus*

FIRST INTRODUCED to Britain in the late 1700s, this native of Australia occurs widely in a variety of fresh, brackish and saltwater habitats, but with a preference for ornamental ponds, lakes and marshes. However, Black Swan has yet to be added to the British List as its population in the UK, largely arising from introductions or escapes, is not considered to be self-sustaining.

*Bird Atlas 2007–11* reports the species as more widespread than previously thought, mainly in the southern half of Britain. In Devon during the Atlas period there were records of this unmistakeable category E species from no fewer than 43 tetrads in twenty 10-km squares across both the wintering and breeding periods. Highly nomadic in its natural range in Australia in response to rainfall or drought, in Devon the species would appear to be more sedentary, although wandering individuals do occur. Birds present (possibly a single roaming individual) in three tetrads on the Axe Estuary during the winter periods, for example, were not recorded there during the breeding period.

Breeding was confirmed in five tetrads, including Exton (Exe Estuary) in 2009, at Exminster Marshes in 2010 and at Morchard Road in 2010. A family group consisting of two adults and three juveniles was seen at Kenwith Castle, Abbotsham, on 23 December 2008; it is not known whether they bred locally (*DBR* 2008).

*Text: Tim Jones & Tim Davis / Photo: Gray Clements*

Balmer *et al.* 2013: 164; Sitters 1988: not treated; Tyler 2010: 165

**Breeding distribution 2007–2013**

Present
Possible
Probable
Confirmed

**Winter-period abundance 2007–13**

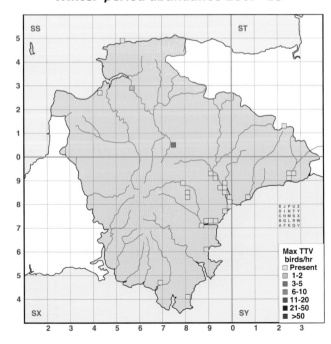

Max TTV
birds/hr
Present
1-2
3-5
6-10
11-20
21-50
>50

# Bewick's Swan
## Cygnus columbianus

Amber listed

BREEDING ON the Siberian tundra and migrating to the relative warmth of western Europe in winter, this rare visitor to Devon was recorded from 15 tetrads in six 10-km squares during the Atlas period, with records from the Avon, Axe, Exe and Taw/Torridge Estuaries, Thurlestone Marsh and Slapton Ley, involving at least seven individuals. The only non-coastal record was of one in flight over Upottery Airfield in December 2011. Most reports were of single birds, with the exception of two at Braunton Marshes in January/February 2009 and two on the Axe Estuary in December 2012, which stayed into January 2013. All records except one (a long-staying 1st-winter bird frequenting the Avon Estuary and Thurlestone Marsh) involved adults.

*Text: Tim Jones & Tim Davis*

Balmer *et al.* 2013: 160; Sitters 1988: not treated; Tyler 2010: 47

# Whooper Swan
## Cygnus cygnus

Amber listed

THE FEW Whooper Swans that reach Devon – where the species is rare, albeit more regularly recorded than Bewick's Swan – are likely to be migration 'overshoots' or wandering birds from the main British and Irish wintering grounds of the Icelandic breeding population. They are typically seen feeding on grassland or autumn-sown cereal crops close to estuaries or other larger wetlands, often in the company of Mute Swans. During the Atlas period there were records for all six winters, covering 32 tetrads in fourteen 10-km squares, with the majority of sightings from the Axe, Exe and Taw/Torridge Estuaries. Other locations included the Erme Estuary, Kingsbridge Estuary, Lundy, Mansands and Upper Tamar Lake. Most records were of one to four birds, but a flock of 12 adults flew up the Taw/Torridge Estuary in November 2008, and six were on Lundy in November 2010. The majority of sightings involved adults, but juveniles were noted in three winters.

*Text: Tim Jones & Tim Davis / Photo: Shaun Barnes*

Balmer *et al.* 2013: 162; Sitters 1988: not treated; Tyler 2010: 48

### Winter-period abundance 2007–13

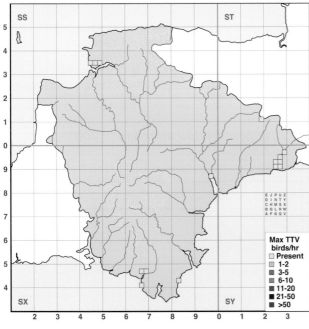

### Winter-period abundance 2007–13

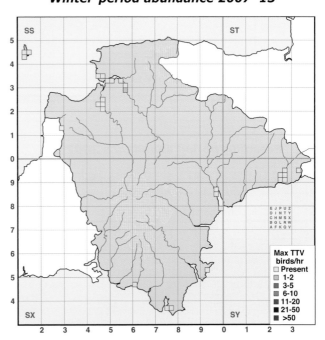

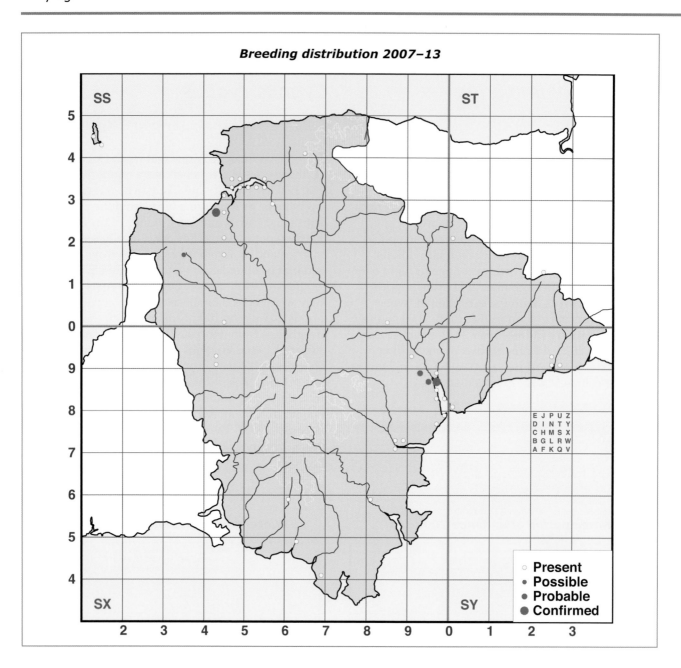

**Breeding distribution 2007–13**

Present
Possible
Probable
Confirmed

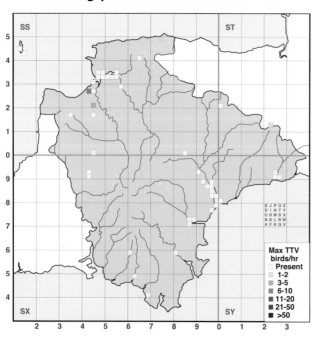

**Breeding-period abundance 2007–13**

Max TTV
birds/hr
Present
1-2
3-5
6-10
11-20
21-50
>50

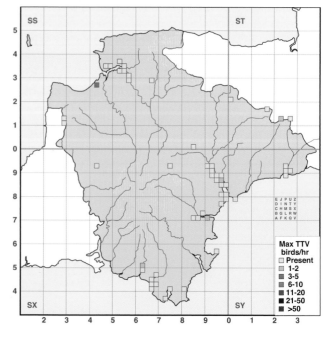

**Winter-period abundance 2007–13**

Max TTV
birds/hr
Present
1-2
3-5
6-10
11-20
21-50
>50

# Greylag Goose
*Anser anser*

Amber listed

ONCE WIDESPREAD in Britain – though there appears to be no evidence of breeding in Devon – the native Greylag Goose population was all but wiped out by wetland loss and over-hunting. While conservation measures were eventually directed at the surviving indigenous Greylags in the far north-west of Britain, a large, naturalized and generally sedentary population, originating from introductions and escapes, grew rapidly during the 20th century. This is the main source for most birds recorded in Devon, including all those involved in recent breeding occurrences. A third population, individuals and small flocks of which occur in Devon from time to time, is composed of migratory Greylag Geese that breed in Iceland and winter in Britain and Ireland. Birds from all three populations favour lowland grassland close to wetlands, while naturalized Greylags often occur in parkland and on ornamental lakes, where they sometimes occur in company with Canada Geese.

*Bird Atlas 2007–11* shows the South West as the only significant gap in Greylag Goose distribution in England; the highest densities in both summer and winter occur in southern and eastern parts of the country. It is therefore not surprising to find that Greylags were recorded from just 73 tetrads in Devon (only 3.3% of the total, though involving thirty-two 10-km squares) and that breeding was confirmed in only two: one on the Exe Estuary and the other close to the north coast at Abbotsham.

The scarcity of Greylags in Devon, contrasting with the relative abundance of Canada Geese, is intriguing. Possible factors discussed by Austin (2002: 19) include slight differences in the type of managed grassland favoured by each species and competitive exclusion of Greylags by Canadas.

Greylags were not mapped by the Devon Tetrad Atlas 1977–85, but it is fairly clear that there has been a gradual increase over the years since then, with breeding first recorded on the Exe Estuary in 2001 (Tyler 2010).

During the Atlas period there was a notable influx of Icelandic Greylags to southern Britain in autumn 2011 and it is likely that this explains the increased number of sightings reported in Devon during winter 2011/12 (*DBR* 2012). The maps show that sightings were more widespread in winter than during the breeding period, which in part reflects the occurrence of passage and/or wintering birds from the Icelandic population, but may also involve movements of naturalized geese from 'up country'.

*Text: Tim Jones & Tim Davis / Photo: Neil Bygrave*

Balmer *et al.* 2013: 172; Sitters 1988: not treated; Tyler 2010: 56

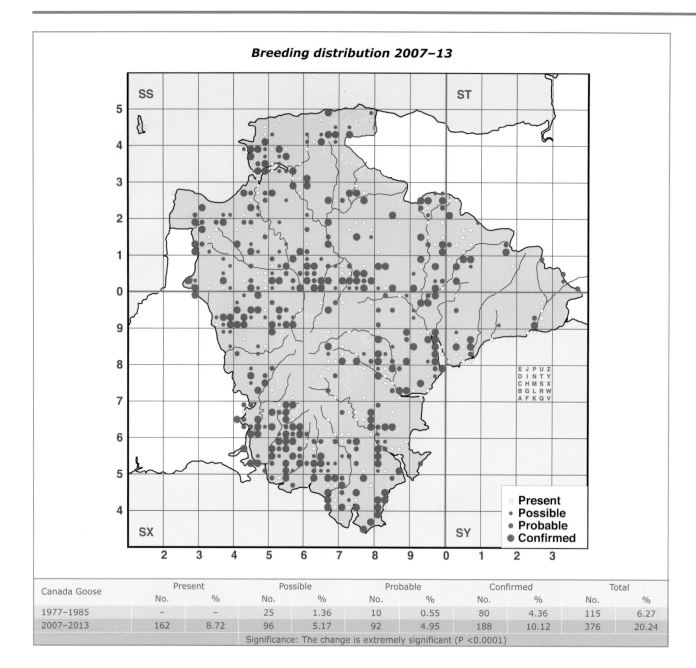

### Breeding distribution 2007–13

Legend:
- ○ Present
- • Possible
- • Probable
- ● Confirmed

| Canada Goose | Present | | Possible | | Probable | | Confirmed | | Total | |
|---|---|---|---|---|---|---|---|---|---|---|
| | No. | % | No. | % | No. | % | No. | % | No. | % |
| 1977–1985 | – | – | 25 | 1.36 | 10 | 0.55 | 80 | 4.36 | 115 | 6.27 |
| 2007–2013 | 162 | 8.72 | 96 | 5.17 | 92 | 4.95 | 188 | 10.12 | 376 | 20.24 |
| | Significance: The change is extremely significant (P <0.0001) | | | | | | | | | |

### Breeding distribution 1977–85

Legend:
- • Possible
- • Probable
- ● Confirmed

### Breeding-period abundance 2007–13

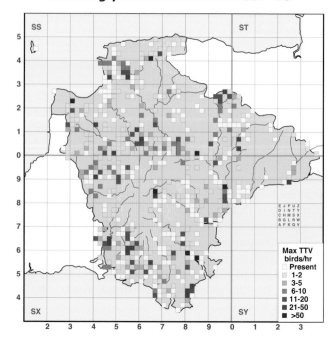

Max TTV birds/hr
- ☐ Present
- 1-2
- 3-5
- 6-10
- 11-20
- 21-50
- >50

# Canada Goose
*Branta canadensis*

*B*IRD ATLAS *2007–11* shows that the naturalized Canada Goose population expanded its range significantly in western Britain during the decades since the *Breeding Atlas 1968–72* and *Winter Atlas 1981–84*. The scale of the increase in Devon is underlined by a comparison of data for the two Devon Atlases.

While the number of tetrads with confirmed breeding records more than doubled between the two surveys, the increase in the number of occupied tetrads was more than fourfold. The *Devon Tetrad Atlas 1977–85* shows many unoccupied 10-km squares during the breeding season, whereas the maps here indicate that is no longer the case, with only a handful of 10-km squares – most on the fringes of the county – in which Canada Geese were not recorded during the 2007–13 breeding periods.

### Winter-period abundance 2007–13

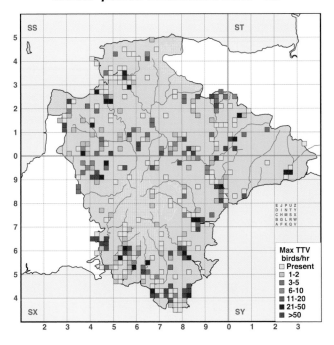

Much of the high ground of Dartmoor and Exmoor is unoccupied in either the breeding or winter period, as are the more rugged sections of the county's coastline, but distribution is otherwise extremely wide. The significantly higher number of occupied tetrads during the breeding period (in comparison with the winter period) reflects dispersal to potentially suitable nesting areas, some of which can be quite small waterbodies. In contrast, birds are more concentrated at favoured feeding grounds during the winter, particularly around estuaries and larger freshwater bodies, including lakes and reservoirs, where suitable grazing (typically arable crops and cultivated grassland) occurs. The seasonal variation in the extent to which Canada Geese are dispersed or concentrated is reflected in the density maps. There are 11 tetrads where counts of more than 50 Canada Geese were recorded during the breeding period, whereas the corresponding number of tetrads for the winter period (34) is more than three times higher.

The *Devon Bird Reports* show that the highest counts during the Atlas period came from the Exe Estuary, Taw/Torridge Estuary, Roadford Reservoir and Portworthy Mica Dam, with the maximum site count being 944 on the Taw/Torridge on 9 December 2009.

It is likely that breeding productivity was adversely affected by several cool wet summers during the Atlas period; this could be one reason why the county WeBS maxima show a slightly declining trend for those years, compared with a general increase prior to 2006. It remains to be seen whether there is additional expansion of this highly adaptable and successful species' Devon range and population in the years ahead, or whether suitable habitat in the county is now 'saturated'.

*Text: Tim Jones & Tim Davis / Photo: Neil Bygrave*

Balmer *et al.* 2013: 174; Sitters 1988: 60; Tyler 2010: 57

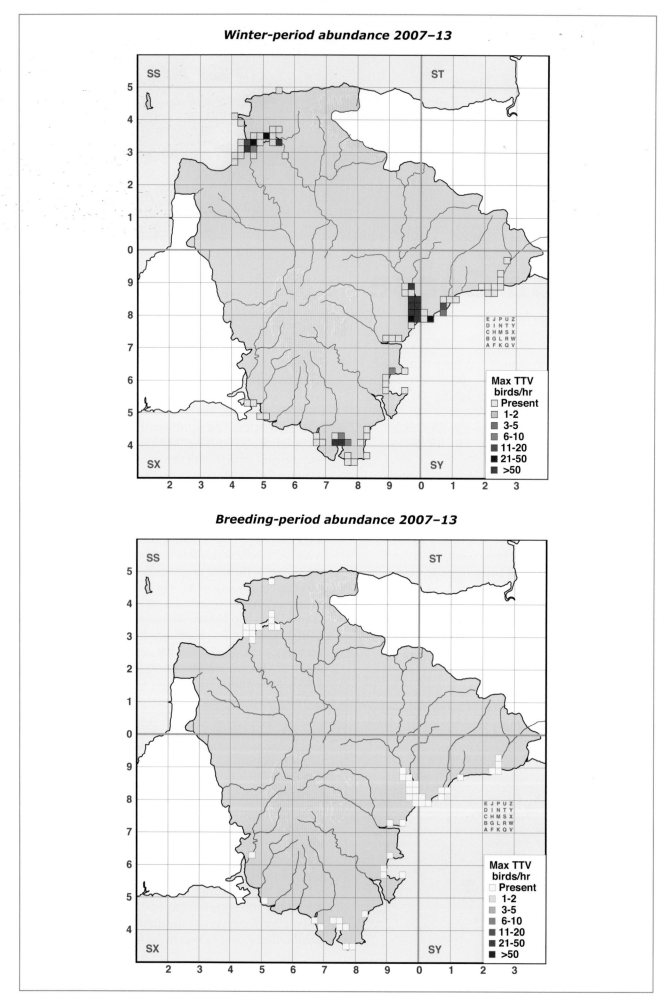

**Winter-period abundance 2007–13**

**Breeding-period abundance 2007–13**

# Brent Goose
*Branta bernicla*

Incorporating:
**Dark-bellied Brent Goose** *B. b. bernicla*
**Pale-bellied Brent Goose** *B. b. hrota*
**Black Brant** *B. nigricans*

BRENT GOOSE is a regularly occurring migrant and wintering species in Devon. The nominate Dark-bellied Brent Goose *B. b. bernicla* (pictured top), which breeds in the Russian Arctic, winters in variable numbers at traditional estuarine sites where the species' preferred food plant, eel-grass, occurs. Small numbers of Pale-bellied Brent Geese (middle photo), of the Canadian breeding population *B. b. hrota*, which winter mainly in Ireland, but also along the coast of north-west France, pass through South Devon on migration, mainly in spring. The Black Brant *B. b. nigricans* (lower photo) which breeds in eastern Siberia, Alaska and western Canada, is a rare vagrant to Devon.

The maps reflect this species' status as the most coastal of the geese that occur regularly in Devon and also – second to the naturalized Canada Goose population – the most abundant. The principal winter strongholds of Dark-bellied Brents on the Exe, Kingsbridge and Taw/Torridge Estuaries stand out, but there are records of smaller numbers from other south coast estuaries and headlands. Flocks of passage migrants and/or birds commuting between feeding grounds are regularly seen from these headlands, including, in spring, Pale-bellied Brent Geese. The Exe Estuary and Seaton Bay are favoured sites for observing passage Pale-bellied Brents in

April/May; more than 250 were in the area on 16 April 2012, though numbers are usually lower than this. Whilst Pale-bellied Brents are also seen in similar areas in autumn, numbers are considerably below those noted in spring. Small numbers of Pale-bellied Brents also occurred on the Taw/Torridge Estuary during the Atlas years, particularly during autumn migration in 2011, when up to 22 were seen in November.

The breeding success of Brent Geese, like that of other species nesting at high latitudes, is hugely dependent on the fickle Arctic summer, where a boom year in fine conditions (or when potential predators of geese encounter an abundance of small-mammal prey) may be followed by several years of low, or even zero, productivity. This is reflected in the significant between-year variation in numbers wintering in Devon and above all in the variable proportion of juveniles within the flocks. The peak monthly WeBS total varied from a low of 1,219 in winter 2009/10, to a high of 2,108 in winter 2007/08. These numbers are also likely to have been influenced by the colder than normal British winters during some of the Atlas years.

Single adult Black Brants were recorded on the Kingsbridge Estuary (December 2007–March 2008), the Exe Estuary (January–March 2009) and the Taw/Torridge Estuary (February–March 2012).

*Text: Tim Jones & Tim Davis / Photos: Andrew Cunningham (main), Neil Bygrave (top), Lee Collins (middle & lower)*

*Brent Goose sponsored by Brent Birders – of South Brent Parish*

Balmer *et al.* 2013: 178; Sitters 1988: not treated; Tyler 2010: 61

# Egyptian Goose
## *Alopochen aegyptiaca*

*B*IRD *ATLAS 2007–11* documents a significant expansion in both range and population size of this introduced African species in comparison with earlier Atlases. However, the main centres of distribution are in East Anglia and south-east England, with few occurring in either summer or winter in western parts of the UK. The Egyptian Geese occurring in South Devon are currently very much on the fringes of the species' range.

Recorded in 30 tetrads from eleven 10-km squares during the winter period and 30 tetrads from nine 10-km squares during the breeding period, the small Devon population appears to be essentially sedentary, being focused on sheltered south coast estuaries, especially the Avon, Dart and Kingsbridge.

Breeding is thought to have first occurred in the county at Newton Abbot in about 2000 but this event lacks adequate documentation. Regular successful breeding began on the Dart Estuary in 2005 and was annual from 2007 to 2011. A pair also raised two young on the Avon Estuary in 2011 and an unsuccessful breeding attempt was made there in 2012. While there are signs that the Devon population is gradually increasing, it remains very small at probably fewer than 20 individuals, and records during the Atlas period generally involved low single-digit counts.

*Text: Tim Jones & Tim Davis / Photo: Mike Langman*

Balmer *et al.* 2013: 184; Sitters 1988: not treated; Tyler 2010: 65

### Breeding distribution 2007-13

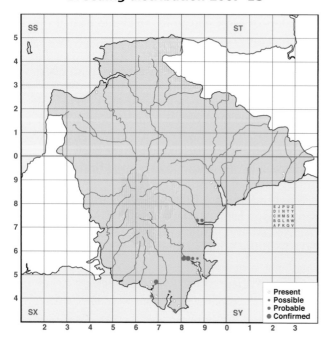

- □ Present
- · Possible
- ● Probable
- ● Confirmed

### Winter-period abundance 2007–13

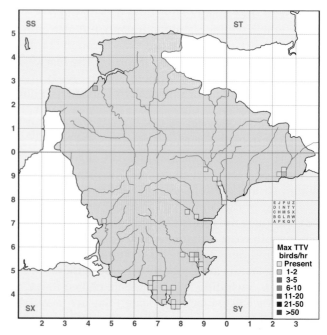

Max TTV birds/hr
- □ Present
- ▫ 1-2
- ▪ 3-5
- ■ 6-10
- ■ 11-20
- ■ 21-50
- ■ >50

# Wigeon
## *Anas penelope*

Amber listed

THE WHISTLING call of the Wigeon is one of the most evocative sounds of winter birdwatching on many of Devon's estuaries. Indeed, this is very much a coastal species of dabbling duck, feeding on eel-grass and algae, but also on cultivated grasses (*BWP*) and flocks are often to be seen fanning out over grazed or mown grassland before beating a hasty retreat to the nearest waterbody at the first hint of danger.

Migrants arrive from northern Eurasian breeding grounds – Tyler (2010) documents a Wigeon cannon-netted on Seaton Marshes that had been ringed in the Khanty-Mansi Region of Russia, a distance of 4,547 kilometres from Seaton – with most vacating the county by the end of March.

The winter distribution map clearly picks out core sites of the Exe, Kingsbridge and Taw/Torridge Estuaries, with smaller numbers occurring at many other south coast estuaries, and passage or 'commuting' flocks often seen from coastal headlands. Although there is a scatter of occupied tetrads inland, numbers are small, with the exception of Tamar Lakes. While there are site-to-site and annual variations (Tyler 2010) there has been little apparent change in overall wintering numbers in the county over the past 15 years, with the peak Devon WeBS total typically in the range of 4,000–6,000 individuals (*DBR* 2012).

Small numbers of birds lingered well into the breeding period at a number of estuarine sites, notably the Exe Estuary, in most years, but there was no evidence of any nesting attempt – although a female and, briefly, a pair were seen in June and early July 2007 at Bowling Green Marsh.

*Text: Tim Jones & Tim Davis*
*Photos: Neil Bygrave (left), Mike Jones (right)*

Balmer *et al.* 2013: 192; Sitters 1988: not treated; Tyler 2010: 70

### Winter-period abundance 2007–13

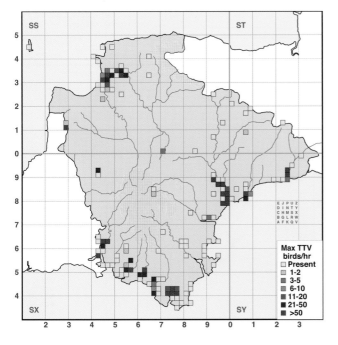

Max TTV birds/hr
☐ Present
1-2
3-5
6-10
11-20
21-50
>50

### Breeding-period abundance 2007–13

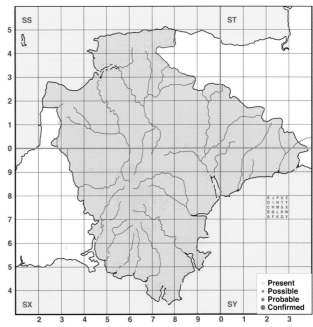

Present
Possible
Probable
Confirmed

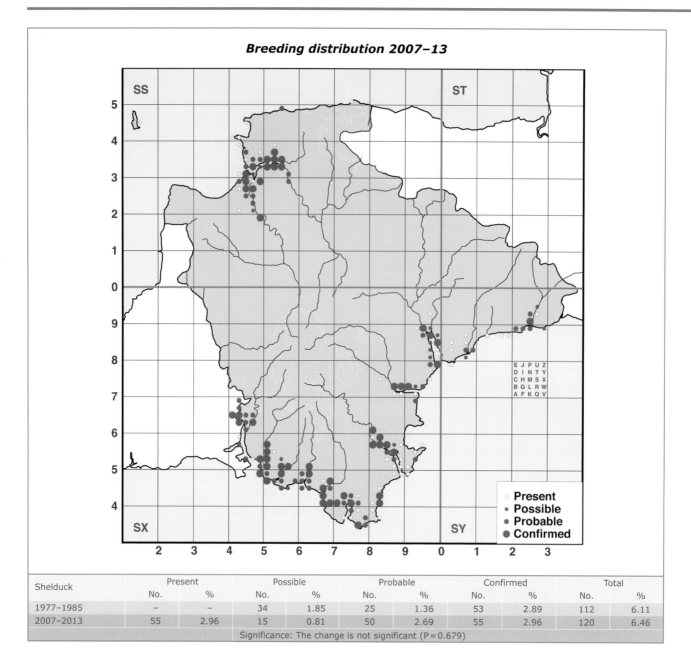

## Breeding distribution 2007–13

| Shelduck | Present | | Possible | | Probable | | Confirmed | | Total | |
|---|---|---|---|---|---|---|---|---|---|---|
| | No. | % | No. | % | No. | % | No. | % | No. | % |
| 1977–1985 | – | – | 34 | 1.85 | 25 | 1.36 | 53 | 2.89 | 112 | 6.11 |
| 2007–2013 | 55 | 2.96 | 15 | 0.81 | 50 | 2.69 | 55 | 2.96 | 120 | 6.46 |
| Significance: The change is not significant (P = 0.679) | | | | | | | | | | |

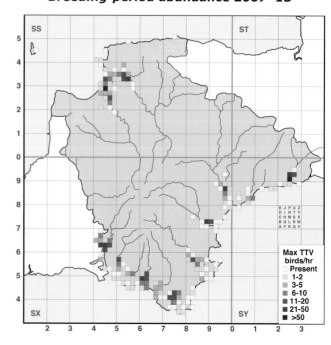

## Breeding distribution 1977–85

## Breeding-period abundance 2007–13

# Shelduck

*Tadorna tadorna*

Amber listed

SHELDUCKS ARE closely associated with estuaries, where they feed on invertebrates (especially small *Hydrobia* snails) on mud- and sand-flats exposed at low tide. They nest in holes, typically old rabbit burrows, often in flood banks and hedge banks on nearby farmland. Large flocks form at favoured, traditional feeding sites in winter, while crèches of juveniles from multiple family parties may be seen at the end of the breeding season. Adult Shelducks largely vacate Devon in the late summer and autumn, with most probably undertaking an international pre-moult migration to the Wadden Sea (Tyler 2010).

The dependence of Shelducks on coastal habitats is reflected in the maps, which show an almost complete absence from inland areas of the county in both the breeding and wintering periods. The concentration of birds around our major estuaries stands out clearly, with particularly notable clusters on the Axe, Exe, Teign, Dart, Kingsbridge, Tamar Complex and Taw/Torridge and it is in these locations that the highest numbers occur in winter. During the period 2007–2011 the highest mean monthly WeBS total for Devon was 1,152 in February (*DBR* 2012). Peak numbers always occur relatively late in the winter as birds return progressively from the moulting grounds. While wintering numbers have been fairly stable over the past 15 years, there is some suggestion of a slight decline, perhaps mirroring a declining trend in the Great Britain WeBS index (*DBR* 2012).

A comparison of the present breeding-period map with the *Devon Tetrad Atlas 1997–85* shows that breeding was confirmed in 53 tetrads in 1977–1985 and in 55 tetrads in 2007–2013, suggesting little overall change (although dedicated surveys conducted by David Price in 1976 and 1992 indicated a 20% increase in the county's breeding population over that period (Price 1977, 1993)). Closer examination of the two Devon Atlases indicates apparent losses in some areas (e.g. Braunton Burrows and parts of the Axe and Exe Estuaries) but gains elsewhere (e.g. parts of south-west Devon). How much these differences reflect real change, local variation in observer effort, or both, is impossible to know. Certainly, disturbance from recreational activities has increased on many of Devon's estuaries over the last 30 years, which could be one reason for localized declines.

*Text: Tim Jones & Tim Davis / Photo: Robin Morrison*
*Shelduck sponsored by Mike Tyler*

Balmer *et al.* 2013: 186; Sitters 1988: 62; Tyler 2010: 66

### Winter-period abundance 2007–13

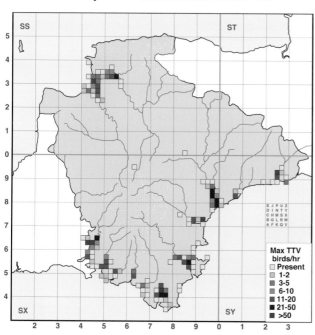

Max TTV birds/hr
☐ Present
☐ 1-2
☐ 3-5
■ 6-10
■ 11-20
■ 21-50
■ >50

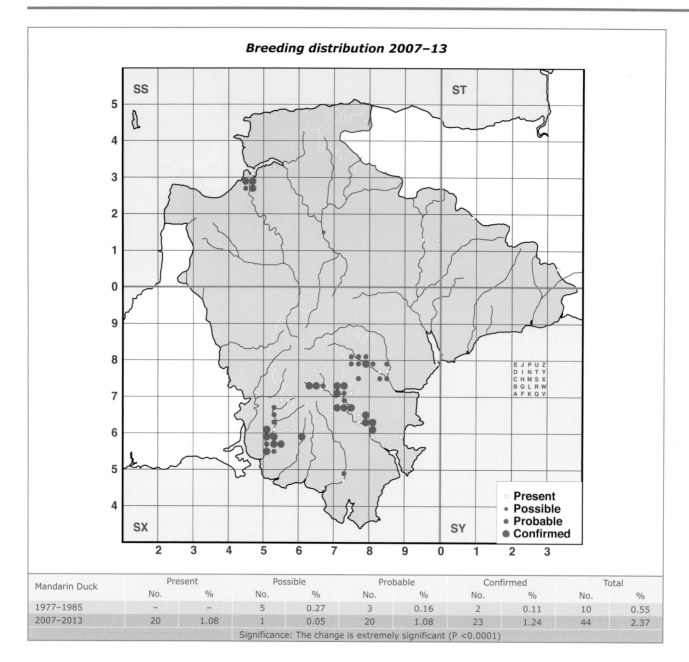

**Breeding distribution 2007–13**

| Mandarin Duck | Present | | Possible | | Probable | | Confirmed | | Total | |
|---|---|---|---|---|---|---|---|---|---|---|
| | No. | % | No. | % | No. | % | No. | % | No. | % |
| 1977–1985 | – | – | 5 | 0.27 | 3 | 0.16 | 2 | 0.11 | 10 | 0.55 |
| 2007–2013 | 20 | 1.08 | 1 | 0.05 | 20 | 1.08 | 23 | 1.24 | 44 | 2.37 |
| Significance: The change is extremely significant (P <0.0001) | | | | | | | | | | |

**Breeding distribution 1977–85**

**Breeding-period abundance 2007–13**

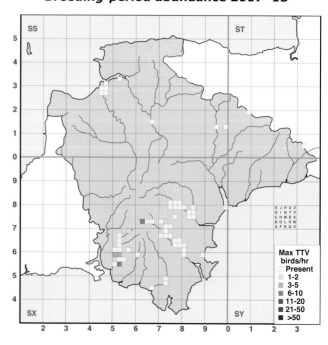

# Mandarin Duck

*Aix galericulata*

Mᴀʟᴇ Mᴀɴᴅᴀʀɪɴs are perhaps the most distinctive and 'ornamental' of the many exotic wildfowl at large in the UK as a consequence of escapes or deliberate releases from captive collections. The first Devon record was of a drake at Burrator Reservoir in 1960, but the species probably only became established in the county from the early 1980s (Tyler 2010).

*Bird Atlas 2007–2011* documents the species' national range expansion and increase in numbers, and shows the main strongholds now being in the south-east of England, the Severn Vale and the Peak District. The maps presented here clearly indicate the establishment and significant growth of the South Devon population since the *Devon Tetrad Atlas 1977–85*. All of the 10-km squares occupied during the breeding periods 2007–2011 represent gains since the *Breeding Atlas 1968–72*. Likewise, all those squares occupied in the winter periods 2007–2011 are also gains since the *Winter Atlas 1981–84*.

Mandarins are hole-nesters and, although they take readily to nestboxes, are most likely to be found breeding in areas where there are mature trees growing alongside smaller rivers. The wooded river valleys of southern Dartmoor and the South Hams are therefore eminently suitable. The middle and upper catchments of the rivers Teign, Dart and Plym are of particular importance throughout the year and form the core of the breeding range in Devon, the only notable outlier being the river Torridge in North Devon. There is a wider scatter of records for the winter period, but this may – in part at least – reflect increased coverage of potential sites during the core months for the Wetland Birds Survey (WeBS).

That numbers are growing in Devon is not in doubt, though a flock of 80 gathered at dusk in Hembury Woods, in the upper reaches of the river Dart near Buckfastleigh, in November 2012 was unprecedented. At least 25 young were hatched at four sites in the county earlier the same year (*DBR* 2012).

*Text: Tim Jones & Tim Davis / Photos: Chris Triggs*
*Mandarin sponsored by Alan Ford*

Balmer *et al.* 2013: 190; Sitters 1988: 64; Tyler 2010: 69

### Winter-period abundance 2007–13

Max TTV birds/hr
☐ Present
◻ 1-2
◼ 3-5
◼ 6-10
◼ 11-20
◼ 21-50
◼ >50

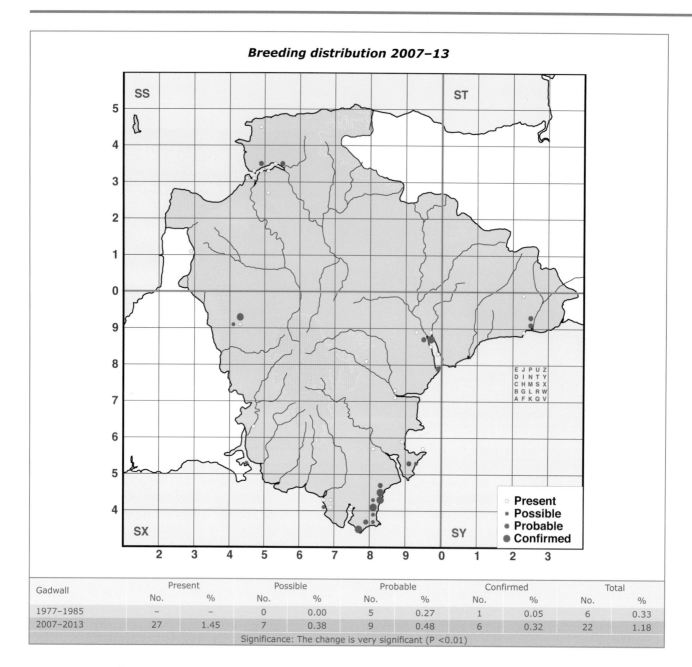

## Breeding distribution 2007–13

| Gadwall | Present | | Possible | | Probable | | Confirmed | | Total | |
|---|---|---|---|---|---|---|---|---|---|---|
| | No. | % | No. | % | No. | % | No. | % | No. | % |
| 1977–1985 | – | – | 0 | 0.00 | 5 | 0.27 | 1 | 0.05 | 6 | 0.33 |
| 2007–2013 | 27 | 1.45 | 7 | 0.38 | 9 | 0.48 | 6 | 0.32 | 22 | 1.18 |
| Significance: The change is very significant (P <0.01) | | | | | | | | | | |

## Breeding distribution 1977–85

## Breeding-period abundance 2007–13

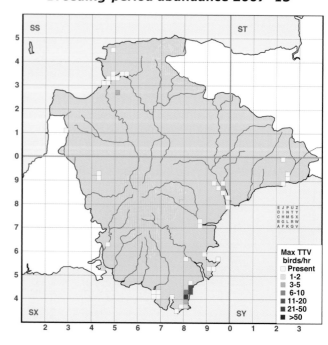

# Gadwall
*Anas strepera*

Amber listed

GADWALL REQUIRE open areas of shallow fresh or brackish water for feeding, and well-vegetated, reasonably undisturbed wetland margins for nesting. Given the relative scarcity of such habitats across most inland regions of the county, it is not surprising that this is very much a coastal and estuarine species in Devon. The only inland site regularly holding more than a handful of birds is Roadford Reservoir, as the maps clearly show.

Numbers of this discreetly refined duck have increased dramatically in Britain and Ireland in recent decades, as shown in *Bird Atlas 2007–2011*. Wetland Bird Survey (WeBS) data show that the UK winter population more than trebled between 1983/84 and 2008/09, while numbers reached a record high in winter 2011/12 (Austin *et al.* 2014). The growth in numbers has been accompanied by a significant expansion of both the breeding and wintering ranges, as shown in the maps, which vividly demonstrate the gains in Devon since the *Devon Tetrad Atlas 1977–85*. Tyler (2010) charts the species' rise from 19th-century vagrant, through annual occurrences since the Second World War, to its current year-round presence in the county.

While numbers remain modest in relation to those 'up country', Devon WeBS counts have confirmed the upward trend – a record 192 Gadwall were counted in December 2012. This was probably partly due to cold-weather movements that month, when up to 96 birds crowded into an ice-free stretch of the Exeter Canal (adjoining the Exe Estuary), with reports also from a number of unusual locations (*DBR* 2012).

Breeding was first confirmed at Slapton Ley in 1984 and has become a regular occurrence since the mid-1990s (Tyler 2010). During the Atlas years, breeding was confirmed at both Beesands and Slapton Leys, Roadford Reservoir, the Exe Estuary and Prawle. In addition there were breeding-season records from several other areas including, in the north of the county, the Taw/Torridge Estuary.

The winter-period map also shows a very close association with coastal habitats, with Beesands, Mansands and Slapton Leys among the more important sites. The highest site count during the Atlas period was 117 at Beesands Ley in January 2010 (*DBR*).

*Text: Tim Jones & Tim Davis / Photo: Chris Proctor*

Balmer *et al.* 2013: 194; Sitters 1988: 298; Tyler 2010: 73

### Winter-period abundance 2007–13

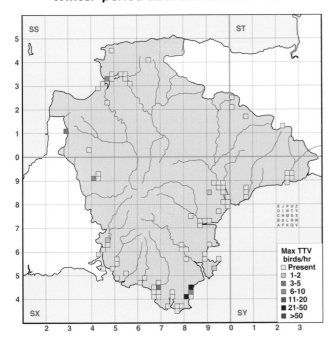

Max TTV birds/hr
- ☐ Present
- ☐ 1-2
- ■ 3-5
- ■ 6-10
- ■ 11-20
- ■ 21-50
- ■ >50

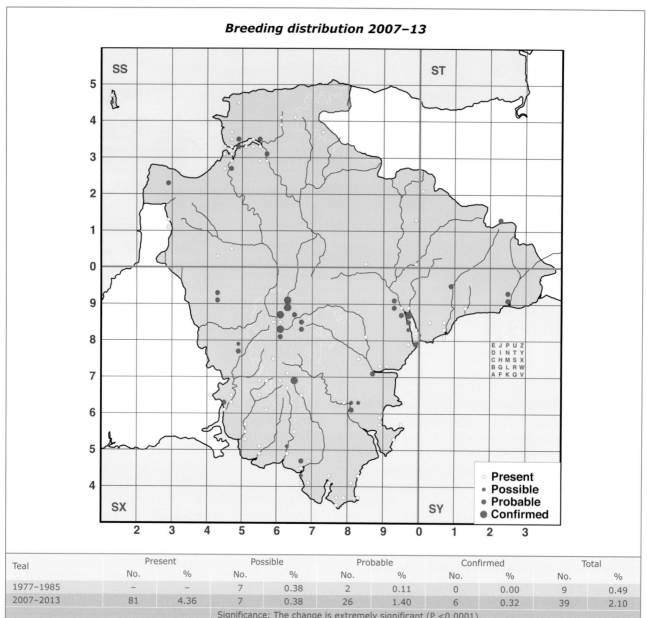

## Breeding distribution 2007–13

| Teal | Present | | Possible | | Probable | | Confirmed | | Total | |
|---|---|---|---|---|---|---|---|---|---|---|
| | No. | % | No. | % | No. | % | No. | % | No. | % |
| 1977–1985 | – | – | 7 | 0.38 | 2 | 0.11 | 0 | 0.00 | 9 | 0.49 |
| 2007–2013 | 81 | 4.36 | 7 | 0.38 | 26 | 1.40 | 6 | 0.32 | 39 | 2.10 |
| Significance: The change is extremely significant (P <0.0001) | | | | | | | | | | |

## Breeding distribution 1977–85

## Breeding-period abundance 2007–13

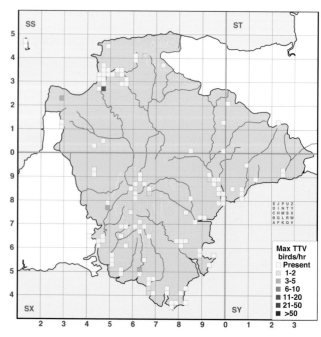

# Teal
## *Anas crecca*

Amber listed

TEAL ARE widespread and locally common passage and winter visitors to Devon, but remain an extremely scarce and sparsely distributed breeding species.

Tyler (2010) reported historical breeding records for Beesands Ley and Slapton Ley, Braunton Marshes and Tamar Lakes, in addition to confirmed breeding at five Dartmoor sites between 1930 and 2006. The *Devon Tetrad Atlas 1977–85* recorded possible breeding in seven tetrads and probable breeding in two tetrads, the latter both on Dartmoor. The breeding map for Teal during the current Atlas period therefore represents something of a high-water mark for the species, at least by the standards of recent decades, with confirmed breeding for five Dartmoor tetrads and one on the Exe Estuary, along with probable breeding evidence for 26 further tetrads involving fifteen 10-km squares.

Outside the breeding season, Teal may occur on virtually any wetland, from small farm ponds and ditches, temporarily flooded areas, to larger riverine and estuarine sites, and this is reflected by the wide scatter of occupied tetrads, involving sixty-six 10-km squares, in the winter-period map. However, larger numbers are confined to relatively few locations, especially the Exe and Taw/Torridge Estuaries. Other tetrads in which counts of more then 50 were made were those containing Tamar Lakes, the Tamar Estuary complex and Claw Moor near Holsworthy. *Bird Atlas 2007–2011* indicates that the number of 10-km squares in Devon showing 'losses' for Teal since the *Breeding Atlas 1988–1991* were outweighed by apparent gains.

WeBS data show that the peak monthly totals for the county varied significantly over the 15-year period between winters 1997/98 and 2011/12. The maximum count during the winter periods for the current Atlas was 2,936 in December 2010. Much of the year-to-year variability is likely to be explained by prevailing weather conditions, since Teal are highly mobile in response to the extent of flooding or the onset of severe cold snaps. December 2010 was a particularly cold month and it may be that birds from smaller, frozen sites within the county concentrated at ice-free coastal wetlands and/or that birds from elsewhere in Britain and northern Europe moved to south-west England.

### Winter-period abundance 2007–13

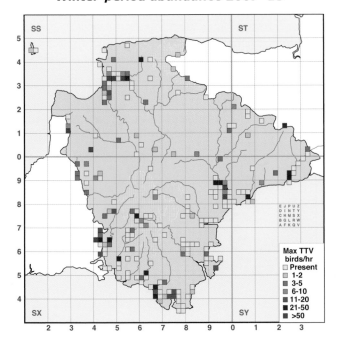

Max TTV
birds/hr
☐ Present
▩ 1-2
▩ 3-5
■ 6-10
■ 11-20
■ 21-50
■ >50

*Text: Tim Jones & Tim Davis / Photo: Dave Scott*
*Teal sponsored by Anne Dudley*

Balmer *et al.* 2013: 196; Sitters 1988: 298; Tyler 2010: 75

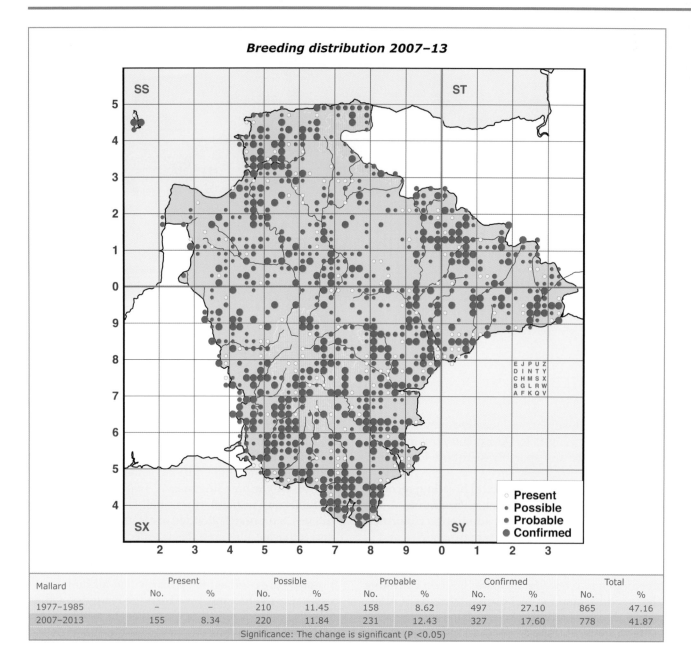

## Breeding distribution 2007–13

| Mallard | Present | | Possible | | Probable | | Confirmed | | Total | |
|---|---|---|---|---|---|---|---|---|---|---|
| | No. | % | No. | % | No. | % | No. | % | No. | % |
| 1977–1985 | – | – | 210 | 11.45 | 158 | 8.62 | 497 | 27.10 | 865 | 47.16 |
| 2007–2013 | 155 | 8.34 | 220 | 11.84 | 231 | 12.43 | 327 | 17.60 | 778 | 41.87 |
| Significance: The change is significant (P <0.05) | | | | | | | | | | |

## Breeding distribution 1977–85

## Breeding-period abundance 2007–13

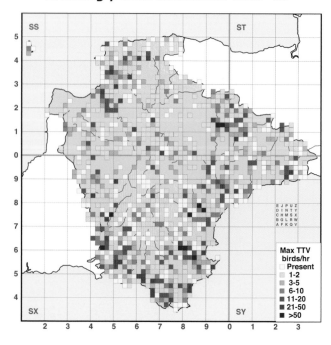

# Mallard

*Anas platyrhynchos*

Amber listed

THE FAMILIAR Mallard is Devon's most widespread duck, having been recorded during the Atlas period in almost every 10-km square in the county, with breeding proven in the vast majority; only a few squares containing fragments of coastline were 'blank'.[1] At tetrad level, however, the picture is more complicated. While the tetrad map for the breeding season shows that Mallard remains a common breeding species (increased by birds reared and released for shooting), a comparison of the statistics for the current Atlas period with those from the *Devon Tetrad Atlas 1977–85* shows a significant drop – of more than one-third – in the number of tetrads in which breeding was confirmed. The overall number of tetrads from which Mallard were recorded, however, showed only a 10% decline.

A comparison of the breeding maps from the two Atlases shows that most of the apparent losses are from inland areas, particularly Mid Devon, to the north and east of Dartmoor, but less so in northernmost parts of the county. It is hard to assess, from these data alone, the extent to which this reflects genuine losses or if differences in recording between the two Atlas periods constitute an important contributory factor. However, *Bird Atlas 2007–2011* showed that the breeding range of Mallard had actually increased slightly in Britain since the *Breeding Atlas 1988–1991*, and that abundance had increased significantly. These findings suggest that the apparent losses in Devon may actually reflect limited survey coverage of some

parts of the county during 2007–2013. Interestingly, there was a roughly fourfold increase in the number of instances of confirmed breeding on Dartmoor during the current Atlas period compared with the *Devon Tetrad Atlas 1977–85*. The number of occupied tetrads on Exmoor also increased.

In winter, Mallards were recorded in just under half (approximately 42%) of all tetrads, with both distribution and – especially – abundance showing the expected bias towards coastal lowlands and major river valleys. The highest numbers were found on the south coast estuaries, the Taw/Torridge Estuary in North Devon and the Grand Western Canal in the east of the county. The overall winter distribution is very similar to that during the breeding season.

The monthly WeBS county totals indicate a stable or increasing trend for the numbers of Mallard wintering in Devon, with maxima of 3,000–3,500 in each winter between 2003/04 and 2011/12 (*DBR* 2012), and a peak during the Atlas winter periods of 3,383 in December 2011. This contrasts with the national WeBS trend, which shows a marked decline since the 1980s in numbers wintering in Britain as a whole (Austin *et al.* 2014).

*Text: Tim Jones & Tim Davis*
*Photos: Andrew Cunningham & (inset) Neil Bygrave*

Balmer *et al.* 2013: 198; Sitters 1988: 66; Tyler 2010: 79

[1] With no reliable way of distinguishing fully between wild and domestic Mallard, the two forms have been amalgamated in the maps.

### Winter-period abundance 2007–13

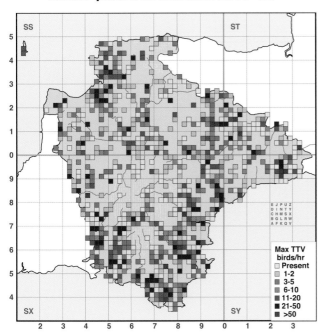

Max TTV birds/hr
☐ Present
1-2
3-5
6-10
11-20
21-50
>50

# Pintail
## *Anas acuta*

Amber listed

PINTAIL, ARGUABLY the most elegant of our winter ducks, is a relatively scarce species in Devon, occurring regularly in winter at just a handful of estuarine sites, notably the Axe, Exe and Kingsbridge Estuaries on the south coast and the Taw/Torridge Estuary in the north – a picture very much confirmed by the map for the Atlas winter period. Numbers vary markedly from year to year, but the maximum monthly WeBS total for Devon only rarely exceeds 200. During the Atlas winter periods, the highest county total was 216 in February 2012, all but eight of these birds occurring on the Exe, Kingsbridge and Taw/Torridge Estuaries.

Records during the Atlas breeding period are all thought to relate to late-departing wintering birds; there was no evidence of breeding during any of the Atlas years and there are no past breeding records for Devon.

*Text: Tim Jones & Tim Davis*
*Photos: Neil Bygrave & (inset) Lee Collins*

Balmer *et al.* 2013: 200; Sitters 1988: not treated; Tyler 2010: 81

### Winter-period abundance 2007–13

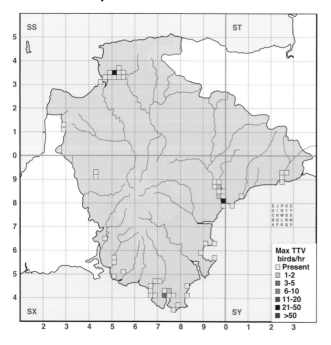

### Breeding-period abundance 2007–13

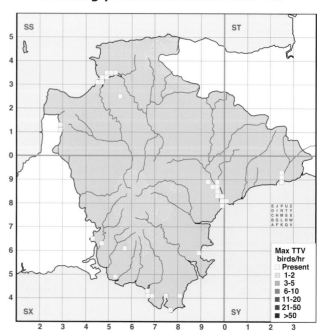

# Garganey

*Anas querquedula*

WHILE WE are used to thinking of wildfowl as long-distance migrants, most are winter visitors to Devon. Garganey is the exception being the only member of the family Anatidae to occur regularly in Britain as a trans-Saharan summer visitor. This attractive Teal-sized bird with a powder-blue forewing and, in the drake, unmistakeable white head-stripe, is scarce in Devon. This is likely to be due in part to the county's westerly location in relation to the main UK breeding range, as shown in *Bird Atlas 2007–11*, but may also reflect the fact that there are relatively few extensive lowland freshwater wetlands with dense marginal vegetation – the species' preferred nesting habitat.

Altogether there were records from 29 tetrads during the Atlas breeding period, involving fourteen 10-km squares. Most records were of passage migrants, generally ones and twos, stopping off briefly at south coast estuaries, especially the Exe. The few scattered dots in North Devon also refer to migrants. Garganey have bred occasionally in Devon, with five confirmed instances up to and including 1998, four of these at Exminster Marshes on the Exe Estuary and one at Slapton Ley (Sitters 1988; Tyler 2010). However, there were no confirmed breeding records during the Atlas years, and though

a pair – the male of which was seen displaying – held territory at Exminster Marshes in spring 2012, there was no stronger evidence that nesting occurred (*DBR* 2012). Other 'probable' breeding dots are shown for the Axe Estuary, Otter Estuary and Slapton Ley.

*Text: Tim Jones & Tim Davis / Photo: Rob Jutsum*
*Garganey sponsored by Andrew Graham*

Balmer *et al.* 2013: 202; Sitters 1988: 298; Tyler 2010: 83

### Breeding distribution 2007-13

Present
Possible
Probable
Confirmed

### Breeding-period abundance 2007–13

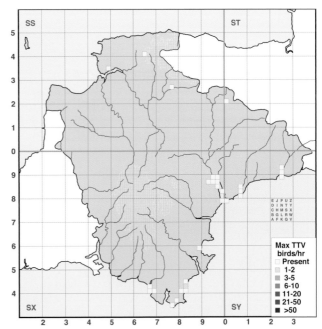

Max TTV
birds/hr
Present
1-2
3-5
6-10
11-20
21-50
>50

| Garganey | Present | | Possible | | Probable | | Confirmed | | Total | |
|---|---|---|---|---|---|---|---|---|---|---|
| | No. | % | No. | % | No. | % | No. | % | No. | % |
| 1977–1985 | – | – | 5 | 0.27 | 3 | 0.16 | 1 | 0.05 | 9 | 0.49 |
| 2007–2013 | 24 | 1.29 | 0 | 0 | 5 | 0.27 | 0 | 0 | 5 | 0.27 |
| Significance: The change is not significant (P=0.275) | | | | | | | | | | |

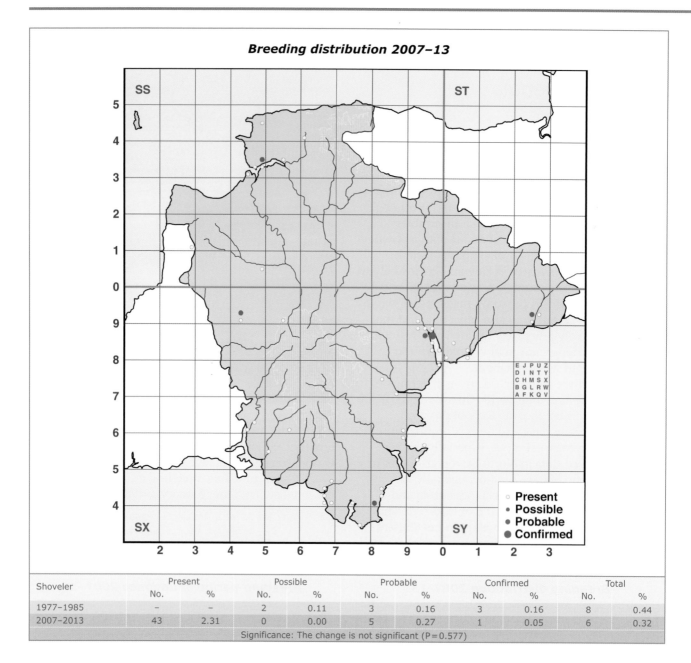

**Breeding distribution 2007–13**

| Shoveler | Present | | Possible | | Probable | | Confirmed | | Total | |
|---|---|---|---|---|---|---|---|---|---|---|
| | No. | % | No. | % | No. | % | No. | % | No. | % |
| 1977–1985 | – | – | 2 | 0.11 | 3 | 0.16 | 3 | 0.16 | 8 | 0.44 |
| 2007–2013 | 43 | 2.31 | 0 | 0.00 | 5 | 0.27 | 1 | 0.05 | 6 | 0.32 |
| Significance: The change is not significant (P=0.577) | | | | | | | | | | |

**Breeding distribution 1977–85**

**Breeding-period abundance 2007–13**

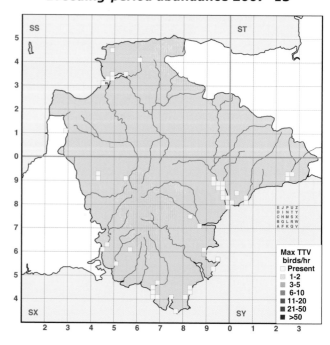

# Shoveler

*Anas clypeata*

Amber listed

THE UNUSUAL bill shape of both sexes, the bold, colourful breeding plumage of the drake and the eye-catching display, often seen in late winter, make Shoveler one of our most charismatic native wildfowl, though in Devon it is a relatively scarce species.

Very much a coastal duck in Devon, favouring estuaries and shallow brackish or freshwater wetlands, it is not surprising that, with the notable exceptions of Roadford Lake and Tamar Lakes, all the higher winter counts of Shovelers during the Atlas years came from the main south coast estuaries, along with the Taw/Torridge Estuary in the north. While there were winter records for 88 tetrads, involving thirty-two 10-km squares, counts of more than ten birds were only received from a handful of tetrads. Indeed, monthly WeBS totals for the whole county during the Atlas years show a modest peak of 149 (in March of winter 2011/12),

with maxima for other winters in the period ranging from 80 in 2010/11 to 129 in 2009/10 (*DBRs*).

Some of the coldest winters of recent decades occurred during the period covered by Atlas fieldwork and this may have served to distort the overall picture in comparison with a run of more 'normal' years. Shovelers wintering in Britain are likely to be particularly affected by cold weather (Holt *et al.* 2012), given their dependence on very shallow wetlands that are vulnerable to freezing, and taking into account that northern Europe is at the edge of the species' winter range. It is likely that many UK-wintering Shovelers will have moved south-west in response to cold weather, with many probably vacating British shores altogether for milder climes (Holt *et al.* 2012). For example, there were noticeably few in Devon during winter 2010/11, which was particularly cold. On the other hand, cold snaps may also have served to increase the number and scatter of occupied tetrads as birds made local movements seeking suitable unfrozen feeding grounds.

Most Shovelers leave Devon in late winter or early spring, with very few remaining (or arriving) to make a breeding attempt. Tyler (2010) lists just nine known occurrences of confirmed breeding prior to this Atlas period, all at either Exminster Marshes or Bowling Green Marsh on the Exe Estuary, in the years 1974 to 2006. This tenuous status as a Devon breeding species is reflected by the paucity of dots on the breeding-season map, recorded in just 49 tetrads, with most of these likely to relate to late-staying winter visitors or passage migrants in early spring. Evidence of nesting was restricted to five tetrads where breeding was 'probable' and a single tetrad (Exe Estuary) where breeding was successful in both 2008 and 2009.

*Text: Tim Jones & Tim Davis*
*Photos: Neil Bygrave & (right) Mike Jones*

Balmer *et al.* 2013: 204; Sitters 1988: 299; Tyler 2010: 85

### Winter-period abundance 2007–13

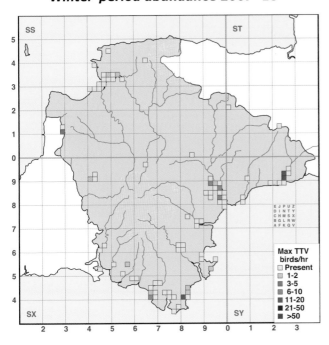

Max TTV
birds/hr
☐ Present
■ 1-2
■ 3-5
■ 6-10
■ 11-20
■ 21-50
■ >50

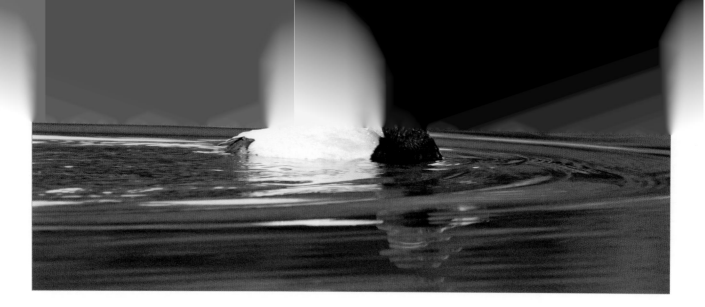

# Pochard
*Aythya ferina*

**Red listed**

THE FIRST confirmed breeding record of Pochard for Devon was as recently as 2000, when ducklings were seen at Slapton Ley (Tyler 2010). During the Atlas period probable breeding was noted at Wrafton Pond (Taw/Torridge Estuary) in 2011 and four young were seen at this site in July 2012, constituting only the second occurrence of successful breeding in the county.

Overall during Atlas fieldwork, Pochard were recorded in 19 tetrads in the breeding period and 70 tetrads in the winter period. With the exception of the Taw/Torridge Estuary breeding record, all of the 'breeding-period' records are considered to involve late-staying wintering birds and/or passage migrants. While there is a wide scatter of records during winter, double-digit counts occurred in only a handful of tetrads, most notably at Beesands Ley

and Slapton Ley. However, the winter-period map of TTV results does not record the WeBS counts of 50 or more which occurred on two occasions (December 2010 and January 2012) at Roadford Reservoir.

WeBS data for Devon showed a sharply declining trend in wintering numbers during the 15 winter periods from 1997/98 to 2011/12 (*DBR* 2012). While peak monthly WeBS totals for the county exceeded 300 during three winters in the late 1990s and early 2000s, all the corresponding maxima for the Atlas years were below 200, with several less than 100. This is very much in line with the national picture, with a 47% decrease in UK wintering numbers between 2000/01 and 2010/11 (Austin *et al.* 2014).

*Text: Tim Jones & Tim Davis / Photo: Andrew Cunningham*

Balmer *et al.* 2013: 210; Sitters 1988: 299; Tyler 2010: 89

### Breeding distribution 2007-13

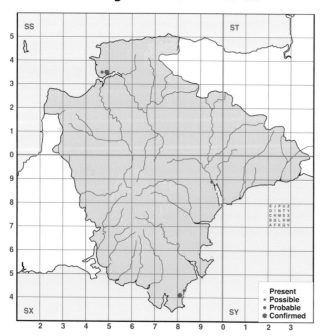

### Winter-period abundance 2007–13

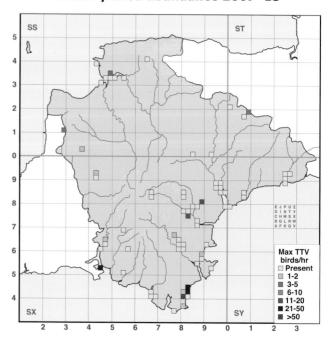

# Scaup
*Aythya marila*

SCAUP IS a winter visitor to Devon, arriving from its breeding grounds that stretch from Siberia, through European Russia, to northern Fennoscandia and Iceland. *Bird Atlas 2007–11* indicates there has been a 57% range expansion nationally since the the *Winter Atlas 1981–84*.

The winter distribution map in *Bird Atlas 2007–11* shows gains since 1981–84 along the whole southern coast of Devon, while in the north it is restricted to Bideford Bay. Numbers occurring in the county are small, and during the Atlas period the species was only recorded from 38 tetrads. Numbers vary, influenced by cold weather in the east of Britain, with recent harsh winters triggering larger influxes than usual, alongside other *Aythya* species.

Arrival dates vary greatly, usually during October, though Scaup have been recorded in September, departing in March–April.

Slapton Ley and nearby Beesands Ley, together with the Exe Estuary and associated sites, are the only locations where Scaup are recorded annually, but they are also recorded fairly regularly from our larger estuaries such as the Taw/Torridge and Kingsbridge Estuaries. Birds are only seen in small numbers: seven birds at Dawlish Warren in winter 2010/11 and 2012/13 together with six on the Kingsbridge Estuary in winter 2010/11 (*DBRs* 2011, 2012, 2013) were the highest counts during the Atlas period. Occasional records occur at inland sites such as Roadford Reservoir.

*Text: Lee Collins / Photo: Laurie Allnatt*

Balmer et al. 2013: 214; Sitters 1988: not treated; Tyler 2010: 96

## Winter-period abundance 2007–13

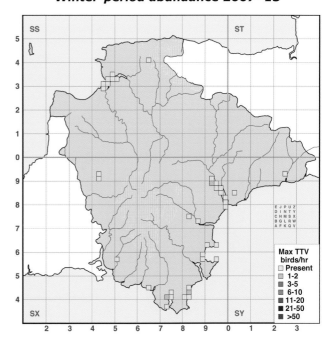

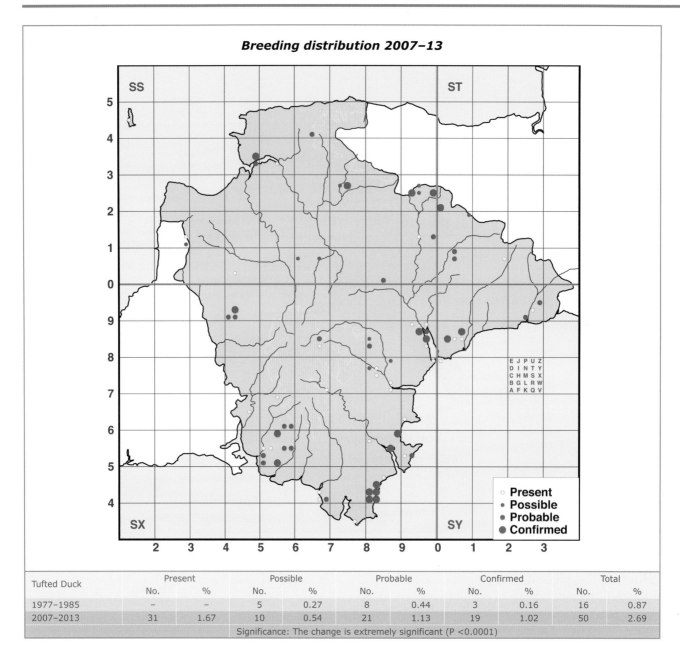

## Breeding distribution 2007–13

| Tufted Duck | Present | | Possible | | Probable | | Confirmed | | Total | |
|---|---|---|---|---|---|---|---|---|---|---|
| | No. | % | No. | % | No. | % | No. | % | No. | % |
| 1977–1985 | – | – | 5 | 0.27 | 8 | 0.44 | 3 | 0.16 | 16 | 0.87 |
| 2007–2013 | 31 | 1.67 | 10 | 0.54 | 21 | 1.13 | 19 | 1.02 | 50 | 2.69 |
| Significance: The change is extremely significant (P <0.0001) | | | | | | | | | | |

## Breeding distribution 1977–85

## Breeding-period abundance 2007–13

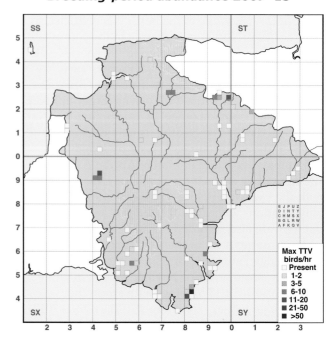

# Tufted Duck

*Aythya fuligula*

As predominantly freshwater diving ducks, Tufted Ducks occur mainly on larger ponds, lakes and reservoirs in winter, occasionally being seen on estuaries or sea-bays. In the breeding season they favour lakes and ponds with dense marginal vegetation and so more often occur at smaller wetlands. *Bird Atlas 2007–11* shows that Devon is very much on the fringes of the species' core British range in both winter and breeding periods.

During fieldwork for the *Devon Tetrad Atlas 1977–85* there were just three confirmed breeding records: two near Ottery St Mary in East Devon and one near Dolton in Mid Devon. However, Tony John noted in his account for the *Tetrad Atlas* that "it would appear that Tufted Ducks are slowly colonising Devon". That this assessment was correct is borne out by the maps for the current Atlas, which show confirmed breeding in no fewer than 19 tetrads in ten 10-km squares, with a wide distribution across the county.

Given that Devon is rather poor in areas of open and deep freshwater bodies, it is probably not surprising that the winter-period maps reveal Tufted Duck to be relatively scarce in both distribution and abundance. Indeed, counts greater than ten during Atlas fieldwork were recorded for only nine tetrads, with Roadford Lake and Slapton and Beesands Leys being by far the most important sites.

WeBS data show that high county totals were recorded during several of the Atlas winters, most likely reflecting cold-weather influxes from elsewhere. The highest monthly total for Devon during the Atlas winter periods was 467 in January 2013. A notable cold-weather influx occurred in December 2010, with "many smaller and/or less regularly used sites holding unusually high numbers" (*DBR* 2010).

*Text: Tim Jones & Tim Davis / Photos: Mike Langman*
*Tufted Duck sponsored by Eileen Marsh*

Balmer *et al.* 2013: 212; Sitters 1988: 68; Tyler 2010: 93

### Winter-period abundance 2007–13

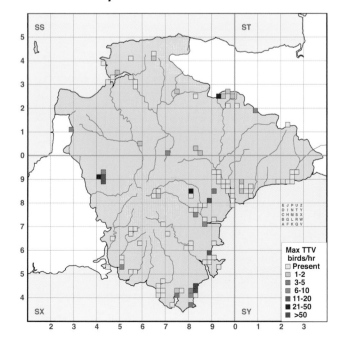

Max TTV birds/hr
- Present
- 1-2
- 3-5
- 6-10
- 11-20
- 21-50
- >50

# Eider
## *Somateria mollissima*

Amber listed

T RADITIONALLY WINTER visitors to Devon, Eiders were recorded from 11 tetrads during the Atlas period, mainly along the South Devon coastline, especially Dawlish Bay and Torbay, as well as off Thurlestone and Salcombe, and around Bideford Bay in the north. They are usually seen between September and April, although they can occur in any month of the year. Numbers are very variable and, over the last few years, the species' absence at many well-watched locations suggests that it is, sadly, becoming a scarcer bird in Devon as it is in winter in some parts of Britain. Reasons suggested for declines in breeding populations in Britain and northern Europe include a change in food supply (Coulson 2010), climate change (Lehikoinen *et al.* 2006) and thiamine deficiency (Balk *et al.* 2009). Fifty Eiders at Dawlish Warren in April 2011 was by far the highest count during the Atlas period, but observations from this site have since fallen considerably, to the extent that it is now no longer a wintering species but more an uncommon migrant.

*Text: Lee Collins / Photos: Paul Sterry/NPL*

Balmer *et al.* 2013: 216, Sitters 1988: not treated, Tyler 2010: 97

### Winter-period abundance 2007–13

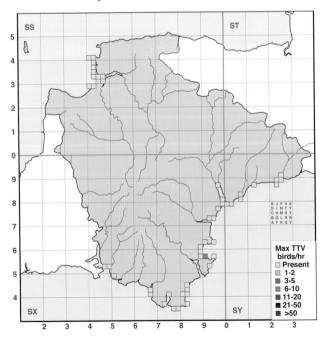

### Breeding-period abundance 2007–13

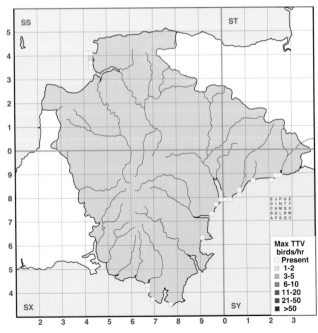

# Long-tailed Duck
*Clangula hyemalis*

**Red listed**

LONG-TAILED DUCKS are scarce winter visitors to Devon and fewer than ten are recorded each year. During the Atlas winter-periods they were recorded in a total of 31 tetrads, but this is more a reflection of their wandering habits than a count of individuals. None was recorded during a TTV.

Birds, nearly always singles, generally appear during late October (*DBRs*), occasionally earlier, and most sightings are from the south coast, with records from North Devon very infrequent. They are generally seen offshore in sheltered bays, but can also venture into river estuaries, notably that of the

Exe. Sightings from well-watched headlands are rare. Most records involve just a single date, suggesting passage birds, but some may remain for much of the winter, particularly in Torbay or Dawlish Bay. Although records away from the coast are very unusual, birds can occasionally occur on inland waterbodies – during the Atlas period one over-wintered at Roadford Reservoir from November 2008 to February 2009.

*Text: Lee Collins / Photo: Lee Collins*

Balmer *et al.* 2013: 218; Sitters 1988: not treated; Tyler 2010: 99

### Winter-period abundance 2007–13

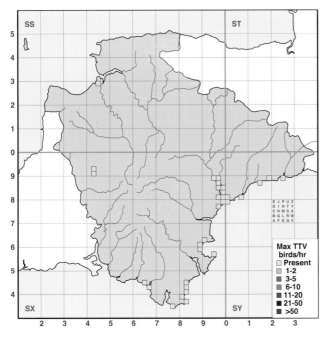

### Breeding-period abundance 2007–13

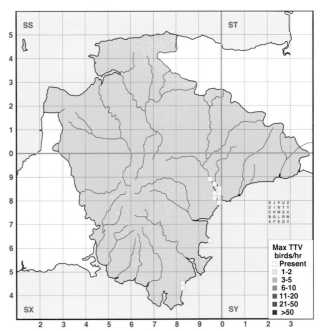

# Common Scoter

*Melanitta nigra*

**Red listed**

ALTHOUGH USUALLY thought of as a winter visitor, Common Scoter is Devon's commonest sea duck and can be found in every month of the year, with non-breeders present during the summer. During the winter period, Common Scoters were recorded in 71 tetrads. The strikingly similar total of 68 tetrads for the summer period reflects not only the presence of summering non-breeders, but also the fact that this Atlas period embraces spring passage, post-breeding movements and early autumn passage.

Records came from all along the southern coast, and on the north coast mainly from around Bideford Bay. Common Scoters were recorded off Lundy in all but one year (2008) during the Atlas period, mostly in small numbers but exceptionally 25 on 26 October 2012 (*LFS Annual Report 2012*). Most sightings came from well-watched bays or headlands, where passage counts accounted for many of the high monthly counts which peaked annually at 200–300 individuals during the Atlas years (*DBRs* 2007–2013). Many of the larger counts were recorded in late summer and/or during the winter. Common Scoters are rare inland in Devon, with records less than annual.

*Bird Atlas 2007–11* records a 39% national expansion in winter range since the *Winter Atlas 1981–84*, with gains most evident in areas of lower winter abundance. Locally, the winter distribution change map since the *Winter Atlas 1981–84* shows gains in many parts of Devon, away from the Wembury area.

*Text: Lee Collins / Photo: Chris Proctor*

Balmer *et al.* 2013: 220; Sitters 1988: not treated; Tyler 2010: 101

### Winter-period abundance 2007–13

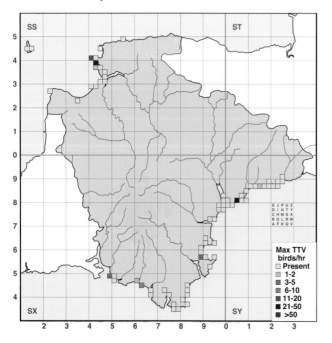

### Breeding-period abundance 2007–13

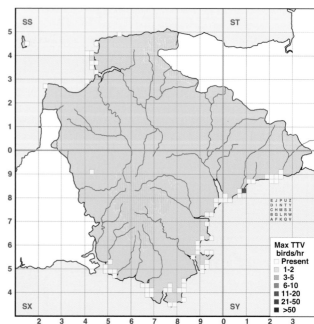

# Velvet Scoter
*Melanitta fusca*                                                    **Red listed**

THIS THICKSET sea-duck is a winter visitor to Devon and was recorded in 31 tetrads during the Atlas period. The *Bird Atlas 2007–11* winter distribution map shows gains in most Devon sites since the *Winter Atlas 1981–84*. Although not a common bird in Devon, it may be found at any coastal site, although most records have come from bays along the South Devon coastline and Bideford Bay in the north.

Velvet Scoters tend to remain well offshore, either within a Common Scoter flock or on their own and can easily be missed, especially in unsettled conditions. A wing-flap or a brief flash of white during its open-winged dive can help to confirm the species' presence. The same white secondaries, visible even at great distance, make flight identification easy and it is often observed on passage at key sites.

Velvet Scoters appear from late October and depart by April. Counts are generally of single birds or small parties, although 13 were seen in Start Bay in February 2008 and 12 immature birds frequented Seaton Bay in February 2011.

*Text: Lee Collins / Photo: Paul Sterry/NPL*

Balmer *et al.* 2013: 222; Sitters 1988: not treated; Tyler 2010: 104

### Winter-period abundance 2007–13

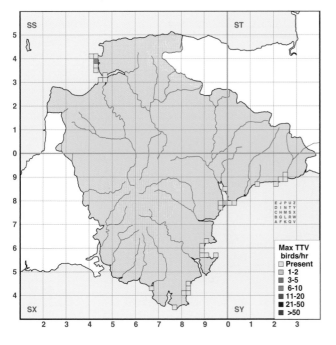

### Breeding-period abundance 2007–13

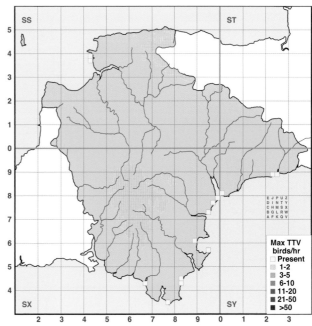

# Goldeneye
## *Bucephala clangula*

Amber listed

A SMALL diving duck, the Goldeneye is a bird of estuaries and inland waters, feeding mainly on molluscs and crustaceans and a small amount of insects. The number wintering in Britain is currently decreasing and was estimated to be 20,000 for the years 2004/5 to 2008/9 (Musgrove *et al.* 2013). The British breeding population for 2006–10 was estimated to be 200 pairs (Musgrove *et al.* 2013).

In Devon, Goldeneyes are uncommon winter visitors and passage migrants, arriving in September and October, with the highest numbers occurring between November and March, although a few may linger into April. Occasionally one or two birds have also been recorded during the breeding season but there has never been any suggestion of breeding (Tyler 2010).

Numbers in Devon each winter have never been very high, with only the Exe and Kingsbridge estuaries, together with Slapton Ley and Roadford Reservoir, reaching double figures on a regular basis. Smaller numbers are to be found on other estuaries such as the Taw/Torridge, Tamar and freshwater sites such as Kennick and Trenchford Reservoirs. There was some apparent evidence of higher numbers being seen during the harsher winters of 2009–11 with high counts during this period of 21 at Kingsbridge in January 2011, 22 on the Exe in February 2012 and 19 at Slapton in January 2010. Roadford Reservoir holds good numbers on a regular basis and 18 were recorded from here in December 2012 (*DBR*s 2008–2013).

*Text: Ray Jones / Photo: Dave Scott*

Balmer *et al.* 2013: 224; Sitters 1988: not treated; Tyler 2010: 106

### Winter-period abundance 2007–13

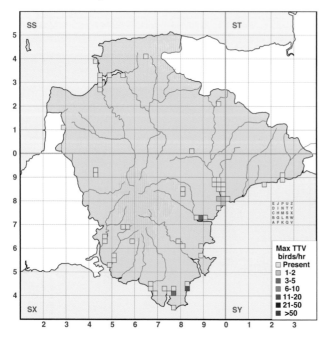

### Breeding-period abundance 2007–13

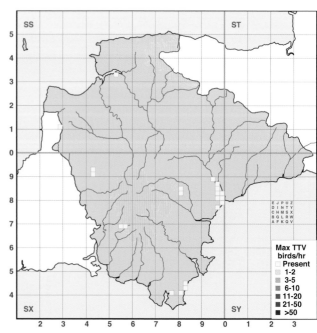

# Ruddy Duck
## Oxyura jamaicensis

An American species of marshy lakes and ponds, the Ruddy Duck was introduced into wildlife collections in Britain in the 1930s (RSPB 2009) These included the Wildfowl & Wetlands Trust at Slimbridge where, during the 1950s, a number of birds escaped and, together with subsequent escapes from other wildlife collections, established feral populations on reservoirs, particularly of the West Midlands. Subsequently, further feral populations became established in both Britain and mainland Europe, and the species began to hybridize with the closely related and endangered White-headed Duck *Oxyura leucocephala*, especially in Spain, reducing the already declining population of White-headed Ducks to a new low.

As a consequence of this hybridization and, under pressure from conservationists, the European Commission decided on a programme to eradicate the Ruddy Duck throughout Europe in order to protect the native White-headed Duck. This programme commenced in 1999 and in Britain by 2012, numbers had been reduced by 6,500, and it was estimated there were only 40 individuals, of which just two were adult females, left in Britain by 2014 (Musgrove *et al.* 2013: 86; AHVLA 2014).

In Devon numbers have always been low, although there was an unprecedented count of 76 at Slapton in January 1982 (Tyler 2010). There have been records in all months of the year at various sites, but the main location was always Slapton Ley, where the species first bred in 2001 and subsequently

in 2004, 2005 and 2007. There was one record of breeding during the Atlas period when two broods were reared at Slapton in 2009.

While some Ruddy Ducks in Britain may escape the cull due to the withholding of known breeding sites, there were no records in 2013 and its continuing presence in Devon looks unlikely.

*Text: Ray Jones / Photo: Chris Proctor*

Balmer *et al.* 2013: 232; Sitters 1988: not treated; Tyler 2010: 113

### Breeding distribution 2007-13

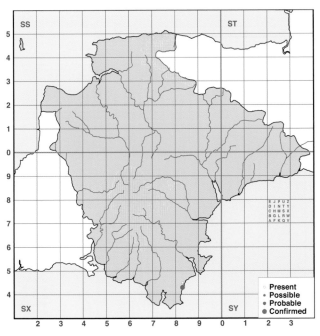

- Present
- • Possible
- • Probable
- ● Confirmed

### Winter-period abundance 2007–13

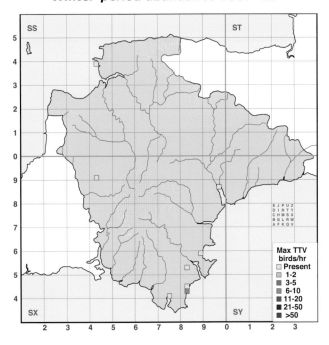

Max TTV birds/hr
- □ Present
- ▫ 1-2
- ▫ 3-5
- ■ 6-10
- ■ 11-20
- ■ 21-50
- ■ >50

## Breeding distribution 2007–13

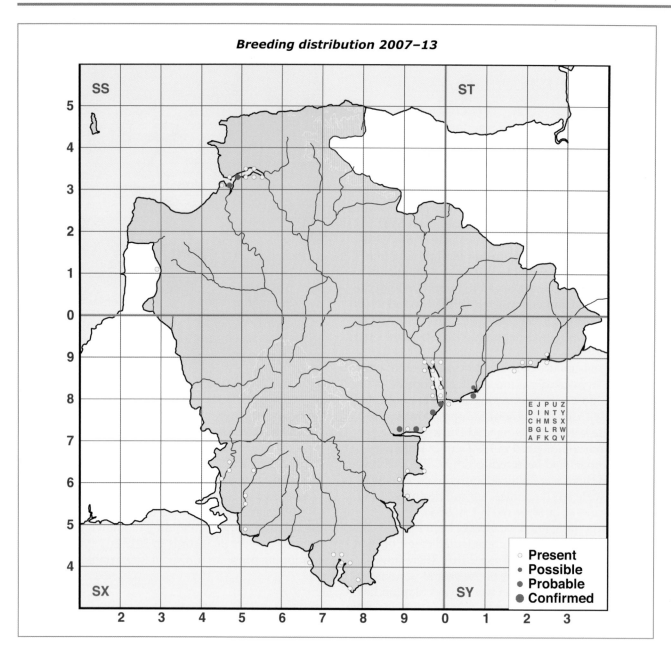

Present
Possible
Probable
Confirmed

## Breeding-period abundance 2007–13

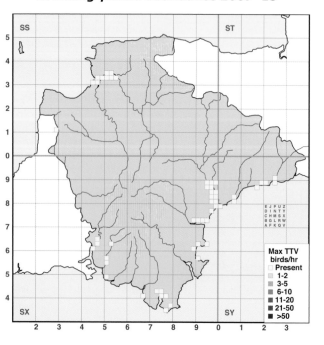

Max TTV
birds/hr
Present
1-2
3-5
6-10
11-20
21-50
>50

## Winter-period abundance 2007–13

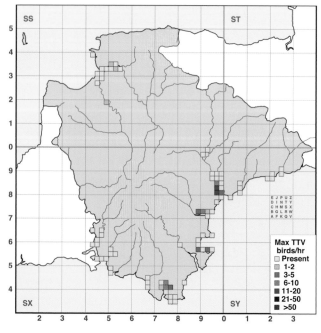

Max TTV
birds/hr
Present
1-2
3-5
6-10
11-20
21-50
>50

# Red-breasted Merganser
## *Mergus serrator*

THE RED-BREASTED MERGANSER is, in winter, a bird of shallow marine environments feeding predominantly on small fish, supplemented at times by aquatic insects and crustaceans. It nests on the ground among sheltering vegetation, by freshwater lakes in northern Eurasia south to the United Kingdom, northern North America, Iceland, Greenland, China and Japan. It winters in Europe south to the Mediterranean, Black and Caspian Seas, and along the Pacific and Atlantic coasts of North America.

During the latter half of the last century numbers increased dramatically in Britain, and this was reflected in an increase in the numbers seen in Devon. The European summer population is estimated at about 80,000 pairs (BTO BirdFacts), while *Bird Atlas 2007–11* estimates the British and Irish population at 2,200 pairs. The wintering British population was estimated at 8,400 for the period 2004/05 to 2008/09 (Musgrove *et al.* 2013).

In Devon, the Red-breasted Merganser is a fairly common winter visitor and passage migrant, rarely staying into summer. The most important site for the species in Devon is undoubtedly the Exe Estuary, where numbers are sometimes of national importance (98). Other important sites are the Kingsbridge and Teign Estuaries and Torbay. The species is also found on other estuaries in both north (Taw/Torridge) and south (Axe and Plym) of the county and occasionally on freshwater sites such as Tamar Lakes.

The first returning migrants generally arrive in October, with counts usually peaking in November and December. Numbers may be boosted at times when the weather is severe elsewhere in Britain, and in the Exe Estuary complex may exceed 100 and in March 2009 an extraordinary 140 birds were recorded during the WeBS count. Most leave by the end of March but a few may linger into April, with occasional non-breeders staying throughout the summer.

The first recorded breeding in Devon was at Dawlish Warren in 1993 and the species has occasionally bred in subsequent years, the last record being in 2003 when young were seen at Dawlish Warren and on the Teign Estuary. Birds have been seen during the breeding season in subsequent years (2009, 2010 & 2012) on the Exe but breeding has not been observed.

Devon is perhaps a southerly extremity of the Red-breasted Merganser's breeding range and climate change may mean that breeding in the county in the foreseeable future is unlikely.

*Text: Ray Jones / Photo: Barry Bowden*

Balmer *et al.* 2013: 228; Sitters 1988: not treated; Tyler 2010: 109

## Breeding distribution 2007–13

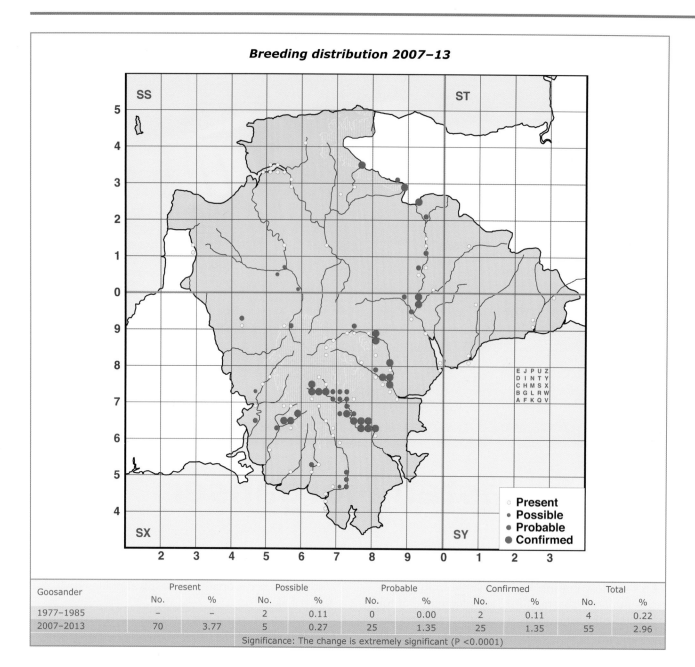

| Goosander | Present | | Possible | | Probable | | Confirmed | | Total | |
|---|---|---|---|---|---|---|---|---|---|---|
| | No. | % | No. | % | No. | % | No. | % | No. | % |
| 1977–1985 | – | – | 2 | 0.11 | 0 | 0.00 | 2 | 0.11 | 4 | 0.22 |
| 2007–2013 | 70 | 3.77 | 5 | 0.27 | 25 | 1.35 | 25 | 1.35 | 55 | 2.96 |
| Significance: The change is extremely significant (P <0.0001) | | | | | | | | | | |

## Breeding distribution 1977–85
## Breeding-period abundance 2007–13

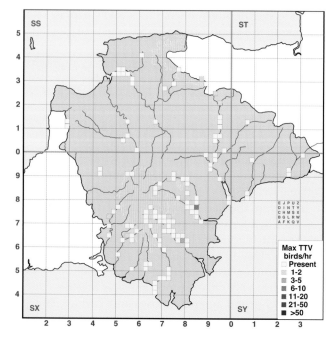

# Goosander
*Mergus merganser*

GOOSANDERS ARE now regularly seen inland in winter on rivers and reservoirs in Devon, and occasionally on the coast. Following a southward spread in range during the 20th century, Goosanders bred for the first time in Devon at Staverton on the River Dart in 1980 (Tyler 2010). Prior to this they were winter visitors in small numbers. In the *Devon Tetrad Atlas 1977–85*, breeding was confirmed in four tetrads, all on the River Dart, with two further records of possible breeding in West Devon. In the current Devon Atlas, confirmed breeding was recorded in 25 tetrads, on the rivers Plym, Dart, Bovey, Teign and Exe, and the River Barle in north-east Devon on Exmoor; Goosanders also probably bred in 25 tetrads and possibly in a further five. However, there are still very few breeding registrations in north-west Devon or to the east of the Exe Estuary.

During the *Winter Atlas 1981–84*, Goosanders were only recorded in south-west Devon and along the Exe catchment, but they are now much more widely distributed in winter, with a number of records, particularly in South Devon around Dartmoor and its rivers. Goosanders feed along stretches of rivers during the day, returning in late afternoon to roost on Dartmoor reservoirs such as Avon Dam, Burrator, Venford, Meldon, Fernworthy and Hennock. The largest roost count was of 104 at Roadford Reservoir in January 1997. Coordinated counts on the Dartmoor reservoirs show that numbers usually peak in January and February, totalling 70–90 birds in winters 2009/10 to 2012/13 (Smaldon 2013). It is not fully understood whether the state of the rivers can be a significant factor in the number of birds coming to roosts (Smaldon *in litt.*). The majority of birds in these roosts are females and first-winter males ('brownheads'), adult males usually making up less than a third. Most of those roosting on Dartmoor are found on the western side; numbers roosting at Fernworthy and Hennock rarely reach double figures. Some birds come in to roost when there is very little light and dawn counts have revealed larger numbers than dusk counts at some sites.

Wintering numbers may well decline in future, as studies of Goosander, Goldeneye and Tufted Duck have shown that numbers wintering in northern Scandinavia have increased, whereas there have been large declines in the south of their wintering range, in France, Denmark, the Netherlands and Switzerland (Lehikoinen *et al.* 2013).

*Text: A W G John / Photo: Ron Champion*
*Goosander sponsored by Brent Birders – of South Brent Parish*

Balmer *et al.* 2013: 230; Sitters 1988: 299; Tyler 2010: 111

### Winter-period abundance 2007–13

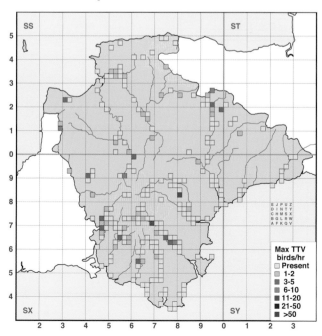

Max TTV birds/hr
- □ Present
- 1-2
- 3-5
- 6-10
- 11-20
- 21-50
- >50

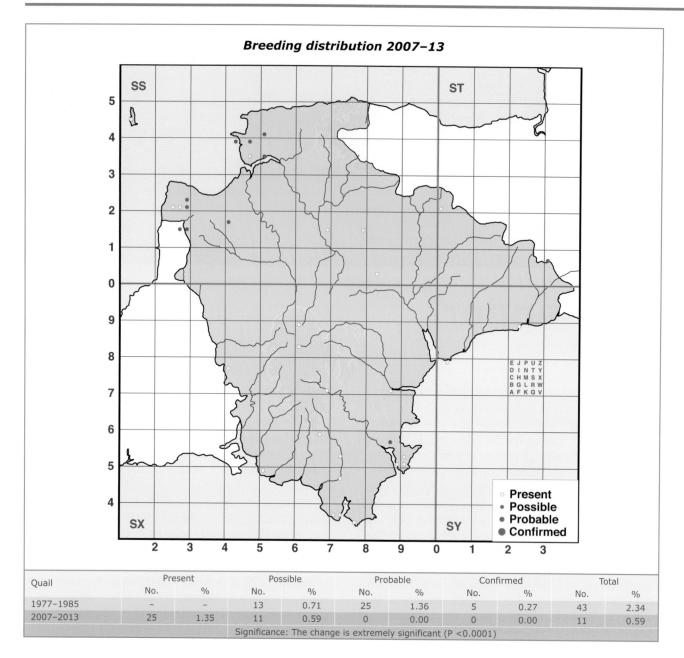

**Breeding distribution 2007–13**

| Quail | Present | | Possible | | Probable | | Confirmed | | Total | |
|---|---|---|---|---|---|---|---|---|---|---|
| | No. | % | No. | % | No. | % | No. | % | No. | % |
| 1977–1985 | – | – | 13 | 0.71 | 25 | 1.36 | 5 | 0.27 | 43 | 2.34 |
| 2007–2013 | 25 | 1.35 | 11 | 0.59 | 0 | 0.00 | 0 | 0.00 | 11 | 0.59 |
| Significance: The change is extremely significant (P <0.0001) | | | | | | | | | | |

**Breeding distribution 1977–85**

**Breeding-period abundance 2007–13**

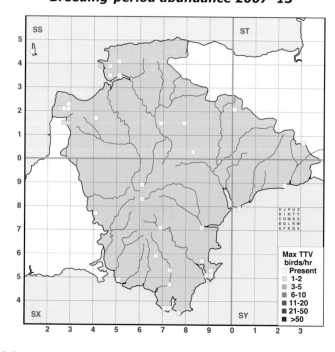

# Quail
*Coturnix coturnix*

Amber listed

THE QUAIL breeds in Europe, north and central Asia, and east and southern Africa, and winters from the Mediterranean and Middle East south to Central Africa. It prefers drier, well-drained soils with sufficient vegetation for concealment. Cereal crops and long grass are particularly favoured, where it feeds on seeds and insects. Very rarely seen, its presence is often detected only by its distinctive '*wet-my-lips*' call. Proof of breeding can be difficult to obtain unless the nest is found or young are observed.

In Britain, the Quail is at the western edge of its range, with an estimated 540 males in an average summer (Musgrove *et al.* 2013). Most arrivals in Devon are during May to July with the number of records received annually rarely exceeding ten; only three were recorded in the years 2012 and 2013, but 16 were noted in 2011. On Lundy, the majority of records refer to single birds in spring. Birds migrating across the county are occasionally taken at night by Peregrines (Dixon & Drewitt 2012).

During the *Devon Tetrad Atlas 1977–85*, Quail were found possibly or probably breeding in 43 tetrads, with confirmed breeding in five. Concentrations occurred around Crediton, where it was heard almost annually, and north of Barnstaple. At that time it was estimated that there were 10–20 pairs per year in Devon, with possibly 50–100 pairs in the Quail year of 1970. Its status as a breeding bird in Devon was considered likely to remain precarious and this seems to have been borne out by the current survey, during which Quail were detected in only 36 tetrads, with none in its former Crediton area stronghold and few north of Barnstaple. No breeding was confirmed during the period of the Atlas; the last was in 1995 at North Molton Ridge, when 12 young were observed (Tyler 2010).

The reduction of food such as invertebrates and weed seeds resulting from pesticide and herbicide use, together with the conversion of many former cereal fields to intensively managed pasture, particularly in the north of the county, have probably reduced habitat quality and extent, and it seems likely Quail will not regain its position as a breeding bird in Devon.

*Text: Ray Jones / Photo: Simon Price*

Balmer *et al.* 2013: 246; Sitters 1988: 82; Tyler 2010: 122

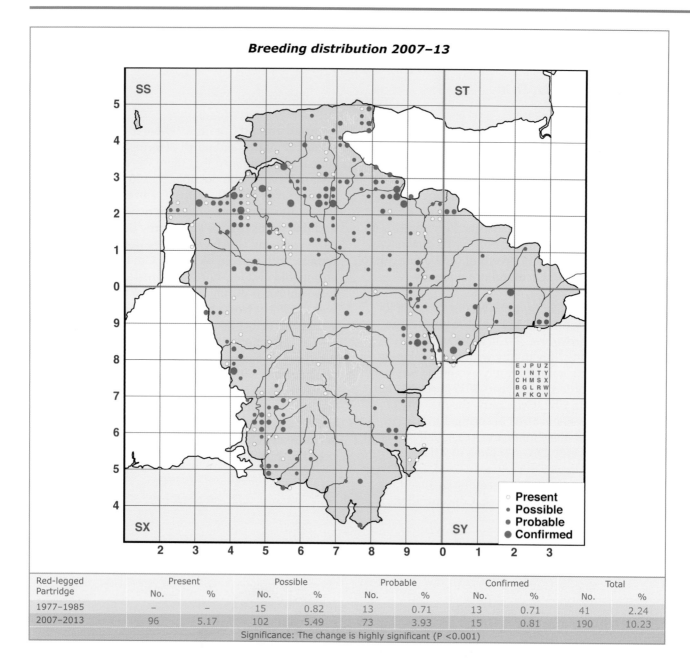

**Breeding distribution 2007–13**

| Red-legged Partridge | Present | | Possible | | Probable | | Confirmed | | Total | |
|---|---|---|---|---|---|---|---|---|---|---|
| | No. | % | No. | % | No. | % | No. | % | No. | % |
| 1977–1985 | – | – | 15 | 0.82 | 13 | 0.71 | 13 | 0.71 | 41 | 2.24 |
| 2007–2013 | 96 | 5.17 | 102 | 5.49 | 73 | 3.93 | 15 | 0.81 | 190 | 10.23 |
| Significance: The change is highly significant (P <0.001) | | | | | | | | | | |

**Breeding distribution 1977–85**

**Breeding-period abundance 2007–13**

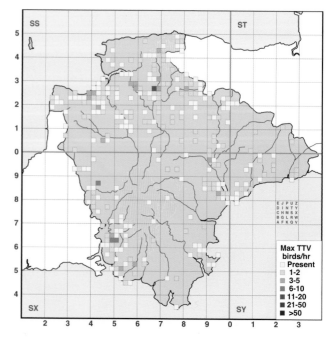

# Red-legged Partridge
## *Alectoris rufa*

RED-LEGGED PARTRIDGES are sedentary birds breeding naturally in France, Spain and Portugal. They were introduced into Britain in 1790, in Suffolk (Tyler 2010). The species prefers areas of low rainfall on arable farmland, sandy heaths, chalk downland and coastal meadows, where it feeds on seeds, leaves and small invertebrates. The wetter climate and large areas of grassland in Devon are not ideal habitat for the species and limit its ability to maintain its numbers and spread naturally.

The European breeding populations is estimated at 2–4.5 million pairs (Birdlife International 2014), with a British population of 82,000 territories in 2009 (Musgrove *et al.* 2013). Large numbers are regularly released for shooting, particularly in eastern counties; around 6.5 million annually in recent years (PACEC 2006). From 1970, most released birds were hybrids between Red-legged Partridge and either Chukar *Alectoris chukar* or Rock Partridge *Alectoris graeca*. However, from 1992, release of hybrids was prohibited under the 1981 Wildlife and Countryside Act.

In Devon the Red-legged Partridge was probably introduced in the 1840s (Tyler 2010) but, despite many subsequent introductions, has never been able to establish itself in significant numbers. The *Devon Tetrad Atlas 1977–85* suggests that the main areas of population were associated with releases, with its stronghold being in East Devon. Since that time, again almost certainly through releases, it has spread further in East Devon, particularly along the Exe basin and is now also found in both the north and south-west of the county, where numbers in 1977–85 had been very low. The species is sparsely distributed in the south and west of the county and is almost absent from Dartmoor where the habitat is not suitable. It is absent from Lundy.

The *Devon Tetrad Atlas 1977–85* estimated the county population at between 50 and 100 pairs, but estimating actual breeding numbers is difficult due to continued releases. Despite the highly significant increase in possible breeding records since the last Atlas, there is little evidence that many released birds breed successfully. Numbers are generally reported in ones and twos, with very few proven records of breeding received.

*Text: Ray Jones / Photo: Alex Carlisle*

Balmer *et al.* 2013: 242; Sitters 1988: 78; Tyler 2010: 119

### Winter-period abundance 2007–13

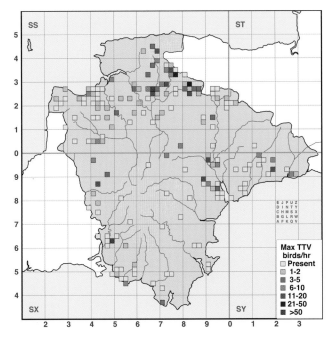

Max TTV birds/hr
☐ Present
1-2
3-5
6-10
11-20
21-50
>50

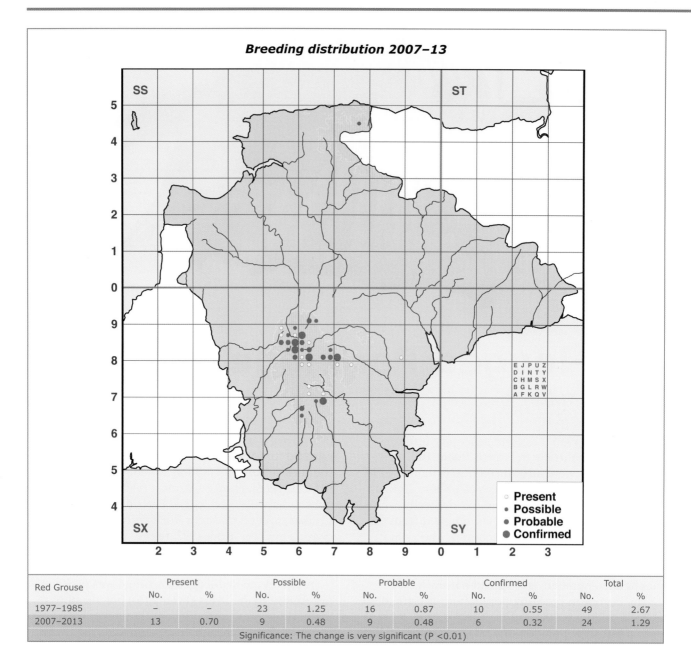

## Breeding distribution 2007–13

| Red Grouse | Present | | Possible | | Probable | | Confirmed | | Total | |
|---|---|---|---|---|---|---|---|---|---|---|
| | No. | % | No. | % | No. | % | No. | % | No. | % |
| 1977–1985 | – | – | 23 | 1.25 | 16 | 0.87 | 10 | 0.55 | 49 | 2.67 |
| 2007–2013 | 13 | 0.70 | 9 | 0.48 | 9 | 0.48 | 6 | 0.32 | 24 | 1.29 |
| Significance: The change is very significant (P <0.01) | | | | | | | | | | |

## Breeding distribution 1977–85

## Breeding-period abundance 2007–13

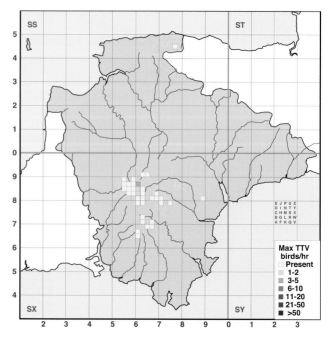

# Red Grouse

*Lagopus lagopus scoticus*

Amber listed

RED GROUSE is endemic to the British Isles and is now regarded as a subspecies of Willow Ptarmigan *L. l. lagopus*. It is a bird of heather moorland, feeding on the shoots, seeds and flowers of heather and, occasionally, insects. The British population was estimated at 230,000 pairs in 2009 (Musgrove *et al.* 2013).

In Devon it is an introduced species of the high heather moors of Dartmoor and Exmoor, occurring mostly above 450 metres, but occasionally lower. It was first introduced to Exmoor in 1820 and further introductions took place in 1915/16 on both Exmoor and Dartmoor. It was also introduced, without success, to Lundy in 1920. The Dartmoor population is the only one in England south of the Pennines.

Numbers on Exmoor since the 1930s were always low and the *Devon Tetrad Atlas 1977–85* estimated

there were only 6–12 pairs in 1985. It had been thought to be extinct on Exmoor from 2000, but a number of records were received in 2003 that may have arisen from an undisclosed release in the foot-and-mouth year of 2001. It is also possible that lack of disturbance during that year may have allowed a small residual population to breed much more successfully than usual. The last record from Exmoor was in 2009.

On Dartmoor there has been a decline since the *Devon Tetrad Atlas 1977–85*, when birds were found in 41 tetrads, with confirmed breeding in seven. The Dartmoor population was estimated to be between 70 and 100 pairs at that time and could be found in small numbers over a wide area, with the exception of the central moors. During the current Atlas period, birds were found in 24 tetrads with confirmed breeding in six. However, because of the secretive nature of the species, it is possible some may have been overlooked.

Causes for the decline include overgrazing resulting in a reduction of available food, increased disturbance by walkers and dogs, excessive swaling and a decline in habitat management resulting in loss of heather. However, climate change is also a critical factor given that this is an upland species that in Devon is well beyond the southern limit of its natural range.

Overall, the Dartmoor population appears to be in gradual decline and although improved management of the heather may help to arrest this, Dartmoor may possibly be too wet and the heather too sparse for the Red Grouse to really thrive. The next Atlas may record that the species is absent from Devon.

*Text: Ray Jones / Photo: Dave Scott*
*Red Grouse sponsored by June Smalley*

Balmer *et al.* 2013: 234; Sitters 1988: 76; Tyler 2010: 114

### Winter-period abundance 2007–13

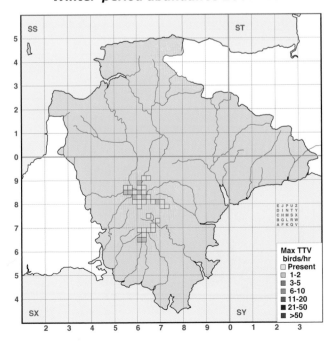

Max TTV
birds/hr
☐ Present
1-2
3-5
6-10
11-20
21-50
>50

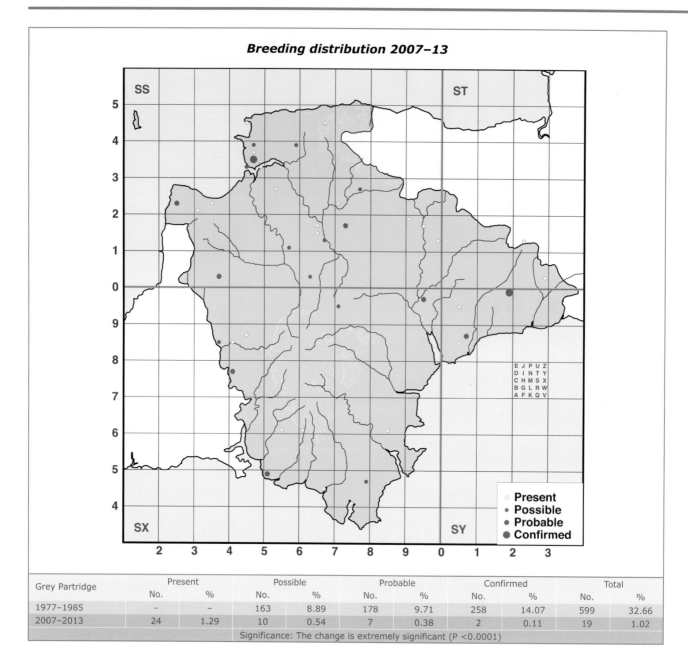

**Breeding distribution 2007–13**

| Grey Partridge | Present | | Possible | | Probable | | Confirmed | | Total | |
|---|---|---|---|---|---|---|---|---|---|---|
| | No. | % | No. | % | No. | % | No. | % | No. | % |
| 1977–1985 | – | – | 163 | 8.89 | 178 | 9.71 | 258 | 14.07 | 599 | 32.66 |
| 2007–2013 | 24 | 1.29 | 10 | 0.54 | 7 | 0.38 | 2 | 0.11 | 19 | 1.02 |
| | Significance: The change is extremely significant (P <0.0001) | | | | | | | | | |

**Breeding distribution 1977–85**

**Breeding-period abundance 2007–13**

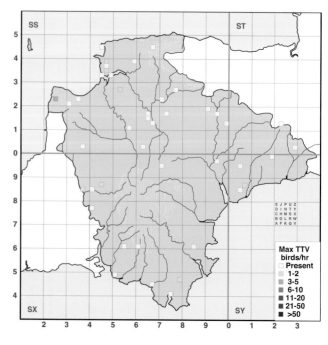

# Grey Partridge
## *Perdix perdix*

**Red listed**

GREY PARTRIDGE is a ground-feeding and nesting bird native to Europe and northern and central Asia. It prefers dry arable land with ground cover no higher than its head. Adults feed mainly on seeds and shoots whilst insects form an essential part of the diet of young chicks.

In Devon it prefers cultivated fields with a strong bias towards high-quality farmland. It has declined by up to 85% in the last 25 years throughout Britain, particularly in areas of intensive cultivation. The situation in Devon is certainly no better and probably even worse. Comparison of the breeding map in the *Devon Tetrad Atlas 1977–85* with the breeding map in the current Atlas shows how dramatically the situation has changed. In the previous Atlas, the Grey Partridge was still widespread, despite a decline since the 1940s, with an estimated population of 1,000–2,000 pairs. Its stronghold at that time was in the Crediton area, with small concentrations near Barnstaple, the Otter Valley and east of the Exe; Grey Partridges were found in 599 tetrads with breeding confirmed in 258. In the current Atlas, Grey Partridges were only found in 43 tetrads; a decline of 93%, with breeding confirmed in only two. The species may be under-recorded due to the difficulty in locating birds but this is unlikely to affect the figures to any great extent.

Primary reasons for the massive national decline are changes in farmland management in an effort to increase yields. Increased use of insecticides and herbicides severely reduces the amount of food available to chicks, whose diet is almost exclusively insects, and the early cutting of grass for silage and the subsequent lack of cover has led to increased predation of hens during the breeding season. Other factors include changes in hedgerow management that can reduce cover, reduced predator control, increased mortality caused by severe winter conditions and wet breeding seasons (Potts 2012). In Devon, a decline in cereal cultivation may also be a factor.

Overall, the future for the Grey Partridge in Devon looks grim, unless there is a dramatic change in agricultural policy and practices. This, however, is looking very unlikely. Rather, farming methods are more likely to intensify to meet the needs of a growing human population. Numbers of birds released for shooting are small and are unlikely to affect overall numbers, but most, if not all, of the current records may derive from these. This may well be the only reason there are still Grey Partridges in the county.

Will there still be Grey Partridges in Devon in the next Atlas in 25 or so years' time?

*Text: Ray Jones / Photo: Dave Scott*

Balmer *et al.* 2013: 244; Sitters 1988: 80; Tyler 2010: 120

### Winter-period abundance 2007–13

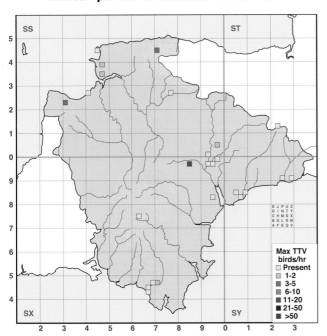

Max TTV birds/hr
- ☐ Present
- ☐ 1-2
- ☐ 3-5
- ■ 6-10
- ■ 11-20
- ■ 21-50
- ■ >50

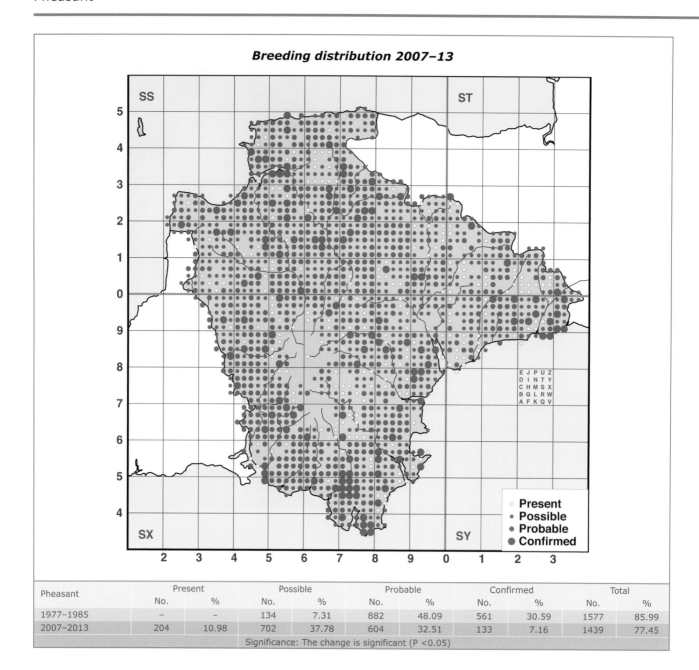

**Breeding distribution 2007–13**

| Pheasant | Present | | Possible | | Probable | | Confirmed | | Total | |
|---|---|---|---|---|---|---|---|---|---|---|
| | No. | % | No. | % | No. | % | No. | % | No. | % |
| 1977–1985 | – | – | 134 | 7.31 | 882 | 48.09 | 561 | 30.59 | 1577 | 85.99 |
| 2007–2013 | 204 | 10.98 | 702 | 37.78 | 604 | 32.51 | 133 | 7.16 | 1439 | 77.45 |
| Significance: The change is significant (P <0.05) | | | | | | | | | | |

**Breeding distribution 1977–85**

**Breeding-period abundance 2007–13**

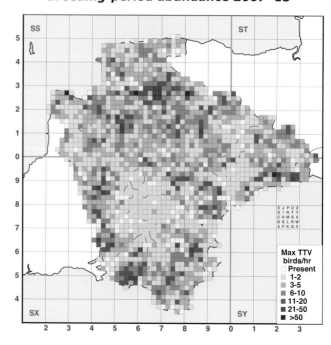

# Pheasant
## *Phasianus colchicus*

PHEASANTS WERE probably introduced into Britain from southern Russia in mediaeval times; these birds are believed to have been of the subspecies *P. c. colchicus*. Numbers in Britain were supplemented by further introductions in the 18th and 19th centuries of other races from the Far East, such as *P. c. torquatus* (BWP). Hybridization between these subspecies has given rise to the variations in plumage seen throughout Britain today.

Pheasants are sedentary and rarely move more than a few kilometres. They need open farmland with plenty of nearby cover, preferably with dense undergrowth to avoid predators. They are very much ground-living birds, feeding mainly on seeds and fruits and nesting in a shallow depression in dense undergrowth.

They are widespread throughout Britain and numbers can, at times, exceed 35 million in Britain (*Bird Atlas 2007–11*). In Devon, as elsewhere, the wild population is boosted each autumn by birds reared and released for shooting and most records refer to these.

The *Devon Tetrad Atlas 1977–85* showed the Pheasant to be widespread throughout the whole of the county, with the exception of the high moors of Dartmoor and Exmoor and larger towns and cities. It was found in 1,577 tetrads, with confirmed breeding in 561. In comparison, the current Atlas found Pheasants in 1,638 tetrads but with confirmed breeding in only 133. Both of these confirmed breeding figures are probably an underestimate as, owing to its preference for dense cover, breeding is difficult to confirm unless the nest is found or young are seen.

Comparison of the breeding status in the two Atlases shows that distribution has changed little. The *Devon Tetrad Atlas 1977–85* estimated there were 10,000–15,000 during the breeding season and there is little reason to doubt this has changed very much, although the numbers released have increased in recent years. Its ground-nesting habit makes it vulnerable to predation during the breeding season by, amongst others, Foxes, Stoats and Carrion Crows. However, numbers are maintained by releases of birds for shooting each autumn, although few released birds breed successfully.

*Text: Ray Jones / Photo: Neil Bygrave*

Balmer *et al.* 2013: 248; Sitters 1988: 84; Tyler 2010: 124

### Winter-period abundance 2007–13

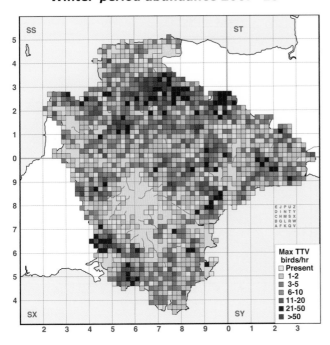

Max TTV birds/hr
- □ Present
- □ 1-2
- ▨ 3-5
- ▤ 6-10
- ■ 11-20
- ■ 21-50
- ■ >50

# Red-throated Diver

*Gavia stellata*

THE SMALLEST and commonest diver in the county, Red-throated Divers appear along Devon's shores from October until late April/early May, with the occasional summer record. During the Atlas period the species was recorded from 70 tetrads. They are widespread along the south coast, mainly in Dawlish Bay, Torbay, Seaton and Start Bay, and around Bideford Bay in the north. The largest annual counts are often in January/February off Hartland Point, where more than 100 are seen in most years. Inland records are very rare. Large passage counts of over 70 birds have been noted during winter and spring (DBRs) and may reflect either long-distance or local movements.

There are few winter distribution changes since the *Winter Atlas 1981–84*, with gains only in Bideford Bay and Torbay and no losses, suggesting a stable wintering population.

*Text: Lee Collins*

*Red-throated Diver sponsored by Bob Heckford*

Balmer *et al.* 2013: 256; Sitters 1988: not treated; Tyler 2010: 126

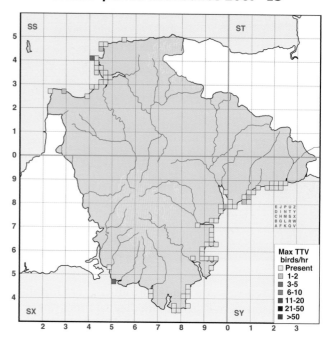

***Winter-period abundance 2007–13***

Max TTV birds/hr
- ☐ Present
- ☐ 1-2
- ■ 3-5
- ■ 6-10
- ■ 11-20
- ■ 21-50
- ■ >50

# Black-throated Diver

*Gavia arctica*

Amber listed

DEVON'S SCARCEST diver, this species was recorded in 40 tetrads during Atlas fieldwork. Although it can be seen anywhere along the coast, most records came from Torbay, Start Bay and Dawlish Bay, with good passage counts also recorded from Prawle Point. Most sightings were of single birds, with gatherings of more than three uncommon. According to *Bird Atlas 2007–11* there has been a 51% winter range expansion since the *Winter Atlas 1981–84*. Although it seems likely that some of these apparent gains resulted from improved coverage and better identification, in Devon there have been increases during the Atlas period along both coasts, with the exception of the Plymouth area (DBRs).

*Text: Lee Collins*

*Black-throated Diver sponsored by Bob Heckford*

Balmer *et al.* 2013: 258; Sitters 1988: not treated; Tyler 2010: 128

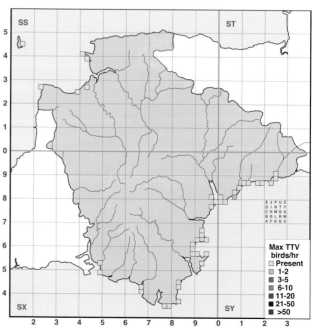

***Winter-period abundance 2007–13***

Max TTV birds/hr
- ☐ Present
- ☐ 1-2
- ■ 3-5
- ■ 6-10
- ■ 11-20
- ■ 21-50
- ■ >50

# Great Northern Diver
*Gavia immer*                                                    Amber listed

ITS HUGE frame, casual wing-beats and large trailing legs give the Great Northern Diver a unique flight profile. This, the largest diver to winter in Devon, is also the most widely distributed, and was recorded from 84 tetrads during the Atlas period. Frequenting deeper water than the other divers, they are usually seen singly, but some locations, such as Torbay, support double-figure numbers in most winters. Passage birds are regularly seen from headlands or well-watched bays and can form many of the larger annual counts – at least 68 off Berry Head in April 2010 was exceptional. It is also the commonest diver to be seen either during overland passage or on inland freshwater lakes and reservoirs.

*Bird Atlas 2007–11* states that there has been a 39% increase since the *Winter Atlas 1981–84* in the number of 10-km squares in which the species was recorded; the BTO maps indicate increases throughout Devon, mainly along the south coast, but also in Bideford Bay and around Lundy, a picture reflected in the winter-period map for Devon.

*Text: Lee Collins / Photo: Dave Norman*

Balmer *et al.* 2013: 260; Sitters 1988: not treated; Tyler 2010: 129

### Winter-period abundance 2007–13

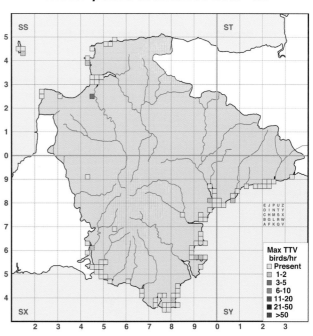

Max TTV birds/hr
☐ Present
▢ 1-2
▧ 3-5
◼ 6-10
◼ 11-20
◼ 21-50
◼ >50

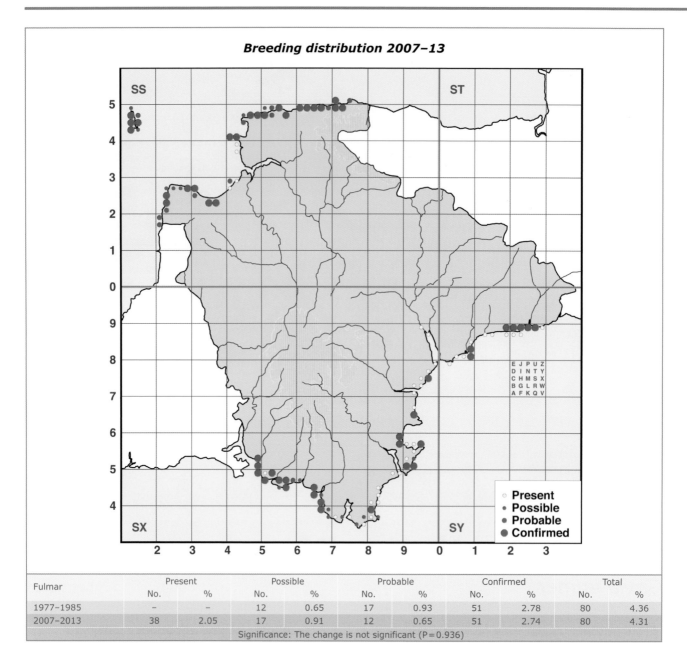

## Breeding distribution 2007–13

| Fulmar | Present | | Possible | | Probable | | Confirmed | | Total | |
|---|---|---|---|---|---|---|---|---|---|---|
| | No. | % | No. | % | No. | % | No. | % | No. | % |
| 1977–1985 | – | – | 12 | 0.65 | 17 | 0.93 | 51 | 2.78 | 80 | 4.36 |
| 2007–2013 | 38 | 2.05 | 17 | 0.91 | 12 | 0.65 | 51 | 2.74 | 80 | 4.31 |
| Significance: The change is not significant (P=0.936) | | | | | | | | | | |

## Breeding distribution 1977–85

## Breeding-period abundance 2007–13

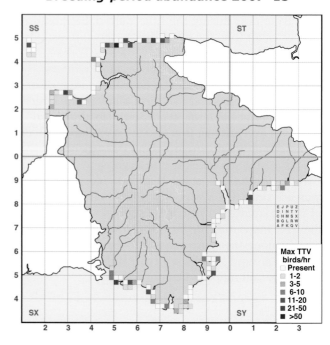

# Fulmar

*Fulmaris glacialis*

Amber listed

WITH THEIR easy gliding flight, Fulmars are a relatively common sight during the breeding season on cliff faces around both the North and South Devon coastline. The county's first breeding record was as recently as 1944, on Lundy, and within a few years Fulmars had colonized both coastlines of the mainland.

Proving breeding can be difficult as birds may prospect suitable nesting ledges and caves for years before settling down to breed. Cliffs occupied by apparently sitting birds even in mid-spring may be deserted in June. Lundy undoubtedly holds the most significant breeding population and was reported to hold 40% of pairs (Seabird 2000). In 2009 a late breeding season survey on the Island recorded 209 occupied sites.

Inclusion of the 'present' category in this survey showed Fulmars to be present in 6.14% of Devon tetrads. If the 'present' category in this atlas is excluded, the numbers of tetrads with probable breeding are remarkably similar to that of the *Devon Tetrad Atlas 1977–85*. National surveys show a reduction in both numbers and breeding productivity since the 1990s with a marked decline since the turn of the century; but this was not identified in this survey.

From the end of August to mid-September, after breeding, Fulmars move out to sea where both adult and immature birds moult. During the winter most Fulmars remain at sea and are slow to return inshore, but in Devon birds generally return to breeding ledges from late February onward (and on Lundy they can reoccupy the ledges from December and hence may also have been recorded during winter surveys). Fulmars were recorded present in 94 tetrads (5.06%). 'Blue' or dark-phase Fulmars, thought to originate from northern colonies, are seen infrequently during the winter, but there were exceptional numbers, perhaps as many as 14 birds, noted in 2008 and 11 in 2012, contrasting with one in 2009 and none in 2007, 2010 and 2013.

While there is no significant change in numbers recorded between this survey and that for the *Devon Tetrad Atlas 1977–85*, the further reduction of the South West's fishing fleet and the introduction of regulations prohibiting the discard of unwanted catch may have future implications for a species whose initial range expansion was linked to the fishing industry.

### Winter-period abundance 2007–13

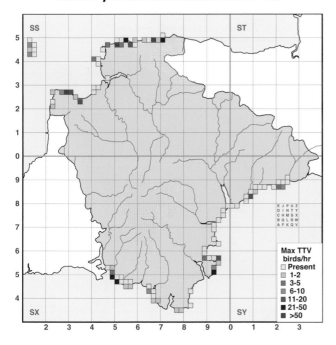

Max TTV birds/hr
☐ Present
☐ 1-2
☐ 3-5
■ 6-10
■ 11-20
■ 21-50
■ >50

*Text: Mike Langman*
*Photos: Barry Bowden (left) & Dave Scott*
*Fulmar sponsored by Exmoor National Park Authority*

**EXMOOR**
NATIONAL PARK

Balmer *et al.* 2013: 262; Sitters 1988: 50; Tyler 2010: 132

# Cory's Shearwater

*Calonectris borealis*

ORY'S SHEARWATER, which breeds in the Mediterranean and on Atlantic islands, including the Canarian and Madeiran archipelagos, is a rare and sporadic visitor to Devon waters, occurring mostly during midsummer.

Sightings of this large Atlantic shearwater depend largely on food supply and/or weather bringing birds closer to shore than normal before they move back into the western approaches. Unsurprisingly, the majority of Atlas-period records came from well-watched headlands, particularly Berry Head, Start Point and Prawle Point. There were also records from Seaton, Dawlish Warren, Thurlestone and Lundy but, surprisingly, no records from the mainland coast of North Devon.

The year-to-year variability in numbers occurring off Devon was demonstrated during the Atlas period with, for example, just single birds in 2009 (May), 2010 (July) and 2012 (July) but several hundred in 2008 (June to August) (*DBRs*).

*Text: Mike Langman*

Balmer *et al.* 2013: not treated; Sitters 1988: not treated; Tyler 2010: 136

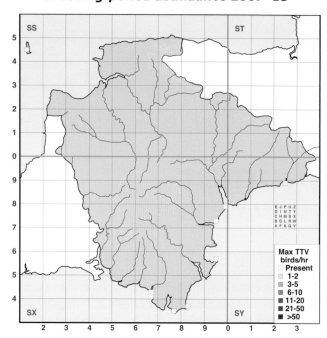

*Breeding-period abundance 2007–13*

# Great Shearwater

*Puffinus gravis*

REAT SHEARWATER is a rare passage visitor, breeding on islands in the South Atlantic during our winter and moving into the north-west Atlantic during our spring, then migrating south through the eastern Atlantic mostly between August and October.

Occurrences of Great Shearwater off Devon are dictated by variations in food availability and prevailing weather patterns. During the Atlas period, all of the records came from four south coast sites and, as expected, during the summer months the well-watched Berry Head and Start Point picked up the bulk of the sightings. The best year during the Atlas period was 2008 with eight birds recorded, the poorest 2009 with only one (*DBRs*).

*Text: Mike Langman*

Balmer *et al.* 2013: not treated; Sitters 1988: not treated; Tyler 2010: 137

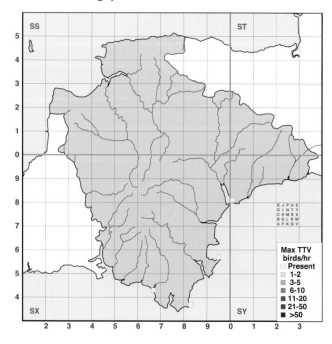

*Breeding-period abundance 2007–13*

# Sooty Shearwater

## *Puffinus griseus*

A SCARCE, mostly autumn, passage migrant breeding on islands in the southern Atlantic and Pacific oceans, Sooty Shearwaters are usually seen from well-watched headlands in Devon during July to November, when strong south-westerly winds combined with poor visibility force birds into the English and Bristol Channels.

Records during the Atlas period came mainly from along the south coast and from only four tetrads in the north (including Lundy). Poor numbers were recorded in 2013 (perhaps as few as 30 birds) but exceptional numbers in 2009, including a peak passage of 582 noted off Berry Head on 2 September 2009. Passage can still occur as late as November (records from six tetrads), though this falls within the Atlas winter period. True winter and spring records are very rare however; during the Atlas years there were records of singles from both Torbay and Dawlish Warren in January 2011.

*Text: Mike Langman / Photo: Mark Darlaston*

Balmer *et al.* 2013: not treated; Sitters 1988: not treated; Tyler 2010: 137

### Winter-period abundance 2007–13

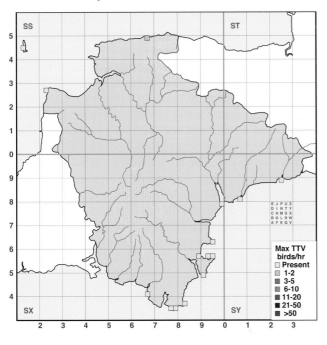

### Breeding-period abundance 2007–13

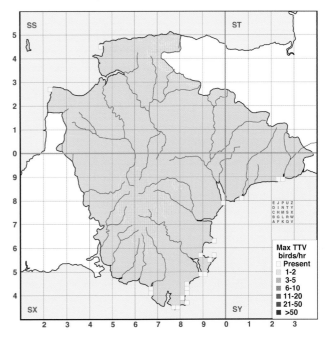

121

# Manx Shearwater

*Puffinus puffinus*

THIS OCEANIC species is often seen in large numbers from Devon coasts, but its only known breeding location is on Lundy. Birds arrive to nest in late March and remain until October when the last fledged young leave to spend the winter in the South Atlantic; Atlas records for the winter period will almost certainly be of birds heading south in late autumn or early arrivals in the spring.

On Lundy they nest in burrows on the steep grassy slopes above the cliffs, mainly along the west coast. There are no reliable estimates of breeding numbers prior to 2000, but in 2001 a survey involving playing calls at all holes and recording responses provided the first representative figure of just 310 nesting pairs (Price & Booker 2002). Prior to 2001 few, if any, young were being reared (Taylor 1985), apparently because of predation by rats.

A Seabird Recovery programme was undertaken, and in 2004 the island was declared rat-free. Without mammalian predation, many more young fledged and the population grew rapidly. A repeat survey in 2008 found 1,127 pairs; the increase was entirely due to immigration, as shearwaters do not breed until five–six years old. The latest survey, in 2013, estimated 3,451 pairs – a tenfold increase in ten years (Booker & Price 2014b, Price & Booker 2014).

The inland dot in the 10-km square SX87 refers to a juvenile found in Chudleigh in September 2008 and released from Teignmouth Pier later the same day (*DBR* 2008).

*Text: David Price / Photo: Mark Darlaston*
*Manx Shearwater sponsored by Tony & Ann Taylor*

Balmer *et al.* 2013: 264; Sitters 1988: 292; Tyler 2010: 140

### Breeding distribution 2007-13

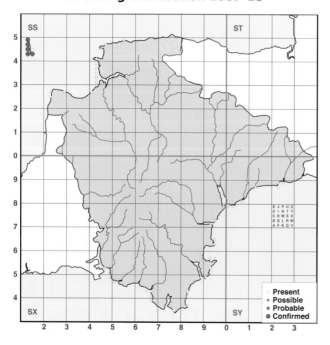

Present
Possible
Probable
Confirmed

# Balearic Shearwater

## Puffinus mauretanicus

**Red listed**

WITH A breeding population estimated at just 3,193 pairs (Arcos 2011) and confined to the Balearic Islands, the Balearic Shearwater is classed as critically endangered.

Balearic Shearwaters have shown a general trend of increasing numbers in Devon over the last decade. During the Atlas period they were recorded in 24 tetrads (1.29%), primarily on the south coast. Most occurrences are during the post-breeding period, June to September, when non-breeding birds disperse north to feed and moult. Lyme Bay is known to be a particularly important area for the species at this time (SeaWatch SW 2007–2011).

Annual counts in Devon varied considerably during the survey period (see table). There is evidence to show a further movement north into the Bristol Channel during the late autumn, with peak counts here during October and even November; for example, 16 from Hartland Point on 25 November 2011, 127 from Hartland Point on 17 October 2013 and 23 from Lundy on 21 October 2013 (*DBRs*).

*Text: Mike Langman / Photo: Mark Darlaston*

Balmer *et al.* 2013: 265; Sitters 1988: not treated; Tyler 2010: 142

| Balearic Shearwater Annual counts, 2007–2013 | |
|---|---|
| **Year** | **Count** |
| 2007 | 570 |
| 2008 | 1,335 |
| 2009 | 887 |
| 2010 | 926 |
| 2011 | 4,104 |
| 2012 | 1,794 |
| 2013 | 2,662 |

### Breeding-period abundance 2007–13

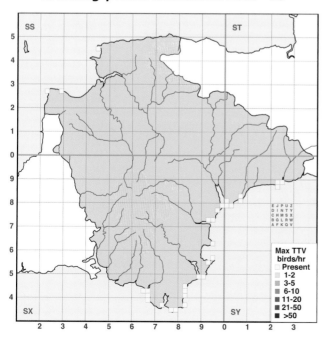

### Winter-period abundance 2007–13

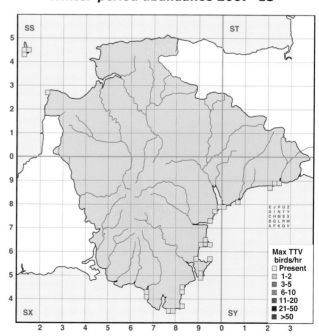

# Storm Petrel

*Hydrobates pelagicus*

THIS REGULARLY recorded tiny pelagic species has a chequered history in the county. Its nocturnal lifestyle, long-range feeding excursions and inaccessible nesting sites, which must be free from mammalian predators, have made it very difficult to confirm breeding.

Breeding occurred on the south coast on Thatcher Rock, Torbay in 1874 and as late as 1950. More recently birds ringed in Ireland, Scotland and the Channel Islands have been controlled during the

summer, using tape lures, at Hartland Point and Prawle, and birds ringed at Hartland Point, Prawle Point and Lundy have been controlled at: Gwennap Head, Cornwall; Hartlepool; Portland Bill; on the Isles of Scilly, Isle of Man and Wales (Tyler 2010). It is clear that Storm Petrels showing brood patches caught and ringed in Devon may well have travelled long distances to feed around our coast.

Following the eradication of rats on Lundy in 2004, it was only a matter of time before breeding on

### Breeding-period abundance 2007–13

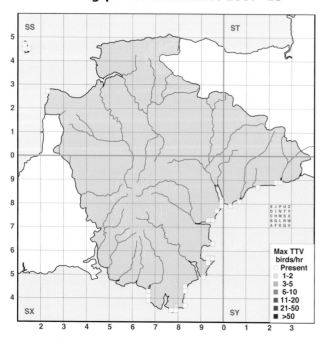

### Winter-period abundance 2007–13

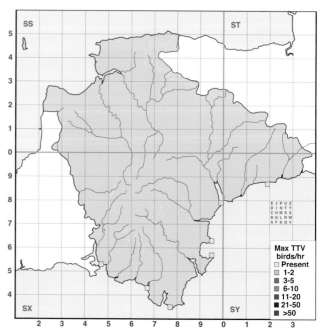

the island was confirmed, and in 2014 a chick was discovered. There is little doubt that breeding numbers on Lundy will increase in the future.

Most Storm Petrels, as their name suggests, are seen after sustained periods of stormy weather and south westerly winds. Food supply is also a factor, with good numbers of birds sometimes noted close to shore in calm summer conditions, mainly from Hartland Point, Prawle Point, Dawlish Warren and Berry Head. Over the seven-year Atlas period they were recorded in 23 (1.24%) tetrads, mostly during April–September, and in very small numbers from the south coast October–November. There was a single February sighting in 2008. Numbers vary considerably between years; 1,467 were counted in 2007 and 1,217 in 2009, while 2013 was very poor with just 74 (*DBRs*). From April to November, fishermen and ferry passengers to Lundy and France/Spain regularly report Storm Petrels, sometimes in good numbers, out of sight of shore-based watchers.

Since the closure of raw sewage outfalls in the 1990s, far fewer birds have been noted off South Devon headlands such as Hope's Nose and Sharkham Point, where they would regularly patter-feed over the sewage slick.

*Text: Mike Langman / Photo: Mark Darlaston*

Balmer *et al.* 2013: 266; Sitters 1988: not treated; Tyler 2010: 144

# Leach's Petrel
## *Oceanodroma leucorhoa*

**Amber listed**

LEACH'S PETREL is a rare passage/winter migrant to Devon. It breeds on islands and coastlines of the northern Atlantic and Pacific Oceans and winters further south as far as equatorial waters. In Devon it is mostly recorded after severe west to south-west gales during late autumn.

Unlike Storm Petrels, Leach's Petrels are prone to be 'wrecked' by storms, usually onto windward coastlines and bays. These weakened birds are usually pursued relentlessly by avian predators, and observers have sometimes witnessed them being killed. Two were taken by a Peregrine at Thurlestone on 29 November 2009 and the remains of a Leach's Petrel were found at a Peregrine plucking site in Exeter in 2009 (*DBR* 2009). There are historic reports of moribund or dead birds found well inland. Two were found in 2009, at Hooe, Plymouth on 25 November and at Roborough on 3 December.

Passage of multiple individuals has been recorded occasionally, as birds blown into the Bristol and English Channel make their way back out to the Atlantic Ocean as winds subside. During the Atlas period, Leach's Petrels were recorded in 14 tetrads, all within the autumn and early winter months of September to December. Apart from 2009, which was an exceptional year with 14 records of 37 birds, there were just three other records of single birds during the Atlas period, in 2007, 2012 and 2013 (*DBRs*).

*Text: Mike Langman*

Balmer *et al.* 2013: 267; Sitters 1988: not treated; Tyler 2010: 146

### *Winter-period abundance 2007–13*

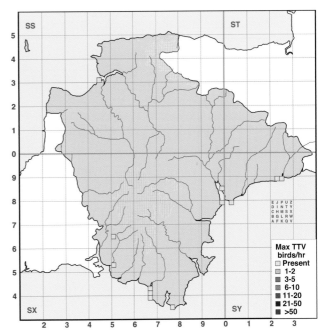

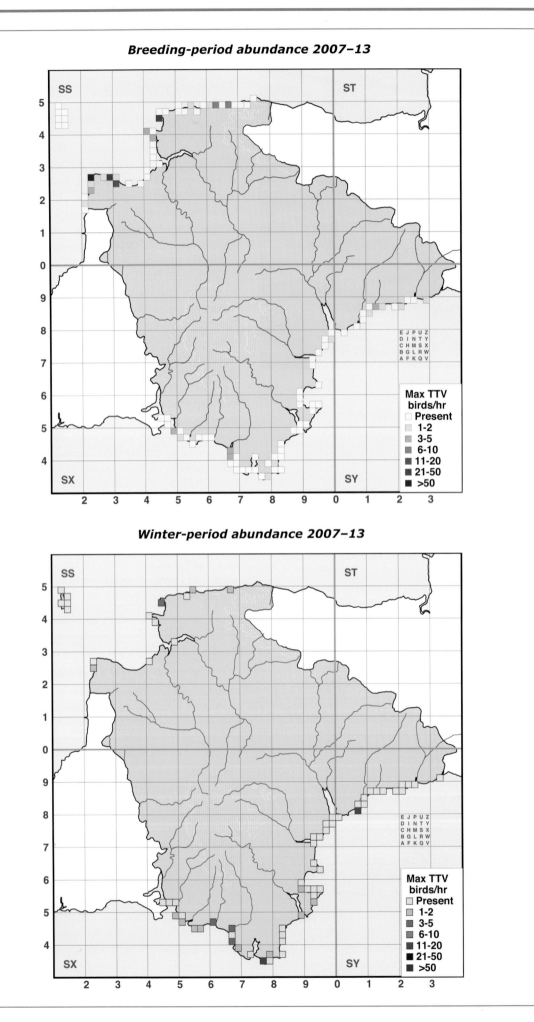

**Breeding-period abundance 2007–13**

Max TTV
birds/hr
- Present
- 1-2
- 3-5
- 6-10
- 11-20
- 21-50
- >50

**Winter-period abundance 2007–13**

Max TTV
birds/hr
- Present
- 1-2
- 3-5
- 6-10
- 11-20
- 21-50
- >50

# Gannet
*Morus bassanus*

Amber listed

Gannets spend their entire lives at sea except when breeding and only very occasionally are storm-driven birds found inland. They last bred in Devon (on Lundy) over 100 years ago (Davis & Jones 2007), and the nearest breeding colonies to Devon are now at Grassholm, Dyfed (70 km from Hartland Point), with about 39,000 pairs; and two colonies, Les Étacs and Ortac, on Alderney (110 km from Start Point), where there are about 6,000 pairs altogether (Mead 2000).

The species is present all year round in Devon coastal waters. Numbers recorded during Atlas counts tended to be highest on the north coast in summer, with records from 44 northern coastal tetrads, including timed counts of over 50 per hour off Hartland Point and more than six per hour in eight other tetrads. In winter, sightings were more widespread off southern coasts, although in lower numbers; on the north coast there were records from only 13 tetrads, although counts of over 50 per hour were recorded around Lundy, and also Morte Point. The higher summer figures for the north coast probably reflect the relative closeness of the Grassholm colony, North Devon waters being well within feeding range for Gannets breeding on

Grassholm. However, it is also likely that many of the birds seen round the Devon coast in summer are non-breeders, probably following Mackerel shoals as they move inshore in late summer. Ringing recoveries show that some birds from Alderney reach the southern coasts of Devon (Tyler 2010).

Gannets in British waters are partly migratory, moving south in winter to the Bay of Biscay and points south as far as Mauretania, with young birds moving farthest (Wernham *et al.* 2002). Some remain in the English Channel, although it is likely that their strong flight enables them to move to more productive fishing grounds during rough weather. Gannet populations in British waters have increased markedly in the last 100 years and several new colonies have been established, such as the Alderney colonies in 1940 and 1946 (Mead 2000). Some of the increase may be a result of birds exploiting discards from fishing boats, in which case stricter regulation of this practice may lead to population stabilisation, or even a decline.

*Text: J M Lock / Photo: Dave Scott*
*Gannet sponsored by Peter Upstone*

Balmer *et al.* 2013: 268 Sitters 1988: not treated; Tyler 2010: 148

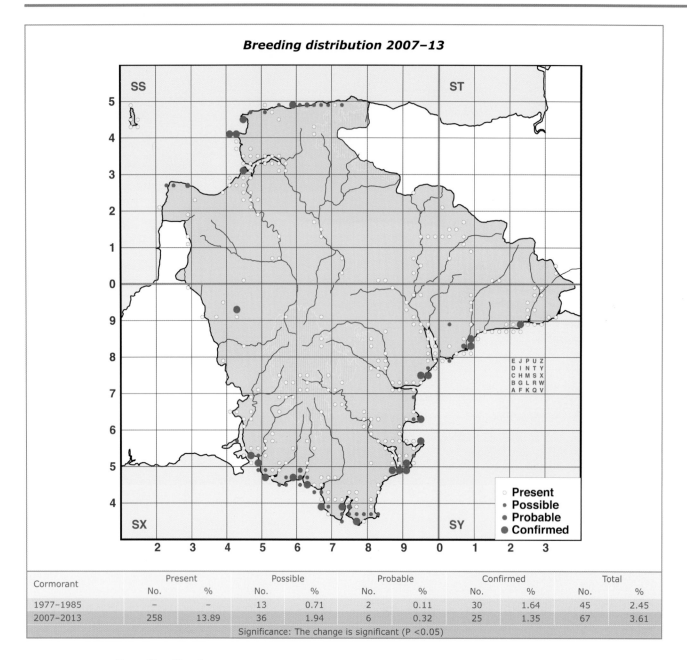

### Breeding distribution 2007–13

| Cormorant | Present | | Possible | | Probable | | Confirmed | | Total | |
|---|---|---|---|---|---|---|---|---|---|---|
| | No. | % | No. | % | No. | % | No. | % | No. | % |
| 1977–1985 | – | – | 13 | 0.71 | 2 | 0.11 | 30 | 1.64 | 45 | 2.45 |
| 2007–2013 | 258 | 13.89 | 36 | 1.94 | 6 | 0.32 | 25 | 1.35 | 67 | 3.61 |
| Significance: The change is significant (P <0.05) | | | | | | | | | | |

### Breeding distribution 1977–85

### Breeding-period abundance 2007–13

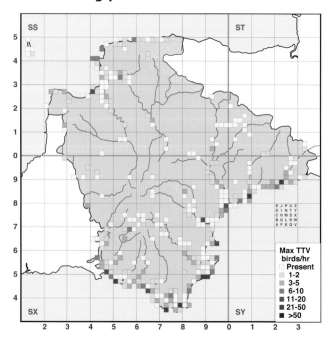

# Cormorant

*Phalacrocorax carbo*

CORMORANTS ARE resident fish-eating birds of coastal waters, feeding in shallow water and also making extensive use of rivers and freshwater lakes where their activities make them unpopular with anglers. Atlas records show that they even use the upper reaches of rivers on Dartmoor.

Birds of the North Atlantic race *P. c. carbo* can be found all round Devon's coast, but are scarce on Lundy, where they last bred in 1959. In Devon, breeding is almost exclusively on coastal cliffs, although at least one pair nested at Roadford Reservoir in 2013.

There has been little change in abundance or distribution of breeding birds since the *Devon Tetrad*

*Atlas 1977–85* survey. There are now rather fewer tetrads in North Devon with confirmed breeding, as there are on the south coast east of the Exe, but the numbers of confirmed breeding sites west of the Exe are almost the same in the two surveys. However, the breeding categories of possible, probable and confirmed combined suggests a significant expansion in breeding range within the county. It is not, however, possible to say whether there has been any change in the total population as numbers in each tetrad were not recorded in the *Devon Tetrad Atlas 1977–85*. If one assumes between five and ten breeding pairs per occupied tetrad, then the total Devon breeding population may lie within the range 350 to 700 pairs. *Bird Atlas 2007–11* states that, in Britain as a whole, the breeding population has increased by 30% since the *Breeding Atlas 1968–72*; the wintering population too has increased, mainly at inland sites. These increases will largely be due to the species receiving full protection under the Wildlife and Countryside Act 1981. Cormorants can still be controlled under licence where they are causing substantial damage to fisheries.

Most of Devon's Cormorants are sedentary, and stay around our coasts and estuaries throughout the year, but ringing recoveries show that at least some juveniles disperse south in winter to the coasts of France and Spain.

Continental Cormorants *P. c. sinensis* are recorded in ones and twos in most years, mainly on the south coast and mainly in freshwater or estuarine habitats, but identification of this subspecies is difficult (Langman 2005).

*Text: J M Lock / Photo: Neil Bygrave*

Balmer *et al.* 2013: 270; Sitters 1988: 52; Tyler 2010: 150

### Winter-period abundance 2007–13

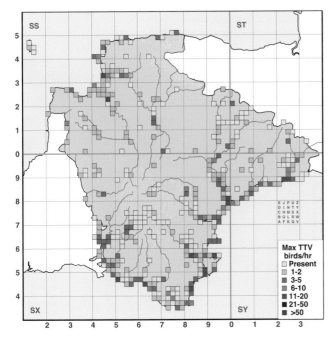

Max TTV birds/hr
☐ Present
1-2
3-5
6-10
11-20
21-50
>50

# Breeding distribution 2007–13

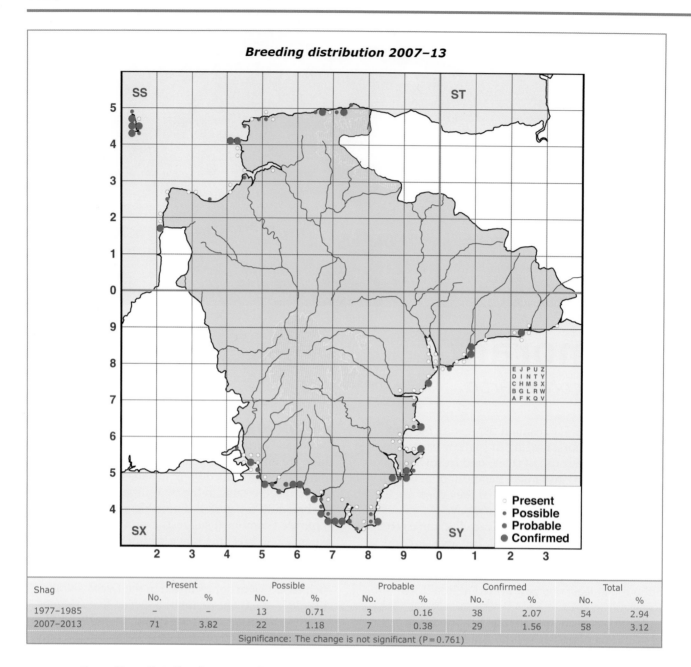

| Shag | Present | | Possible | | Probable | | Confirmed | | Total | |
|---|---|---|---|---|---|---|---|---|---|---|
| | No. | % | No. | % | No. | % | No. | % | No. | % |
| 1977–1985 | – | – | 13 | 0.71 | 3 | 0.16 | 38 | 2.07 | 54 | 2.94 |
| 2007–2013 | 71 | 3.82 | 22 | 1.18 | 7 | 0.38 | 29 | 1.56 | 58 | 3.12 |
| Significance: The change is not significant (P=0.761) | | | | | | | | | | |

## Breeding distribution 1977–85

## Breeding-period abundance 2007–13

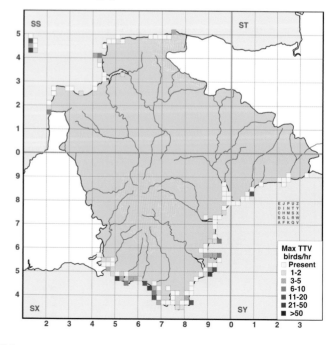

# Shag
*Phalacrocorax aristotelis*

**Red listed**

SHAGS DIFFER from Cormorants not only in their smaller size and green, not bluish, gloss, but also in being almost exclusively maritime. The winter density map shows this difference very clearly. As a rule, only storm-driven juveniles are found inland and, while birds may feed in the lower reaches of estuaries, the bulk of their food is obtained from coastal waters. They feed more in mid-water than do Cormorants, and eat more open-water fish, rather than bottom-living species. Shags are also more gregarious than Cormorants and often form feeding flocks that may comprise up to several hundred birds. Such flocks have been recorded off the mouth of the Exe, with 310 counted in November 2010.

More Shags were recorded from the south coast than the north during Atlas fieldwork. Unlike Cormorants, they breed on Lundy where there were 112 pairs in 2013 (Booker & Price 2014a). Comparison with the *Devon Tetrad Atlas 1977–85* survey suggests a slight decline in the numbers of tetrads with breeding confirmed – 29, rather than 38 tetrads. However, the total number of breeding tetrads (56) was virtually the same as in the previous survey (58).

Numbers of breeding Shags are difficult to estimate because the nests are often tucked into clefts and hollows. An apparent decline on Lundy from c.130 pairs in the 1950s to about half that number by 2000 may simply have reflected the particularly thorough censusing of Shags for research purposes during the 1950s (Davis & Jones 2007). However, an increase since the island was declared rat free in 2004 suggests that nest predation by rats may have been an issue in the past. However, assuming an average colony size of ten, there may have been between 400 and 600 breeding pairs of Shags in Devon during the Atlas period.

Adult Shags are virtually sedentary but juveniles disperse fairly widely, and there are recoveries of Lundy-ringed birds from north-west France as well as from Cornwall and Dorset. One or two have reached southern Ireland and a single Lundy-ringed bird was shot in Denmark. 'Wrecked' juveniles have been recovered in central and eastern England.

*Text: J M Lock / Photo: Mark Darlaston*

Balmer *et al.* 2013: 272; Sitters 1988: 54; Tyler 2010: 155

### Winter-period abundance 2007–13

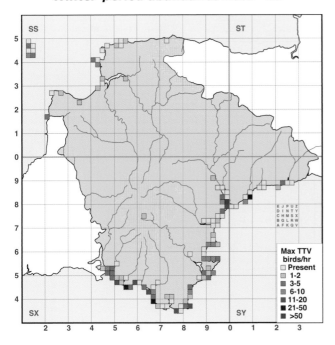

Max TTV birds/hr
- ☐ Present
- ☐ 1-2
- ☐ 3-5
- ☐ 6-10
- ■ 11-20
- ■ 21-50
- ■ >50

# Bittern
*Botaurus stellaris*

Amber listed

THE BITTERN is a camouflaged specialist reedbed hunter. Males are known for their far-carrying booming call. In Devon it is mostly a winter visitor and very scarce passage migrant, mainly from September to March, and particularly during severe winters affecting Britain and north-west Europe. The harsh weather of early 2010 and winter 2010/11 produced many more Devon records than usual.

Winter records came from most of the county's estuaries or larger coastal marshlands, particularly those with reedbeds. The majority of occupied tetrads were around the Exe Estuary, with others at Slapton Ley and South Milton, South Huish and Thurlestone marshes. Proving the presence of more than one individual at any site is extremely difficult, but sightings involving two individuals came from Sherpa Marsh (Taw/Torridge Estuary) in January 2010, Exe Estuary wetlands in December 2010 and 2011 and Slapton Ley in November 2012. A GPS-tagged bird from northern Holland wintered at Slapton Ley in 2011/12 and again in 2012/13.

Bitterns are increasing as a breeding species in Britain due to reedbed creation schemes, targeted reedbed management, improving water quality and careful protection. Breeding probably occurred in Devon in 1996 and 1997, since booming was heard and putative juveniles seen in summer (*DBRs*), but not since, although there were a few summer records during the Atlas period. Hope remains that the

species may breed again in Devon, particularly given the proximity of the significant breeding population in the Somerset Levels (Ballance *et al.* 2014).

*Text: Robert Hurrell / Photo: Chris Townend*
*Bittern sponsored by Roberta Emslie-Henry*

Balmer *et al.* 2013: 274; Sitters 1988: not treated; Tyler 2010: 157

### Breeding-period abundance 2007–13

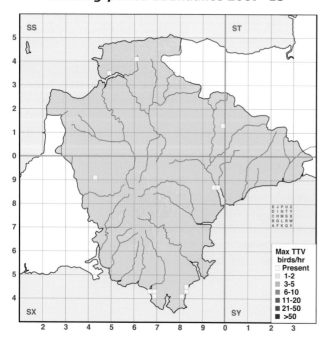

### Winter-period abundance 2007–13

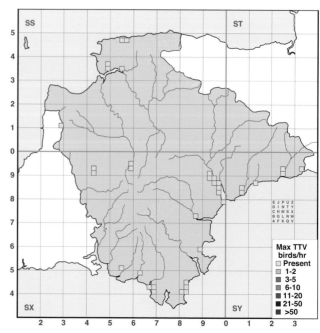

# Cattle Egret

*Bubulcus ibis*

THE WELL-NAMED Cattle Egret is most often found with livestock in grass fields. Prior to 2005 the species was no more than a vagrant in Devon with only three records since 1805, the year of the first British record. Sightings are now virtually annual, with exceptional influxes in the 2007/08 and 2008/09 winters involving well over 40 individuals.

On the riverine systems of the Plym, Yealm and Exe they feed by day in fields, often with livestock, and often with Little Egrets. At dusk they join Little Egret roosts.

The winter distribution map shows that virtually all records came from within four kilometres of an estuary or other waterbody. Most winter TTV records came from the Exe and Taw/Torridge Estuaries, with up to five birds present. Other records came from around south coast estuaries and rivers although the absence of records from the Dart catchment is surprising. In 2008, 40 birds were recorded and multiple records came from six sites. Most North Devon records were from the Taw/Torridge where a maximum count of five was seen; from South Devon similar counts came from Tamerton Foliot and Kingsbridge whilst three birds were seen at South Huish and Exminster Marshes as well as singles and twos from numerous other sites. At least 14 birds occurred in 2009 with a new county maximum of eight birds in the Kingsbridge area in early January. In the following years between three and seven individuals were recorded.

Summer records, all of single birds, came mainly from south coast estuaries, Seaton Marshes and the Taw/Torridge Estuary.

In view of the confirmation of breeding in Somerset in 2008, the possibility of this species breeding in Devon in the future no longer seems fanciful.

*Text: Robert Hurrell / Photo: Rob Jutsum*
*Cattle Egret sponsored by Nikki & Peter Jeffcote*

Balmer *et al.* 2013: 278; Sitters 1988: not treated; Tyler 2010: 163

## Breeding-period abundance 2007–13

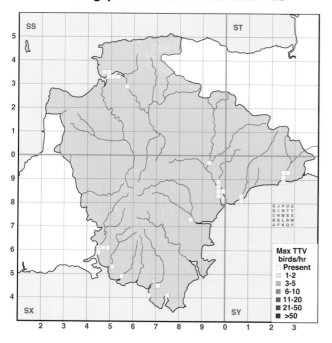

## Winter-period abundance 2007–13

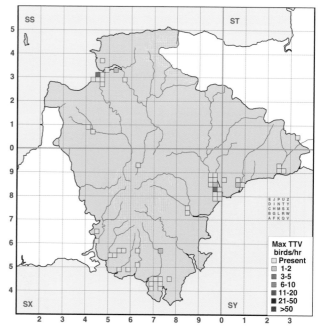

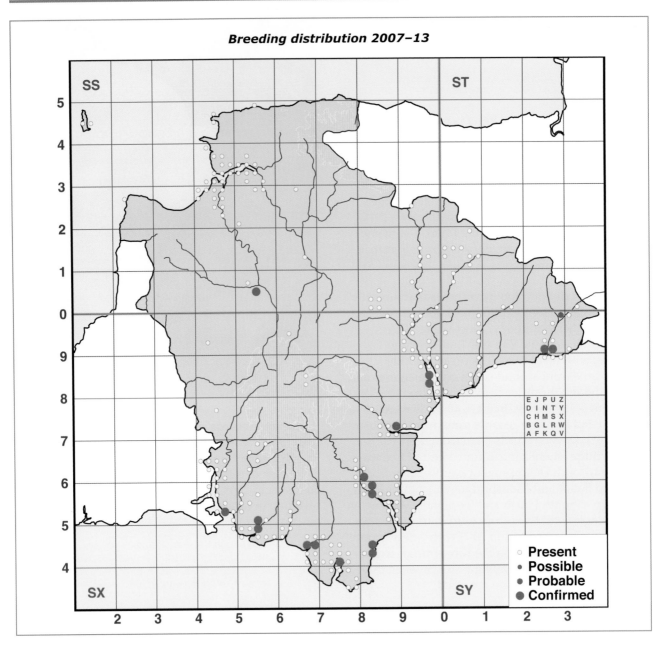

**Breeding distribution 2007–13**

Present
Possible
Probable
Confirmed

**Breeding-period abundance 2007–13**

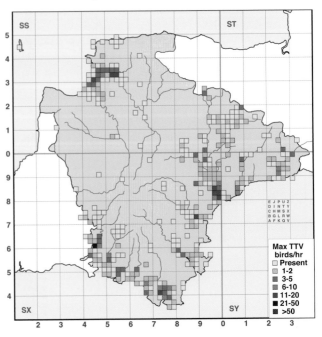

**Winter-period abundance 2007–13**

Max TTV
birds/hr
Present
1-2
3-5
6-10
11-20
21-50
>50

# Little Egret
*Egretta garzetta*

THIS ELEGANT all-white heron is most often found within estuaries and marshlands, but also on open rocky coasts, inland lakes, ponds, along rivers and in fields, often with livestock. During the breeding season they sport feathery white plumes, strikingly revealed during their territorial interactions and courtship.

Prior to 1989, Little Egret was a rare vagrant to Devon but a dramatic northward extension of its breeding range and post-breeding dispersal from north-west France has occurred since (*DBR* 1990). An influx of at least 40 birds in autumn 1989 was followed by wintering in every subsequent year. The table below illustrates the striking increase in summer and winter maximum WeBS county totals from 1997 to 2007, peaking at 550 in September 2007, but which has since fallen back by more than 20% in both summer and winter.

The *Devon Tetrad Atlas 1977–85* did not mention this species, which bred for the first time in the UK in Dorset in 1996 and in Devon in 2002 (Whitehall 2002). Proving breeding can be difficult because Little Egrets tend to choose densely vegetated and secluded nesting areas (Tabb 2004, Hurrell & Hurrell 2014). During the Atlas recording period all but one of the confirmed breeding sites was from the south coast. These were the Axe, Exe, Teign, Dart, Kingbridge, Avon and Yealm Estuaries, Drake's Island and Slapton Ley. The single inland breeding site was within the Torridge catchment. Nesting was not recorded at every site in all years.

Both the winter and summer TTV maps confirm a distribution strongly associated with estuaries and rivers. The highest winter TTV concentration was on the Tamar Estuary with 21–50 birds. This estuary is an EU Special Protection Area for both wintering and passage Little Egrets. Most birds using the Tamar Estuary roost and breed on Drake's Island (*DBRs* 2007, 2008, 2009, 2010).

The summer TTV map shows presence in 197 tetrads (10.6%), while this rises to 330 (17.8%) for the winter map. The highest summer TTV counts came from the Exe (>50) and Avon (21–50) estuaries. During WeBS counts over the Atlas period, 50 or more birds were recorded at Drake's Island, and on the Exe, Taw/Torridge and Teign Estuaries (*DBRs*).

It is hoped that Little Egret numbers will at least be maintained and that the breeding population may colonize new breeding sites in the north of the county.

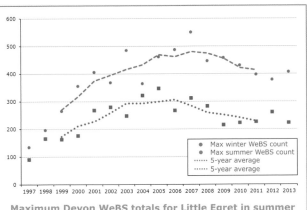

**Maximum Devon WeBS totals for Little Egret in summer (March–September) and winter (October–February), 1997–2013. Source: *DBRs*.**

*Text: Robert Hurrell / Photo: Barry Bowden*
*Little Egret sponsored by Robert Hurrell*

Balmer *et al.* 2013: 276; Sitters 1988: not treated; Tyler 2010: 165

# Great White Egret
## *Ardea alba*

THIS LARGE white heron is currently a vagrant to Devon, though given the species' status as an increasing year-round resident on the nearby Somerset Levels, where breeding was confirmed for the first time in Britain in 2012, it may well become more common here and indeed colonize, as did the Little Egret.

Records during the Atlas period came from April to December (peaking in April/May and September/October) with none overwintering.

Late summer records, from six tetrads, all on the south coast, were associated with the larger coastal or estuarine marshlands: Axe Estuary (2011), Exe Estuary (2012) and the South Milton, South Huish and Thurlestone Marsh complex. Spring singletons were also seen at the same estuaries in 2011–2013. (An indication of the source of at least some of these birds was provided when a bird colour-ringed as a nestling at Lac de Grand-Lieu, Loire-Atlantique, France in 2001, was sighted on the Exe Estuary in August 2003.) Single birds were also present within the Slapton Ley reedbeds in November 2009 and near the Dart Estuary. North Devon records all came from the Taw/Torridge estuary in September 2010 and October 2012.

*Text: Robert Hurrell / Photo: David Land*

Balmer *et al.* 2013: 279; Sitters 1988: not treated; Tyler 2010: 167

**Breeding-period abundance 2007–13**

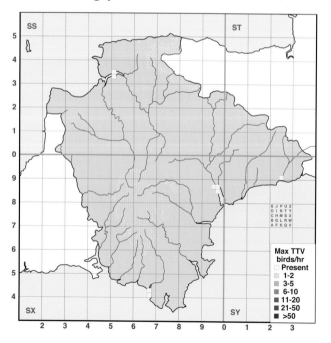

**Winter-period abundance 2007–13**

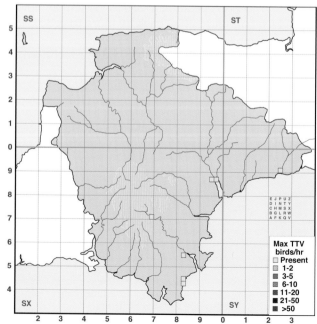

Max TTV birds/hr
- Present
- 1-2
- 3-5
- 6-10
- 11-20
- 21-50
- >50

# Glossy Ibis
*Plegadis falcinellus*

Glossy Ibises are rare vagrants to Devon. During the Atlas period they were recorded from south coast estuaries – Plym, Avon, Kingsbridge, Exe and Otter – mainly in winter, sometimes singly but more usually in small flocks of mainly juvenile birds, although up to 21 were seen together (*DBR* 2010). They are usually seen feeding in areas of wet grassland and at water margins. Colour-ringing has shown that most of these birds originate from the very large breeding colony in Doñana, southern Spain, where the species first nested in 1996 (*DBR* 2010).

*Text: J M Lock / Photo: Chris Townend*

Balmer *et al.* 2013: 282; Sitters 1988: not treated; Tyler 2010: 173

### Winter-period abundance 2007–13

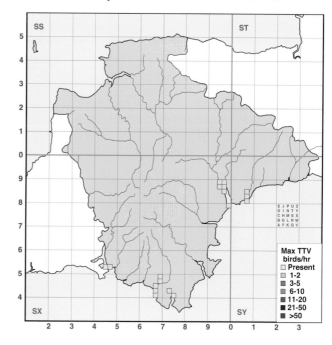

Max TTV
birds/hr
☐ Present
◻ 1-2
▨ 3-5
▨ 6-10
■ 11-20
■ 21-50
■ >50

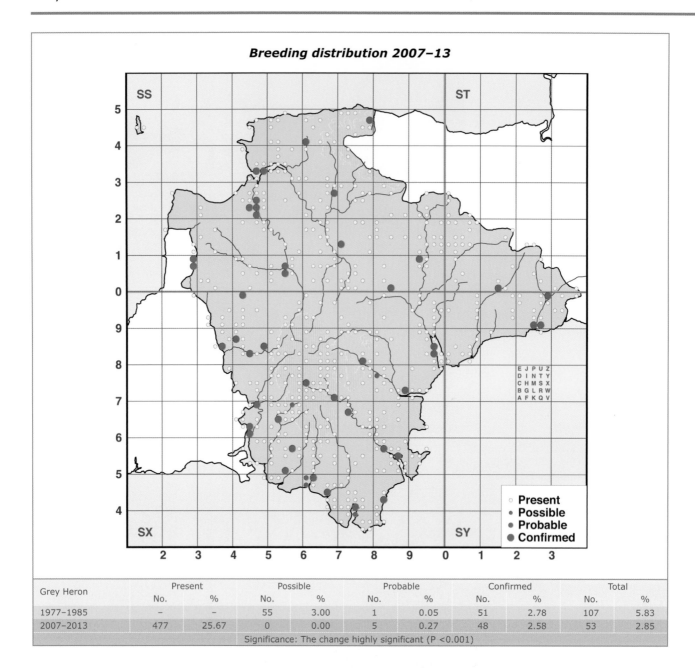

**Breeding distribution 2007–13**

| Grey Heron | Present | | Possible | | Probable | | Confirmed | | Total | |
|---|---|---|---|---|---|---|---|---|---|---|
| | No. | % | No. | % | No. | % | No. | % | No. | % |
| 1977–1985 | – | – | 55 | 3.00 | 1 | 0.05 | 51 | 2.78 | 107 | 5.83 |
| 2007–2013 | 477 | 25.67 | 0 | 0.00 | 5 | 0.27 | 48 | 2.58 | 53 | 2.85 |
| Significance: The change highly significant (P <0.001) | | | | | | | | | | |

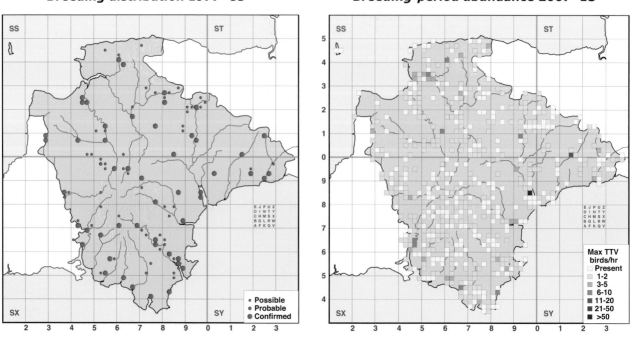

**Breeding distribution 1977–85**

**Breeding-period abundance 2007–13**

# Grey Heron
## *Ardea cinerea*

THIS PATIENT hunter is an adaptable and mobile species frequenting estuarine and inland waterways, lakes, leats, ponds, bogs, marshes, reedbeds, fields and the coast. The totals for tetrads with confirmed or probable breeding sites in both the present survey and in the *Devon Tetrad Atlas 1977–1985* were very similar. This initially appears to suggest little change between the two surveys. However, some former sites are no longer used, for example where woodland has been felled, while new sites have appeared elsewhere. In the *Devon Tetrad Atlas*, of the 33 heronries recorded, 20 contained one to nine nests, ten held 10 to 19 nests, with three sites having 20 nests or more (Arlington 28, Powderham 28 and Puslinch 20). During the present Atlas period, 20 of the 25 heronries recorded contained one to seven nests, five held between 10 and 16 nests, and only one had 20 nests or more (Powderham 22, with Arlington having declined to four nests and Puslinch none).

Data from the BTO Heronries Census show a continuing national decline since 2007, with approximately 11,500 nests in 2011; 11,200 nests in 2012 and provisionally about 10,080 nests in 2013 (a 10% reduction since 2012) (*DBR* 2013).

The figure (after Rogers 2008) shows WeBS county totals for Grey Heron during both summer and winter periods from 1997 to 2013. There has been a marked decline since 2007. Winter numbers fell in 2008, as did the maximum summer WeBS count in 2009, indicating an overall 30–40% reduction in numbers for both seasons. Over the Atlas period the Devon population was severely reduced. Harsh winters and wet springs and summers may have been partly responsible.

The winter-period map shows records for 542 tetrads (29.2%) with a wide inland distribution including much of Dartmoor and Exmoor and most watercourses from their headwaters to the coast. The highest winter TTV counts came from an Exe Estuary tetrad that held between 20 and 50 birds. Elsewhere, counts of six to ten birds came from tetrads on the River Axe, the Tamar Estuary Complex, Lower Tamar Lake and the Taw/Torridge Estuary.

Since the Atlas summer period includes late winter, post-breeding dispersal and early autumn, the mapped distribution is equally widespread. Records came from 500 tetrads, (26.9%) of the total. Many of these records were of presence on or near estuaries, rivers, the Grand Western Canal and much of Dartmoor and Exmoor. All tetrads with TTV counts of six or more birds were within at most 10 km of a heronry and it is likely most of these records refer to foraging breeders.

*Text: Robert Hurrell / Photo: Neil Bygrave*
*Grey Heron sponsored by*
*Axe Vale & District Conservation Society*

Balmer *et al.* 2013: 280; Sitters 1988: 56; Tyler 2010: 168

### Winter-period abundance 2007–13

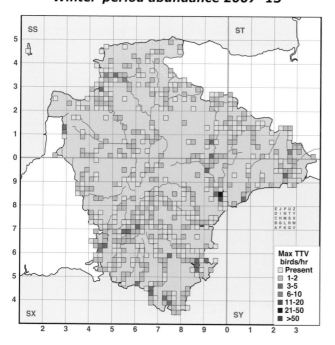

Max TTV birds/hr
- ☐ Present
- 1-2
- 3-5
- 6-10
- 11-20
- 21-50
- >50

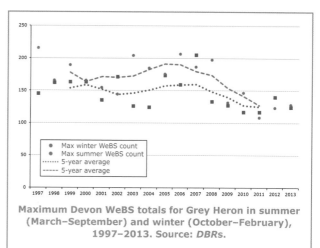

- • Max winter WeBS count
- • Max summer WeBS count
- ······ 5-year average
- - - - 5-year average

**Maximum Devon WeBS totals for Grey Heron in summer (March–September) and winter (October–February), 1997–2013. Source: *DBRs*.**

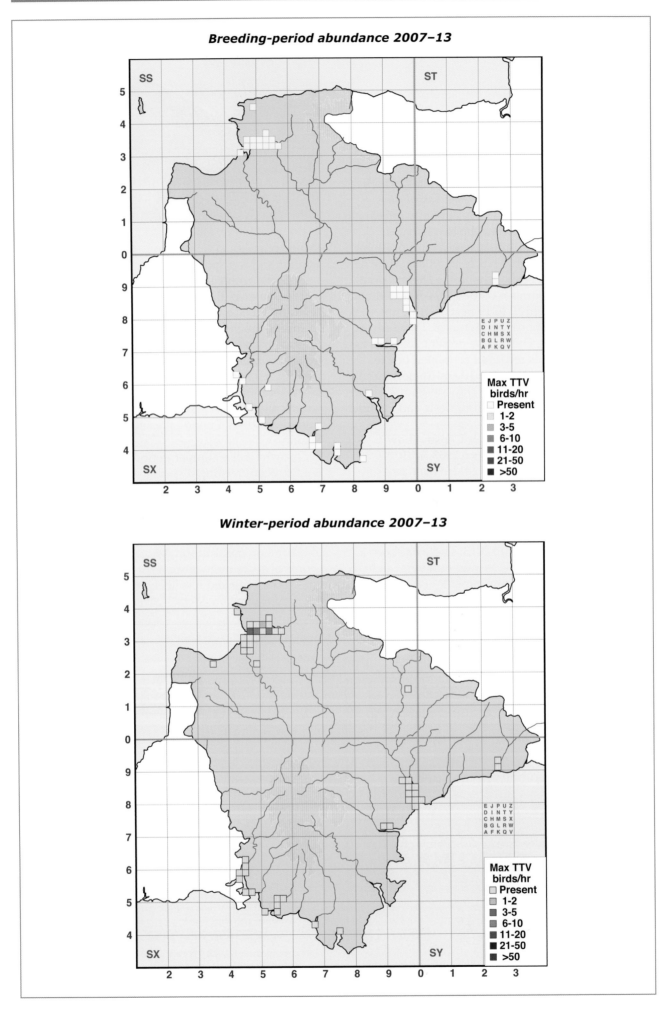

**Breeding-period abundance 2007–13**

Max TTV
birds/hr
Present
1-2
3-5
6-10
11-20
21-50
>50

**Winter-period abundance 2007–13**

Max TTV
birds/hr
Present
1-2
3-5
6-10
11-20
21-50
>50

# Spoonbill
## *Platalea leucorodia*

**Amber listed**

Since they feed by wading and sweeping their extraordinary bills from side to side to 'filter' invertebrates and small fish from the water, Spoonbills are very much birds of extensive, shallow wetlands. While they choose reedbeds and scrubby trees for their mainly continental European nesting colonies, outside the breeding season Spoonbills in Devon typically occur on estuaries and tidal lagoons.

Spoonbills were recorded from no fewer than 50 tetrads during the Atlas winter periods, with the Taw/Torridge Estuary being the main site, though there are also notable clusters for the Exe Estuary and the Tamar Complex, and more scattered records for several other south coast estuaries.

In the early 1980s, at the time of fieldwork for the *Winter Atlas 1981–84*, Spoonbills were vagrants to Devon, but records have been annual since 1987 and a regular wintering tradition has become established on the Taw/Torridge Estuary (Jones & Davis 2009: 19). This tradition was maintained throughout the Atlas period, with a maximum of 13 birds during the winter of 2011/12 (*DBR*s). Although Spoonbills are no longer a rarity in Devon, the total number present in the county at any one time still only occasionally reaches double figures.

Colour-marking (leg-rings and leg-flags) shows that several of the birds using the Taw/Torridge in winter originated from breeding colonies in The Netherlands, while one, 'FJ9', which returned to North Devon in successive winters, was hatched at the Doñana Biological Station in southern Spain (Davis & Jones 2010: 34). FJ9, a female, has also been seen in Somerset, Dorset and Nottinghamshire and was present on the north Norfolk coast in the summers of 2011 and 2012. In April 2011, she was seen exhibiting courtship behaviour in the breeding colony at Holkham, the UK's first nesting colony of Spoonbills for 300 years (Davis 2011). Colour-marking has also revealed exchanges of birds between the Taw/Torridge and Exe Estuaries.

The only truly inland record during the Atlas period concerned one at Chettiscombe (near Tiverton) in January 2008 (*DBR*).

While Spoonbills were recorded in 33 tetrads during the Atlas breeding periods, these are all considered to have been lingering wintering birds (most of which appear to have been immature in any case) or passage migrants. There was no suggestion of breeding behaviour and Tyler (2010) implies that there are no known historical records of nesting in the county.

While numbers in Devon remain small, there seems every likelihood of Spoonbill becoming more firmly established as a British breeding species, and of a corresponding increase in birds using the county outside the breeding season. However, there seems no immediate likelihood of Spoonbills nesting in Devon; not least because of the very restricted area of potentially suitable habitat.

*Text: Tim Davis & Tim Jones / Photo: Chris Triggs*
*Spoonbill sponsored by*
*Taw & Torridge Branch of Devon Birds*

Balmer *et al.* 2013: 283; Sitters 1988: not treated; Tyler 2010: 175

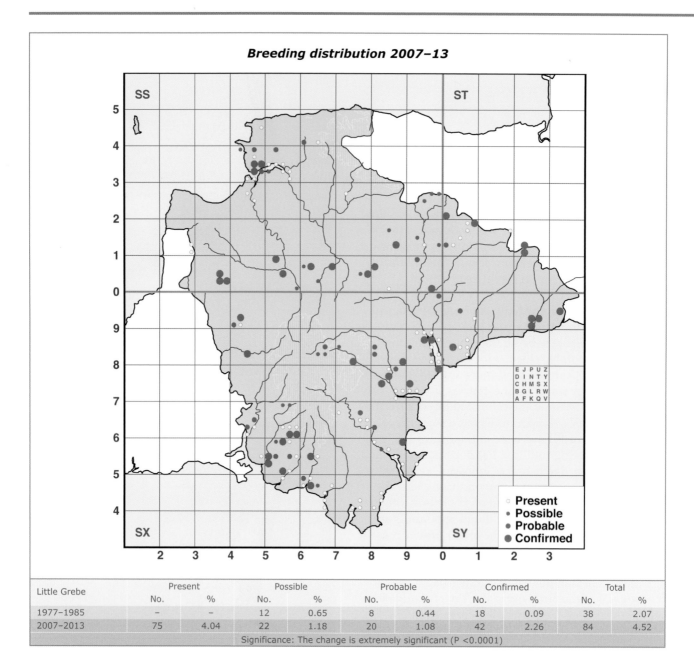

## Breeding distribution 2007–13

| Little Grebe | Present | | Possible | | Probable | | Confirmed | | Total | |
|---|---|---|---|---|---|---|---|---|---|---|
| | No. | % | No. | % | No. | % | No. | % | No. | % |
| 1977–1985 | – | – | 12 | 0.65 | 8 | 0.44 | 18 | 0.09 | 38 | 2.07 |
| 2007–2013 | 75 | 4.04 | 22 | 1.18 | 20 | 1.08 | 42 | 2.26 | 84 | 4.52 |
| Significance: The change is extremely significant (P <0.0001) | | | | | | | | | | |

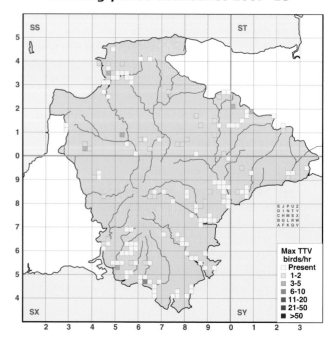

## Breeding distribution 1977–85

## Breeding-period abundance 2007–13

# Little Grebe
## *Tachybaptus ruficollis*

Little Grebes often draw attention to themselves through their far-carrying 'whinnying' call, which can be heard throughout the year but most often during the breeding season. More catholic in its habitat requirements than Great Crested Grebe, the diminutive 'dabchick' occurs in a wide variety of coastal and inland wetlands, including many that are small, shallow and densely vegetated.

During the present Atlas period, possible, probable or confirmed breeding was recorded in a total of 84 tetrads in thirty-six 10-km squares. This compares with 38 tetrads in twenty-four 10-km squares during the *Devon Tetrad Atlas 1977–85* – a significant expansion in the Devon breeding range during the last 30 years or so. This is in line with a notable expansion in South West England generally, as noted in *Bird Atlas 2007–11*. The number of Devon tetrads for which breeding was confirmed increased from 18 to 42 (more than 130%). The *Devon Tetrad Atlas 1977–88* stated "… it seems unlikely that more than 20–30 pairs breed in any one year". It is clear that the species is now both more widespread and probably more numerous. Assuming a conservative average of one pair per tetrad from which confirmed or probable breeding was recorded, and assuming that nesting did not occur in all tetrads in every year, the Devon breeding population during the current Atlas period may have been in the range 50–70 pairs.

The winter-period TTV map shows presence in 199 tetrads in fifty-five 10-km squares, with the number of occupied 10-km squares noticeably higher than in the *Winter Atlas 1981–84*. The highest

### Winter-period abundance 2007–13

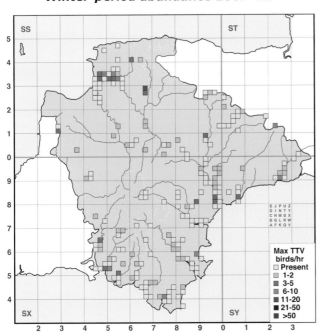

Max TTV birds/hr
- ☐ Present
- 1-2
- 3-5
- 6-10
- 11-20
- 21-50
- >50

densities are around the coastlines, particularly the south coast estuaries and bays, and the Taw/Torridge Estuary in the north. Though inland records were widespread, generally only very small numbers were involved. During the six winter periods of the Atlas years, the maximum monthly WeBS totals for Devon were remarkably consistent, varying between 142 in December 2008 and 158 in December 2011. The Kingsbridge Estuary was the most important individual site, with highest counts ranging between 25 and 38 birds. The Tavy and Taw/Torridge Estuaries were also consistently important sites (with peak counts of at least 15 birds in most winters), while other key locations (holding similar numbers in some winters) included the Axe, Dart, Exe and Plym Estuaries, the River Dart at Dartington, Lopwell Dam and Radford Lake.

In common with Great Crested Grebe, the UK WeBS index for Little Grebe indicates a steady increase of wintering numbers between the early 1980s (when national population monitoring of grebes commenced) and the early 2000s, followed by a decline during the *Devon Tetrad Atlas* period. However, there was no indication that this recent fall in numbers for the UK as a whole was reflected in Devon.

*Text: Tim Jones & Tim Davis / Photo: Neil Bygrave*
*Little Grebe sponsored by Amanda Carpenter*

Balmer *et al.* 2013: 284; Sitters 1988: 46; Tyler 2010: 177

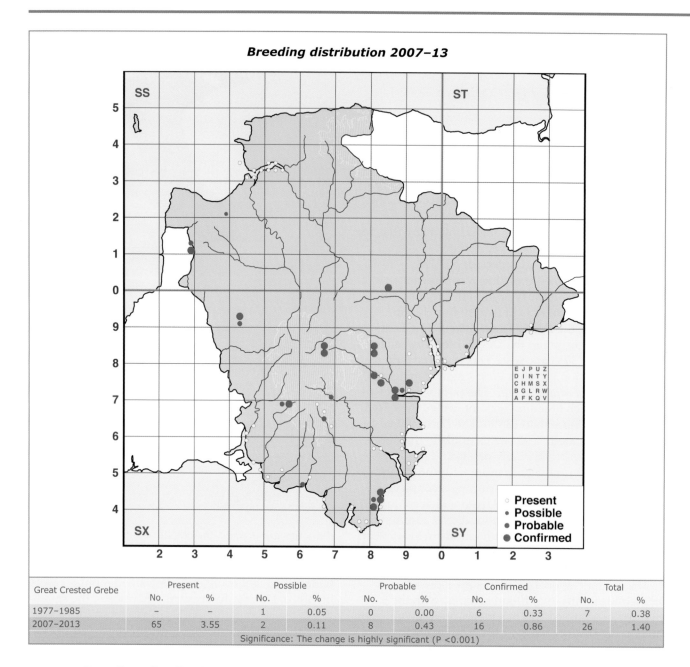

## Breeding distribution 2007–13

| Great Crested Grebe | Present | | Possible | | Probable | | Confirmed | | Total | |
|---|---|---|---|---|---|---|---|---|---|---|
| | No. | % | No. | % | No. | % | No. | % | No. | % |
| 1977–1985 | – | – | 1 | 0.05 | 0 | 0.00 | 6 | 0.33 | 7 | 0.38 |
| 2007–2013 | 65 | 3.55 | 2 | 0.11 | 8 | 0.43 | 16 | 0.86 | 26 | 1.40 |
| Significance: The change is highly significant (P <0.001) | | | | | | | | | | |

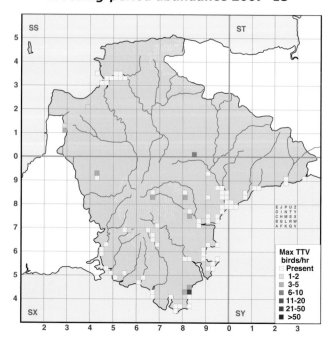

## Breeding distribution 1977–85

## Breeding-period abundance 2007–13

# Great Crested Grebe
## *Podiceps cristatus*

STRIKINGLY BEAUTIFUL plumage and a spectacular courtship display make the Great Crested Grebe one of Devon's most impressive breeding birds, but one that occurs in only small numbers owing to the scarcity of suitable nesting habitat. Ideally, each pair requires at least one hectare of open water, combined with ample, but not too dense aquatic vegetation, as well as a suitable supply of fish and sufficient feeding areas not exceeding five metres in depth (Snow & Perrins 1998). Such conditions are extremely localized in the county.

The breeding-period maps for the current Atlas show occurrence in 92 tetrads but it is likely that many tetrads with 'presence only' involve the large numbers of wintering birds still present in March, as shown by data in *Devon Bird Reports*. The *Devon Tetrad Atlas 1977–85* shows confirmed breeding for six tetrads in three 10-km squares, while for the current Atlas period it was confirmed in 16 tetrads spread over fifteen 10-km squares and involving 12 different sites; a highly significant expansion. However, many of these sites supported only one pair and breeding was only regular at six sites. The maximum number of successful pairs in Devon probably did not exceed 15 in any Atlas year (*DBRs*).

The winter-period map shows records for 109 tetrads in thirty-two 10-km squares. As would be expected, given the species' requirement for extensive areas of relatively shallow water, these are concentrated along the south coast estuaries and

bays, and larger inland waters. Atlas TTVs do not fully capture the magnitude of peak numbers at key wintering sites shown by data in the *DBRs*. The most important sites (those holding at least 20 individuals) during the Atlas period were the Exe Estuary & Dawlish Bay, Kingsbridge Estuary, Roadford Reservoir, Seaton (offshore), Slapton Ley, Tamar Complex and Torbay & Babbacombe. The highest county WeBS total was 212 in December 2010, while the maximum count from an individual site was 242 at Torbay & Babbacombe in February 2010.

Comparison with the *Winter Atlas 1981–1984* suggests that the number of Devon 10-km squares from which the species was recorded was significantly higher during the present Atlas winter period. This presumably reflects the expansion in the UK winter range, which grew by 22% between the *Winter Atlas* and *Bird Atlas 2007–2011*. The UK WeBS index shows that wintering numbers increased significantly between the early 1980s and the early 2000s, but have declined since.

*Text: Tim Jones & Tim Davis / Photo: Adrian Davey*
*Great Crested Grebe sponsored by Miriam Guard*

Balmer *et al.* 2013: 286; Sitters 1988: 48; Tyler 2010: 179

### Winter-period abundance 2007–13

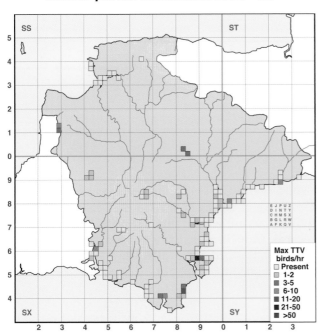

Max TTV birds/hr
- □ Present
- ▨ 1-2
- ▨ 3-5
- ▨ 6-10
- ▨ 11-20
- ■ 21-50
- ■ >50

# Red-necked Grebe

*Podiceps grisegena*

**Red listed**

RED-NECKED GREBES are scarce winter visitors to Devon, favouring bays along the south coast, especially Dawlish Bay and Torbay, and, to a lesser extent, the Taw/Torridge Estuary in the north. Birds generally arrive during October and November and leave between early March and early May. During this survey the species was recorded in 36 tetrads, all of which are coastal.

The winter of 2010/2011 saw a maximum of 45 records of possibly 10 birds. With the British wintering population for the period 2004/5 to 2008/9 estimated at 55 birds (Musgrove *et al.* 2011: 88) the south-west coast appears to be an important area for the species.

*Text: Lee Collins / Photo: Adrian Davey*

Balmer *et al.* 2013: 288; Sitters 1988: not treated; Tyler 2010: 182

# Slavonian Grebe

*Podiceps auritus*

**Red listed**

SLAVONIAN GREBES are winter visitors to Devon's shores, favouring sheltered bays and estuaries. The Exe Estuary and nearby coastal waters have historically been their main site, although numbers here have steadily declined over recent years, to the point where finding any offshore can be a challenge. In this survey the species was recorded from 48 tetrads, mostly on the south coast, with the principal sites away from the Exe being Start Bay, Torbay and Thurlestone Bay.

Birds generally return in late October and depart in late March or early April. One individual, released from care in 2008, lingered year-round at the lower end of the Exe Estuary throughout the remainder of the Atlas period.

*Text: Lee Collins*

Balmer *et al.* 2013: 290; Sitters 1988: not treated; Tyler 2010: 183

# Black-necked Grebe

*Podiceps nigricollis*

**Amber listed**

BLACK-NECKED GREBES are winter visitors and passage migrants in Devon, favouring sheltered coastal bays such as Dawlish Bay, Slapton Ley, Start Bay and Thurlestone. It was recorded in 26 tetrads, all on the south coast and its stronghold remains Torbay where, although numbers fluctuate between years, double-digit counts have been recorded with up to 23 in 2009. Spring passage could find birds anywhere along our coastline.

Birds generally appear in Devon waters from late October, and depart in late March. Occasional individuals are seen in summer, with Atlas-period records, from Slapton, Exmouth and Thurlestone Bay, with the bird at the latter site staying for two weeks in late June 2012.

*Text: Lee Collins*

Balmer *et al.* 2013: 292; Sitters 1988: not treated; Tyler 2010: 185

# Honey-buzzard

*Pernis apivorus*

Amber listed

HONEY-BUZZARDS ARE summer migrants to the UK, returning in May and leaving by September/October. Since the *Devon Tetrad Atlas 1977–85* this unique raptor has ceased to be a regular breeding species in Devon, with no breeding records during the period 2007–2013. The once-famous Haldon ridge population peaked at around two pairs and last bred successfully in 1995. A lack of continuity of returning adults meant that this small population was lost; a trend not reflected in the New Forest – the largest established population in southern England – where the population actually increased around 1997 (Wiseman 2012), the time of Devon's loss.

Speculation in the *Devon Tetrad Atlas 1977–85* that the previous year's young returned the following year as sub-adults is almost certainly incorrect, as the young do not return to breeding areas in their first calendar year, so that the immature birds described in that account were either returning or new adults.

During the March–September Atlas period there were accepted records of migrants passing over 13 tetrads, mostly in separate 10-km squares. These had a coastal bias (see map) and were mostly during the peak migration months of May and September. All records were subject to approval by the Devon Birds Records Committee since Common Buzzards in Devon are very variable in plumage and can be mistaken for this species.

## Breeding-period abundance 2007–13

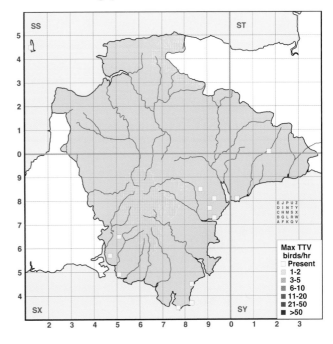

Max TTV birds/hr
- Present
- 1-2
- 3-5
- 6-10
- 11-20
- 21-50
- >50

*Text: Mark Darlaston / Photo: Paul Sterry/NPL*
*Honey-buzzard sponsored by Malcolm McVail*

Balmer *et al.* 2013: 303; Sitters 1988: 293; Tyler 2010: 187

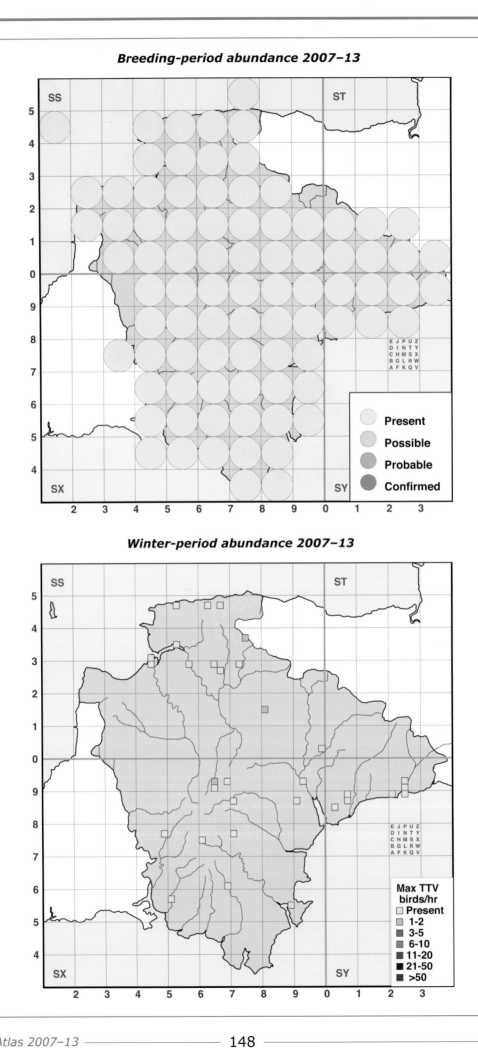

**Breeding-period abundance 2007–13**

Present
Possible
Probable
Confirmed

**Winter-period abundance 2007–13**

Max TTV
birds/hr
Present
1-2
3-5
6-10
11-20
21-50
>50

# Red Kite
*Milvus milvus*

THE RE-ESTABLISHMENT of Red Kites in southern England and elsewhere in the UK is one of the great raptor conservation success stories of recent years. As shown by *Bird Atlas 2007–11*, the expansion of breeding range has yet to reach Devon, though an influx of non-breeders arrived in Devon from late March through to July in each year of the current survey. Arrivals appear to be initiated by anticyclonic weather, which provides favourable conditions for soaring flight, apparently prompting many non-breeding kites to 'go for a wander', a good number reaching the South West.

The increased UK population, now at least 1,600 pairs (Musgrove *et al.* 2013: 88), is almost certainly the origin of these wandering birds (Darlaston 2009). These itinerant birds throw up a dilemma in the interpretation of Atlas data, as they were often seen over potentially suitable breeding habitat. By definition, these could therefore be classed as 'possible' breeders, yet most surveyors tended to record them simply as 'present' or 'migrant', with just two tetrads included in the 'possible breeding' category (based on habitat suitability alone). There was no higher level of breeding evidence (probable or confirmed) in any tetrad. Hence the 'breeding period' map should be viewed as the overall distribution of birds. Although the species was

recorded in a relatively large number of tetrads, the proportion of tetrads that include potentially suitable breeding habitat is unknown. All are therefore shown as 'present' for consistency in map presentation.

Over the six-year period, Red Kites were seen in 289 (15.6%) tetrads during March–September, a dramatic increase compared to the time of the *Devon Tetrad Atlas 1977–85* which did not mention this species. Sightings were well distributed throughout Devon, highlighted by the fact that at the 10-km level they were seen in 93% of squares. By comparison, the October–February distribution was much reduced, with records from only 32 tetrads (1.7%), indicating that by the winter the majority of birds have moved back to their natal areas. What the maps really show is that during the Atlas period an unknown number of Red Kites wandered over most of Devon, particularly during the breeding season.

Given the continued expansion in southern England, it can only be a matter of time before the Red Kite is re-established as a breeding species in Devon.

*Text: Mark Darlaston / Photo: Andy Brown*
*Red Kite sponsored by Gerald & Barbara Shapley*

Balmer *et al.* 2013: 294; Sitters 1988: not treated; Tyler 2010: 191

# Marsh Harrier
## *Circus aeruginosus*

**Amber listed**

*B*IRD *ATLAS 2007–11* shows that Marsh Harriers have expanded their range in the UK since the *Breeding Atlas 1988–1991*, with the breeding population estimated at 320–380 pairs (Musgrove *et al.* 2013). While the largest proportion is migratory, some birds remain in this country throughout the year. Their favoured nesting habitats are areas of reedbed (fens), although some now nest in cereals. Devon's reedbeds are rather small compared to more extensive ones elsewhere in the UK, and are restricted to the South Hams leys and some estuaries, thus limiting the species' potential breeding range in the county.

Most of Devon's Marsh Harriers are also migratory, but since 2002 the species has been present year round, with one or two females frequenting the South Hams leys during the winter. Just prior to the start of Atlas fieldwork there was a failed breeding attempt in 2006, when a male also took up residence for one season (Whitehall 2008). There were no further recorded breeding attempts during the Atlas period, although at least one female continued to frequent the area.

The map for the March–September period shows just one 10-km square with 'possible' breeding (records of a resident female in suitable habitat), while birds were recorded as present in a further 43 tetrads in twenty-one 10-km squares mainly in the south of the county. The Atlas methodology throws up the conundrum of how to interpret records of birds over potentially suitable habitat when the majority are likely to be migrants. Most records were submitted as 'present' or 'migrant', although many would qualify as 'possible' based on habitat (though much restricted), so the map needs to be viewed with this caveat in mind.

The October–February distribution was more restricted to coastal areas, but indicated a similar pattern of habitat use, albeit with records from less than half the number of tetrads than the 'breeding' period.

*Text: Mark Darlaston / Photo: Paul Sterry/NPL*
*Marsh Harrier sponsored by Nikki and Peter Jeffcote*

Balmer *et al.* 2013: 298; Sitters 1988: not treated; Tyler 2010: 195

### Breeding distribution 2007–13

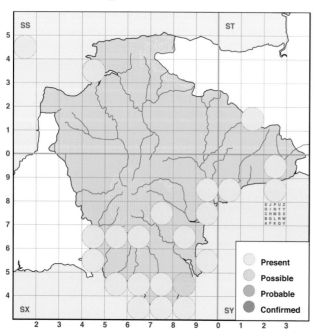

- Present
- Possible
- Probable
- Confirmed

### Winter-period abundance 2007–13

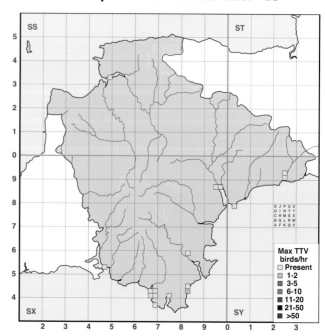

Max TTV birds/hr
- Present
- 1-2
- 3-5
- 6-10
- 11-20
- 21-50
- >50

# Hen Harrier

*Circus cyaneus*

## Red listed

IN DEVON, Hen Harriers occur as both winter visitors and passage migrants. They favour areas of semi-natural vegetation (rough grassland and heathland), which is found extensively on Dartmoor and Exmoor and to a lesser extent on the East Devon commons, remnant Culm grasslands, along both coasts (especially the South Hams) and around some estuaries (notably the Exe, Axe and Taw/Torridge). Both maps highlight their association with these habitats, which provide suitable hunting and roosting habitat.

During the October–February Atlas period, Hen Harriers were recorded in 139 tetrads (7.5%), while all TTV counts came from Dartmoor, Exmoor and Bursdon Moor, highlighting these areas as strongholds for this species in winter, although numbers were generally low.

During March–September there was no evidence of any breeding (probable or confirmed) and the species' status in Devon remains non-breeding. While some of the wintering areas, particularly areas of heather moorland on Exmoor and Dartmoor, could be viewed as also including suitable breeding habitat, records for March and April need to be interpreted with care. Many Hen Harriers have not yet left their wintering grounds in early spring and/or are moving through on migration. There were few sightings after May and although single birds were seen as late as July, these records appear to

relate to an occasional non-breeding (summering) bird or early migrant. From late August–September, birds start to move south from their northern breeding grounds. The distribution of March–September sightings is broadly similar to that in October–February, although restricted to only 69 tetrads (3.7%). All were roving records; there were none during TTVs.

*Text: Mark Darlaston / Photo: Mark Darlaston*
*Hen Harrier sponsored by The Dartmoor Study Group*

Balmer *et al.* 2013: 300; Sitters 1988: not treated; Tyler 2010: 196

### Summer-period abundance 2007–13

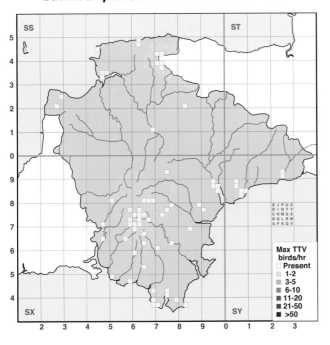

### Winter-period abundance 2007–13

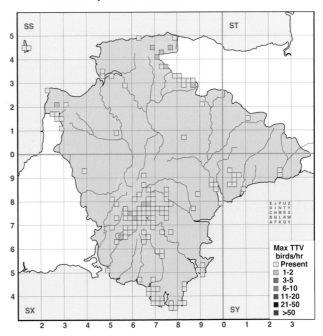

# Goshawk
## *Accipiter gentilis*

SINCE THE *Devon Tetrad Atlas 1977–85*, Goshawks have made a welcome return as a regular breeding species in Devon. They prefer mature conifer plantations for nesting, but may hunt over open farmland as well as in woodland. The early colonizers in Devon mostly favoured mature larch, but plantations of this deciduous conifer have been greatly reduced in extent in Devon, most having been clear-felled – mainly during the Atlas period – to combat the spread of the fungal disease *Phytophthora ramorum* in many parts of the county. Much to the relief of Devon Goshawk workers, birds nesting in larch switched to other conifer species, which are now the main breeding habitat, although nests have also been found in oak and beech, showing the potential of deciduous woodland.

Despite their size, Goshawks are very elusive birds of prey and the majority of proven breeding records came through Schedule 1 licence returns to the BTO rather than the general Atlas survey – without these returns the species would be greatly under-recorded. Licence holders dedicate much time to locating and protecting nests by ensuring that woodland managers are aware of their locality, so that trees due for felling are not cut during the breeding season. Unfortunately, despite being protected, Goshawks are also persecuted, with proven incidents occurring in Devon during the Atlas period (*DBR* 2012). For this reason it has been decided not to provide maps of the distribution of the species in Devon.

During the period March–September Goshawks were recorded in 42 (2.3%) tetrads in twenty-one 10-km squares, of which 18 had confirmed breeding, three probable and three possible. The distribution showed that most were within a core area, with a few outliers, although there were large areas of Devon with none recorded.

During October–February in the survey period, Goshawks were recorded in 22 (1.2%) tetrads in seventeen 10-km squares, with a wider distribution than in the breeding season, although the majority were still within the core breeding range.

*Text & Photos: Mark Darlaston*
*Goshawk sponsored by Julia & George Harris*

Balmer *et al.* 2013: 304; Sitters 1988: 299; Tyler 2010: 202

| Goshawk | Present | | Possible | | Probable | | Confirmed | | Total | |
|---|---|---|---|---|---|---|---|---|---|---|
| | No. | % | No. | % | No. | % | No. | % | No. | % |
| 1977–1985 | – | – | 1 | 0.05 | 1 | 0.05 | 0 | 0.00 | 2 | 0.11 |
| 2007–2013 | 18 | 0.97 | 3 | 0.16 | 3 | 0.16 | 18 | 0.97 | 24 | 1.29 |
| Significance: The change is extremely significant (P <0.0001) | | | | | | | | | | |

# Osprey
## Pandion haliaetus

**Amber listed**

Wᴵᴛʜ ᴀ UK population estimated at 200–250 pairs (Musgrove *et al.* 2013) the Osprey is now a regular sight in Devon. Migrants are more evident on the coast, particularly estuaries, where birds stop to refuel on spring or autumn migration between their African winter quarters and northern European breeding sites. In Devon there are always more records in autumn than spring, as birds tend to linger for longer in autumn, and numbers are boosted by juveniles making their first migration.

The March–September map includes the periods when birds are moving north through the spring and then south from late August through September. Ospreys were recorded in 120 tetrads (6.5%), with a strong coastal bias. The extensive Exe Estuary, unsurprisingly, shows the highest number of tetrads, with other concentrations around the Taw/Torridge, Axe, Teign and Kingsbridge Estuaries. A few birds were also recorded inland.

Some late-autumn migrants are included in the October–March Atlas map; such records were mostly in October, although a notably late bird was on the Kingsbridge Estuary in early December 2011. At the other end of the 'winter' period, an early spring migrant was on the Plym Estuary on 19 February 2008.

There was no evidence of breeding for Ospreys during the Atlas period, though breeding has occurred in the past (Tyler 2010) and many of Devon's estuaries continue to provide suitable habitat. Perhaps with a little help (such as the provision of artificial nest platforms), the return of this magnificent raptor as a breeding species in Devon is a real possibility.

*Text: Mark Darlaston / Photos: Dave Scott*
*Osprey sponsored by Lizzie & Roger Little*

Balmer *et al.* 2013: 314; Sitters 1988: not treated; Tyler 2010: 209

### Breeding-period abundance 2007–13

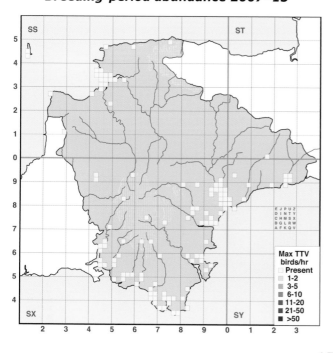

Max TTV birds/hr
☐ Present
1-2
3-5
6-10
11-20
21-50
>50

### Winter-period abundance 2007–13

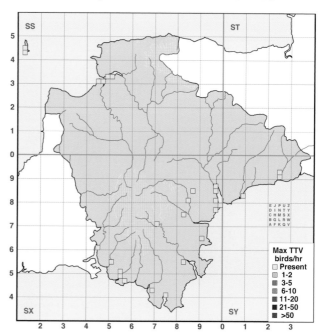

Max TTV birds/hr
☐ Present
1-2
3-5
6-10
11-20
21-50
>50

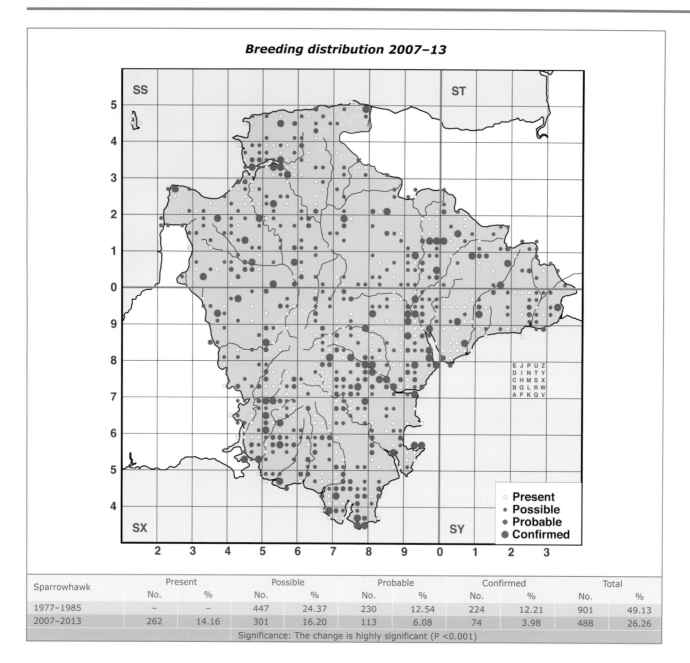

### Breeding distribution 2007–13

| Sparrowhawk | Present | | Possible | | Probable | | Confirmed | | Total | |
|---|---|---|---|---|---|---|---|---|---|---|
| | No. | % | No. | % | No. | % | No. | % | No. | % |
| 1977–1985 | – | – | 447 | 24.37 | 230 | 12.54 | 224 | 12.21 | 901 | 49.13 |
| 2007–2013 | 262 | 14.16 | 301 | 16.20 | 113 | 6.08 | 74 | 3.98 | 488 | 26.26 |
| Significance: The change is highly significant (P <0.001) | | | | | | | | | | |

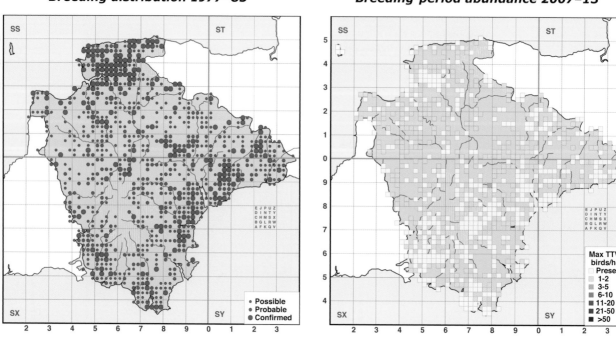

### Breeding distribution 1977–85

### Breeding-period abundance 2007–13

# Sparrowhawk

## *Accipiter nisus*

THE SPARROWHAWK is Devon's second most abundant raptor and has a UK population of 35,000 pairs (Musgrove *et al.* 2013). In Devon, Sparrowhawks are year-round residents with some evidence of birds moving through as migrants, particularly in autumn at coastal locations. They require trees for nesting, with a preference for conifers, and hence they are associated with areas of woodland, ranging from extensive forests to small groups of trees, sometimes in urban localities. Devon provides ample habitat, apart from areas of higher moorland devoid of woodland, highlighted by the widespread distribution found during the Atlas survey, with records for 40.4% of tetrads during the period March–September and 42.1% during October–February.

The Sparrowhawk is not the easiest species for which to prove breeding and the Atlas methodology almost certainly led to underestimation, highlighted by the fact that only 4% of tetrads show confirmed breeding, with a further 22.3% indicating possible or probable breeding. If these results are taken at face value, there has been a highly significant reduction since the *Devon Tetrad Atlas 1977–85*, when 49.1% of tetrads showed breeding evidence (12.2% confirmed and 36.9% probable/possible). However, 'presence' during the breeding season (40.4% of tetrads for the current Atlas; no comparable figure is available from the *Devon Tetrad Atlas 1977–85*) is perhaps a more realistic measure of likely breeding distribution.

When viewed at the 10-km level, almost all 10-km squares show some breeding evidence in both Atlas surveys and this may be a better scale to evaluate this species. However, even at this level the present Atlas shows no breeding evidence for the 10-km square containing the Torquay area and coastal woodland where there is ample suitable habitat and which must surely hold breeding Sparrowhawks, thereby highlighting how easily this species can be overlooked! If there has been a decline, it is unlikely to be as dramatic as the current Atlas data suggest, as no major decline is apparent in *Bird Atlas 2007–11* – which shows little change since the *Breeding Atlas 1988–91*. Taking all factors into account, it is probable that the Devon Sparrowhawk population is relatively stable.

*Text: Mark Darlaston / Photo: Charlie Fleming*
*Sparrowhawk sponsored by Geoff Moores*

Balmer *et al.* 2013: 306; Sitters 1988: 70; Tyler 2010: 203

### Winter-period abundance 2007–13

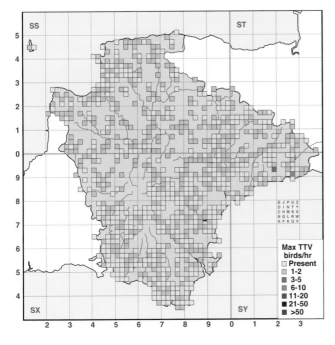

Max TTV birds/hr
- ☐ Present
- 1-2
- 3-5
- 6-10
- 11-20
- 21-50
- >50

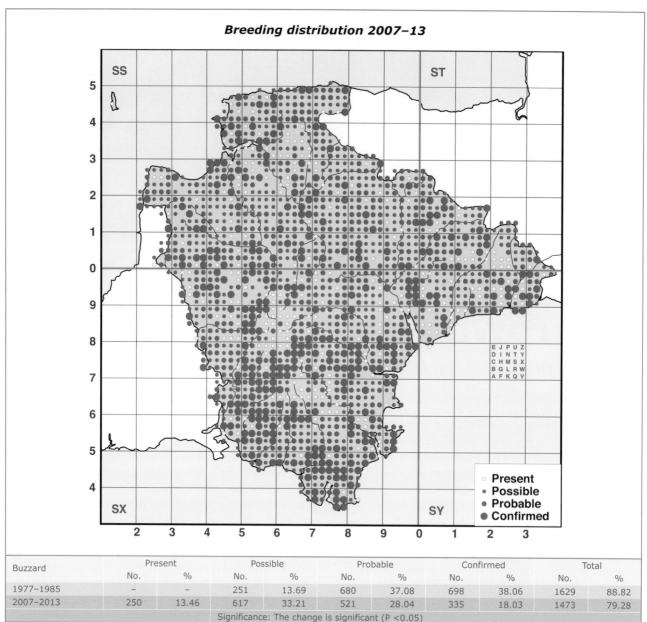

**Breeding distribution 2007–13**

| Buzzard | Present | | Possible | | Probable | | Confirmed | | Total | |
|---|---|---|---|---|---|---|---|---|---|---|
| | No. | % | No. | % | No. | % | No. | % | No. | % |
| 1977–1985 | – | – | 251 | 13.69 | 680 | 37.08 | 698 | 38.06 | 1629 | 88.82 |
| 2007–2013 | 250 | 13.46 | 617 | 33.21 | 521 | 28.04 | 335 | 18.03 | 1473 | 79.28 |
| Significance: The change is significant (P <0.05) | | | | | | | | | | |

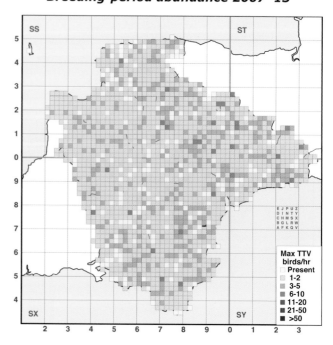

**Breeding distribution 1977–85**

**Breeding-period abundance 2007–13**

# Buzzard
## *Buteo buteo*

BUZZARDS HAVE long been familiar features in the skies above Devon's varied farmed and wilder landscapes, most notably over well-wooded country across rolling farmlands, along river valleys, on Dartmoor and Exmoor, and other hill districts. A few pairs still breed on sea cliffs along rugged sections of both coasts. The Buzzard population is comprised of sedentary and highly territorial pairs whose vocal aerial spring displays provide strong evidence of likely breeding, though not all pairs may actually breed in every year. Confirmation of breeding is time-consuming, whether through searching woods for occupied nests, waiting to hear the often noisy recently fledged young, or chancing upon and provoking angry demonstrations by parents with youngsters hidden nearby.

The breeding-period maps show that Buzzards were present in 92% of tetrads (compared to 89% in the *Devon Tetrad Atlas 1977–85*) and were only absent from the high, treeless parts of Dartmoor. Locally they have spread to breed well inside the Plymouth city limits as well as reaching new coastal sites, and perhaps extending further up on to Dartmoor as conifer plantations have matured. Breeding densities in Devon (and beyond) rarely exceed one to two pairs per tetrad (Sitters 1988, Dare 2015) but some pairs may have nest sites in adjoining tetrads. The TTV map for the breeding period shows that one or two Buzzards were noted in 83% of tetrads, three or four in 14%, and five to ten birds in 3%. The last group probably referred to soaring parties of neighbouring pairs, but might also have included itinerant individuals.

The main breeding map shows that the proportions of tetrads in which breeding was proven (18%) or deemed probable (33%) were much lower than during the 1980s survey (43% and 42%, respectively). These discrepancies are indicative of the differing methodologies employed during the two surveys as there is no evidence (anecdotal or otherwise) of recent local declines in Buzzard numbers or breeding performance (*DBRs* 2007–2013). The *Devon Tetrad Atlas 1977–85* estimated 1,500–2,000 pairs of Buzzards were breeding in Devon. Present numbers are probably higher, given the recent dramatic increases in Somerset and throughout Britain. A re-assessment of Devon's Buzzard population is long overdue.

The winter distribution is similar, with only the highest parts of Dartmoor lacking Buzzards. The sedentary population then includes many first-winter and older immature birds, resulting in higher TTV counts. Winter densities, however, seem generally low – one or two birds in 79% of tetrads – reflecting the species' more covert behaviour in winter. More than four birds were observed in only 4% of tetrads, mainly in eastern and north-eastern districts. Maximum counts of 10 to 16 birds, in ten tetrads, exceeded local breeding numbers and were probably linked to small gatherings of immature birds feeding in fields (Dare 1999).

### Winter-period abundance 2007–13

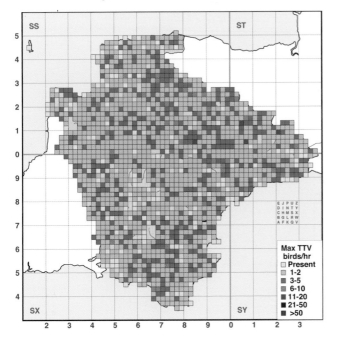

| | Max TTV birds/hr |
|---|---|
| ☐ | Present |
| | 1-2 |
| | 3-5 |
| | 6-10 |
| | 11-20 |
| | 21-50 |
| | >50 |

*Text: Peter Dare / Photos: Mark Darlaston (top) & Adrian Davey*
*Buzzard sponsored by Lizzie & Roger Little*
Balmer *et al.* 2013: 308; Sitters 1988: 72; Tyler 2010: 205

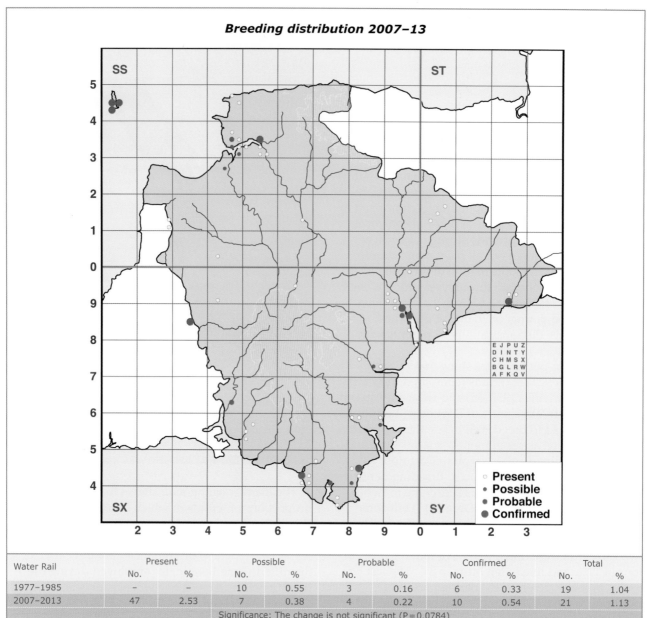

**Breeding distribution 2007–13**

| Water Rail | Present | | Possible | | Probable | | Confirmed | | Total | |
|---|---|---|---|---|---|---|---|---|---|---|
| | No. | % | No. | % | No. | % | No. | % | No. | % |
| 1977–1985 | – | – | 10 | 0.55 | 3 | 0.16 | 6 | 0.33 | 19 | 1.04 |
| 2007–2013 | 47 | 2.53 | 7 | 0.38 | 4 | 0.22 | 10 | 0.54 | 21 | 1.13 |
| Significance: The change is not significant (P = 0.0784) | | | | | | | | | | |

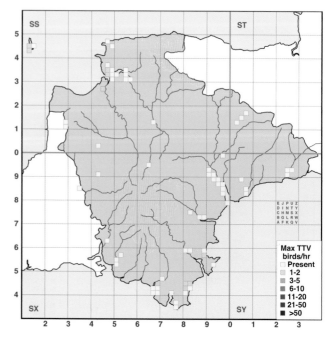

**Breeding distribution 1977–85**

**Breeding-period abundance 2007–13**

# Water Rail
*Rallus aquaticus*

THE WATER Rail is a shy, skulking bird, most likely to be located by its 'squealing pig' call. It frequents dense and moderately tall aquatic vegetation on muddy ground beside fresh or brackish waters, but is very secretive and easily overlooked. In Devon its requirements are only met in a few small areas such as estuarine reedbeds and freshwater marshes, and it is rare on the higher ground of Dartmoor and is not normally found on Exmoor. It is omnivorous, feeding mainly on small fish, birds or mammals, which it either kills itself or finds as carrion, but in winter it feeds mainly on vegetation such as roots and shoots, berries, seeds and fruit (Cramp *et al.* 1980).

The Devon population is augmented by passage migrants and winter visitors to estuaries, rivers and some freshwater lakes and canals. Wintering birds are much easier to observe, particularly when they emerge from cover looking for food in extreme conditions. The main passage period is August to October (Tyler 2010) with birds migrating mainly at night, but there appears to be very little spring passage.

Water Rails become even more secretive during the breeding season and nest within dense cover. It is therefore likely that more breed in Devon than indicated by the present Atlas. Confirmation of breeding can generally only be obtained by glimpses of young that have recently left the nest.

During the Atlas period, breeding was confirmed in ten tetrads compared with six in the *Devon Tetrad Atlas 1977–1985*. Confirmed breeding records came from the Avon, Axe, Exe and Taw/Torridge Estuaries and also from Roadford Reservoir, Slapton Ley and Lundy, with the latter reporting up to four broods annually. The 1977–85 survey recorded confirmed breeding only at Slapton Ley, the Taw/Torridge Estuary and Witheridge. The creation of new reedbeds at some wetland nature reserves has probably benefited the species. Sitters estimated a breeding population of 10–15 pairs, possibly up to 20, whereas present records suggest a breeding population of 20–25 pairs, though the apparent increase is not statistically significant.

*Text: Ray Jones / Photo: Charlie Fleming*
*Water Rail sponsored by The Lundy Squealers*

Balmer *et al.* 2013: 324; Sitters 1988: 86; Tyler 2010: 222

### Winter-period abundance 2007–13

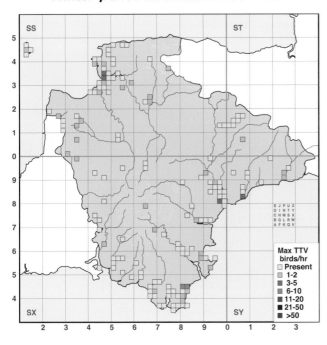

Max TTV
birds/hr
☐ Present
▨ 1-2
▨ 3-5
▧ 6-10
■ 11-20
■ 21-50
■ >50

# Corncrake
## *Crex crex*
### Red listed

THE CORNCRAKE is a very secretive bird that spends most of its time in the tall vegetation of hay fields or damp wildflower meadows, where it feeds on small invertebrates or seeds. It is much more likely to be heard than seen.

The current British population is estimated as 1,200 males in summer with its main breeding areas on the Scottish islands (BTO BirdFacts). In Devon, although it has bred in the past – the last confirmed breeding occurred in Shillingford in 1987 – it is now a scarce passage migrant. During the Atlas years only one to three records were received annually from six different tetrads. Four of these concerned singles in 2008, 2009, 2011 and 2013 identified by feathers found at a Peregrine nest site on St Michael's Church in Exeter (Dixon & Drewitt 2012).

Any birds arriving in Devon in late April or early May are likely to be on passage to the Scottish breeding grounds, while those in autumn are likely be returning birds, including young raised in the current year.

The Corncrake has declined dramatically over its Western European breeding range, primarily due to changes in farming practices. Indeed, the *Devon Tetrad Atlas 1977–85* indicated that the Corncrake was unlikely to return to Devon as a breeding bird unless there were dramatic changes in agricultural practice, particularly in the production of winter animal feed. Late-harvested hay fields have virtually disappeared and given way to silage production, with multiple cutting and quick-growing grass aided by fertilizers. It is impossible for these silage fields to host ground-nesting birds, including the Corncrake.

*Text: Ray Jones / Photo: Mark Darlaston*

Balmer *et al.* 2013: 327; Sitters 1988: 300; Tyler 2010: 227

### Breeding-period abundance 2007–13

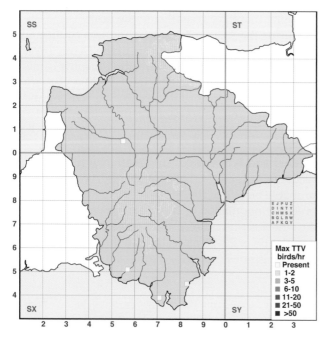

Max TTV birds/hr
Present
1-2
3-5
6-10
11-20
21-50
>50

### Breeding distribution 1977–85

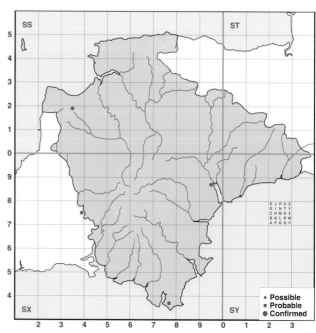

• Possible
• Probable
• Confirmed

# Crane
## Grus grus

CRANES ARE vagrants to Devon, often seen singly but also as small flocks. They are birds of open moist grasslands and are omnivorous, taking mainly seeds, fruits and leaves but also insects, amphibians and even small birds. Most European Cranes are migratory, breeding in northern Europe and wintering in southern Spain and North Africa. Until the 16th century, Cranes bred in Britain (although records can be confusing because the word 'crane' was also applied to herons).

Since 1981 a small population has bred in Norfolk and there are now several small colonies in eastern England. From 2010 the Great Crane Project, led by the Wildfowl & Wetlands Trust, began to release captive-raised birds on the Somerset Levels with the aim of re-establishing the species as a breeding bird in the region.

During the Atlas period, Cranes were recorded from seven tetrads, mainly during the summer, and largely around the Exe and Otter Estuaries. None of the birds stayed long and it seems likely that these were wandering individuals from the Somerset flock, although all released birds are ringed and individuals seen in Devon were not reported as ringed. If, as seems likely, the Somerset birds become established and start to breed, then one may confidently predict that Cranes will appear more frequently in Devon in the future.

*Text: J M Lock / Photo: David Land*
*Crane sponsored by Janet Teare*

Balmer *et al.* 2013: 332; Sitters 1988: not treated; Tyler 2010: 232

### Breeding-period abundance 2007–13

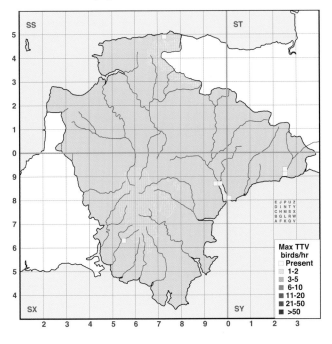

### Winter-period abundance 2007–13

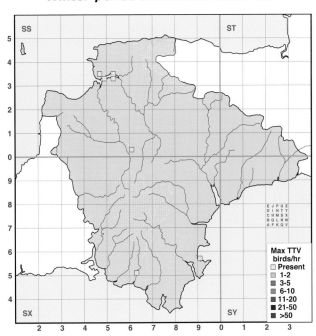

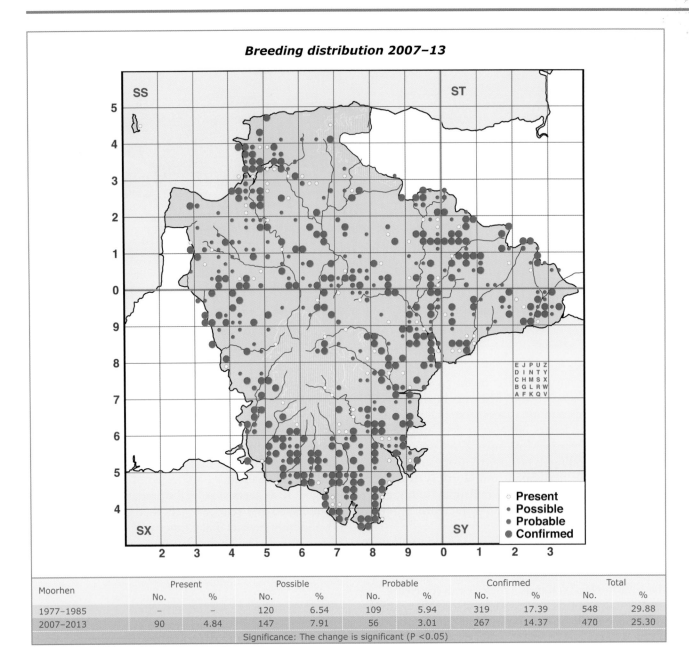

## Breeding distribution 2007–13

| Moorhen | Present | | Possible | | Probable | | Confirmed | | Total | |
|---|---|---|---|---|---|---|---|---|---|---|
| | No. | % | No. | % | No. | % | No. | % | No. | % |
| 1977–1985 | – | – | 120 | 6.54 | 109 | 5.94 | 319 | 17.39 | 548 | 29.88 |
| 2007–2013 | 90 | 4.84 | 147 | 7.91 | 56 | 3.01 | 267 | 14.37 | 470 | 25.30 |
| Significance: The change is significant (P <0.05) | | | | | | | | | | |

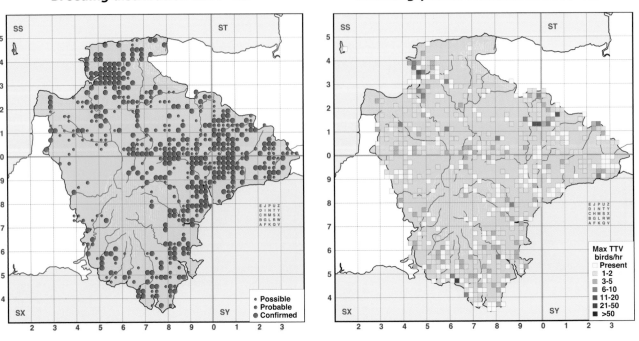

## Breeding distribution 1977–85

## Breeding-period abundance 2007–13

# Moorhen
## *Gallinula chloropus*

MOORHENS ARE common in much of Devon, frequenting slow-moving eutrophic freshwater bodies with bankside and emergent vegetation, where they feed on plant material, invertebrates and small fish. However, they are mostly absent from the higher ground of Exmoor and Dartmoor owing to the acidic wetlands and typically narrow, fast-flowing streams and rivers that characterize these areas leading to very restricted availability of suitable habitat; farm ponds are sometimes an exception. Devon's Moorhens are probably largely sedentary but there is likely to be some immigration in autumn and winter (Wernham *et al.* 2002).

The breeding and winter distribution of Moorhens in the county are very similar, although winter numbers are generally higher. Some of the differences between the summer and winter figures may be explained by the species' skulking habits, particularly in the breeding season, when it may be overlooked within dense bankside vegetation.

The *Devon Tetrad Atlas 1977–85* showed confirmed breeding in 318 tetrads, with possible/probable breeding in another 220 tetrads, compared with 267 confirmed and 203 possible/probable tetrads in the current atlas. While this is a slight decline in recorded breeding, it is likely that tetrads where birds were present also represented undetected breeding.

The largest concentrations of both wintering and breeding Moorhens in Devon are found along the Grand Western Canal, with 40–80 broods recorded annually in the current Atlas years and over 100

individuals recorded in most winter months. Other breeding concentrations were noted in the Aveton Gifford area where 20+ nests were found each year, the Prawle area and Exminster Marshes. Areas holding good wintering numbers included the Axe, Exe and Taw/Torridge Estuaries.

The *Devon Tetrad Atlas 1977–85* estimated the Devon population as 1,500–2,000 pairs, based on an average of three–four pairs per occupied tetrad. A similar calculation based on the data for this Atlas period would give an estimate of 1,700–2,200 pairs.

With two to three and sometimes four broods produced per pair per year, populations recover to previous levels very quickly following adverse conditions, such that the future of the Moorhen in Devon currently looks secure.

*Text: Ray Jones / Photos: Neil Bygrave (top), Gray Clements*

Balmer *et al.* 2013: 328; Sitters 1988: 88; Tyler 2010: 229

### Winter-period abundance 2007–13

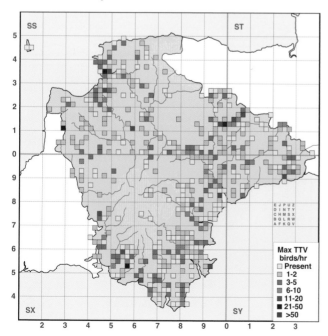

Max TTV birds/hr
- ☐ Present
- 1-2
- 3-5
- 6-10
- 11-20
- 21-50
- >50

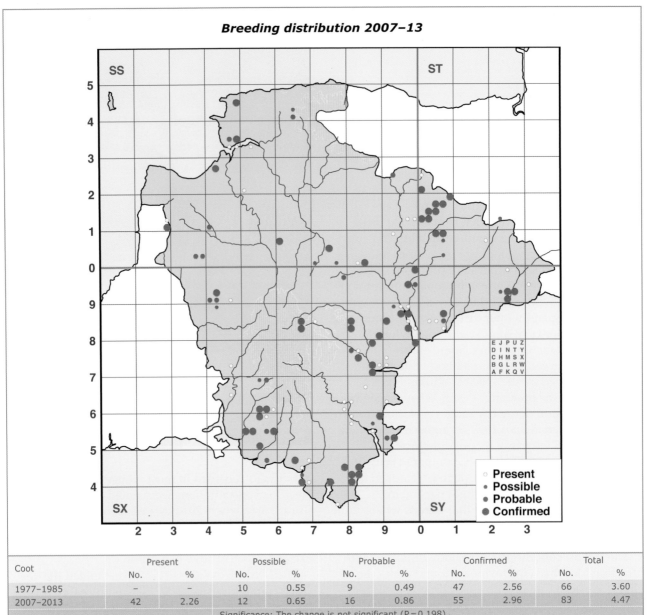

## Breeding distribution 2007–13

| Coot | Present | | Possible | | Probable | | Confirmed | | Total | |
|---|---|---|---|---|---|---|---|---|---|---|
| | No. | % | No. | % | No. | % | No. | % | No. | % |
| 1977–1985 | – | – | 10 | 0.55 | 9 | 0.49 | 47 | 2.56 | 66 | 3.60 |
| 2007–2013 | 42 | 2.26 | 12 | 0.65 | 16 | 0.86 | 55 | 2.96 | 83 | 4.47 |
| Significance: The change is not significant (P=0.198) | | | | | | | | | | |

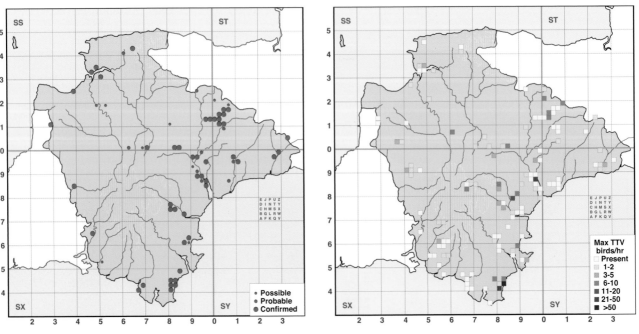

## Breeding distribution 1977–85

## Breeding-period abundance 2007–13

# Coot
## *Fulica atra*

COOTS REQUIRE large, fairly shallow eutrophic waters such as freshwater lakes, reservoirs, gravel pits, lakes and ponds with abundant floating or submerged vegetation. They feed on vegetation, snails and insect larvae. In exceptional winter weather they will also use rivers, estuaries and, occasionally, the sea.

Their distribution in Devon is determined by a lack of suitable habitat, particularly at higher elevations and they do not normally occur on Exmoor or Dartmoor where the reservoirs are generally too deep and acidic, with little submerged vegetation. The particular habitat requirements of the species mean that its summer and winter distributions in Devon are similar, although wintering numbers in suitable habitats are generally higher.

The Coot's main breeding site in Devon is Slapton

Ley, with up to 70 pairs (*DBR* 2008), smaller breeding numbers occurring on the Axe and Exe Estuaries, Beesands Ley, Dawlish Warren, Hennock Reservoirs, Huntsham Lake and Mansands Ley. The Grand Western Canal, which in the *Devon Tetrad Atlas 1977–85* was the second most important area, has, since 2001, for unknown reasons, had low breeding productivity, numbers in 2013 being at an all-time low.

The numbers of Coot in winter are supplemented by the arrival of many migrant birds, generally from Scandinavia and the Low Countries (Wernham *et al.* 2002). The numbers of these migrants, which usually arrive at night, can fluctuate greatly and this appears to be mainly related to weather, with highest numbers being seen during severe conditions. At Slapton Ley, in particular, many hundreds of birds can occur in harsh weather in winter, though numbers can sometimes be adversely affected by algal growth (Whitehall 2003). High wintering numbers may also be seen at Roadford Reservoir (324 birds in December 2011) and on the Exe Estuary reserves (over 290 birds in December 2010), with smaller numbers at Beesands Ley, Decoy Lakes (Newton Abbot), Hennock Reservoirs, Rackerhayes Lake and Tamar Lakes. Higher numbers in autumn suggest that migrating birds may also pass through.

Nationally, the Coot has experienced a long-term increase since the late 1960s, but trends over the five years to 2012 suggest a slight downturn (BTO BirdTrends 2014). In Devon, the Coot has slightly increased its breeding distribution since the *Devon Tetrad Atlas 1977–85*, with confirmed breeding in 55 tetrads compared to 47. Tyler (2010) suggests there are now fewer breeding pairs but this does not appear to be borne out by the Atlas data.

### Winter-period abundance 2007–13

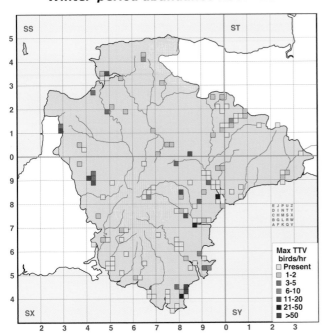

Max TTV birds/hr
- ☐ Present
- 1-2
- 3-5
- 6-10
- 11-20
- 21-50
- >50

*Text: Ray Jones / Photo: Paul Nunn*
*Coot sponsored by Doug & Annie Howes*

Balmer *et al.* 2013: 330; Sitters 1988: 90; Tyler 2010: 230

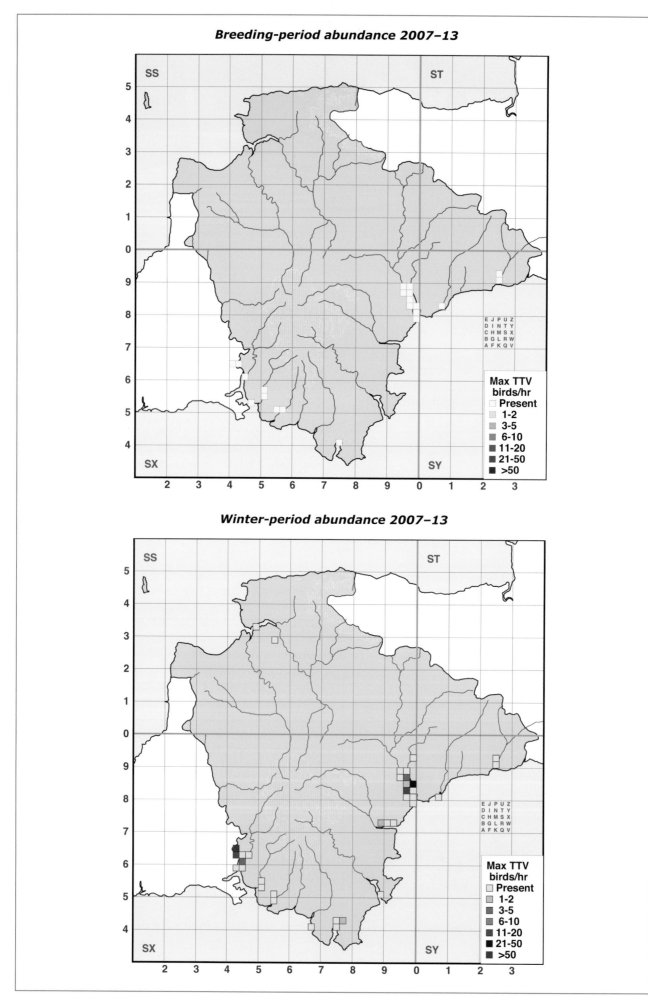

**Breeding-period abundance 2007–13**

SS

ST

Max TTV
birds/hr
Present
1-2
3-5
6-10
11-20
21-50
>50

SX

SY

**Winter-period abundance 2007–13**

SS

ST

Max TTV
birds/hr
Present
1-2
3-5
6-10
11-20
21-50
>50

SX

SY

# Avocet
## *Recurvirostra avosetta*

THE AVOCET's behaviour is as singular as its plumage and bill shape. Equally at home striding across mudflats or swimming in shallow water, its feeding behaviour can range from a gentle 'scything' of polychaete worms from soft mud to a frenzied attack on shoals of mysid shrimps. High-tide roosts may also be on *terra firma* or afloat.

In Devon, Avocets are primarily winter visitors to the mudflats of the upper reaches of the Tamar Complex and Exe Estuary from late October to early March. They also occur on passage, and over the years, singles or small groups have occurred in all months, and from almost all estuaries and occasionally coastal and inland sites. However, they have not bred, and in spite of the huge (1,663%) expansion of the national breeding population since the *Breeding Atlas 1968–72*, *Bird Atlas 2007–11* shows no breeding in England west of the Solent.

Distribution *within* estuaries is affected primarily by the distribution of soft mud, which tends to be in the upper reaches, but mud, worms and Avocets can move downstream after strong river flows scour the upper flats. In general, flocks are scattered and mobile, and distribution at any one time is affected not only by flow rates, but also by tidal state and weather.

The distribution in Devon has not changed since the 1960s when small numbers wintered on the Tamar and later the Exe, then the only wintering sites in the British Isles. Subsequently, wintering numbers have increased rapidly to a current level of over 7,500 birds nationally, and there has been a 165% range expansion since the *Winter Atlas 1981–84*. In contrast, the Tamar and Exe numbers appear to have stabilized (see figure), although there are problems in obtaining accurate counts (Reay & Kent 2011).

In view of the rapid colonization of new sites throughout southern Britain, particularly over the last 25 years, it is perhaps surprising that none of the other Devon estuaries have become regular wintering sites.

*Text: Peter Reay / Photos: Neil Bygrave & (inset) Richard Hargeaves*
*Avocet sponsored by John & Anita Shaw*

Balmer *et al.* 2013: 338; Sitters 1988: not treated; Tyler 2010: 238

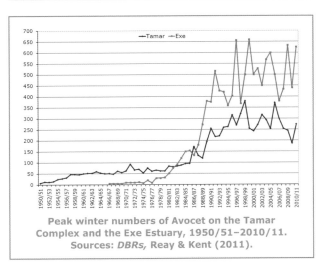

**Peak winter numbers of Avocet on the Tamar Complex and the Exe Estuary, 1950/51–2010/11. Sources: *DBRs*, Reay & Kent (2011).**

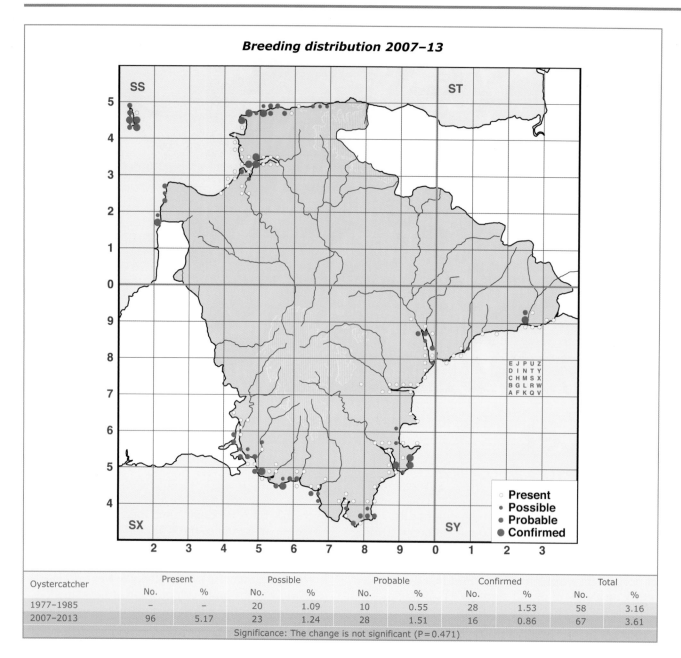

## Breeding distribution 2007–13

| Oystercatcher | Present | | Possible | | Probable | | Confirmed | | Total | |
|---|---|---|---|---|---|---|---|---|---|---|
| | No. | % | No. | % | No. | % | No. | % | No. | % |
| 1977–1985 | – | – | 20 | 1.09 | 10 | 0.55 | 28 | 1.53 | 58 | 3.16 |
| 2007–2013 | 96 | 5.17 | 23 | 1.24 | 28 | 1.51 | 16 | 0.86 | 67 | 3.61 |
| Significance: The change is not significant (P = 0.471) | | | | | | | | | | |

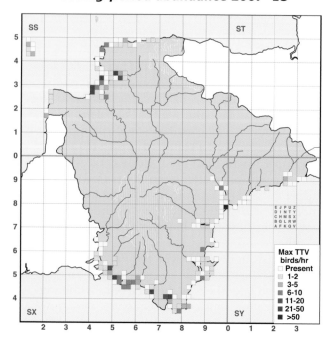

## Breeding distribution 1977–85

## Breeding-period abundance 2007–13

# Oystercatcher
## *Haematopus ostralegus*

Amber listed

WITH THEIR shrill calls and striking plumage, Oystercatchers are a familiar feature of Devon's coasts and estuaries. They occur as scarce breeders, as fairly numerous winter visitors, as non-breeding summer visitors and as passage migrants.

The summer map shows that Oystercatchers nest sparsely in Devon, with just seven confirmed breeding records on the north coast and six on the south coast. The only concentration is on Lundy where the population was estimated at 18 pairs in both 2008 and 2013. On the mainland, nesting has been regular at Yelland on the Taw/Torridge Estuary, with five nests in 2007 and three pairs in 2008. Most other records of confirmed and probable breeding relate to just one pair per occupied tetrad.

Devon's breeding population comprises at least the 18 pairs on Lundy, say four on the Taw, and probably one each in the ten remaining mainland tetrads in which breeding was confirmed (though breeding may not be regular in some); a total of about 30 pairs. Breeding was 'probable' in a further 25 mainland tetrads and 'possible' in 24, but whether breeding really occurred in those areas is uncertain, and any conclusion is confounded by the presence of many immature non-breeders (see below). Several 'probable' records are from well-watched areas, such as Plymouth and Prawle Point, for which it is likely that there would have been better evidence if the birds really had bred. Therefore, the breeding population is tentatively estimated at 30–60 pairs; not dissimilar from estimates of 25–50 pairs in the

1960s (Dare 1970) and 28–58 pairs in the early 1980s (*Devon Tetrad Atlas 1977–85*). Thus there is no evidence that the breeding population has changed significantly over the past 50 years.

The winter map shows that Oystercatchers are widely distributed along both coasts, with major concentrations on the Exe and Taw/Torridge Estuaries. On the Exe, midwinter numbers peaked during 1986–1996 at around 4,000 and have since declined to about 2,000, but numbers on the Taw/Torridge have increased from below 1,000 during 1998–2003 to more than 1,000 in most years since, with more than 2,000 in December 2012 (*DBRs*). Elsewhere the only sites that regularly support more than 100 are the Teign Estuary (300–400) and the Kingsbridge Estuary (100–200) (*DBRs*).

Ringing recoveries from the Exe wintering population show that most breed in Scotland, where *Bird Atlas 2007–11* indicates the breeding population to have declined by 30% between 1995 and 2011. This partly explains the 50% decline on the Exe, but also suggests that conditions for Oystercatchers on the Exe may have deteriorated, and/or they have improved on the Taw/Torridge.

Young Oystercatchers remain in their Devon wintering areas until they first move away to breed when they are three or four years old (Ens *et al.* 1996). Thus, substantial numbers of non-breeding immatures can be found on the county's coasts and estuaries throughout the summer months, with concentrations on the Exe and Taw/Torridge (mean 2008–2012 June counts of 334 and 329 respectively; *DBRs*).

*Text: Humphrey Sitters / Photo: Mike Jones*
*Oystercatcher sponsored by Nick & Gill Townsend*

Balmer *et al.* 2013: 336; Sitters 1988: 92; Tyler 2010: 235

### Winter-period abundance 2007–13

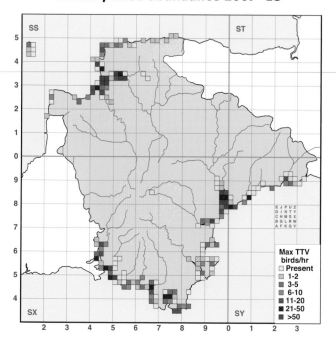

Max TTV birds/hr
- ☐ Present
- 1-2
- 3-5
- 6-10
- 11-20
- 21-50
- >50

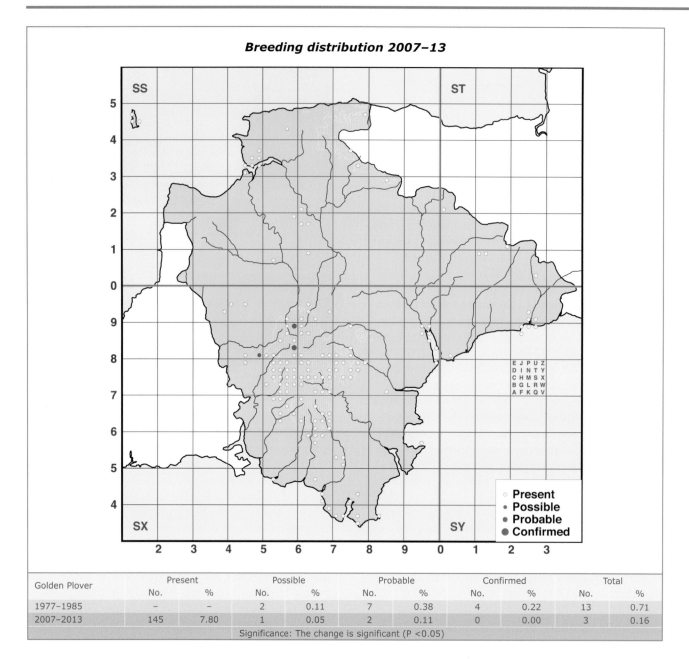

**Breeding distribution 2007–13**

| Golden Plover | Present | | Possible | | Probable | | Confirmed | | Total | |
|---|---|---|---|---|---|---|---|---|---|---|
| | No. | % | No. | % | No. | % | No. | % | No. | % |
| 1977–1985 | – | – | 2 | 0.11 | 7 | 0.38 | 4 | 0.22 | 13 | 0.71 |
| 2007–2013 | 145 | 7.80 | 1 | 0.05 | 2 | 0.11 | 0 | 0.00 | 3 | 0.16 |
| Significance: The change is significant (P <0.05) | | | | | | | | | | |

**Breeding distribution 1977–85**

**Breeding-period abundance 2007–13**

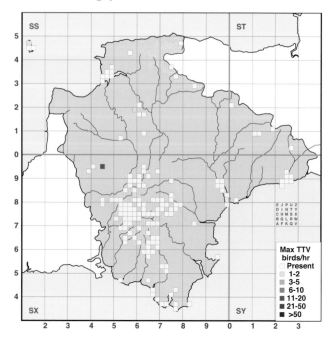

# Golden Plover
## *Pluvialis apricaria*

IN BRITAIN the Golden Plover breeds in uplands and winters on lowland farmland, extensive grassland and coastal grazing marshes. Its English breeding strongholds are the Yorkshire Dales, South Pennines and the Peak District.

There is no apparent long-term trend in the British breeding population, although the BTO's Breeding Bird Survey indicates a 6% decline between 1995 and 2012 (Harris *et al.* 2014). However, some upland birds, including Golden Plover, are increasingly affected by higher summer temperatures, which causes problems for their Crane fly (Tipulidae) prey (Pearce-Higgins *et al.* 2010) and there is some evidence of losses in the south of the breeding range, including Devon, where successful breeding has not been proven in the last ten years. The last proven breeding was on Dartmoor in 2004 and the last birds holding territory were seen in 2008 (*DBR*). There is some evidence that the height of vegetation within the preferred nesting areas is no longer suitable since Golden Plovers prefer vegetation that is not too tall for them to see over, and not so thick as to prevent them running about (*BWP*).

The species' decline as a breeding bird in Devon is reflected in the two county Atlases; in the *Devon Tetrad Atlas 1977–85*, Golden Plovers were suspected of breeding in 13 tetrads (1%) in Devon but during the current Atlas period this had fallen to just three tetrads with no evidence of nesting. It is likely that the Golden Plover no longer breeds in Devon. Golden Plovers recorded in Devon in April may well be birds that winter far to the south in Iberia or even North Africa, on passage to breeding sites further north (Wernham *et al.* 2002).

On migration and in winter, Golden Plovers are attracted to mown grass or close-grazed pastures and other farmland of open character, including grazing marshes. On the coast they tend to neglect tidal flats of mud or sand, although they may use them for roosting, and to prefer open ground above the foreshore, which they commonly share with Lapwings. The Devon winter distribution reflects these habitat preferences.

Wintering Golden Plovers are relatively common and widespread in the county, having been recorded in 352 tetrads (19%) during the October to March period. Flocks vary considerably in size and are highly mobile. Sites that are favoured if conditions are right include the grazing marshes adjoining the Taw/Torridge Estuary where 4,220 were recorded in December 2012, on Dartmoor (2,000 in November 2012) and on Upottery Airfield (1,000 in January 2012). This was a year when numbers were higher than usual, although it is difficult to make useful comparisons in a species where many may be on open fields well inland and not regularly counted. Flocks begin to build up in October and the number of birds in the county, around 5,500 in recent years, remains relatively stable until March.

*Text: John Waldon / Photo: Steve Hatch*
*Golden Plover sponsored by John Howes*

Balmer *et al.* 2013: 348; Sitters 1988: 96; Tyler 2010: 253

### Winter-period abundance 2007–13

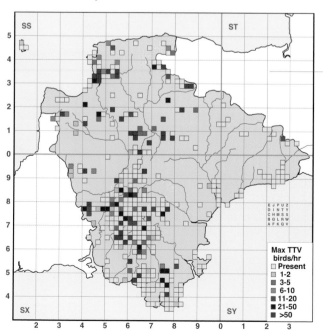

Max TTV birds/hr
- ☐ Present
- ☐ 1-2
- ☐ 3-5
- ■ 6-10
- ■ 11-20
- ■ 21-50
- ■ >50

# Grey Plover
## *Pluvialis squatarola*

I N THE UK the Grey Plover is a passage migrant and winter visitor. It breeds on arctic tundras from western Siberia to eastern Canada, and winters as far south as South Africa. Those wintering in western Europe come from a breeding population in northern Russia, and in England wintering birds have a south-eastern distribution, with most found between The Wash and the Solent. The UK wintering population declined by 13% between 2000 and 2010 and was estimated to be 43,000 in 2008–09 (Musgrove *et al.* 2011).

In Devon, the distribution has not changed significantly in recent years and remains concentrated in the Exe and Taw/Torridge Estuaries with Kingsbridge hosting lower numbers. Although small numbers can be seen along the coast and at waterbodies throughout the county, the concentration at these few sites reflects the presence of the birds' preferred feeding areas in the intertidal zone, on broad mudflats or sandy beaches, and to a lesser extent on wet grassland and saltings. Grey Plovers often defend the same feeding area from one year to the next (Townsend *et al.* 1984). The main wintering sites are the Exe and Taw/Torridge Estuaries, and – to a lesser extent – other estuaries with extensive intertidal flats. However, the overall numbers wintering in Devon have declined since the 1990s and WeBS total counts of more than 500 birds (575 in January 2013) were exceptional during the Atlas period, whereas in February 1995 the Taw/Torridge Estuary held over 650 and in February 1998 the Exe Estuary held 573 (*DBRs*). The reasons for the change in wintering population numbers are not clear (*Bird Atlas 2007–11*).

A small passage of birds begins in August in most years but wintering numbers typically only start to build up in earnest during November. These birds leave mainly in February/March, with a modest spring passage accounting for some that linger into April or May.

*Text: John Waldon / Photo: Neil Bygrave*

Balmer *et al.* 2013: 350; Sitters 1988: not treated; Tyler 2010: 256

### Winter-period abundance 2007–13

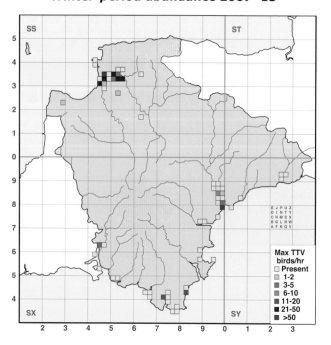

### Breeding-period abundance 2007–13

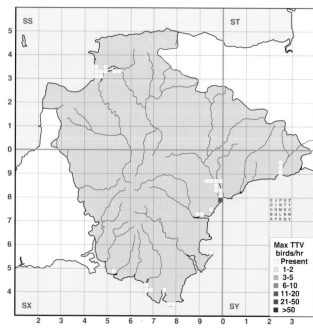

# Little Ringed Plover
## *Charadrius dubius*

Lɪᴛᴛʟᴇ Rɪɴɢᴇᴅ Pʟᴏᴠᴇʀ is a summer migrant that has relatively recently become established as a breeding species in Devon. Though nesting did not occur in the UK until 1938, by 2007 the population was estimated at 1,200 pairs centred on the Midlands, the South East and northern England (Conway *et al.* in press). The species is renowned for nesting in man-made habitats such as quarries, gravel pits, spoil heaps and sewage works, with only 3% of nesting attempts occurring on natural sites such as riverine shingle (Parrinder 1989).

As elsewhere in Britain, the Little Ringed Plover is an early spring migrant in Devon, arriving during March and April, usually on wetlands close to the county's main estuaries of the Exe and Taw/Torridge, although other estuaries such as the Axe and Teign are used. Nesting can also be early, with some eggs already laid in April. This potentially overlaps with the continued arrival of migrants destined for breeding sites further north, sometimes making it difficult to separate local breeders from passage birds. Breeding in Devon was first proven in 2002 and has been suspected or proven throughout the Atlas years – but never more than single nests at disparate sites in any one year. Post-breeding migration is less noticeable than in the spring and starts in July, peaking in August.

There are no winter records of this small wader in Devon, which is unsurprising as almost all those that

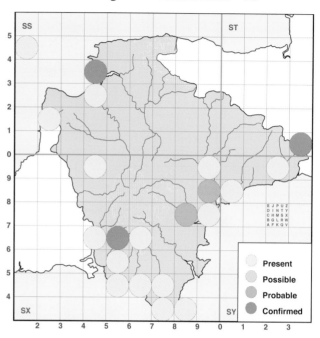

**Breeding distribution 2007–13**

Legend:
- Present
- Possible
- Probable
- Confirmed

nest in Europe winter south of the Sahara, from Senegal to Kenya (Brown & Grice 2005).

*Text: John Waldon / Photo: Lee Collins*
*Little Ringed Plover sponsored by John Waldon*

Balmer *et al.* 2013: 342; Sitters 1988: not treated; Tyler 2010: 243

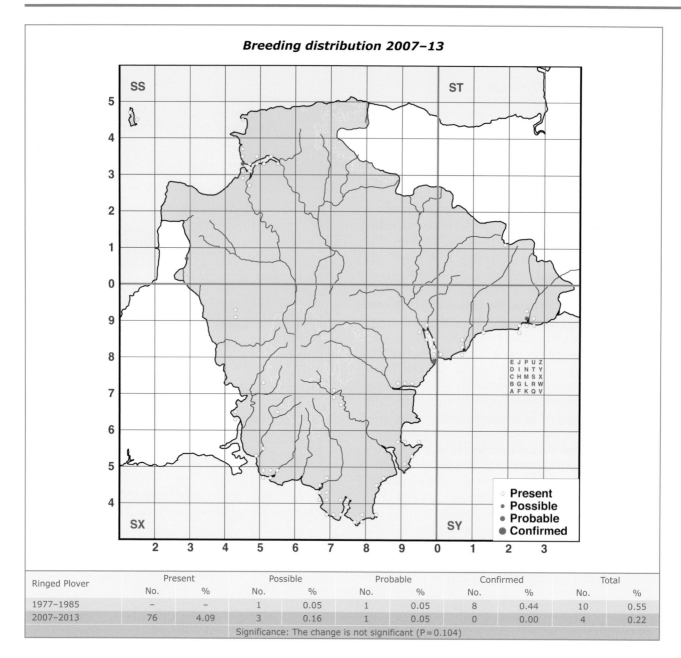

### Breeding distribution 2007–13

| Ringed Plover | Present | | Possible | | Probable | | Confirmed | | Total | |
|---|---|---|---|---|---|---|---|---|---|---|
| | No. | % | No. | % | No. | % | No. | % | No. | % |
| 1977–1985 | – | – | 1 | 0.05 | 1 | 0.05 | 8 | 0.44 | 10 | 0.55 |
| 2007–2013 | 76 | 4.09 | 3 | 0.16 | 1 | 0.05 | 0 | 0.00 | 4 | 0.22 |
| Significance: The change is not significant (P = 0.104) | | | | | | | | | | |

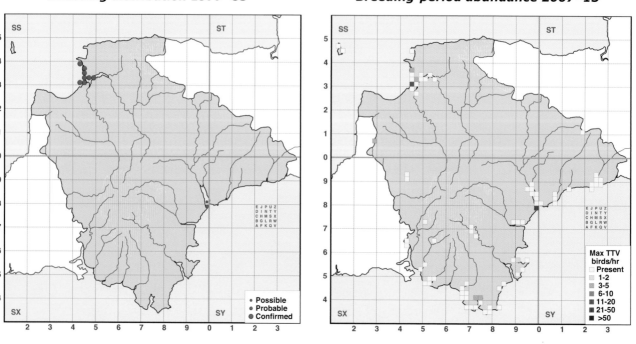

### Breeding distribution 1977–85

### Breeding-period abundance 2007–13

# Ringed Plover
## *Charadrius hiaticula*

**Red listed**

RINGED PLOVERS are recorded in every month of the year in Devon. Whilst successful breeding has not been recorded in the county since 2009, a small number do summer and there is a significant passage through the county of birds breeding further north. There is also a regular wintering population usually restricted to the larger estuaries.

Ringed Plovers usually nest above the high-tide line on sandy or shingle beaches, and appear always to have avoided the generally long narrow beaches of South West England. Although D'Urban & Mathew (1892) stated that it "breeds all round the coast wherever there is a pebbly beach", breeding has, in recent years, been restricted to the Taw/Torridge Estuary and Dawlish Warren, a situation confirmed by the current Atlas. On the Taw/Torridge Estuary there were up to 12 breeding pairs between 1977 and 1985 but nesting has occurred only occasionally since then and with little success, due mainly to recreational disturbance (Turner 2009), and not confirmed at all during the Atlas period. At Dawlish Warren breeding possibly took place in 2009 and a bird was holding territory in 2010. Disturbance by people and dogs as well as changes to the profile of the beach are also considered to be contributing factors and may be relevant elsewhere in the county.

The UK's annual wintering population was estimated to be 36,000 in 2009, made up of birds that had nested in the UK and birds from the Baltic and Wadden Sea (Musgrove *et al.* 2011). Monitoring has established that there has been a long-term 36% decline in the UK wintering population (Holt *et al.* 2012), thought to be a consequence of climate change (Maclean *et al.* 2008). This is mirrored in Devon where reference to the WeBS county totals for December shows that although it varies considerably from year to year there does seem a downward trend over the last ten years (see figure).

An impressive number of Ringed Plovers breeding in Greenland, Canada, Iceland and Fennoscandia pass through Britain to winter as far south as West Africa. Some of these passage birds appear in Devon, especially on the Taw/Torridge Estuary and on the Exe Estuary (Collins 2014). This southbound movement can be significant in late summer, with a mean August county WeBS total of 450 during the period 2008 to 2012 (*DBR* 2013). A smaller peak is recorded in May as birds return to their breeding grounds.

*Text: John Waldon / Photo: Dave Scott*

Balmer *et al.* 2013: 344; Sitters 1988: 94; Tyler 2010: 245

### Winter-period abundance 2007–13

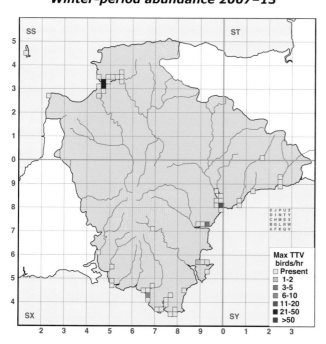

Max TTV birds/hr
- ☐ Present
- 1-2
- 3-5
- 6-10
- 11-20
- 21-50
- >50

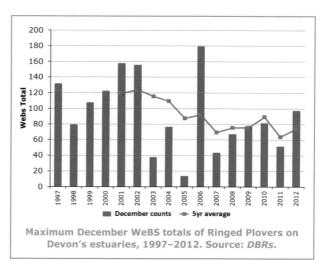

December counts — 5yr average

**Maximum December WeBS totals of Ringed Plovers on Devon's estuaries, 1997–2012. Source: *DBRs*.**

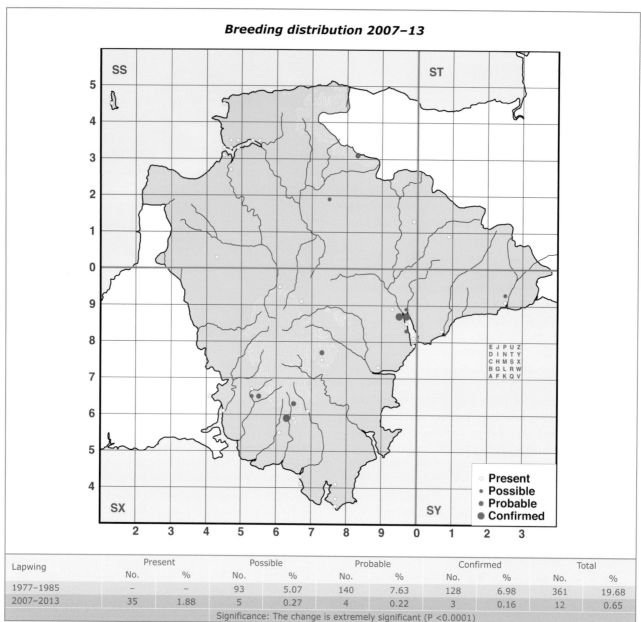

## Breeding distribution 2007–13

| Lapwing | Present | | Possible | | Probable | | Confirmed | | Total | |
|---|---|---|---|---|---|---|---|---|---|---|
| | No. | % | No. | % | No. | % | No. | % | No. | % |
| 1977–1985 | – | – | 93 | 5.07 | 140 | 7.63 | 128 | 6.98 | 361 | 19.68 |
| 2007–2013 | 35 | 1.88 | 5 | 0.27 | 4 | 0.22 | 3 | 0.16 | 12 | 0.65 |
| Significance: The change is extremely significant (P <0.0001) | | | | | | | | | | |

## Breeding distribution 1977–85

## Breeding-period abundance 2007–13

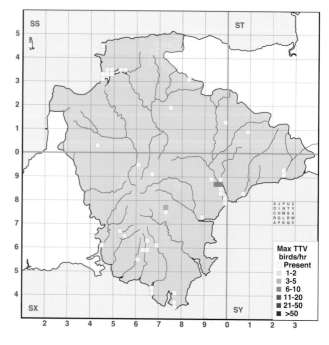

# Lapwing
## *Vanellus vanellus*
### Red listed

LAPWINGS ARE iconic birds associated with a range of open habitats including moorland, pastures, arable farmland and estuaries. Their distinctive black and white plumage and distinctive *'peewit'* call makes them easily identifiable, and the spectacle of their erratic tumbling display flight over the breeding territory can be enjoyed from late February to May.

The loss of breeding Lapwings, in terms of both range and abundance, is vividly demonstrated in *Bird Atlas 2007–11* and is particularly striking in western Britain. Declines in Devon have been discussed by Smaldon (2005), Davis & Jones (2007) and Tyler (2010). The *Devon Tetrad Atlas 1977–85* showed that breeding was widespread across the county, with the highest densities occurring in East Devon and on Dartmoor. Altogether during the 1977–85 survey, breeding evidence was recorded for 361 tetrads (19.7%). The corresponding figure for the current Atlas was only 12 tetrads (1.7%), a decline of 96.8%, with confirmed breeding restricted to the Exe Estuary RSPB reserves and southern Dartmoor.

On the Exe Estuary RSPB reserves – now the most important remaining area of the county for breeding Lapwings – numbers during the Atlas period fluctuated between 12 pairs in 2011 and 19 pairs in 2012. Only six young fledged in 2011, but following the installation of an anti-predator fence that year (after the breeding season) at Exminster Marshes, the number of fledged young increased dramatically to

29 in 2012 and 38 in 2013. Other proactive conservation measures have included rush and grass (*Deschampsia*) control and careful management of water levels, especially in spring, to ensure the grassland does not become too dry. This probably explains why breeding on the Exe was wholly restricted to RSPB-managed land. On Dartmoor, detailed monitoring between 2005 and 2013 showed a reduction in the number of Lapwing breeding sites from five tetrads to just a single tetrad, in which no more than four pairs now breed (Avon 2007; *DBRs*).

The reasons for the decline have been linked to habitat loss and degradation due to changes in agricultural practices, notably the change from spring to autumn sowing of cereals, drainage of grasslands and loss of mixed farmland (BTO BirdTrends 2014). Weather conditions and predation (particularly by Carrion Crows and foxes) are key factors affecting the success of Devon's few remaining breeding pairs.

During autumn and winter, Lapwings are generally seen in flocks, and numbers increase significantly as winter migrants arrive. The majority in winter are found around Devon's estuaries, especially the Taw/Torridge, Axe and Exe. The peak WeBS county total during the Atlas period reached 4,657 during a period of snow and frost in January 2009, while the maximum site count was 5,000 on the Axe Estuary in January 2013 (*DBRs*). Even allowing for cold-weather influxes midway through the Atlas period, a comparison of mean January WeBS totals for 2002–2006 (4,395 ) and 2008–2012 (3,289) suggests a decline in wintering numbers. *Bird Atlas 2007–11* reports evidence of increased wintering around eastern British estuaries, citing climate change as a possible factor.

*Text: Jon Avon / Photo: Roy Churchill*
*Lapwing sponsored by James Diamond*

Balmer *et al.* 2013: 352; Sitters 1988: 98; Tyler 2010: 258

### Winter-period abundance 2007–13

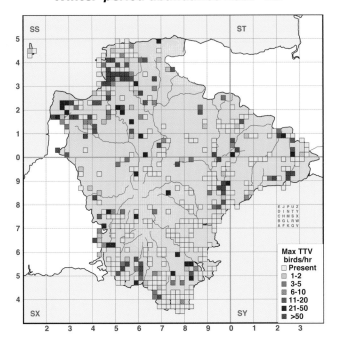

Max TTV birds/hr
- ☐ Present
- 1-2
- 3-5
- 6-10
- 11-20
- 21-50
- >50

# Dotterel
*Charadrius morinellus*

DOTTERELS ARE mainly scarce passage migrants to Devon moorlands and coastal agricultural land, with most records between mid-April and mid-May and in late August and September.

The breeding-period records relate to three birds on Brendon Common, Exmoor, on 2 May 2008, one on north-west Dartmoor on 8 May 2011, one on Lundy during May 2011 and two in May 2013 as well as two on 31 August 2010, one at Salcombe in September 2011 and single birds in the Bolberry Down area in September 2009 and 2011.

Winter records, such as the bird seen at Prawle on 4 January 2010, are extremely rare and there have only been seven in the county since records began. More Dotterels are recorded in Devon on autumn passage, with five such records during the Atlas years.

Given the county's extensive moorlands and the fact that there have been sporadic breeding records well south of the main range (e.g. Ireland and the Netherlands), it is possible that the odd pair of Dotterels might even breed in Devon occasionally. It is also likely that the abundance of suitable habitat and relative sparseness of birdwatchers mean more Dotterels occur on passage than are ever actually recorded.

*Text: Humphrey Sitters / Photo: Andrew Cunningham*

Balmer *et al.* 2013: 346; Sitters 1988: not treated; Tyler 2010: 251

### Breeding-period abundance 2007–13

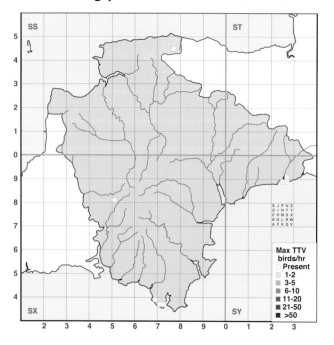

### Winter-period abundance 2007–13

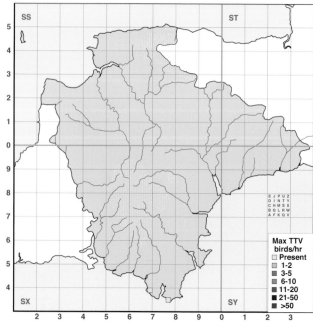

# Whimbrel
## *Numenius phaeopus*

**Red listed**

THE FAR-CARRYING, rapidly repeated whistling call of Whimbrels en route to breeding grounds in Scotland, Iceland, Fennoscandia and western Russia (Wernham *et al.* 2002) is one of the most evocative sounds of spring migration around our estuaries and coasts. However, as the maps show, there are also widespread records from inland parts of the county and regular instances of overwintering by very small numbers.

During the March–September Atlas period, records came from 166 tetrads in fifty 10-km squares. The first spring migrants typically appeared during the first week of April (though nine were on the Exe Estuary on 13 March 2012), with passage peaking between mid-April and mid-May and continuing into June. The two most important sites were the Exe Estuary and Thurlestone Bay, where maxima for the Atlas years were 805 on 3 May 2009 and 362 on 24 April 2010 respectively (*DBRs*). In 2008, Thurlestone Bay also saw "a steady flow from mid-April to mid-May totalling over 1,000 birds" (*DBR*). Other regular sites on the south coast that regularly held good numbers in spring included the Axe Estuary/Seaton Bay, the Prawle area, Slapton Sands and Wembury Beach. On the north coast the Taw/Torridge Estuary was the most important site, with a maximum count of 222 on 13 May 2013; TTVs for the Atlas did not necessarily capture these often fleeting arrivals.

Southbound migration is much less marked than spring passage; it also occurs very early, with the peak in all Atlas years occurring in July, typically the last week of the month; e.g. 54 at Dawlish Warren (Exe Estuary) on 23 July 2012. Maximum site counts for other years were almost all less than 40.

Some of the occupied tetrads shown on the October–February map relate to migrants. However, single wintering birds occurred in each of the Atlas years, with south coast records from the Exe, Kingsbridge, Otter and Plym Estuaries, Tamar Complex, Plymouth Sound, Thurlestone Bay and Wembury. Very unusually, seven were seen on the Taw/Torridge Estuary on 14 January 2013.

Most inland records occurred in spring, when singles and small groups were heard in flight (including at night), but some birds were seen when they paused to rest or feed on moorland and grassland, and at reservoirs.

*Text: Tim Jones & Tim Davis / Photo: Steve Hatch*
*Whimbrel sponsored by John Dixon*

Balmer *et al.* 2013: 374; Sitters 1988: not treated; Tyler 2010: 294

### Breeding-period abundance 2007–13

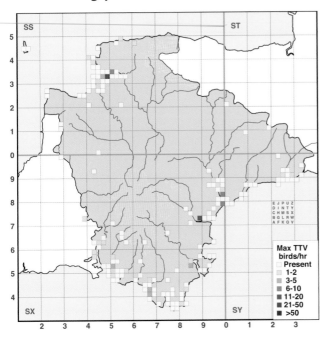

### Winter-period abundance 2007–13

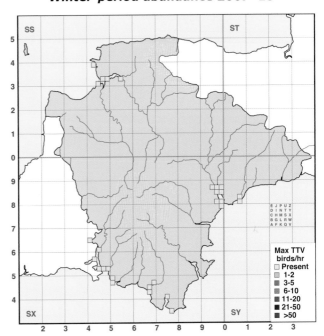

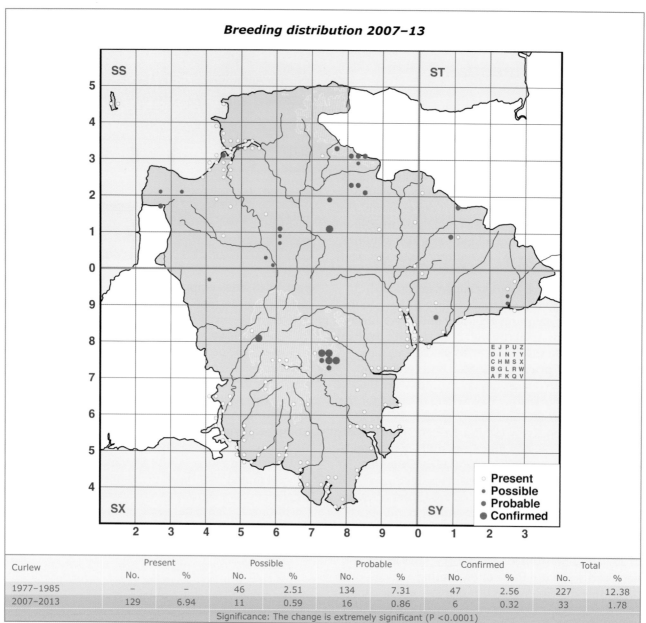

## Breeding distribution 2007–13

| Curlew | Present | | Possible | | Probable | | Confirmed | | Total | |
|---|---|---|---|---|---|---|---|---|---|---|
| | No. | % | No. | % | No. | % | No. | % | No. | % |
| 1977–1985 | – | – | 46 | 2.51 | 134 | 7.31 | 47 | 2.56 | 227 | 12.38 |
| 2007–2013 | 129 | 6.94 | 11 | 0.59 | 16 | 0.86 | 6 | 0.32 | 33 | 1.78 |
| | Significance: The change is extremely significant (P <0.0001) | | | | | | | | | |

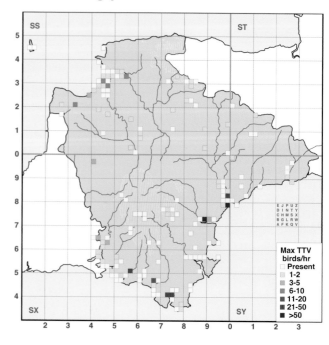

## Breeding distribution 1977–85

## Breeding-period abundance 2007–13

# Curlew
## *Numenius arquata*

**Red listed**

CURLEWS ARE familiar birds, seen feeding or roosting on Devon's estuaries throughout the year, especially those of the Exe and Taw/Torridge. Their instantly recognizable and far-carrying '*curlee*' calls draw attention to their presence day and night, while on the breeding grounds the bubbling spring song can also be heard over considerable distances. However, once settled on their breeding territories they can be much more difficult to locate; despite being the largest British wader, their camouflaged plumage conceals them well.

Curlews were noted on Dartmoor in the early 19th century (Turton & Kingston 1830). Moore (1969) referred to them nesting commonly throughout the county and increasing again following heavy mortality in the winter of 1962/3. A survey of the breeding birds of Dartmoor in 1979 showed an estimated 23 pairs (Mudge 1981). The *Devon Tetrad Atlas 1977–85* estimated the breeding population to be 200–250 breeding pairs but also identified and documented the start of a downturn in both population and range. Habitat loss through drainage and fragmentation were recognized as major factors, especially in the Culm grasslands. The decline is well documented in the *Devon Bird Reports*, which confirm the cessation of breeding at many previously well-known and traditional sites. In 1990, the population was estimated at 21 pairs (*DBR* 1991) but since 2008 has remained in single figures with few young fledged.

During 1977–85, Curlews were recorded in 227 tetrads (12%) with confirmed breeding in 47, whereas the current Atlas found breeding evidence in only 33 tetrads with breeding confirmed in just six, representing a reduction of over 85%. This reflects a national trend of steep decline since the 1970s (BTO BirdTrends 2014) and Europe-wide decline since the 1980s (PECBMS). The breeding-period map shows almost countywide extinction in previous strongholds away from Dartmoor, but even there the losses are striking.

A very small but apparently stable population of four pairs has continued to breed on east Dartmoor and two young were successfully fledged there in 2007. Monitoring has shown frequent predation by Carrion Crows and though some crow removal resulted in more clutches hatching, chick survival remained poor. In both 2011 and 2012, single chicks reached three to four weeks in age before disappearing due to suspected predation (possibly by crows, but potentially by Buzzards, Foxes or Badgers). Further monitoring by Dartmoor National Park and the Duchy of Cornwall may reveal precisely why chicks are failing to fledge.

Large numbers of birds are seen during autumn passage (July–September) and mainly on the county's estuaries during the winter months. The Exe (1,869 in February 2013), Taw/Torridge (1,508 in January 2012) and Kingsbridge Estuaries (420 in October 2012) hold the largest numbers, with that of the Exe being by far the greatest. During the Atlas period, the county WeBS total peaked in January 2012 with 3,337 birds recorded (*DBR*).

The future for Curlew as a breeding species in Devon looks bleak; any conservation measures applied to help this remaining population rear young need to be robust and well supported.

*Text: Jon Avon / Photo: Neil Bygrave*
*Curlew sponsored by Jon Avon*

Balmer *et al.* 2013: 376; Sitters 1988: 106; Tyler 2010: 296

### Winter-period abundance 2007–13

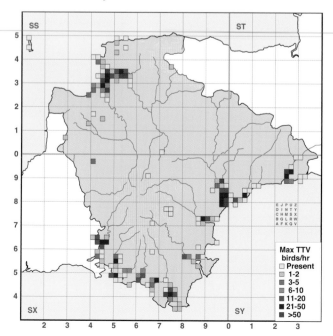

Max TTV birds/hr
☐ Present
1-2
3-5
6-10
11-20
21-50
>50

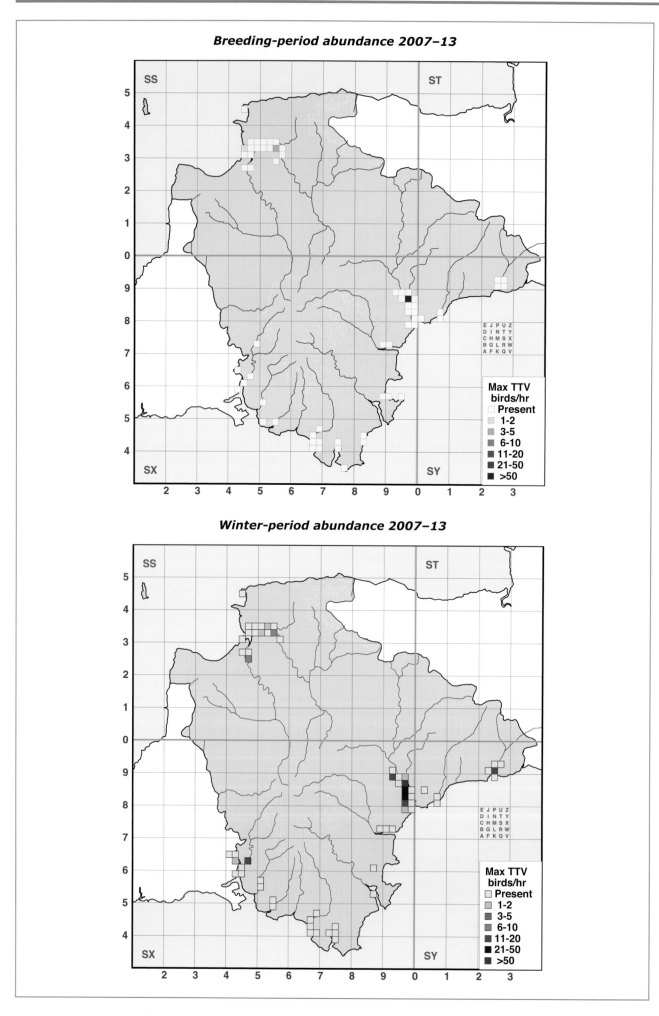

Breeding-period abundance 2007–13

Winter-period abundance 2007–13

Max TTV birds/hr
Present
1-2
3-5
6-10
11-20
21-50
>50

# Black-tailed Godwit

*Limosa limosa*                                                   **Red listed**

THE BLACK-TAILED Godwit feeds by probing into soft mud or soil, and is more or less restricted to estuaries and other coastal wetlands. It does occasionally occur inland in Devon, particularly on passage, but hardly ever on the open coast. Black-tailed Godwits occur throughout the year, with the highest numbers from August to March. Wintering birds belong to the Icelandic subspecies *islandica*, but the nominate race *limosa* may occur on passage, although there are no confirmed records (Langman *et al.* 2007). Both subspecies breed in small numbers in Britain, but summer-period birds in Devon are either on passage or are non-breeders, especially on the Exe Estuary, where only in June are numbers likely to dip below 100. Colour-ringed birds have clearly demonstrated the link with Iceland and other wintering and passage sites in Britain and continental Europe, demonstrating various degrees of site fidelity and movements between sites within a season (Adams 2006).

The Exe Estuary (including surrounding marshes) is by far the most important site, not only in Devon but in South West England, with winter numbers regularly peaking at over 1,000 – well above the threshold for international importance (the only wader species to achieve this globally significant level in Devon; *DBR* 2011). Almost all other Devon records come from the Tamar Complex (above Tamar Bridge) and the Axe Estuary, both supporting 50–100 birds; the Taw/Torridge Estuary with up to 50 and the Kingsbridge Estuary and South Huish area with fewer than 20. On the winter abundance map, the great majority of tetrads show simple presence. All tetrads showing a high level of occupancy were within the four main estuaries, with only the Exe including tetrads where more than 20 birds were counted. The patchy nature of the species' distribution is underlined by its occurrence in only 60 tetrads (3.23%) in winter and 42 (2.26%) in the breeding season.

Black-tailed Godwit was not included in the *Devon Tetrad Atlas 1977–85*, but both numbers and distribution differ from the time of the *Winter Atlas*

*1981–84*. Numbers on the Exe have increased (it was rare for more than 800 to be counted in the early 1980s (Price 2010)) and in the earlier period there was no regular wintering other than on the Exe and Tamar. The changes seen in Devon are all part of the national five-fold increase in wintering numbers since the early 1980s and the 177% range expansion reported in *Bird Atlas 2007–11*. This national expansion includes a notable increase in the use of inland sites, but this has not occurred so far in Devon.

*Text: Peter Reay / Photos: Neil Bygrave*
*Black-tailed Godwit sponsored by Axe Estuary Ringing Group*

Balmer *et al.* 2013: 370; Sitters 1988: not treated; Tyler 2010: 289

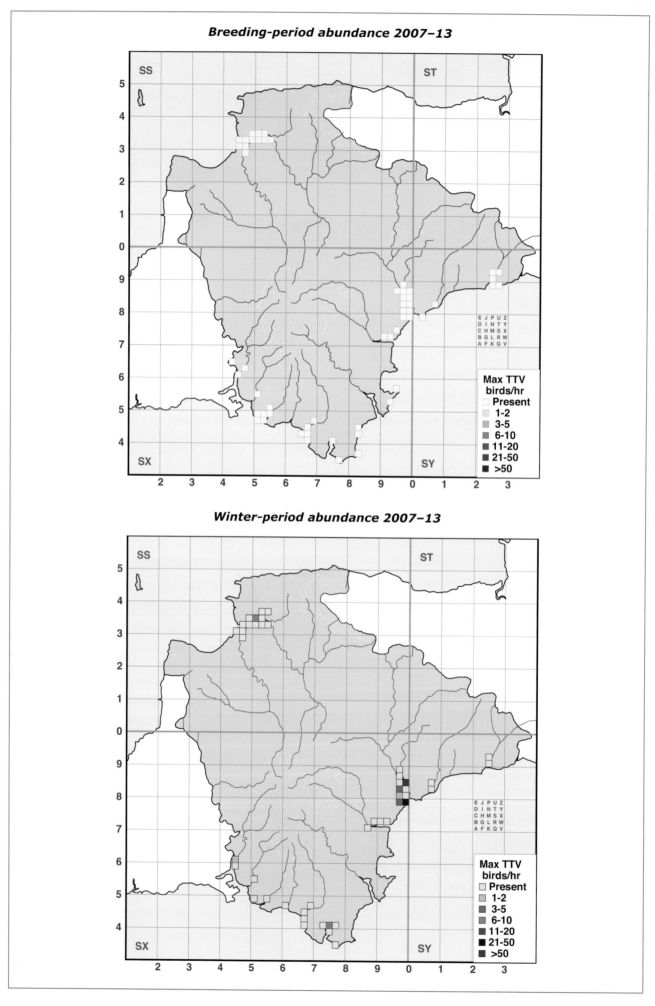

**Breeding-period abundance 2007–13**

**Winter-period abundance 2007–13**

Max TTV
birds/hr
☐ Present
1-2
3-5
6-10
11-20
21-50
>50

# Bar-tailed Godwit

*Limosa lapponica*

Bar-tailed Godwits feed by probing into mud and sand, and although very much an estuarine species, there are occasional occurrences on the open coast, and even inland. The species is recorded throughout the year in Devon, but the highest numbers are in winter. Wintering birds belong to the nominate race *lapponica* which breeds from north-east Europe to western Siberia, but many passage birds are of the race *taymyrensis* which breeds in central Siberia (BTO pers. com.). Breeding-season birds in Devon are either on passage (including those over the sea) or non-breeders, especially on the Exe Estuary, where up to 50 can be expected between May and July.

The Exe Estuary is by far the most important site, not only in Devon but in South West England, with winter numbers regularly peaking at over 200 in the late 2000s. Most other records come from the Taw/Torridge Estuary with up to 100, Kingsbridge Estuary with about 20 and Axe Estuary with about five, but records of occasional single birds have come from several other sites. On the wintering map, most tetrads indicate presence only, with just one site, the Exe Estuary, holding more than 20 birds. The species' patchy distribution is shown by its occurrence in only 45 tetrads (2.42%) in winter and 38 (2.05%) during the summer period.

Bar-tailed Godwit was not included in the *Devon Tetrad Atlas 1977–85*, but numbers are significantly lower than at the time of the *Winter Atlas 1981–84*, when peaks of over 500 were regularly seen on the Exe Estuary. At that time, the Taw/Torridge and Kingsbridge Estuaries were the only other regular sites, with peaks on both of around 20 birds. *Bird Atlas 2007–11* shows there has been a 19% range expansion in Britain since the *Winter Atlas 1981–84*, but a more recent decline in numbers associated with an eastwards shift in wintering areas linked to milder winters (Maclean *et al.* 2008). On the Exe, along with a 60% decline in monthly means since the 1970s, the peak month has changed from December to February, perhaps reflecting a greater relative importance of *taymyrensis* birds on passage (Price 2010).

*Text: Peter Reay*

*Photos: Neil Bygrave (top) & Roy Churchill (inset)*

Balmer *et al.* 2013: 372; Sitters 1988: not treated; Tyler 2010: 292

# Turnstone
## *Arenaria interpres*

**Amber listed**

THEIR CRYPTIC plumage means that a group of Turnstones busily picking about on seaweed-covered rocks can easily pass unnoticed. They can be found in Devon throughout the year, due to the overlapping presence of wintering birds and spring and autumn passage migrants. Numbers dip to a minimum in June, when most are on their Arctic breeding grounds (Wernham *et al.* 2002).

The maps confirm the Turnstone's status as one of our most strictly coastal waders, with no Atlas records from inland localities.

The UK WeBS trend shows that wintering Turnstone numbers have been declining since the mid-1980s. At the end of the Atlas period, numbers were close to the all-time lows of recent winters

(Austin *et al.* 2014). In Devon, most were present around south coast estuaries and bays. The most important site was the Exe Estuary, followed by the Taw/Torridge Estuary; secondary sites included Dawlish seafront, the Plym Estuary, Plymouth Sound, Torbay and Wembury Beach. During the core winter months of December to February, the peak WeBS total occurred in January in all except one winter, varying between 156 (January 2008) and 400 (December 2011); the highest single site count was 180 on the Exe Estuary in January 2009 (*DBRs*).

Away from the Taw/Torridge Estuary, Westward Ho! and Downend, the maps show that Turnstones are scarce along the north coast, though this might partly reflect difficulty of access for observers.

Adults begin to return from the breeding grounds in July, with substantial arrivals of adults and juveniles by August–September; for example, 175 on the Exe Estuary in August 2010 and 113 on the Taw/Torridge Estuary in September 2011 (*DBRs*). At least some of these probably passed on and wintered further south (the August WeBS total was often higher than that for September); others probably overwintered.

During most Atlas years there was little evidence of spring passage influxes after the departure of wintering birds by the end of April.

*Text: Tim Jones & Tim Davis / Photo: Steve Hatch*

Balmer *et al.* 2013: 288; Sitters 1988: not treated; Tyler 2010: 311

### *Breeding-period abundance 2007–13*

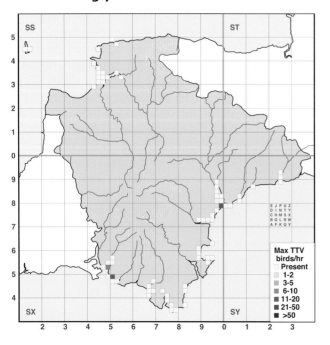

### *Winter-period abundance 2007–13*

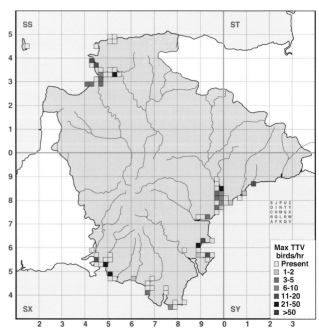

# Knot
*Calidris canutus*

IN DEVON, Knots are mainly winter visitors in modest numbers to just two estuaries, the Exe and the Taw/Torridge. They also occur in smaller numbers on most of Devon's other estuaries in winter and on passage.

The map for March–September includes some wintering birds, which may not leave until April or May, together with northbound passage migrants from elsewhere. Generally, the last adults leave in the first week of June and the first to return arrive in late July; there are very few records between these dates. The map for the October–February period relates largely to Devon's wintering population since most autumn migrants have passed through before then, mainly in August–September.

Between 2007 and 2013, peak winter numbers on the Exe fluctuated between 176 and 350 and on the Taw/Torridge between 67 and 164. Much of this variation can probably be explained by different numbers of juveniles arising from annual fluctuation in breeding success.

The Knots that occur in Devon belong to the subspecies *C. c. islandica* which breeds in north-east Canada and Greenland and winters in north-west Europe (Sitters & Tomkovich 2010). The *islandica* population has been estimated at about 450,000 individuals, of which 320,000 winter in the British Isles (over half on The Wash). Those that occur in Devon are therefore only a tiny proportion.

*Text: Humphrey Sitters / Photo: Gary Thoburn*

Balmer *et al.* 2013: 354; Sitters 1988: not treated; Tyler 2010: 261

### Breeding-period abundance 2007–13

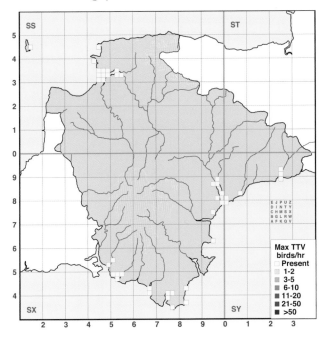

### Winter-period abundance 2007–13

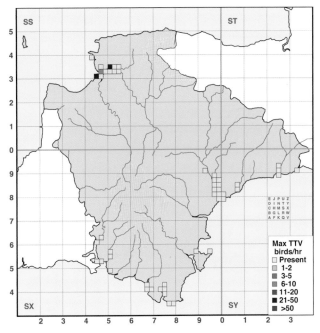

# Ruff

*Calidris pugnax*

**Red listed**

RUFF ARE primarily scarce passage migrants in Devon, though small numbers also occur in most winters. Tyler (2010) charts the species' changing fortunes in the county, with a significant increase in the mid 20th century followed by a decline, especially in wintering numbers. Given the tiny size of the UK breeding population (*Bird Atlas 2007–11*), the vast majority of Ruff occurring in the county are continental breeding birds moving to and from mainly sub-Saharan wintering grounds (Wernham *et al.* 2002).

Most Atlas records were from the Avon, Axe, Exe and Taw/Torridge Estuaries, with only scattered occurrences elsewhere. The *Devon Bird Reports* for the Atlas years show that the total number of Ruff present at any one site only reached double figures on three occasions: ten on the Exe Estuary in September 2008, 14 on the Axe Estuary in January 2010 and ten on the Axe in February 2012.

All of the Atlas breeding-period records can be safely attributed to late-staying wintering individuals and/or spring and autumn passage migrants. Northbound migrants occur well into May, while the first returning failed breeders can arrive as early as June, with juveniles passing through from late summer. Similarly, at least some of the winter-period records are likely to relate to migrants still passing south in October. Ruff are generally very scarce in midwinter, though hard-weather influxes can occur. Most WeBS county totals for December to February during the Atlas years were in the range one to four birds. The higher counts mentioned above were probably associated with cold spells, when birds moved to comparatively mild coastal areas from frozen inland and continental wintering sites (*Bird Atlas 2007–11*).

*Text: Tim Jones & Tim Davis / Photo: Rob Jutsum*

Balmer *et al.* 2013: 362; Sitters 1988: not treated; Tyler 2010: 279

### Breeding-period abundance 2007–13

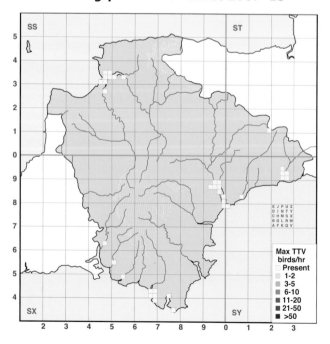

### Winter-period abundance 2007–13

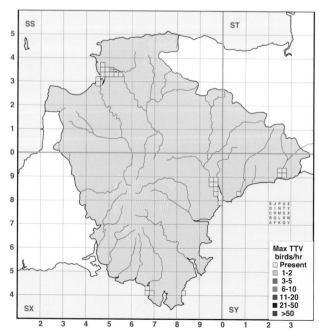

# Curlew Sandpiper
*Calidris ferruginea*
Amber listed

CURLEW SANDPIPERS occur on Devon marshes and estuaries mainly as scarce passage migrants in autumn. Spring records are sparse and winter records are no more than occasional.

The summer-period records, whilst including those that probably relate to northbound migrants in spring – such as one on the Taw/Torridge Estuary on 10 April 2010, one at Bowling Green Marsh on 3 and 5 May 2011, one on Dawlish Warren on 5 May 2012, one on Exminster Marshes on 9 May 2012 and one on the Axe Estuary on 23 May 2012 – also include September migrants which are recorded from all of the major Devon estuaries. Three July records are also likely to be of adults returning early from the breeding grounds: two at Bowling Green Marsh on 31 July 2008, one at South Huish in July 2010 and three at Dawlish Warren on 25/26 July 2012.

The winter records relate to a probable late southbound juvenile at Bowling Green Marsh on 18 November, and single wandering wintering birds on the Taw/Torridge Estuary in November and December 2011, on the Plym Estuary on 12 February 2012 and at Slapton Ley on 27 December 2012.

Many more Curlew Sandpipers occur in Devon in autumn than at any other time of year, with peak numbers in September. Most are juveniles and numbers fluctuate depending on the success of the breeding season. During the Atlas years the aggregate of September records varied from a low of eight in 2012 to a maximum of 49 in 2010.

*Text: Humphrey Sitters / Photo: Roy Churchill*

Balmer *et al.* 2013: 359; Sitters 1988: not treated; Tyler 2010: 271

### Breeding-period abundance 2007–13

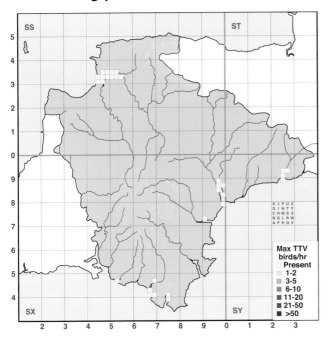

### Winter-period abundance 2007–13

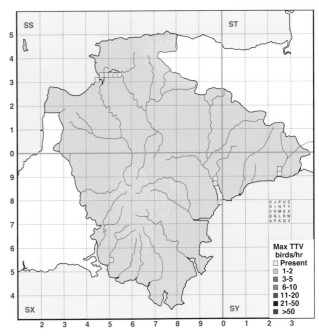

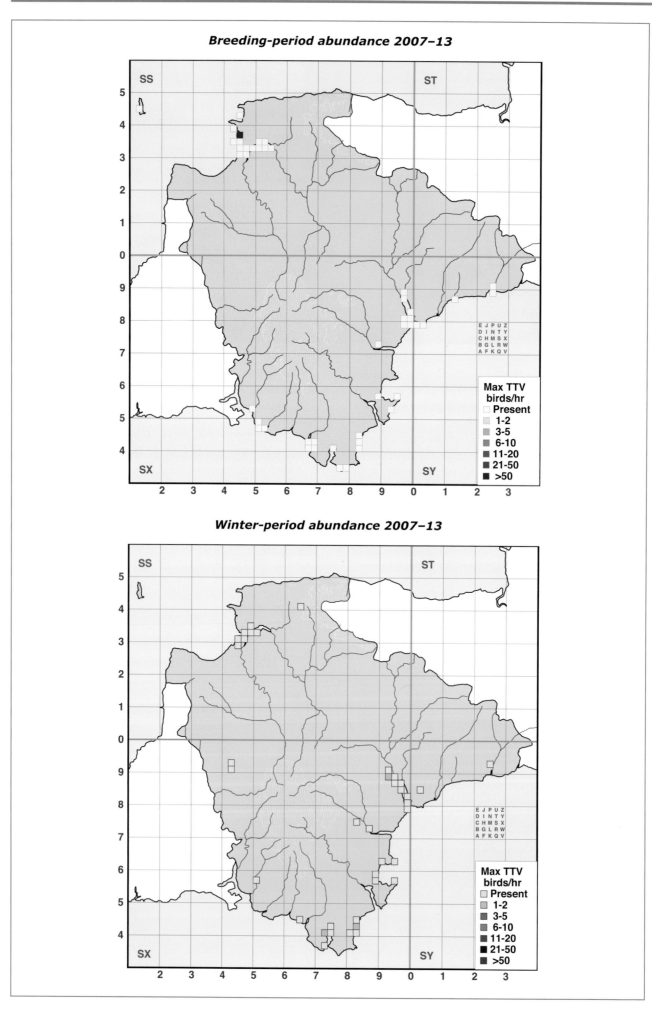

**Breeding-period abundance 2007–13**

**Winter-period abundance 2007–13**

# Sanderling
*Calidris alba*

THE SANDERLING's affinity for sandy beaches goes a long way to explaining the distributions shown in the maps; especially the focus on Saunton Sands and the Taw/Torridge Estuary and to a lesser extent the Exe Estuary and Thurlestone Bay. They are most common as passage migrants in spring and autumn, also occurring in winter, albeit in lower numbers.

The summer map is mainly a reflection of the distribution of Sanderlings on passage in April, May and July to September when most are to be found at Saunton Sands, the Taw/Torridge Estuary and the Exe Estuary. Smaller numbers also occur on passage at a wide variety of other coastal sites, though at some of them, such as Prawle Point and Thurlestone Bay, much larger numbers are occasionally recorded.

The winter map indicates that the main wintering area is Saunton Sands and the Taw/Torridge Estuary, with only small numbers elsewhere.

Although Sanderlings can be found both on passage and in winter in the Saunton Sands and Taw/Torridge Estuary area and on the Exe Estuary, their patterns of occurrence in these places are quite different (see figure). The Exe supports only 20–30 in winter, but large numbers occur in May and early June (e.g. 180 on 8 June 2010). Smaller numbers are recorded on the Exe during southbound migration, but very few after September. In contrast, the Saunton and Taw/Torridge area has a larger wintering population and much more prolonged spring (February–May) and autumn (July–November) passage. The differences in the patterns of southward migration suggest that the Exe is used mainly by adults and that a higher proportion of juveniles, which migrate later, use the North Devon sites.

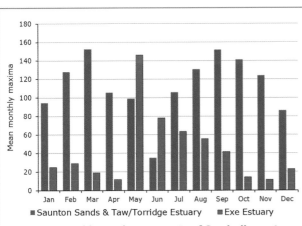

**Mean monthly maximum counts of Sanderlings at Saunton Sands and on the nearby Taw/Torridge Estuary, and on the Exe Estuary during 2008–2012. Source: *DBRs*.**

*Text: Humphrey Sitters*
*Photos: Robert Jutsum & (inset) Lee Collins*
*Sanderling sponsored by Robert Jutsum*

Balmer *et al.* 2013: 356; Sitters 1988: not treated; Tyler 2010: 263

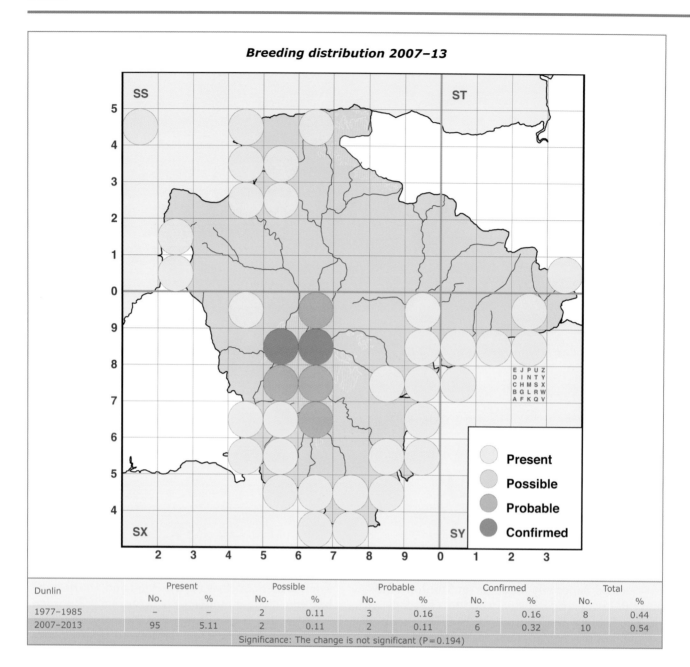

### Breeding distribution 2007–13

| Dunlin | Present | | Possible | | Probable | | Confirmed | | Total | |
|---|---|---|---|---|---|---|---|---|---|---|
| | No. | % | No. | % | No. | % | No. | % | No. | % |
| 1977–1985 | – | – | 2 | 0.11 | 3 | 0.16 | 3 | 0.16 | 8 | 0.44 |
| 2007–2013 | 95 | 5.11 | 2 | 0.11 | 2 | 0.11 | 6 | 0.32 | 10 | 0.54 |
| Significance: The change is not significant (P=0.194) | | | | | | | | | | |

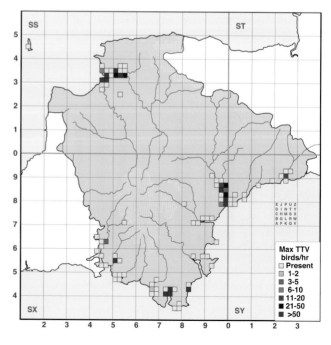

### Breeding distribution 1977–85

### Winter-period abundance 2007–13

# Dunlin

*Calidris alpina*

Amber listed

DUNLIN CAN be seen every month of the year feeding on or around Devon's coasts and estuaries, particularly the Exe Estuary where 3,000–4,000 can occur in the winter months, with a maximum during the Atlas period of 4,885 in December 2010 (*DBR*). Good numbers can also be found wintering on the Taw/Torridge, Plym, Tamar and Kingsbridge Estuaries. The total Devon wintering population often exceeds 5,000 and peaks in the period November–February. December 2010 also saw the WeBS county total peak at 7,333, no doubt a consequence of hard-weather movements given the conditions prevailing at the time. However, numbers wintering in the UK are in long-term decline, falling by more than a quarter between the winters of 1987/88 and 2012/13 (Holt *et al.* 2015).

Devon's wintering Dunlins belong mostly to the subspecies *Calidris alpina alpina*, which breeds in northern Scandinavia and north-west Russia (Delany *et al.* 2009) and may be joined by some *C. a. schinzii*. Numbers fluctuate considerably during spring passage, which peaks in April/May, when migrants of three subspecies (*alpina*, *schinzii* and *arctica*) move north from their wintering grounds through Britain to northern breeding grounds as far afield as Greenland and western Siberia, depending on the subspecies involved. Autumn passage begins from mid-July and continues into October with occasional late birds in November such as those in 2008 on Lundy and in the Yealm Estuary.

Devon has a small breeding population restricted to the highest areas of blanket bog on northern Dartmoor – the most southerly breeding location for Dunlin in the world. These are birds of the subspecies *C. a. schinzii* that also breeds in northern Britain, southern Scandinavia, the Baltic, the Faeroes and Iceland. British breeders are thought to winter mainly in north-west Africa (Delany *et al.* 2009). Nesting on Dartmoor was first reported in 1837 (Moore 1969) and the breeding population has been subject to targeted fieldwork since 1956 when the first nest with eggs was found (Moore 1969). The *Devon Tetrad Atlas 1977–85* estimated 10–12 territories in eight tetrads. The current survey found breeding evidence in ten tetrads (within eight of which breeding was confirmed or probable). Both numbers and distribution were similar to those in 1977–85.

The future of Devon's breeding Dunlin population is looking good, in the short term, with all indications of a stable population that is breeding successfully each year. However, disturbance of breeding areas needs to be minimized and the effects of any predation of nests or young are unknown. The biggest challenge in the longer term may come from the impacts of climate change, which are likely to be significant for a species at the southernmost fringe of its breeding range.

*Text: Jon Avon*
*Photos: Neil Bygrave & (inset) Dave Scott*
*Dunlin sponsored by Sue Foster*

Balmer *et al.* 2013: 360; Sitters 1988: 100; Tyler 2010: 274

# Purple Sandpiper

*Charadrius maritima*

Purple Sandpipers are mostly uncommon winter visitors to the rocky coasts of Devon. The breeding origin of the birds that winter in Devon is not known, but they must undergo wing- and tail-feather moult, which lasts approximately two months, before arriving here as most do not appear until November.

Numbers of Purple Sandpipers in Devon increase from November to January and then remain fairly constant at 50–60 until declining in May. Throughout this period small groups can be found scattered along rocky stretches of both coasts. However, only three areas regularly support more than ten birds: Torbay, Prawle and Sidmouth.

Because the presence of the whole Devon wintering population of Purple Sandpipers straddles the Atlas winter and summer periods, the general patterns of distribution shown by the two maps are quite similar, though the species was recorded in twice as many tetrads in October to February than in March to September. The reason for this difference is likely to be that as the birds are present for the whole four months of the winter period, they are more likely to be recorded and in a greater number of tetrads than during the short period – a month or so – that they are present during the early part of the summer period. The absence of records along some of Devon's rocky shorelines, such as the north-west coast around Hartland Point, might be the result of under-recording due to difficulty of access.

*Text: Humphrey Sitters / Photo: Dave Norman*
*Purple Sandpiper sponsored by Opticron*

Balmer *et al.* 2013: 358; Sitters 1988: not treated; Tyler 2010: 273

### Breeding-period abundance 2007–13

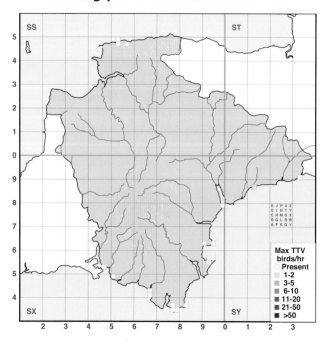

### Winter-period abundance 2007–13

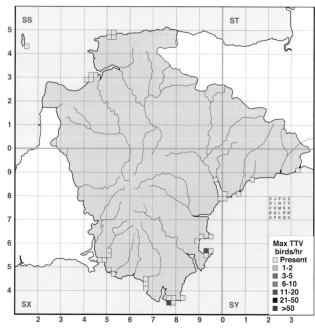

# Little Stint
## *Calidris minuta*

Little Stints are uncommon passage migrants to marshes and estuaries in Devon. They occur mainly in autumn; there are a few records for the spring but hardly any for winter.

The Atlas records include four adults in May and June at Dawlish Warren, Black Hole Marsh and the Yealm Estuary that probably relate to northbound migrants. A single bird, possibly the same individual, was seen during November 2007 and January 2008 on or near the Taw/Torridge Estuary, and another at Bowling Green Marsh on 8 November 2008. The latter may have been a late migrant rather than a wintering bird.

Little Stints occur in greater numbers and with greater regularity during southward migration in autumn. The majority of these are probably juveniles whose numbers vary from year to year depending on the success of the breeding season. Devon records suggest that 2008 and 2010 were probably successful years, with September counts of 22 and 16 respectively, but in the other Atlas years there were only between six and ten (*DBRs*).

*Text: Humphrey Sitters / Photo: Gary Thoburn*

Balmer *et al.* 2013: 355; Sitters 1988: not treated; Tyler 2010: 265

### Breeding-period abundance 2007–13

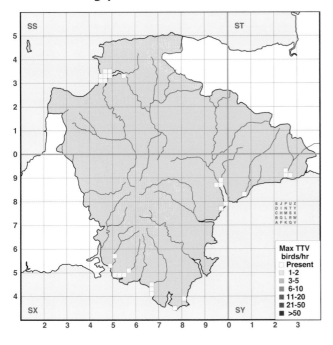

### Winter-period abundance 2007–13

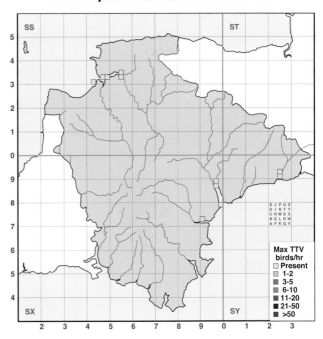

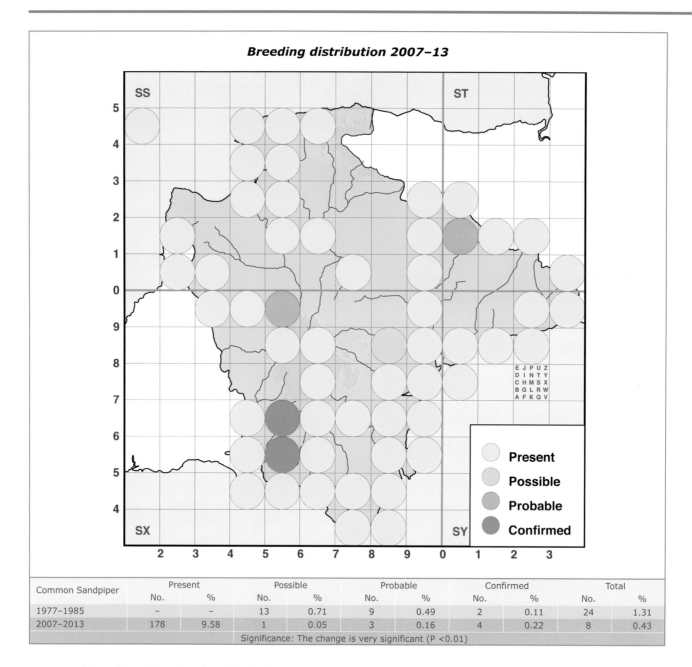

**Breeding distribution 2007–13**

| Common Sandpiper | Present | | Possible | | Probable | | Confirmed | | Total | |
|---|---|---|---|---|---|---|---|---|---|---|
| | No. | % | No. | % | No. | % | No. | % | No. | % |
| 1977–1985 | – | – | 13 | 0.71 | 9 | 0.49 | 2 | 0.11 | 24 | 1.31 |
| 2007–2013 | 178 | 9.58 | 1 | 0.05 | 3 | 0.16 | 4 | 0.22 | 8 | 0.43 |
| | Significance: The change is very significant (P <0.01) | | | | | | | | | |

**Breeding distribution 1977–85**

**Winter-period abundance 2007–13**

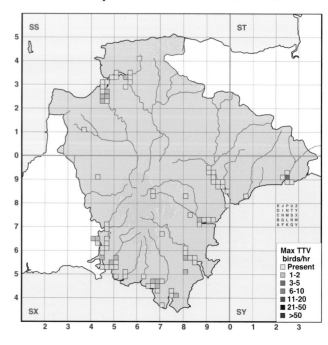

Max TTV
birds/hr
□ Present
□ 1-2
▨ 3-5
▩ 6-10
■ 11-20
■ 21-50
■ >50

# Common Sandpiper

*Actitis hypoleucos*

COMMON SANDPIPERS are frequently seen whilst on passage on lakes and estuaries in spring and autumn, when their stiff-winged flight low over the water and shrill call attract attention. Nationally they breed on the edges of streams and rivers, lakes and reservoirs, but in Devon their nesting sites are quite often on disused china clay pits and associated ponds. Passage birds in May and from late June onwards probably account for many of the 'present' registrations.

In the current Atlas, all four confirmed breeding records, plus one probable, were from two 10-km squares on the south-west edge of Dartmoor: SX55 and SX56. One probable breeding record came from north Dartmoor (SX59), where breeding had been confirmed in the *Devon Tetrad Atlas 1977–85*. There was also one probable breeding record in north-east Devon (ST01), but many, if not all, of the 'present' and 'possible' records are likely to have been passage birds. From the Exe eastwards there were six probable and five possible breeding records during 1977–85, but only one possible in 2007–13. During the national *Breeding Atlas 1988-91*, breeding was confirmed for six 10-km squares. BBS results have shown a long-term decline of 31% since 1995, reflecting a 20% contraction of breeding range in Britain and Ireland since the *Breeding Atlas 1968–72*.

Winter records originated from twenty-four 10-km squares, three more than in the *Winter Atlas 1981–84*, reflecting a 33% expansion of the wintering range nationally since that time. The majority of records came from coastal and estuarine sites, with very few for inland sites. WeBS counts between November and February 2007–13 showed a total county population of between 12 and 19 birds; a substantial proportion of the UK wintering population estimated at a modest 73 birds (*Bird Atlas 2007–11*).

*Text: A W G John / Photo: Tim White*

Balmer *et al.* 2013: 378; Sitters 1988: 110; Tyler 2010: 298

# Green Sandpiper

*Tringa ochropus*

Amber listed

STUMBLING ON a Green Sandpiper – perhaps flushed from a wet ditch, the bird's startlingly white rump contrasting with dark wings, and its urgent high-pitched call gradually fading into the distance – is always an exciting moment. However, this is a relatively scarce and thinly distributed species in Devon, particularly away from a handful of key sites.

Green Sandpipers do not breed in Devon, or indeed anywhere in England or Wales, with only a handful of pairs nesting occasionally in northern Scotland (*Bird Atlas 2007–11*). They occur here as winter visitors and, more commonly, as passage migrants, mainly in late summer and early autumn, when birds move south-west from Fennoscandian and Russian breeding grounds to wintering areas across a broad swathe of western Europe, the Mediterranean and Africa (Wernham *et al.* 2002).

During the winter-period TTVs, Green Sandpipers were recorded in 84 tetrads in thirty 10-km squares. Most were around the Avon, Axe, Exe and Taw/Torridge Estuaries, where freshwater marshes and grazing meadows dissected by drainage ditches provide suitable habitat. During the midwinter period (December to February) the maximum county WeBS totals for the Atlas years were all in the range four to eight birds, with the exception of 11 in February 2009 (*DBRs*), with the highest count for a

single site being eight on the Exe Estuary (including the Exe Valley River Park and Matford) in the same month. The *Winter Atlas 1981–84* shows occupancy in far fewer tetrads than the current Atlas. While the former survey was of shorter duration, it seems likely that a genuine expansion in range and numbers has occurred.

The summer-period map undoubtedly captures a fair number of wintering birds (Wernham *et al.* (2002) indicated that departures from one well-studied UK wintering site do not peak until mid-April), as well as a small number of spring migrants. However the wider scatter of occupied tetrads, especially inland, is likely to reflect the occurrence of return-passage migrants between June and September. During the Atlas years, WeBS county totals all peaked in August (except in 2011, when the highest total was in September), with maxima varying between 11 in August 2008 and 22 in August 2009. The highest count for an individual site was 21 in the South Huish area, just to the south of the Avon Estuary, in August 2010 (*DBRs*).

*Text: Tim Jones & Tim Davis / Photo: Charlie Fleming*
*Green Sandpiper sponsored by Jonathan Aylett*

Balmer *et al.* 2013: 380; Sitters 1988: not treated; Tyler 2010: 301

### Breeding-period abundance 2007–13

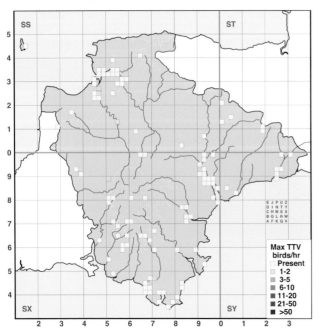

### Winter-period abundance 2007–13

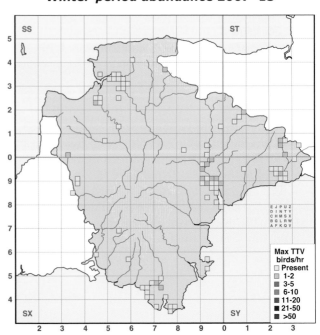

# Spotted Redshank
## Tringa erythropus

SMALL NUMBERS of this scarce passage migrant and winter visitor were recorded annually during the Atlas period. The Exe, Tamar and Taw/Torridge Estuaries regularly held one to five birds between August and March; and occasional singles visited the Axe and Kingsbridge Estuaries. Single spring passage migrants visited south coast freshwater marshes at South Huish and Thurlestone in April–May of some years and a passage bird was on the Yealm Estuary in August 2008. Unusually, single migrants were noted on Lundy and passing Start Point in autumn.

*Text: Peter Dare / Photo: Chris Proctor*

Balmer *et al.* 2013: 382; Sitters 1988: not treated; Tyler 2010: 302

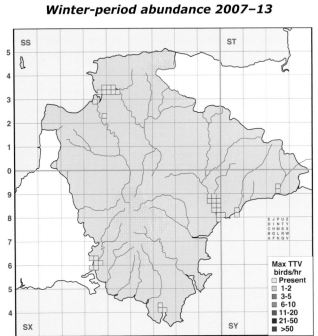

**Winter-period abundance 2007–13**

Max TTV birds/hr
☐ Present
☐ 1-2
■ 3-5
■ 6-10
■ 11-20
■ 21-50
■ >50

---

# Wood Sandpiper
## Tringa glareola

SOME 15–25 autumn passage migrants were reported annually during the Atlas years from coastal freshwater pools and marshes in both the south and north of the county, but especially from the Axe and Exe Estuaries during late June–September when up to six or seven birds occurred together. Occasional birds visited wetlands by the Otter and Taw/Torridge Estuaries, and at Aveton Gifford, Thurlestone and South Huish. There were five inland records, of one to three birds, including singles on Dartmoor (Smallhanger), at Bishops Tawton and Blackhill quarry pool, and three together at Tamar Lakes. Four spring records (involving five individuals) during April and May came from the Taw/Torridge Estuary (Sherpa Marsh), South Huish, Thurlestone and the Avon Estuary.

*Text: Peter Dare*

Balmer *et al.* 2013: 383; Sitters 1988: not treated; Tyler 2010: 307

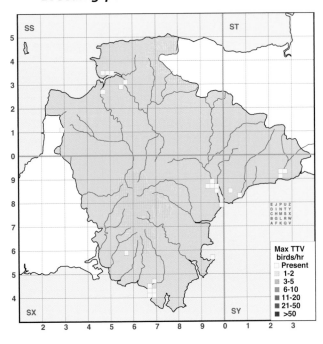

**Breeding-period abundance 2007–13**

Max TTV birds/hr
☐ Present
☐ 1-2
■ 3-5
■ 6-10
■ 11-20
■ 21-50
■ >50

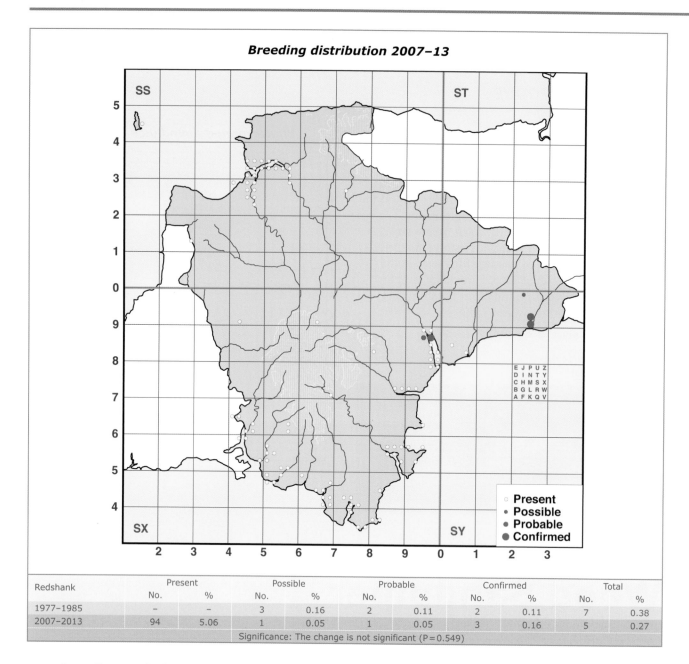

## Breeding distribution 2007–13

Present
Possible
Probable
Confirmed

| Redshank | Present | | Possible | | Probable | | Confirmed | | Total | |
|---|---|---|---|---|---|---|---|---|---|---|
| | No. | % | No. | % | No. | % | No. | % | No. | % |
| 1977–1985 | – | – | 3 | 0.16 | 2 | 0.11 | 2 | 0.11 | 7 | 0.38 |
| 2007–2013 | 94 | 5.06 | 1 | 0.05 | 1 | 0.05 | 3 | 0.16 | 5 | 0.27 |
| Significance: The change is not significant (P=0.549) | | | | | | | | | | |

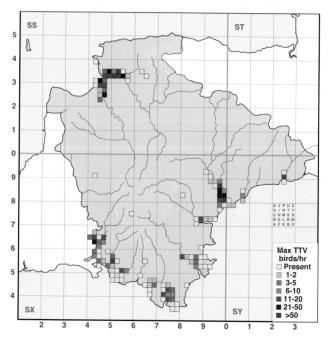

## Breeding-period abundance 2007–13

## Winter-period abundance 2007–13

Max TTV
birds/hr
Present
1-2
3-5
6-10
11-20
21-50
>50

# Redshank
*Tringa totanus*

REDSHANK WINTERING in Devon comprise breeding birds from Britain, Iceland and continental Europe (Tyler 2010) and are found mainly on estuaries, where they probe mud and shallow water for invertebrates. They also occur inland and on the open coast in small numbers, but perhaps more often on passage. The main breeding habitats are damp marshland and grassy fields, often associated with estuaries.

Redshank is a very scarce breeder in Devon (usually fewer than ten pairs annually), but is much more abundant and widespread in winter, with an estimated county population peaking in most years at just over 1,300. November 2009 saw the maximum county total during the Atlas period with an unusually high 1,640 birds recorded in the WeBS count. Post-breeding adults and juveniles begin to arrive on estuaries in late June and leave in March, although there may be sparse passage in other months and probably continued movement within this period.

Redshanks have bred in Devon – one of the few wader species to do so – since at least 1908, though not consistently, and nesting is now almost entirely restricted to the marshes of the Axe and Exe Estuaries, the only sites where breeding evidence was recorded during the current Atlas period (confirmed in three tetrads, probable in one and possible in another – an inland tetrad in the catchment of the Axe). The equivalent figures for the *Devon Tetrad Atlas 1977–85* were two, two and two (also including one 'possible breeding' tetrad inland). So, effectively there has been no change between the two survey periods, against a national contraction, shown in *Bird Atlas 2007–11*, of breeding range in Britain of 44% (mostly since 1988–91) and of population size by 39% during 1995–2010 (Risely *et al.* 2012). Although present in 68 tetrads elsewhere on the breeding-period map, these records would

have comprised passage, non-breeding and early returning birds.

Redshanks are recorded on all the main estuaries in winter, but over 50 were recorded only on the Taw/Torridge, Axe, Exe and Plym Estuaries. The effective restriction to estuaries explains their occurrence in only 124 tetrads (6.7%). Data from *Devon Bird Reports* show that, compared to the early 1980s, overall numbers have decreased by about 23%, reflected by decreases in peak counts at most sites, although there have been increases on the Axe, Plym and Yealm (see table).

*Text: Peter Reay / Photo: Charlie Fleming*
*Redshank sponsored by Seaton Visitor Centre Trust*

Balmer *et al.* 2013: 386; Sitters 1988: 108; Tyler 2010: 308

| Mean peak winter counts for 2008/09–2012/13 and 1982/83–1984/85 for Devon estuaries. Source: DBRs. (The Tamar Complex is excluded because of lack of comparable data for the two time-periods.) | | | |
|---|---|---|---|
| Estuary | 1982/3–1984/5 | 2008/9–2012/13 | Change |
| Exe | 664 | 450 | down |
| Taw/Torridge | 530 | 379 | down |
| Kingsbridge | 196 | 209 | steady |
| Plym | 92 | 179 | up |
| Teign | 88 | 62 | down |
| Axe | 34 | 60 | up |
| Yealm | 30 | 54 | up |
| Dart | 74 | 39 | down |
| Tavy | 80 | 25 | down |
| Avon | 48 | 6 | down |
| Otter | 9 | 6 | steady |
| Erme | 27 | 2 | down |
| County total | 1,496 | 1,158 | down |

# Greenshank
## *Tringa nebularia*
### Amber listed

GREENSHANKS IN Devon are uncommon passage migrants and winter visitors. This elegant pale greenish-grey wader with its unmistakeable '*tew-tew-tew*' call brightens any visit to the coast, especially in winter.

Five Devon estuaries hold nationally important numbers: the Exe, Kingsbridge, Tamar Complex, Taw/Torridge and Yealm. Peak counts of more than 50 occur in most years on the Exe Estuary in August/September, and counts of over 20 occur regularly between July and October on the others. Since 2007, the WeBS county total has peaked in August or September, usually between 130 and 166 (*DBRs*). The scarce inland records are also mainly in August or September.

During the Atlas years, Greenshanks were recorded in 80 tetrads in the winter period and 84 in the summer period (the latter including passage migrants and late-departing wintering birds) with virtually all of the records at coastal or estuarine sites; in the *Winter Atlas 1981–84* they were present in fifteen 10-km squares, compared to 30 for the current Atlas. Monthly WeBS county totals from November to February 2007–13 averaged 66. Numbers wintering in Britain have increased over the last three decades due to milder winters (Maclean *et al.* 2008). Wintering numbers (November–February) on the Exe and Kingsbridge Estuaries and the Tamar Complex showed an increase over the two decades 1989–1998 and 1999–2008, whereas they declined

over the same period on the Taw/Torridge (Tyler 2010). Smaller numbers winter on the Teign, Plym and Avon Estuaries, and occasionally elsewhere.

There is some circumstantial evidence that individuals wintering in Devon are from the Scottish breeding population; birds leave Devon in late March and arrive on the Scottish breeding grounds in early April (*Winter Atlas 1981–84*).

*Text: A W G John / Photo: Neil Bygrave*
*Greenshank sponsored by Colin & Glenys Smith*

Balmer *et al.* 2013: 384; Sitters 1988: not treated; Tyler 2010: 304

### Breeding-period abundance 2007–13

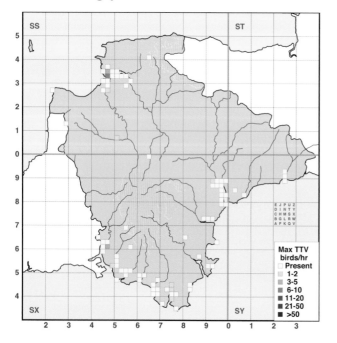

### Winter-period abundance 2007–13

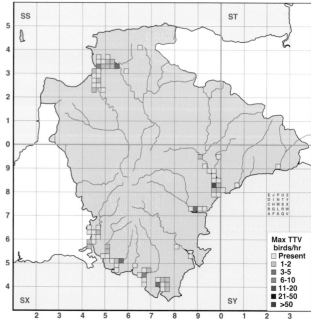

# Jack Snipe
## *Lymnocryptes minimus*

JACK SNIPE may well be one of Devon's most overlooked species. They frequent wet or damp habitats in open country, where access is often limited. Furthermore, they characteristically sit tight until almost trodden on. Their small size, short bill, silence when flushed and habit of dropping back into cover after flying only a short distance contrast markedly with Common Snipe.

Jack Snipe are winter visitors and passage migrants in Devon and are reported annually from wetland habitats, mainly around our coasts and estuaries and on Dartmoor. They arrive from Scandinavian and Russian breeding grounds (Delany *et al.* 2009) from late September onwards and may be present until the end of April, though most records are for December and January. A bird on Dartmoor on 6 September 2011 was exceptionally early, while the latest spring record during the Atlas period was near Braunton on 25 April 2010 (*DBRs*). The breeding-period (March–September) map includes a considerable portion of spring passage as well as early autumn migration, when Jack Snipe pass through Britain to/from wintering grounds that extend through southern and western Europe to north and west Africa (Delany *et al.* 2009).

In good years the total number of Devon records can exceed 20 in a given month; 28 were recorded from widely dispersed locations in January 2010, probably reflecting cold-weather movements given the severe conditions that month. Atlas records came from across the county but particularly Dartmoor and the Exe, Taw/Torridge and Axe Estuaries.

Dartmoor records show a wide scatter but are strongly associated with suitable wetland habitats, especially mire systems. Inland records away from Dartmoor were limited to a handful of tetrads.

*Text: Jon Avon / Photo: David Land*
*Jack Snipe sponsored by Ian Teague*

Balmer *et al.* 2013: 364; Sitters 1988: not treated; Tyler 2010: 280

### Breeding-period abundance 2007–13

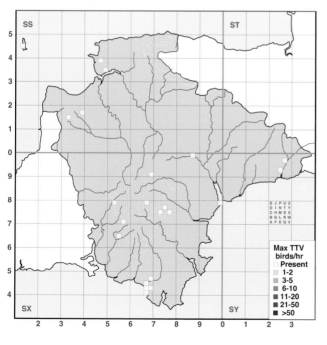

### Winter-period abundance 2007–13

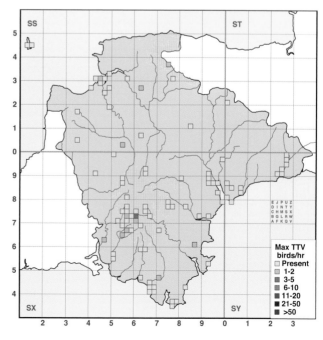

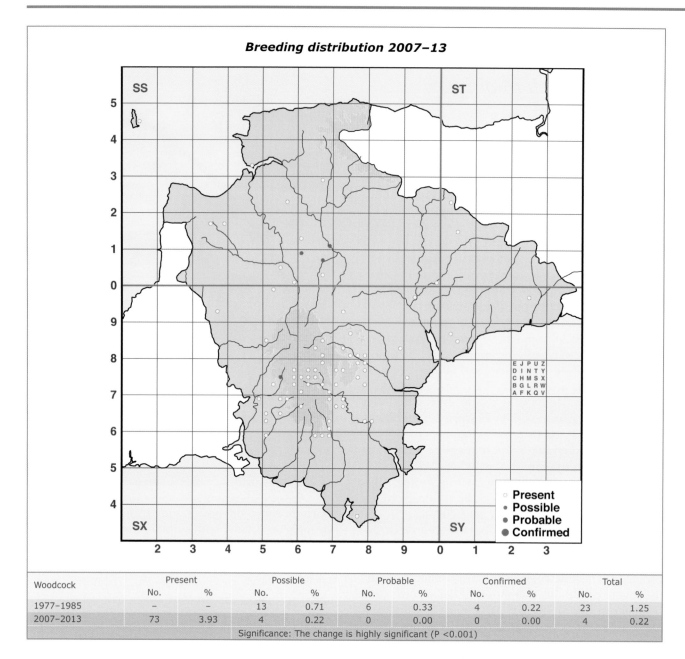

**Breeding distribution 2007–13**

| Woodcock | Present | | Possible | | Probable | | Confirmed | | Total | |
|---|---|---|---|---|---|---|---|---|---|---|
| | No. | % | No. | % | No. | % | No. | % | No. | % |
| 1977–1985 | – | – | 13 | 0.71 | 6 | 0.33 | 4 | 0.22 | 23 | 1.25 |
| 2007–2013 | 73 | 3.93 | 4 | 0.22 | 0 | 0.00 | 0 | 0.00 | 4 | 0.22 |
| Significance: The change is highly significant (P <0.001) | | | | | | | | | | |

**Breeding distribution 1977–85**

**Breeding-period abundance 2007–13**

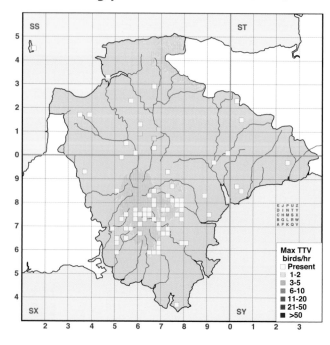

# Woodcock
*Scolopax rusticola*

**Red listed**

OFTEN SEEN as a fleeting glimpse as it twists away through woodland, or overhead at dusk during a roding flight, the Woodcock is abundant in Devon in winter, but an extremely scarce breeder in summer.

In 2007–13, Woodcocks were recorded as possibly breeding in four tetrads, three in a 'cluster' around Winkleigh (in SS60E, SS60T and SS61V) and one near Princetown in SX57M; they were also 'present' in a further 17 tetrads. There were no records of probable or confirmed breeding. In sharp contrast, the *Devon Tetrad Atlas 1977–85* recorded Woodcock in 23 tetrads, including four instances of confirmed breeding, six probable and 13 possible. Between the

*Breeding Atlas 1968–72* and *Bird Atlas 2007–11* there was a 50% decline in the breeding range nationally, and this is reflected in the current Devon picture. The decline may be due to several possible factors, including disturbance (perhaps especially from dogs), drying out of woodlands, overgrazing by deer and declining woodland management (Fuller *et al.* 2005). Sitters (1988) stated that "…during the 1930s Woodcock bred more frequently in Devon than they do today"; they also bred regularly in the 1970s at Venn Ottery and Aylesbeare Commons.

There is a large influx of birds from the continent in autumn, and during harsh winter weather numbers increase further; for instance, BirdTrack reporting rates for Woodcock were two to three times higher in the severe winters of 2009/10 and 2010/11. The winter-period map shows that Woodcock are widespread throughout Devon at this time of year, but with a marked concentration around Dartmoor. Ringing and the use of satellite-tags has shown that wintering birds originate from Scandinavia, the Baltic States and Russia (Hoodless & Powell 2010). Numbers shot annually in the UK, estimated at 200,000 (Wilson 1986), have increased considerably since 1945. However, Woodcock are grossly under-recorded by birdwatchers in winter. Some idea of the numbers present is shown by the fact that over 30 may be found at some sites during winter shoots, especially in cold weather. In 1989 at Tavistock Woodlands around 100 were recorded in both winter periods (*DBR*).

*Text: A W G John / Photo: Ernie Janes/NPL*
*Woodcock sponsored by Hilary Thomas*

Balmer *et al.* 2013: 368; Sitters 1988: 104; Tyler 2010: 287

### Winter-period abundance 2007–13

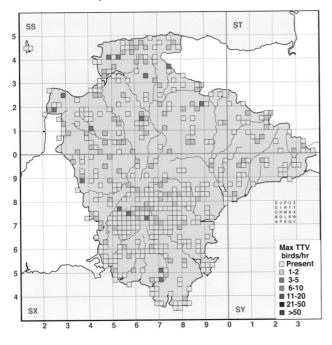

Max TTV birds/hr
- ☐ Present
- 1-2
- 3-5
- 6-10
- 11-20
- 21-50
- >50

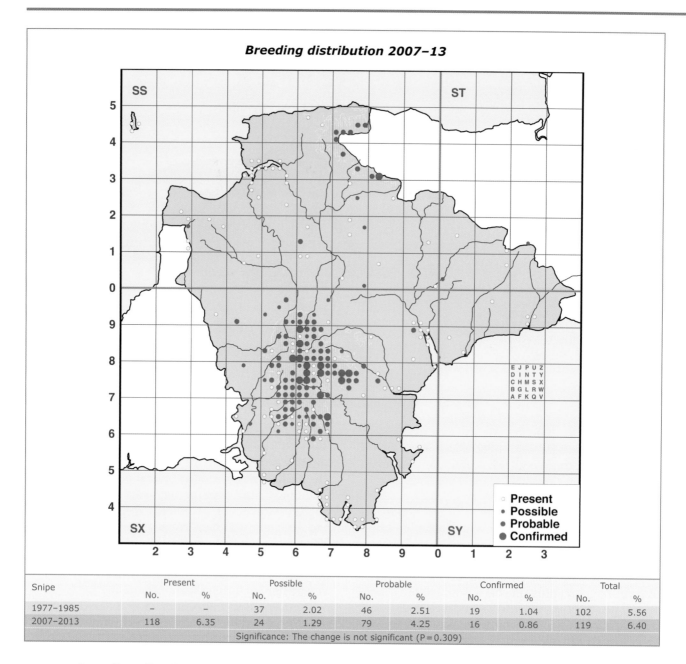

**Breeding distribution 2007–13**

| Snipe | Present | | Possible | | Probable | | Confirmed | | Total | |
|---|---|---|---|---|---|---|---|---|---|---|
| | No. | % | No. | % | No. | % | No. | % | No. | % |
| 1977–1985 | – | – | 37 | 2.02 | 46 | 2.51 | 19 | 1.04 | 102 | 5.56 |
| 2007–2013 | 118 | 6.35 | 24 | 1.29 | 79 | 4.25 | 16 | 0.86 | 119 | 6.40 |
| Significance: The change is not significant (P=0.309) | | | | | | | | | | |

**Breeding distribution 1977–85**

**Breeding-period abundance 2007–13**

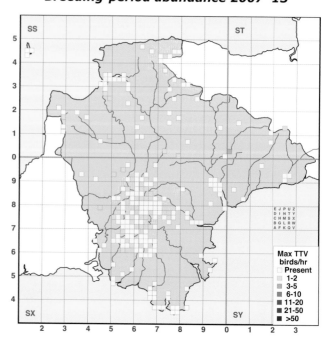

# Snipe
## Gallinago gallinago
Amber listed

$S$NIPE ARE found in a wide range of wetland habitats from estuaries and coastal marshes to the highest points of Dartmoor. They can be seen throughout the year but the population is highest during the autumn and winter. Large numbers of winter migrants arrive from September, with numbers peaking from mid-October until mid-February although migrants may be present or passing through until mid-April (*DBRs*). Snipe can be elusive and the majority of records are of birds accidentally flushed. It is therefore likely that Snipe numbers are consistently underestimated. Moreover, breeding is difficult to prove, with only a few confirmed records annually.

Devon's breeding birds arrive on their territories from mid-March to late April, and nesting occurs from mid-April until late June, after which they vacate the breeding grounds until the following spring. Snipe records on Dartmoor are at their fewest during July and August. It is striking that confirmed breeding during the Atlas period occurred only on the high ground of Dartmoor and Exmoor and this lack of lowland breeding records is a distinct change since the *Devon Tetrad Atlas 1977–85*.

The breeding population in Devon has remained relatively stable, although the current survey suggests a slight increase since 1977–85, with evidence in 119 tetrads (6.4%) during 2008–2013, compared with 102 of tetrads (5.6%) in 1977–85. This contrasts with the trend of decline reported in *Bird*

*Atlas 2007–11*. The breeding distribution is similar to that in the *Devon Tetrad Atlas* which, although having declined in East Devon since 1977–85, shows a considerable increase in the number of tetrads on Dartmoor and Exmoor yielding records of probable and confirmed breeding. The increase on Exmoor may be attributed to the Exmoor Mires Project which has restored over 1,000 hectares of previously drained bog over the entire moor (Exmoor Mires Project).

Surveys on Dartmoor over the last 35 years – 1979 (Mudge 1981), 1986 (Robins & Jutsum 1987), 1977–85 (Sitters 1988) and Geary (2000) – have indicated that numbers and distribution fluctuate on the moor, and Smaldon (2005) concluded that the Dartmoor population was "very healthy if not probably increasing". Monitoring of sites in and around the Widecombe Commons showed increases between 2005 and 2013 (pers. obs.).

Wintering birds were widespread throughout the county, being recorded in 608 tetrads (32.7%) but with an almost 100% presence in the Dartmoor tetrads. With the exception of Dartmoor, winter counts are greatest in the Bovey Basin (327 in January 2013), South Huish area (256 in January 2010), Stover CP Lake (150 in March 2009), Axe Estuary (140 in February 2009) and Mansands Leys (100 in December 2011) (*DBRs*).

Snipe look set to continue to be seen within Devon for the foreseeable future.

*Text: Jon Avon / Photo: Neil Bygrave*
*Snipe sponsored by Michelmore Hughes & Jonathan Aylett*

### Winter-period abundance 2007–13

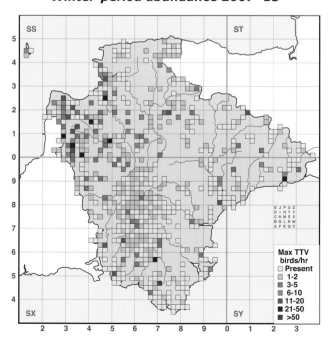

Max TTV birds/hr
☐ Present
☐ 1-2
☐ 3-5
☐ 6-10
■ 11-20
■ 21-50
■ >50

Balmer *et al.* 2013:366; Sitters 1988: 102; Tyler 2010: 282

# Pomarine Skua
## *Stercorarius pomarinus*

POMARINE SKUA is mainly a scarce passage migrant in Devon, though there are occasional winter records. The breeding distribution is circumpolar, but those passing through British waters breed on the Russian tundra, wintering mainly in the Atlantic south of the equator. With their twisted spoon-like tails, 'Poms' are prized seawatchers' birds in spring, sometimes passing watch points in flocks as they fly up the English Channel heading for their Siberian breeding grounds.

Most records of Pomarine Skuas during the Atlas period came during late April through May when birds were moving north, and then from late August through September as they returned south. Summer occurrences are, however, not uncommon and are presumed to be immature birds and non-breeding adults. The March–September map covers all of these periods and shows records from 20 coastal tetrads.

During the spring, Dawlish Bay provided the majority of records while Berry Head produced by far the largest number of sightings in September/ October.

Autumn passage of Pomarine Skuas is often late and protracted and the first juveniles are generally not seen until October. The species is also regularly recorded during the midwinter months, occurring in each of the Atlas years except 2010 (*DBRs*). There has apparently been an increase in shoals of sprats and anchovies off the south coast in winter, and the attendant flocks of seabirds attract both Great and Pomarine Skuas. The winter map (October–February)

mostly reflects late-autumn passage during October and November but midwinter records occurred in ten coastal tetrads. North coast sightings are rare but there were a handful of records from Hartland Point and Lundy between 2009 and 2013 (*DBRs*).

2011 was a record-breaking year for the species in Devon, with 433 birds counted, including an astonishing 88 juveniles off Berry Head on 23 October; the entire Devon total for 2013 was just 79 birds!

*Text: Mike Langman / Photo: Mark Darlaston*

Balmer *et al.* 2013: 391; Sitters 1988: not treated; Tyler 2010: 317

### Breeding-period abundance 2007–13

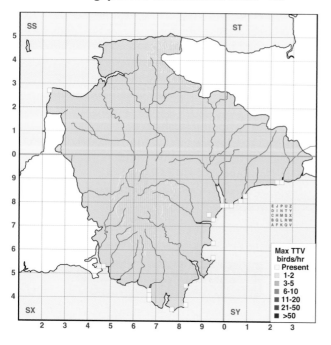

### Winter-period abundance 2007–13

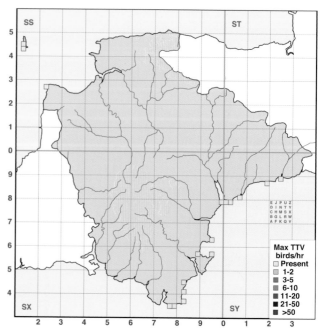

# Arctic Skua

*Stercorarius parasiticus*

**Red listed**

WHILE ARCTIC Skuas are uncommon passage migrants, they are still the most likely skua to be seen in Devon. This aggressive species is fast and agile enough to chase down small gulls and terns, forcing them to regurgitate their last meal or drop any food they are carrying to escape the onslaught.

In Devon the majority of sightings are made during April–May (five-year mean 2008–2012: 8%) and August–November (five-year mean 2008–2012: 86%) but they can occur almost throughout the year, albeit in very small numbers in the winter when most Arctic Skuas are at sea south of the equator.

The March–September map covers the whole of spring migration, from late March through to May, and the first half of autumn passage in August/ September. Arctic Skuas were recorded in 35 coastal tetrads, with the south coast headlands and bays, particularly Berry Head and Dawlish Warren, accounting for most records; there were relatively few sightings along the north coast.

Autumn migration continues into October – when the highest counts of the year are often made, such as the monthly county total of 345 in 2010 (*DBR*) – and regularly extends into November. During this period, Arctic Skuas were recorded in 18 tetrads, all except two in South Devon. Records between December and February are very rare, and confusion with the more regularly wintering Pomarine Skua is a trap for the unwary. During the Atlas period, Arctic Skuas were recorded during these months only in early December 2007 at Prawle Point and Budleigh Salterton (*DBR*).

*Text: Mike Langman / Photo: Mark Darlaston*

Balmer *et al.* 2013: 392; Sitters 1988: not treated; Tyler 2010: 319

## Breeding-period abundance 2007–13

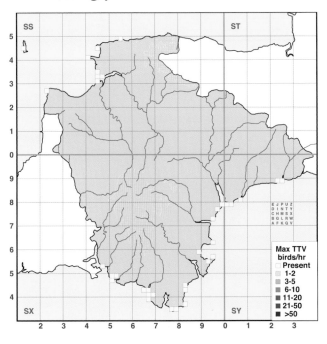

## Winter-period abundance 2007–13

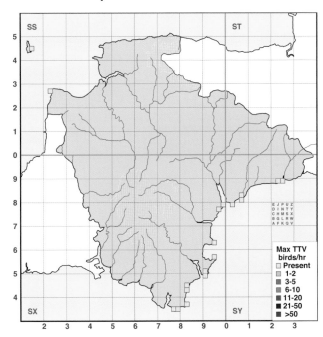

# Long-tailed Skua

*Stercorarius longicaudus*

Long-tailed Skua, the most delicate of the skuas, is a rare passage migrant in Devon, though recorded almost annually. It is the least likely to chase or hunt other seabirds; instead it usually joins seabird flocks picking morsels off the surface in an almost tern-like fashion.

Spring records are very rare and by no means annual, as nearly all Long-tailed Skuas make their way up the west coast of Britain towards their Arctic tundra and Scandinavian mountain breeding grounds during a very short period in May, and rarely venture through the English Channel.

Autumn passage is much more extended, and on a broader front, with many individuals, particularly juveniles, moving through the North Sea into the English Channel before dispersing south into the Atlantic. The breeding-period map (March–September) embraces both spring and early autumn passage, but shows records from just ten coastal tetrads. As with many pelagic birds, weather and food supply dictate the number of birds seen in Devon each year. Strong southerly winds and poor visibility, combined with a good food supply, may result in small numbers of Long-tailed Skuas lingering in Lyme Bay; most notable were about 42 birds seen in late August 2012. Autumn passage continues into October but exceptionally may extend into November.

The winter map, depicting the later autumn passage shows records from seven tetrads.

*Text: Mike Langman / Photo: Dave Scott*

Balmer *et al.* 2013: not treated; Sitters 1988: not treated; Tyler 2010: 321

### Breeding-period abundance 2007–13

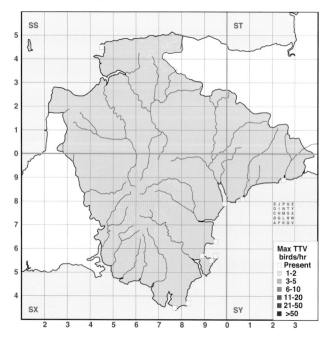

### Winter-period abundance 2007–13

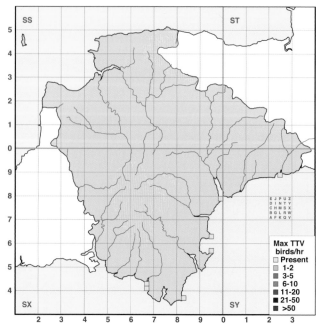

# Great Skua
## *Stercorarius skua*

ALSO KNOWN as 'Bonxies', these bulky aggressive birds breed in the North Atlantic, mainly in Scotland, the Faroes and Iceland. Great Skuas are uncommon spring and autumn passage migrants in Devon but have been recorded in every month, sometimes in the course of a single year, as was the case in 2011 (*DBR*). Records have increased over the last 30 years due partly to a growing North Atlantic population (JNCC Seabird Monitoring Programme) and perhaps also because there are now more observers with an interest in seawatching.

There is a small but regular spring passage of Great Skuas, mostly through the English Channel coast of Devon during March–May, with small numbers of failed breeders or immature birds present in June and July, followed by a larger autumn passage between August and October. Most of these three groups (with the exception of later autumn migrants) are mapped together on the summer-period map (March–September), which shows records for 33 tetrads, mainly on the south coast. There were two particularly good spring passages during the Atlas period, one in May 2007, with approximately 111 birds, and the exceptional total of 313 birds in April 2012 (*DBRs*).

Autumn migration continues into November, with regular midwinter records. Both late migrants and truly midwinter records are included in the winter-period map (October–February), which shows 28 exclusively coastal occupied tetrads. Unlike our other skua species, Great Skuas do not migrate far south in winter and may remain in the western approaches, so that a south-westerly winter gale or storm can push small numbers closer to the Devon coastline, as occurred in January 2011 and both January and December 2012 (*DBRs*).

With diminishing numbers of sand eels and seabirds, combined with reductions in discards from fishing vessels in the North Atlantic, it remains to be seen whether the current size of the Great Skua population and frequency of records will be maintained.

*Text: Mike Langman / Photo: Lee Collins*

Balmer *et al.* 2013: 394; Sitters 1988: not treated; Tyler 2010: 322

### Breeding-period abundance 2007–13

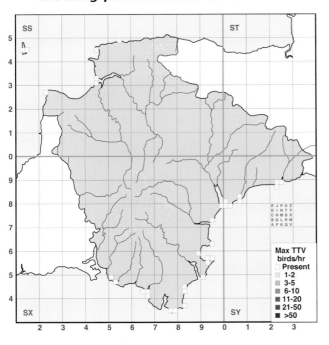

### Winter-period abundance 2007–13

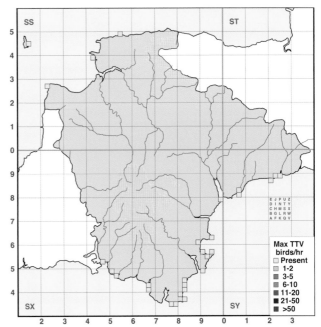

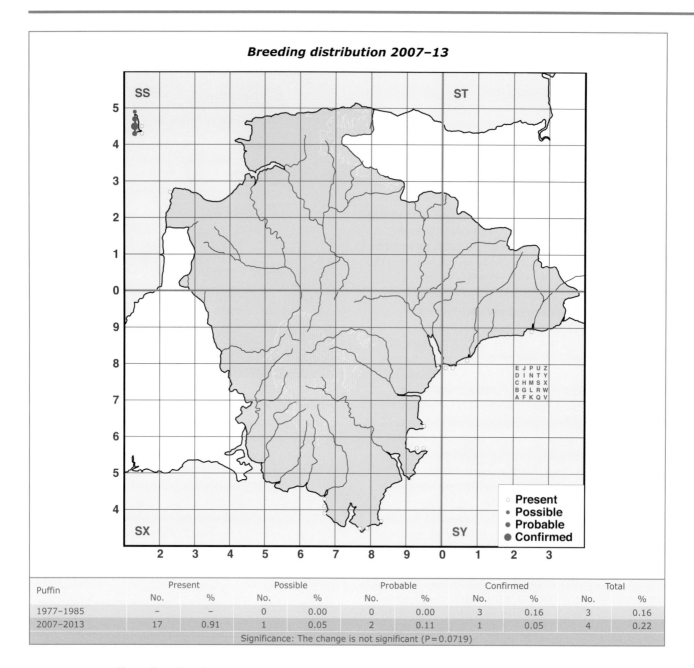

### Breeding distribution 2007–13

| Puffin | Present | | Possible | | Probable | | Confirmed | | Total | |
|---|---|---|---|---|---|---|---|---|---|---|
| | No. | % | No. | % | No. | % | No. | % | No. | % |
| 1977–1985 | – | – | 0 | 0.00 | 0 | 0.00 | 3 | 0.16 | 3 | 0.16 |
| 2007–2013 | 17 | 0.91 | 1 | 0.05 | 2 | 0.11 | 1 | 0.05 | 4 | 0.22 |
| Significance: The change is not significant (P = 0.0719) | | | | | | | | | | |

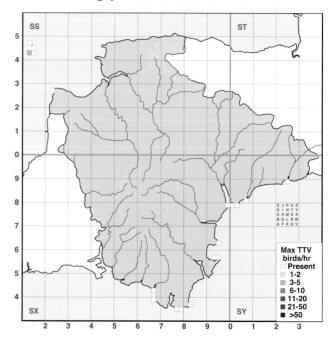

### Breeding distribution 1977–85

### Breeding-period abundance 2007–13

# Puffin

*Fratercula arctica*

**Red listed**

THE PUFFIN is an iconic seabird, much sought after by both birdwatchers and the general public. It is, however, not readily encountered as it is very much an ocean bird, spending most of its life on the open seas and only returning to land to breed at favoured sites, of which there are few in southern England. It is rarely seen elsewhere offshore, as evidenced by just two records from the south coast during the whole Atlas winter period.

In Devon, Puffins breed only on Lundy. They used to nest in huge numbers on the island with an estimate of 3,500 pairs in 1939 (Perry 1940), many of these occupying the thrift-covered slope above Puffin Gully at the far north of the island. The decline in breeding numbers was very rapid, with just 400 pairs remaining by 1954 (Dymond 1980). The population dwindled further until in 1986 – although the maps in the *Devon Tetrad Atlas 1977–85* showed confirmed breeding along the whole of Lundy's western coast – numbers were down to just 39 birds. Subsequently, breeding sites in Jenny's Cove and elsewhere were abandoned and by 2003 there were only single-figure counts of birds present at St Philip's Stone, and breeding was considered doubtful (Taylor 2003).

With huge colonies totalling around 10,000 pairs on the nearby Welsh islands of Skomer and Skokholm, it was apparent that food supply in the neighbouring seas was not a limiting factor, and the presumption was that predation of both birds and eggs by rats was responsible for their decline on Lundy. In 2002, a Seabird Recovery Programme was initiated to eradicate rats from the island, and this target was achieved in 2004.

Immediately, Puffin breeding activity began to improve. The first chick was seen in 2005 and breeding numbers increased in each subsequent year such that, by 2010, 16 pairs were recorded as breeding, with around half successfully fledging young (Saunders & Wheatley 2012). Since then there has been a further increase in numbers and Jenny's Cove has been re-colonized. During the 2013 breeding seabird census, 80 individual Puffins were recorded during early June (Price & Booker 2014).

Elsewhere in South West England, around 200 breeding birds were counted in 2007, 175 of these on the Isles of Scilly. The Lundy colony, in 2013, has therefore grown to account for about 30% of the South West population. Undoubtedly the Seabird Recovery Programme averted the extinction of Puffins as breeding birds in Devon, and there is considerable hope that the colony on Lundy will continue to thrive.

*Text: David Price / Photo: Mike Jones*

*Puffin sponsored by
Lundy Field Society*

Balmer *et al.* 2013: 432; Sitters 1988: 297; Tyler 2010: 385

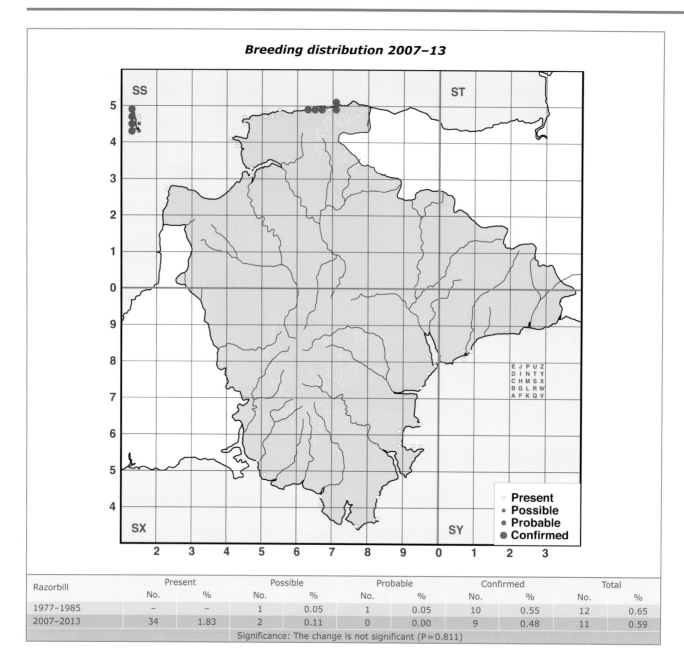

**Breeding distribution 2007–13**

| Razorbill | Present | | Possible | | Probable | | Confirmed | | Total | |
|---|---|---|---|---|---|---|---|---|---|---|
| | No. | % | No. | % | No. | % | No. | % | No. | % |
| 1977–1985 | – | – | 1 | 0.05 | 1 | 0.05 | 10 | 0.55 | 12 | 0.65 |
| 2007–2013 | 34 | 1.83 | 2 | 0.11 | 0 | 0.00 | 9 | 0.48 | 11 | 0.59 |
| Significance: The change is not significant (P=0.811) | | | | | | | | | | |

**Breeding distribution 1977–85**

**Breeding-period abundance 2007–13**

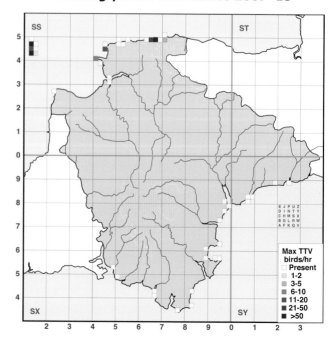

# Razorbill

*Alca torda*

Amber listed

RAZORBILLS SPEND much of the year on the open sea and therefore sightings on land are at a few favoured breeding locations, where they can find high cliffs with plenty of rocky crevices and suitable feeding areas close by. More typically they are seen flying or fishing offshore, with numbers swelled when adverse weather conditions push birds closer to the coast at migration time.

The only recorded breeding sites for Razorbill in Devon are now on Lundy and along a 10-km stretch of the North Devon coast between Lynton and Trentishoe. Birds recorded as 'present' elsewhere during the summer are likely to have been foraging birds or those dispersing after the breeding season.

They no longer breed along the south coast, although the *Devon Tetrad Atlas 1977–85* recorded them at Berry Head and on the Ore Stone off Hope's Nose. Both these sites held fewer than ten pairs, so had a tenuous breeding status.

The frequency and number of winter sightings are often weather-dependent, with birds being driven towards the coast during stormy weather from their open-sea feeding areas. Birds may occasionally visit breeding sites during November or February.

Numbers along the North Devon coast were reported in 2008 as 672 individuals at breeding sites (Porter *et al.* 2009), perhaps representing around 450 pairs (672 x 0.67). This is higher than the 420 birds reported in the *Devon Tetrad Atlas* for 1985, though 734 birds were recorded in 1986 (Porter *et al.* 2009).

On Lundy the majority of birds breed on the craggy towering cliffs along the west coast. Counts at breeding sites since 1970 have hovered between 700 and just under 1,000 individuals, but censuses in 2008 and 2013 recorded increases to 1,045 and 1,324 birds respectively (Price & Booker 2014). This upturn in numbers followed the rat eradication programme of 2002–04 and, as Razorbills often nest in crevices near the cliff tops, they have almost certainly benefited from the absence of this pernicious predator.

Based upon recent figures, the total number of breeding pairs in Devon is perhaps approaching 1,200, representing around 75% of the breeding population in South West England.

*Text: David Price / Photo: Richard Campey*
*Razorbill sponsored by Exmoor National Park Authority*

Balmer *et al.* 2013: 428; Sitters 1988: 122; Tyler 2010: 378

### Winter-period abundance 2007–13

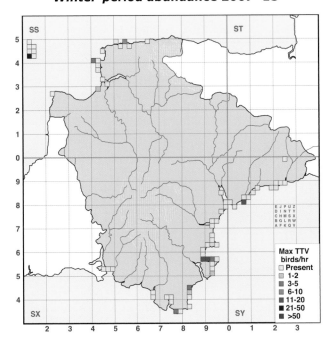

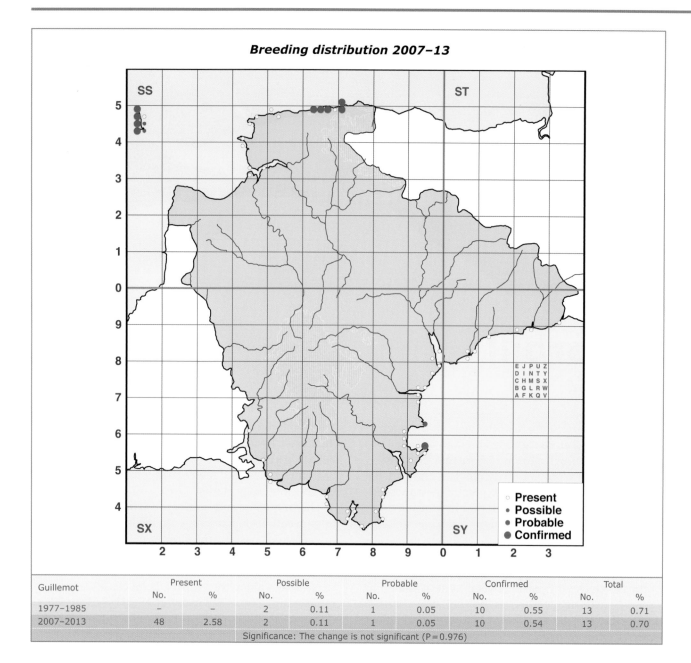

## Breeding distribution 2007–13

| Guillemot | Present | | Possible | | Probable | | Confirmed | | Total | |
|---|---|---|---|---|---|---|---|---|---|---|
| | No. | % | No. | % | No. | % | No. | % | No. | % |
| 1977–1985 | – | – | 2 | 0.11 | 1 | 0.05 | 10 | 0.55 | 13 | 0.71 |
| 2007–2013 | 48 | 2.58 | 2 | 0.11 | 1 | 0.05 | 10 | 0.54 | 13 | 0.70 |
| Significance: The change is not significant (P = 0.976) | | | | | | | | | | |

## Breeding distribution 1977–85

## Breeding-period abundance 2007–13

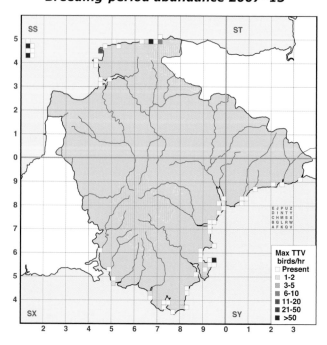

# Guillemot
## *Uria aalge*

Amber listed

THE GUILLEMOT, of which the southern sub-species *U .a. albionis* occurs in Devon, is a typically marine species, only coming onto land to breed. They are vulnerable to ground and avian predators and nest in tightly packed colonies, usually on largely inaccessible cliffs where there are ledges and flat-topped rocks on which they can lay their single egg.

The breeding distribution in Devon is restricted to such sites, the main colonies being on the horizontal limestone ledges of Berry Head on the south coast, the craggy cliffs between Woody Bay and Elwill Bay on the north coast, and the towering rugged west coast of Lundy. Small numbers also breed on the Ore Stone off Hope's Nose. These were the principal sites recorded in the *Devon Tetrad Atlas 1977–85*, and the breeding distribution is virtually unchanged since then.

During the winter, birds spend much of their time out at sea and therefore most of the mapped sightings will have been of birds off the coast, sometimes driven close to land by stormy weather. However, birds also regularly visit breeding sites in winter; hence the higher densities recorded on Lundy (Sherman, in prep.) and Berry Head at this time of year.

Census work on breeding birds uses counts of individuals as pairs are very difficult to determine on closely packed ledges. Based upon such counts at the main colonies, the total for Devon is in the region of 5,000–6,000 birds, which equates (using a conversion factor of 0.67) to around 3,700 pairs (Porter *et al.* 2009). This represents almost 70% of the South West's breeding population.

On Lundy, counts of breeding birds in 1939 probably exceeded 30,000 individuals (Perry 1940), but by the mid-1960s numbers were down to approximately 2,000 birds and varied around this level until the early 2000s. Since then there has been a steady increase to a high of over 4,000 birds in 2013 (Price & Booker 2014). This recent increase coincided with the eradication of rats from Lundy in 2002–04, but has also been apparent to some extent at other sites on the north and south coasts.

Whilst the breeding situation looks promising at the moment, the species is very reliant upon the availability of adequate marine food, particularly when raising young, and is also vulnerable to pollution and severe weather conditions.

*Text: David Price / Photo: Richard Campey*
*Guillemot sponsored by South Devon Branch of Devon Birds*

Balmer *et al.* 2013: 426; Sitters 1988: 120; Tyler 2010: 375

### *Winter-period abundance 2007–13*

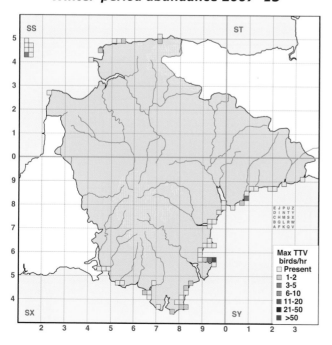

Max TTV birds/hr
- □ Present
- 1-2
- 3-5
- 6-10
- 11-20
- 21-50
- >50

# Black Guillemot

*Cepphus grylle*

Amber listed

I N THE British Isles the Black Guillemot's breeding range is entirely north-western, the main colonies being in western Scotland and around the coast of Ireland. They seldom stray far from these areas during the breeding season and are rarely seen elsewhere during the winter. Sightings in Devon are therefore unusual and noteworthy. The only locations where they were recorded in both winter and summer were off Dawlish Warren and at Berry Head, both seawatching sites well covered by

dedicated observers. Two birds in breeding plumage off Lundy in May and June 2012 constituted the island's first ever records (Davis & Jones 2012), with presumably one of these individuals returning in summer 2013 (Davis & Jones 2013).

*Text: David Price / Photo: David Land*
*Black Guillemot sponsored anonymously*

Balmer *et al.* 2013: 430; Sitters 1988: not treated; Tyler 2010: 382

# Little Auk

*Alle alle*

T HIS HIGH-ARCTIC breeding bird rarely strays far south even in winter, and so any sighting off the Devon coast is unusual. Little Auks are most often recorded in November, particularly when driven inshore by strong winds. All records during the Atlas period were from the south coast, and well-watched sites such as Prawle Point, Berry Head, Hope's Nose, Dawlish Warren and Seaton yielded the majority of sightings. The *Devon Bird Reports* show that the autumn of 2007 produced 15–18 birds, while seven occurred in autumn 2009 but only two or three were reported in other Atlas years.

*Text: David Price*

Balmer *et al.* 2013: 425; Sitters 1988: not treated; Tyler 2010: 384

### Winter-period abundance 2007–13

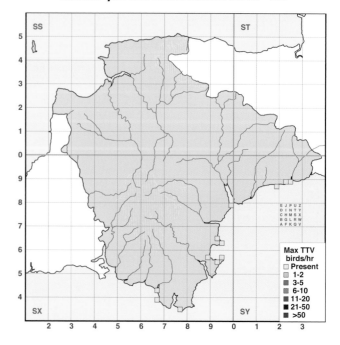

Max TTV birds/hr
- Present
- 1-2
- 3-5
- 6-10
- 11-20
- 21-50
- >50

# Little Tern
## Sternula albifrons

The LITTLE Tern is tiny, dwarfed by Sandwich Terns and noticeably smaller than Common and Arctic Terns. Its size and quick, whippy wing beats make this species easy to identify even at a distance.

Little Terns are passage migrants in Devon and there are no adequately documented breeding records (Tyler 2010). During Atlas fieldwork there were records from 27 tetrads, mostly around the coastal bays of the south coast. Most observations were from a few key sites, particularly between the mouth of the Exe Estuary and Dawlish Bay. The first spring arrivals occur from the second or third week of April, with all first dates during the Atlas years being within the period 11–19 April (*DBRs*). Numbers vary, with singles most common, and counts of between two and six noted annually. Higher counts are less frequent, with the maximum during the Atlas period being eight in May 2008 – far below the all-time peak of 53 in May 1998.

Autumn arrivals can be noted from July onwards, although in many years none appear until August. Sightings are recorded into September but October observations are very scarce. During the Atlas years the highest autumn count was nine in both July 2007 and August 2012, while the latest dates were all in September, with the exception of 2012 when one was off Dawlish Warren on 17 October (*DBRs*).

Nationally, there was a net 30% decline in the number of 10-km squares for which breeding evidence was registered over the 40 years between the *Breeding Atlas 1968–72* and *Bird Atlas 2007–11*). Major efforts are being made to protect known breeding colonies from predation and disturbance, but nests can still be washed out during unusually high tides and storm surges.

*Text: Lee Collins / Photo: Richard Revels/NPL*
*Little Tern sponsored by Bob Heckford*

Balmer *et al.* 2013: 416; Sitters 1988: not treated; Tyler 2010: 360

## Breeding-period abundance 2007–13

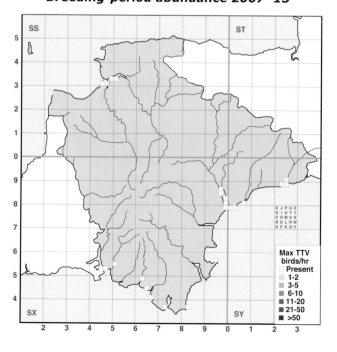

## Winter-period abundance 2007–13

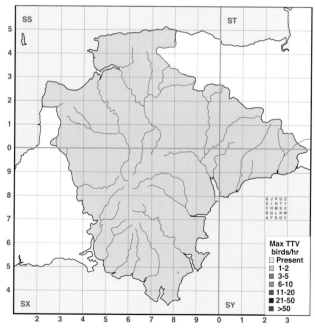

# Sandwich Tern
## *Sterna sandvicensis*

SANDWICH TERN is by far the most frequent and numerous tern in the county, although, like all other terns in Devon, it occurs exclusively as a passage migrant on its way to breeding grounds from winter quarters along the coast of southern and western Africa (Wernham *et al.* 2002).

Arrivals generally appear from mid-March (in the Atlas years, earliest 1 March 2008; *DBR*). A handful of sightings during the period December to February in two Atlas winters (2008/9 and 2012/13) probably referred to birds that had wintered off European coasts.

During the Atlas breeding period (which includes the whole of spring migration and the peak of autumn passage for Sandwich Tern) there were records from over 100 coastal or riparian tetrads, but none from inland ones. Occurrences were widespread along the south coast, although most involved small numbers. Larger counts came from well-watched sites, especially around the mouth of the River Exe.

Spring maxima occurred mainly in April, peaking at 163 at Thurlestone on 28 April 2010. Numbers start to build again in July, with the first juveniles typically appearing mid-month. Birds can appear anywhere along the coast, though Dawlish Warren (Exe Estuary) is the principal site, with counts exceeding 200 in late July or August in all Atlas years. The highest counts were 485 at Dawlish Warren on 16 August 2008 and 400 at Skern (Taw/Torridge Estuary) on 15 August 2012 (*DBRs*).

Reading of colour-rings at Dawlish Warren during the Atlas period showed the occurrence of birds originating from breeding colonies in The Netherlands, Scotland and Wales, demonstrating the importance of the site as a staging area for migrating Sandwich Terns (Collins 2014).

*Text: Lee Collins / Photo: Lee Collins*

Balmer *et al.* 2013: 418; Sitters 1988: not treated; Tyler 2010: 361

### Breeding-period abundance 2007–13

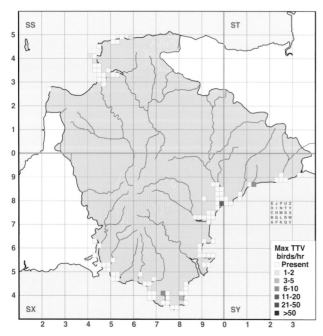

Max TTV birds/hr
☐ Present
1-2
3-5
6-10
11-20
21-50
>50

# Common Tern
## *Sterna hirundo*
Amber listed

THE COMMON Tern is the most frequently seen tern after Sandwich Tern in Devon and was recorded from 41 tetrads during the Atlas surveys. Nationally, the species has slightly extended its breeding distribution over the last 40 years (*Bird Atlas 2007–11*), perhaps due to the provision of nesting platforms on inland waters, though the species remains a passage migrant in Devon. There have been past breeding attempts in the county, the last in 1978 at Dawlish Warren, when a pair laid eggs that were destroyed by holidaymakers (Tyler 2010).

Migrants were recorded all along the south coast, with generally fewer in the north, although the Taw/Torridge Estuary is favoured. There were only one or two inland records. The first spring arrivals are usually in mid-April and sightings continue throughout May. Counts can fluctuate rapidly as successive individuals and small flocks pass through. The highest spring counts during the Atlas period were 300–400 at Dawlish Warren on 3 May 2008 and 400 off South Huish on 24 April 2012.

Returning autumn birds appear generally from early July, with the first juveniles noted during the third week of the month. Birds are seen right through to September, but October sightings are somewhat scarce. As in the spring, counts fluctuate from day to day, with one to several dozen birds recorded. Unsettled conditions can see higher numbers than usual passing through the county – an extraordinary 1,500 were present on the Taw/Torridge Estuary on 16 August 2012, by far the largest count during the Atlas period.

*Text: Lee Collins / Photo: Paul Sterry/NPL*

Balmer *et al.* 2013: 420; Sitters 1988: 300; Tyler 2010: 370

### Breeding-period abundance 2007–13

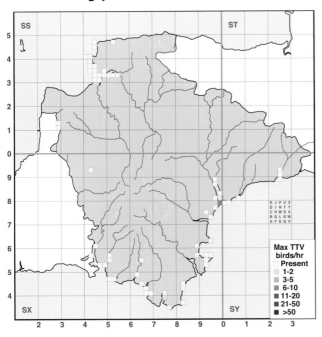

### Winter-period abundance 2007–13

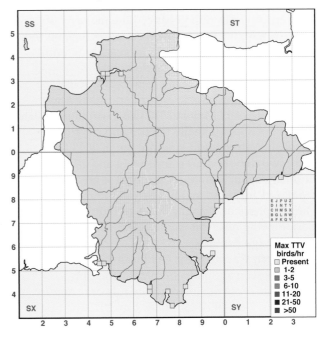

# Black Tern

*Chlidonias niger*

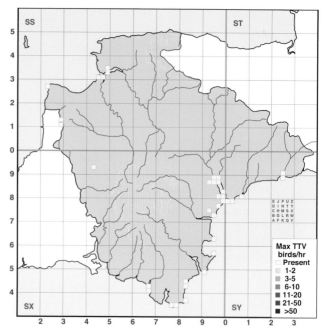

**Breeding-period abundance 2007–13**

Black Terns are scarce passage migrants in Devon, occurring more regularly in late summer and autumn than in spring and often associated with bouts of unsettled weather. During the Atlas period they were recorded from 36 tetrads with the only winter period record being from the Axe Estuary. Since Devon is at the western edge of this species' range, counts are generally low, typically between one and three birds, though two unusually high counts during the Atlas years included 27 off Hartland Point on 6 September 2010 and 25 off Orcombe Point on 3 May 2011 (*DBRs*).

Text: Lee Collins

Balmer *et al.* 2013: 417; Sitters 1988: not treated; Tyler 2010: 364

---

# Roseate Tern

*Sterna dougallii*

**Red listed**

Roseate Terns have declined greatly in the British Isles and now 97% of the population breeds in just three colonies: Coquet Island, Northumberland; Rockabill, Ireland; and Lady's Island Lake, Ireland (*Bird Atlas 2007–11*). However, the improved success of these since 1986 (Newton 2004), thanks to practical conservation measures, means that more passage birds are now being seen in Devon, with records from 16 tetrads during the Atlas period. Dawlish Warren and Exmouth produced the majority of reports, with others coming from elsewhere on the south coast, mainly at regular seawatching points such as Berry Head and Prawle Point.

The first spring migrants generally appear between the third week in April and early May (a first date of 19 May in 2012 was exceptionally late) feeding offshore, usually in ones and twos off Dawlish Warren and Exmouth, but in 2013 there were two double-digit counts of 14 and 20. Autumn birds are again seen in ones and twos and appear from mid-July, and sightings continue through to early September with the latest seen during the Atlas period being on 2 October at Charleton Bay on the Kingsbridge Estuary.

Dawlish Warren is the key location in Devon and birds are seen annually among the massing Sandwich Terns during mid/late July and August. Many carry metal rings and in July 2013 the first field reading of such a ring established that the bird had originated from Coquet Island.

Text: Lee Collins
Roseate Tern sponsored by Dr David Cabot

Balmer *et al.* 2013: 424; Sitters 1988: not treated; Tyler 2010: 372

**Breeding-period abundance 2007–13**

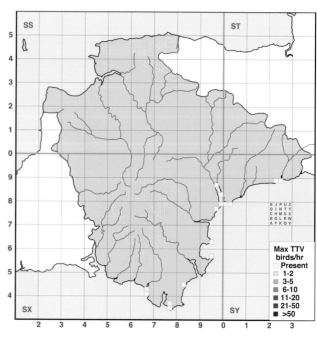

# Arctic Tern
## *Sterna paradisaea*

Amber listed

THE ARCTIC Tern's world-spanning annual migrations from the Arctic to the Antarctic are truly incredible. This species is a passage migrant in Devon that was recorded in 18 tetrads during the Atlas period, reflecting its scarcity relative to the Common Tern, which was present in 41 tetrads. Sightings came mainly from well-watched coastal sites, but much like Common Tern it also has a tendency to undertake overland passage and turn up at inland waterbodies, although this happens only occasionally in Devon, usually less than annually.

The first birds appear from mid-April, a little later than Common Terns, although Arctic Terns are probably under-recorded because of the difficulty of distinguishing them from Common Terns, so that many records are of 'Commic' Terns. Our first autumn birds can be noted as early as July, although August is more typical. Larger counts, including juveniles, are generally noted in September, with 2012 being the peak year during the Atlas period when 28 were seen from Dawlish/Exe Estuary and ten from Torbay/Berry Head.

*Text: Lee Collins / Photo: Mark Darlaston*

Balmer *et al.* 2013: 422; Sitters 1988: not treated; Tyler 2010: 374

### *Breeding-period abundance 2007–13*

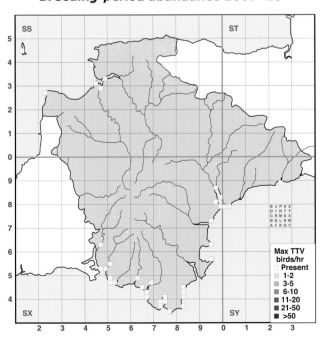

### *Winter-period abundance 2007–13*

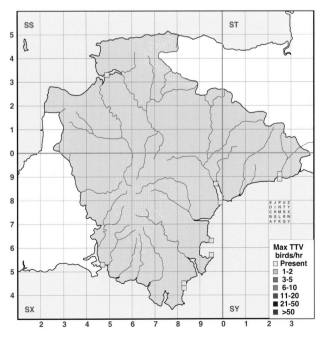

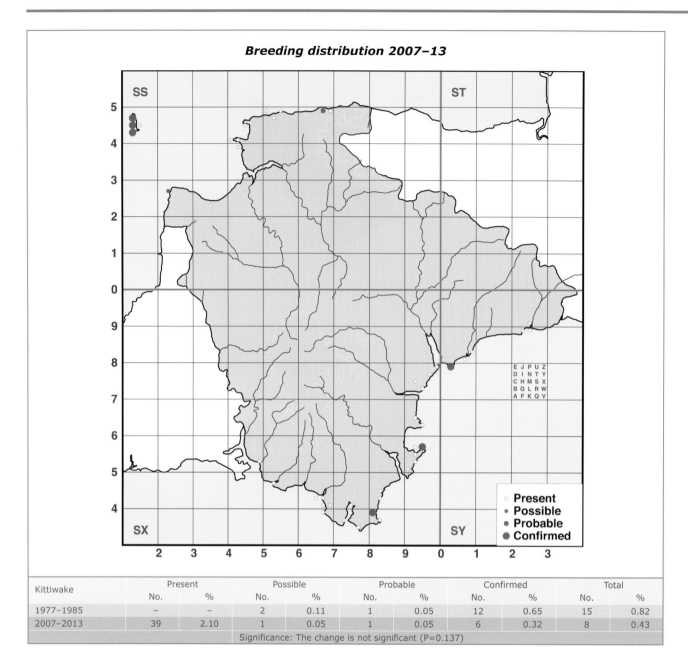

## Breeding distribution 2007–13

| Kittiwake | Present | | Possible | | Probable | | Confirmed | | Total | |
|---|---|---|---|---|---|---|---|---|---|---|
| | No. | % | No. | % | No. | % | No. | % | No. | % |
| 1977–1985 | – | – | 2 | 0.11 | 1 | 0.05 | 12 | 0.65 | 15 | 0.82 |
| 2007–2013 | 39 | 2.10 | 1 | 0.05 | 1 | 0.05 | 6 | 0.32 | 8 | 0.43 |
| Significance: The change is not significant (P=0.137) | | | | | | | | | | |

## Breeding distribution 1977–85

## Breeding-period abundance 2007–13

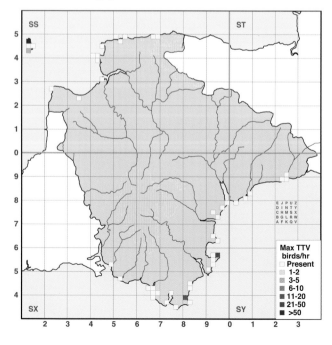

# Kittiwake

*Rissa tridactyla*

**Red listed**

THE KITTIWAKE is the most pelagic of our breeding gull species, traditionally nesting in dense colonies on sea-cliffs, where their nests are often perilously close to the waves. The noise, smell and sheer busyness of a thriving colony of Kittiwakes can be almost bewildering. They have always been confined to a few scattered breeding cliffs – Lundy, Torbay and the north coast of Exmoor, with a few pairs elsewhere (Tyler 2010) – but the current Atlas paints a somewhat depressing picture. The colonies around Torbay are now restricted to Berry Head, whilst most of the colonies near Start Point have disappeared and the north coast of mainland Devon held just a single colony of some 90–100 apparently occupied nests west of Woody Bay in 2014 (*DBR*). On Lundy, Kittiwake numbers have undergone a sizeable decline since the *Devon Tetrad Atlas 1977–85*; the 127 apparently occupied nests recorded in 2013 was the lowest number since records began (Price & Booker 2014). There have been some gains, primarily a new colony at Straight Point just east of Exmouth, but this is only a partial offset for the wider losses.

The cause – or causes – of this wholesale decline are not well understood. Warming coastal waters could be forcing a change in the distribution or abundance of Kittiwake's favoured prey species – this would affect both survival of adults and their breeding productivity (Harris & Wanless 1997; Price & Booker 2014). Poor weather during the breeding season may also play a role at times; for example, in

2012 the lower sections of the two colonies on Lundy were washed away before the chicks had fledged (*DBR*).

In winter, Kittiwakes can be found patchily along both coasts in small numbers, individuals often taking refuge from rough conditions offshore or exploiting available food during their winter wanderings. The turbulent waters around Lundy and the approaches of the Bristol Channel perhaps offer richer pickings than mainland coastal waters; for example, at least 1,500 Kittiwakes were off Lundy's east coast in February 2009 during a cold snap with strong easterly winds (*LFS Annual Report 2009*). Occasional birds occur inland, particularly following extremely stormy conditions.

A comparison of *Bird Atlas 2007–11* with the *Winter Atlas 1981–84* shows that Kittiwakes were recorded in many fewer tetrads in winter in the former survey, and that this decline occurred throughout the UK. The loss has been greatest to the north-west of the UK, but the reasons remain something of a mystery.

*Text: Jeremy Barker / Photo: Paul Sterry/NPL*

Balmer *et al.* 2013: 396; Sitters 1988: 118; Tyler 2010: 327

### Winter-period abundance 2007–13

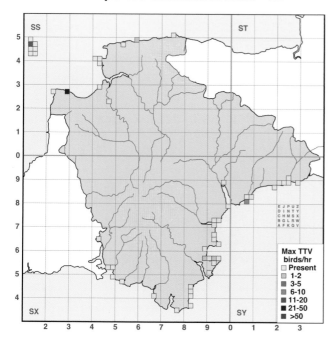

Max TTV birds/hr
- ☐ Present
- 1-2
- 3-5
- 6-10
- 11-20
- 21-50
- >50

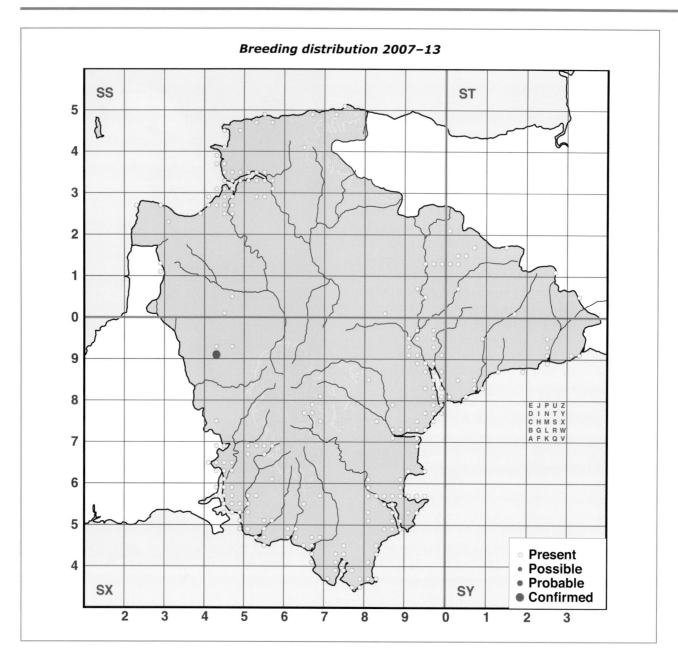

## Breeding distribution 2007–13

Present
Possible
Probable
Confirmed

## Breeding-period abundance 2007–13

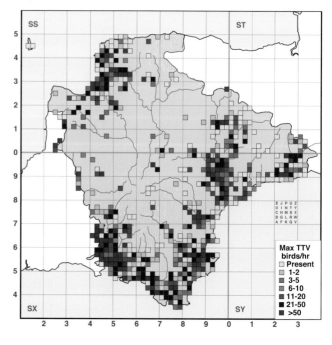

Max TTV
birds/hr
Present
1-2
3-5
6-10
11-20
21-50
>50

## Winter-period abundance 2007–13

Max TTV
birds/hr
Present
1-2
3-5
6-10
11-20
21-50
>50

# Black-headed Gull

*Chroicocephalus ridibundus*

Amber listed

THOUGH FAMILIAR and widespread in winter, the Black-headed Gull is a scarce breeding bird in the South West, perhaps limited by a lack of suitable large shallow waters. Breeding in Devon has always been small-scale and erratic, with the recent attempts at Roadford Lake (*DBR* 2011) being the first instances of confirmed breeding since the late 1950s, when there was a small colony around Braunton Marsh (Tyler 2010). Summering birds – predominantly immatures – occur sparsely along both coasts, concentrated on the main estuaries.

In winter, Black-headed Gulls are found commonly along both coasts and along the floodplains of the major river systems in the county, with few birds found in mid-Devon and the uplands. Sightings of ringed individuals suggest that the wintering population is partly made up of birds from northern Europe, including other parts of the UK, and also show that some individuals are highly faithful to wintering sites, returning to the same stretch of river year on year (pers. obs.). Whilst the species remains common, annual winter counts of roosting birds on the Exe Estuary indicate a substantial decline since the 1980s (see figure). This is in line with a gradual national decline since the early 1990s (Banks *et al.* 2009), perhaps because milder winters mean that birds do not need to move so far south and west.

*Text: Jeremy Barker / Photo: Mike Jones*

Balmer *et al.* 2013: 398; Sitters 1988: not treated; Tyler 2010: 331

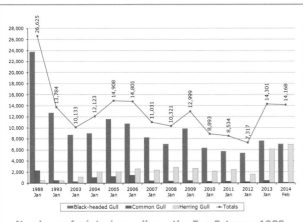

**Numbers of wintering gulls on the Exe Estuary, 1988, 1993 & 2003–2014 (D. Price 2014, unpublished data).**

# Mediterranean Gull

*Larus melanocephalus*

Amber listed

SCAN THROUGH any autumn or winter flock of Black-headed Gulls near the coast these days and there is a strong likelihood you will see one or more Mediterranean Gulls. As the Atlas maps show, the species can be found on any of the main Devon estuaries, with a particular affinity for the Taw/Torridge and Kingsbridge Estuaries in late summer. The former site has recently recorded in excess of a hundred Mediterranean Gulls at a time with a peak count of 146 in August 2012 (*DBR*). Winter birds are more widely distributed, with Torbay, Plymouth and the Otter and Exe Estuaries also recording multiple birds. Although not widely recorded inland, it is surely overlooked amongst the large flocks of inland Black-headed Gulls.

As a species that has rapidly increased its range, not only in the UK but across continental Europe, Mediterranean Gulls are popular study subjects. Colour-ringing has shown that the birds which turn up in Devon in autumn may have been hatched as far east as Poland or Hungary (Robinson 2005) and that they may breed in very different areas year on year – moving from the Mediterranean to the North Sea, for instance (Boldreghini *et al.* 1992). Colour-ringed birds whose rings have been read have originated from Denmark and Poland (*DBRs*). Despite all this, there are probably no suitable breeding sites in Devon – in Britain, Mediterranean Gulls tend to nest amongst colonies of Black-headed Gull, which itself has only a toehold in the county.

*Text: Jeremy Barker / Photo: Paul Nunn*

Balmer *et al.* 2013: 400; Sitters 1988: not treated; Tyler 2010: 338

### Breeding-period abundance 2007–13

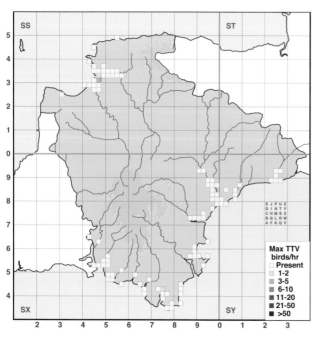

Max TTV birds/hr
- ☐ Present
- ☐ 1-2
- ☐ 3-5
- ☐ 6-10
- ■ 11-20
- ■ 21-50
- ■ >50

### Winter-period abundance 2007–13

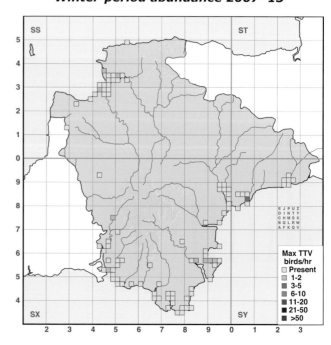

Max TTV birds/hr
- ☐ Present
- ☐ 1-2
- ☐ 3-5
- ☐ 6-10
- ■ 11-20
- ■ 21-50
- ■ >50

# Common Gull

*Larus canus*

Amber listed

A NON-BREEDING visitor to the county, Common Gulls are widely distributed along the lowlands of both Devon coasts. They are regularly encountered through the winter, particularly around urban amenity grasslands and the lower floodplains of the main river systems, though they are perhaps overlooked to some degree amongst flocks of Black-headed Gulls. The winter-period (October–February) map shows a strong focus on peri-urban and coastal areas, with a scatter of records through the rest of the county, perhaps of birds associating with agricultural activities such as ploughing or muck-spreading.

Summer-period records tend to relate to a few lingering birds, which may well not breed that year and have no strong urge to head north to the breeding colonies. These may be joined later on by birds that have failed to breed and have returned early to their winter quarters.

There may have been a slight decline in the number of birds wintering in Devon as there has been some apparent redistribution of birds away from the far south-west of the British Isles since the *Winter Atlas 1981–84*. However, the species is not well monitored by WeBS counts, which occur when birds are widely dispersed inland, and consistent roost counts only take place on the Exe (see figure in Black-headed Gull account, page 227). These roost counts imply a decline in wintering numbers, but it is impossible to determine whether this is a county-wide phenomenon.

*Text: Jeremy Barker / Photo: Rob Jutsum*

Balmer *et al.* 2013: 402; Sitters 1988: 112; Tyler 2010: 341

### Breeding-period abundance 2007–13

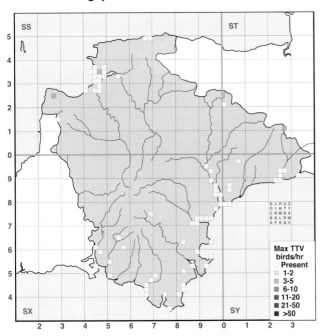

### Winter-period abundance 2007–13

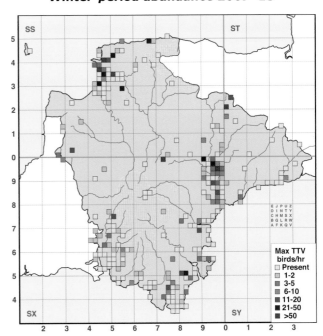

# Little Gull
*Hydrocoloeus minutus*

Lᴵᴛᴛʟᴇ Gᴜʟʟs are predominantly recorded in Devon during their spring and autumn migrations, mainly along the south coast. Records during the Atlas period show a typical spread: spring passage birds concentrated between Thurlestone and the Axe, with a handful of records on the Taw/Torridge Estuary, and a wider scatter of late-autumn and winter birds along both coasts.

Little Gulls are extending their breeding range westwards through Europe (BirdLife International 2004). *Bird Atlas 2007–11* shows that records in the UK during the breeding season are increasing.

*Text: Jeremy Barker / Photo: Paul Sterry/NPL*

Balmer *et al.* 2013: 404; Sitters 1988: not treated; Tyler 2010: 334

### Breeding-period abundance 2007–13

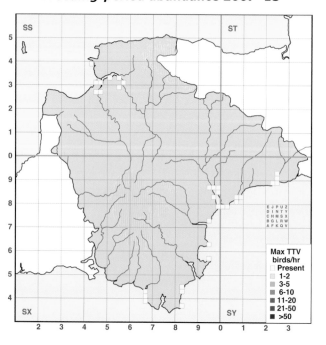

### Winter-period abundance 2007–13

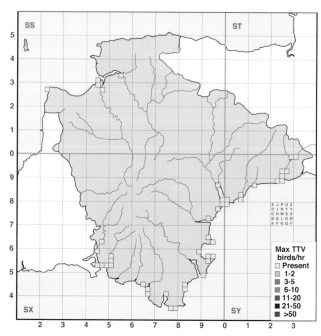

# Yellow-legged Gull
## *Larus michahellis*
Amber listed

ONE OF the 'large white-headed gull' complex, once considered a subspecies of the Herring Gull, the Yellow-legged Gull is scarce but regular in Devon, with a record 109 individuals seen in 2011. Records come mainly from the south coast, with the exception of single occurrences during the Atlas years on the Taw/Torridge Estuary and near Roadford Lake. Like Caspian Gull, this species is usually found by dedicated gull-watchers amongst gatherings of other large gulls. Most records are of juvenile and first-winter birds from July onwards,

presumably dispersing from the growing breeding colonies along the French coast (*Bird Atlas 2007–11*). With a generally expanding trend in northern Europe, we can probably expect to see these birds more often in the future, although the taxonomy of large gulls is likely to undergo further changes to confuse us all!

*Text: Jeremy Barker / Photo: Mark Darlaston*

Balmer *et al.* 2013: 410; Sitters 1988: not treated; Tyler 2010: 351

### Breeding-period abundance 2007–13

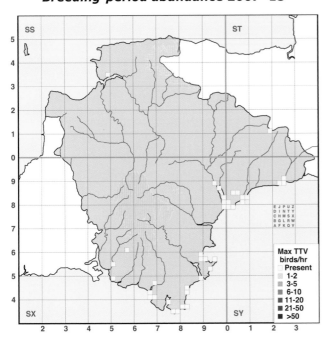

### Winter-period abundance 2007–13

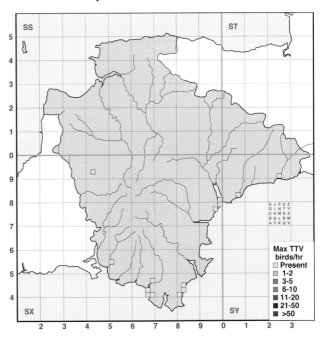

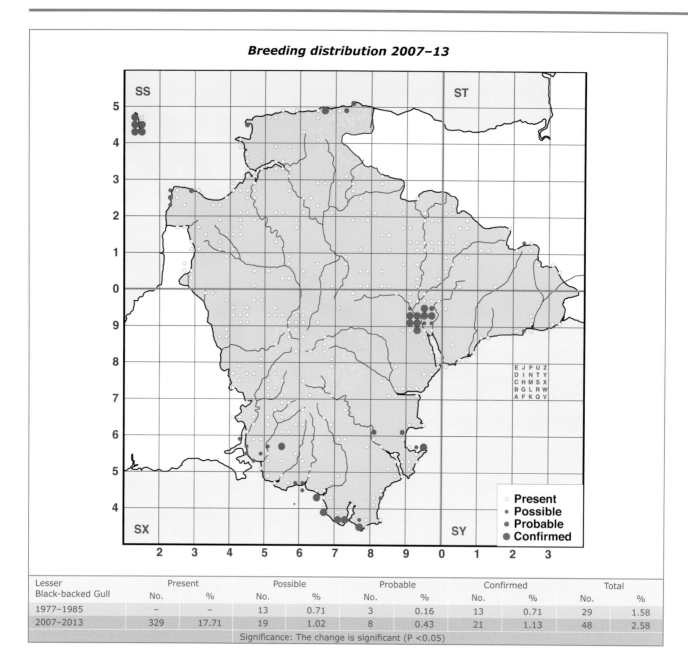

### Breeding distribution 2007–13

| Lesser Black-backed Gull | Present | | Possible | | Probable | | Confirmed | | Total | |
|---|---|---|---|---|---|---|---|---|---|---|
| | No. | % | No. | % | No. | % | No. | % | No. | % |
| 1977–1985 | – | – | 13 | 0.71 | 3 | 0.16 | 13 | 0.71 | 29 | 1.58 |
| 2007–2013 | 329 | 17.71 | 19 | 1.02 | 8 | 0.43 | 21 | 1.13 | 48 | 2.58 |
| Significance: The change is significant (P <0.05) | | | | | | | | | | |

### Breeding distribution 1977–85

### Breeding-period abundance 2007–13

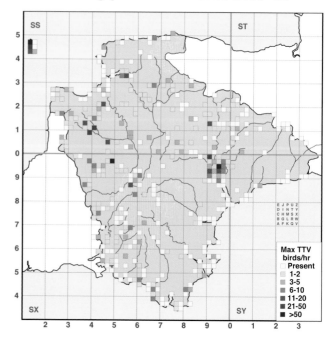

# Lesser Black-backed Gull

*Larus fuscus*

Amber listed

THE LESSER Black-backed Gull is less frequently encountered than the similar-sized Herring Gull, but can be seen in fairly similar situations. Breeding birds can be found scattered along both the north and south coasts, but the bulk of the Devon population nests on Lundy and on Exeter's rooftops.

Like the Herring Gull, the Lesser Black-back is a species which appears to be in the process of a major ecological shift from coast to town, but unlike Herring Gulls, Lesser Black-backs seem not to have taken so readily to the suburbs. Prior to and during the *Devon Tetrad Atlas 1977–85*, this was very much a coastal species, with the bulk of the breeding population on Lundy and scattered amongst Herring Gull colonies on both coasts of the mainland. Since then, and as with Herring Gulls, birds breeding in urban areas have been significantly more productive than those in traditional coastal sites. This difference in productivity is in line with populations further north and east in the UK and is the main driver of what is often seen as a switch in nesting-habitat choice (e.g. Ross-Smith *et al.* 2014). The preference of broader, flatter roofs for nesting may be rooted in their natural preference for broad, grassy coastal slopes and island plateaux, rather than the cliff ledges and outcrops that Herring Gulls prefer.

Coastal populations in natural habitats have declined, including those on Lundy where – despite the eradication of rats in the early 2000s – numbers fell from 444 pairs in 2004 to 242 apparently occupied territories in 2013 (*DBR* 2013). On the mainland, the species has all but vanished from the north coast around Ilfracombe and many of the south coast populations have either shrunk or disappeared. Breeding success is also poor at Prawle, where birds are regularly monitored; again in line with the differing fortunes for coastal and urban breeders.

While much of the UK population has traditionally wintered around the Iberian Peninsula and the north-west coast of Africa (BTO 2012) – from where many colour-ring sightings of Lundy-ringed nestlings have been reported (Davis & Jones 2007) – the species is increasingly frequent in the UK in winter. Lesser Black-backs are rather evenly recorded across the county in winter, although there is something of a concentration of birds across mid-Devon, and comparison with the *Winter Atlas 1981-84* shows a definite increase in inland records. The annual Exe Estuary counts rarely record double figures (*cf.* several thousand Herring Gulls), but this is a species which prefers to roost on fresh water: counts at Roadford and Fernworthy Reservoirs can run to several thousands in late autumn and winter.

### Winter-period abundance 2007–13

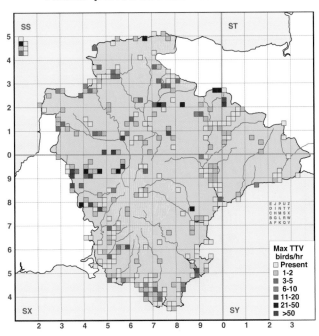

*Text: Jeremy Barker / Photo: Dave Smallshire*

Balmer *et al.* 2013: 406; Sitters 1988: 112; Tyler 2010: 345

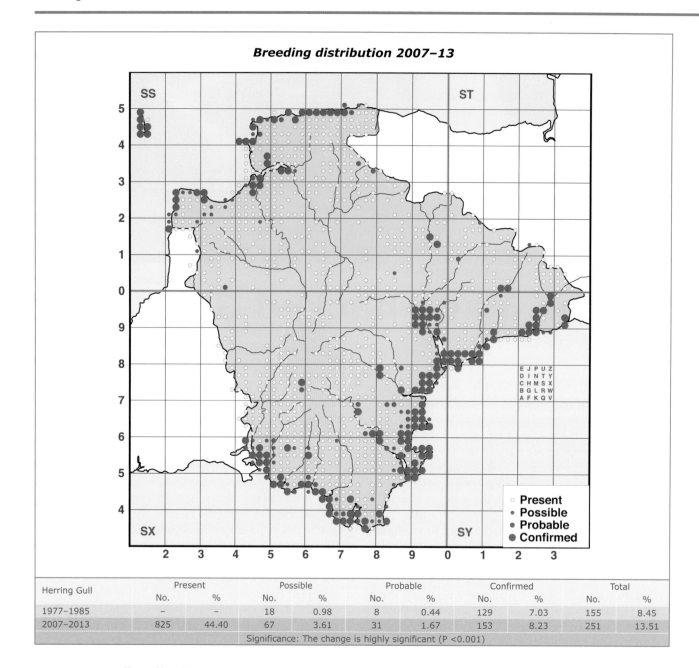

**Breeding distribution 2007–13**

| Herring Gull | Present | | Possible | | Probable | | Confirmed | | Total | |
|---|---|---|---|---|---|---|---|---|---|---|
| | No. | % | No. | % | No. | % | No. | % | No. | % |
| 1977–1985 | – | – | 18 | 0.98 | 8 | 0.44 | 129 | 7.03 | 155 | 8.45 |
| 2007–2013 | 825 | 44.40 | 67 | 3.61 | 31 | 1.67 | 153 | 8.23 | 251 | 13.51 |
| Significance: The change is highly significant (P <0.001) | | | | | | | | | | |

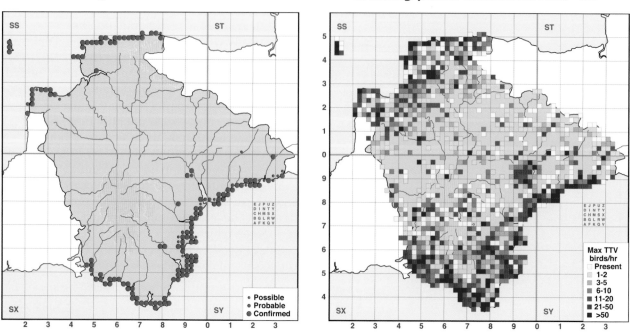

**Breeding distribution 1977–85**

**Breeding-period abundance 2007–13**

# Herring Gull
## *Larus argentatus*

**Red listed**

THE FAMILIAR and ubiquitous 'seagull' of the Devon coasts and towns, the Herring Gull is the most widespread and abundant of the county's large gulls all year round. They can be found almost anywhere, whether searching for food behind the plough, loafing on moorland reservoirs, nesting on suburban roofs or pirating chips on the seafront.

Breeding populations across the UK are in broad decline, sufficient to warrant listing as a species of conservation concern (Robinson 2005), although the status and productivity of the urban population seems open to conjecture. Certainly there has been an increase across the UK in the incidence of rooftop nesting, along with a decline in coastal nesting, but whether the increase in towns compensates for the coastal decline is not clear. The difficulty lies in determining the productivity of urban birds – rooftop vantage points are not easy to come by.

Since the *Devon Tetrad Atlas 1977–85*, the species has shown a marked change in distribution, abandoning some of the coastal cliffs of the north and east coasts and taking up residence on inland rooftops. The spread inland since the 1980s has led to Herring Gulls successfully breeding on roofs as far inland as Okehampton and as high on the moor as Princetown. As breeding productivity in urban situations tends to outstrip that of coastal colonies (Rock 2005), this shift in distribution may yet continue, despite the efforts of local councils to suppress urban gull populations.

### Winter-period abundance 2007–13

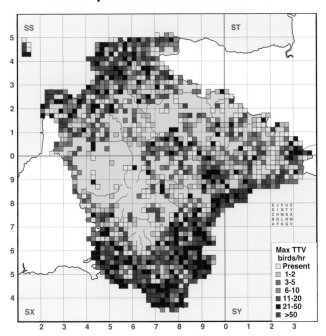

In winter, Herring Gulls can be found more-or-less throughout the county, though they tend not to use the high-altitude moorland or the inland Culm Measures, where there is probably little food for them to find. WeBS counts show that while birds use all the major estuaries in the county, the Exe consistently provides the highest numbers, with a peak, usually in January, of between 2,200 and 2,800; but a very high count of 6,174 birds was made in January 2013 (*DBR*). Counts in Torbay can be in the order of 8,000. Although breeding and winter distributions are broadly similar, the density maps illustrate an increased wintering population. This is likely to consist mainly of birds from within the UK, but may be augmented by some individuals of the nominate subspecies from northern Europe (our birds are *L. a. argenteus*). Certainly this is the only species to have increased steadily over the past few years on the annual Exe Estuary gull count (see figure in the Black-headed Gull account, page 227), though there is little data available to suggest the origins of these birds.

*Text: Jeremy Barker / Photo: Mark Darlaston*
*Herring Gull sponsored by Michael Cockram of Dawlish*

Balmer *et al.* 2013: 408; Sitters 1988: 114; Tyler 2010: 348

# Iceland Gull

## Larus glaucoides

Amber listed

ICELAND GULL is a winter visitor and passage migrant from the high Arctic, with Devon being very much at the edge of the species' range. Individuals tend to turn up either amidst gatherings of other large gulls, often at well-watched roosts (e.g. Axe, Exe and Taw/Torridge Estuaries, Slapton Ley) or around food-rich areas such as sewage outfalls and fishing ports. The number seen during most of the Atlas years was less than ten but 12 were seen in 2009, half of which were on the Axe Estuary, and a country-wide influx in 2012, discussed in detail by Fray *et al.* (2012), saw 31 birds recorded in Devon, most of which were on the south coast.

The Atlas winter-period map (October–February) shows records from both the north and south coasts of the county, but none inland. Individuals can be rather mobile, so that in some cases the same bird may have been recorded in multiple tetrads over the course of a winter. Devon records during the Atlas years mostly referred to the nominate race *L. g. glaucoides*, which breeds in Greenland. The race that breeds in Arctic Canada, *L. g. kumlieni* – known as 'Kumlien's Gull' (and regarded by some authors as a separate species) – was recorded just once during the period, for the first time in 25 years, when a third-year bird was at Brixham between 15 January and 24 February 2012 (*DBR*).

*Text: Jeremy Barker / Photo: David Land*

Balmer *et al.* 2013: 412; Sitters 1988: not treated; Tyler 2010: 353

### Winter-period abundance 2007–13

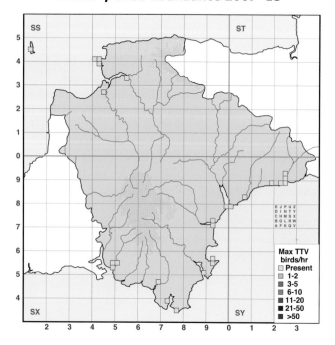

Max TTV birds/hr
- ☐ Present
- 1-2
- 3-5
- 6-10
- 11-20
- 21-50
- >50

# Glaucous Gull

*Larus hyperboreus*

Amber listed

GLAUCOUS GULLS breed throughout the Arctic and winter south along the Atlantic and Pacific coasts to about the latitude of the UK. They are scarce winter visitors to Devon, usually appearing around fishing ports, landfill sites or sewage outfalls. Most records are of first- or second-winter birds which wander further than birds of breeding age. In an average winter, one or two are found somewhere along the county's coastline. Severe weather in the northern Atlantic may drive more Glaucous Gulls towards the UK and result in a larger tally of records than normal, with the number of records in Devon approaching double figures in a very good season. Records were annual during the Atlas years, varying from three in 2011 to seven in 2010 (a year in which there were spells of particularly harsh winter weather) (*DBRs*).

Individuals may wander widely during the course of a winter, which can give the impression that the species is more numerous than it really is (an impression reinforced by the aggregation of data from multiple winters). Mapped clusters of dots may therefore refer to the same bird being recorded in adjacent tetrads; for instance, during the course of a single winter, identifiable individuals have been recorded between Northam Burrows and Baggy Point on the north coast, and between Budleigh Salterton and Thurlestone on the south coast.

*Text: Jeremy Barker / Photo: Lee Collins*

Balmer *et al.* 2013: 413; Sitters 1988: npt treated; Tyler 2010: 355

### Breeding-period abundance 2007–13

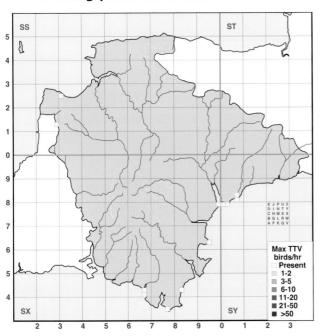

### Winter-period abundance 2007–13

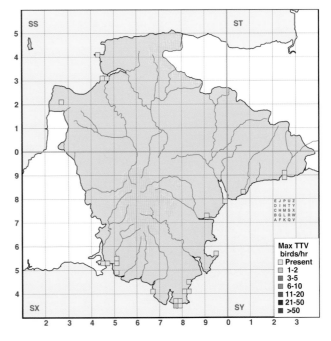

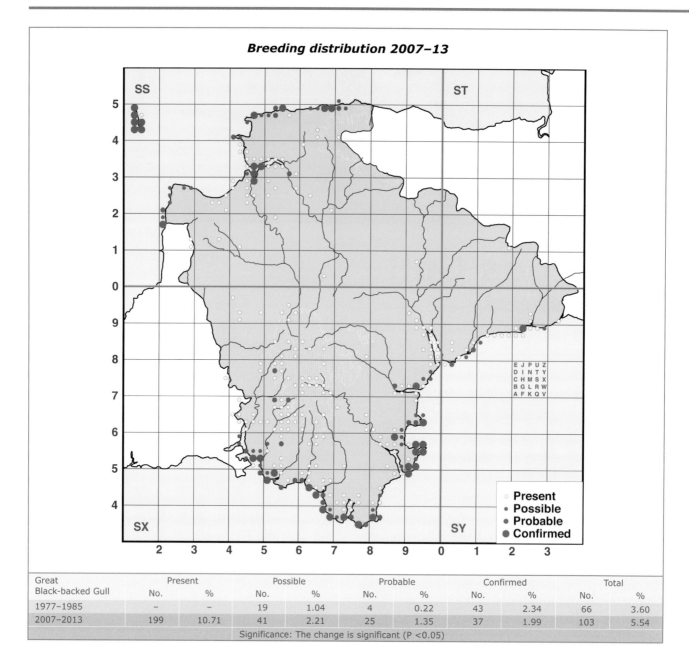

### Breeding distribution 2007–13

| Great Black-backed Gull | Present | | Possible | | Probable | | Confirmed | | Total | |
|---|---|---|---|---|---|---|---|---|---|---|
| | No. | % | No. | % | No. | % | No. | % | No. | % |
| 1977–1985 | – | – | 19 | 1.04 | 4 | 0.22 | 43 | 2.34 | 66 | 3.60 |
| 2007–2013 | 199 | 10.71 | 41 | 2.21 | 25 | 1.35 | 37 | 1.99 | 103 | 5.54 |
| Significance: The change is significant (P <0.05) | | | | | | | | | | |

### Breeding distribution 1977–85

### Breeding-period abundance 2007–13

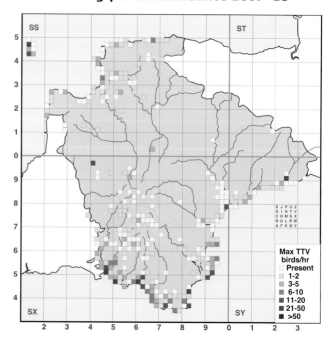

# Great Black-backed Gull

*Larus marinus*

THE SCARCEST – and the largest – of our resident large gulls, Great Black-backed Gulls are nonetheless a familiar sight to anyone who frequents the coast. They can be found in just about any coastal habitat, but favour larger estuaries and rocky coasts. Great Black-backs are not as gregarious when breeding as other large gulls. The highest breeding density in the county is on Lundy, where breeding censuses in 2008 and 2013 recorded 57 and 50 pairs respectively. On the mainland, however, they are distributed along both coasts at fairly low densities, using suitably undisturbed promontories or islets.

In common with Herring and Lesser Black-backed Gulls, numbers have declined somewhat since the *Devon Tetrad Atlas 1977–85* and breeding distribution has changed. Instances of both probable and confirmed breeding along the north coast were considerably fewer for the current Atlas, while on both coasts there seems to be a shift towards breeding in built-up areas and away from the open coastline between settlements. Some suggestion of a spread inland is also hinted at, with records of at least possible breeding well up into the western fringes of Dartmoor. The reasons for increased breeding in towns are likely to include a general decline in fish waste from fisheries, fewer open landfill sites and a reduction in the amount of raw sewage being pumped into the sea. Great Black-backs have been slower to adopt the highly urbanized habits of Herring and Lesser Black-backed Gulls, but should they also take to rooftops, might there be a similar change in population trends, with coastal birds suffering reduced productivity and urban birds proving more successful?

In winter, Great Black-backs are widespread around the Devon coast and numbers are highly variable, with significant increases during periods of stormy weather when birds seek shelter inshore. UK breeders are joined in winter by wanderers from elsewhere along the European Atlantic coast and as far afield as Iceland (Collins 2014). This species remains more strictly coastal in Devon than either Herring or Lesser Black-backed Gulls, although occasional birds can be found almost anywhere. However, inland records most frequently come from reservoirs, which birds use for bathing and resting. Some favoured sites, notably Roadford Reservoir, are situated at some considerable distance from the coast.

## Winter-period abundance 2007–13

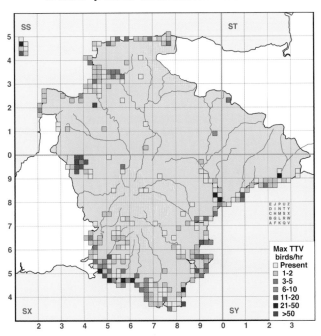

Max TTV birds/hr
- □ Present
- 1-2
- 3-5
- 6-10
- 11-20
- 21-50
- >50

*Text: Jeremy Barker / Photo: Neil Bygrave*

Balmer *et al.* 2013: 414; Sitters 1988: 116; Tyler 2010: 357

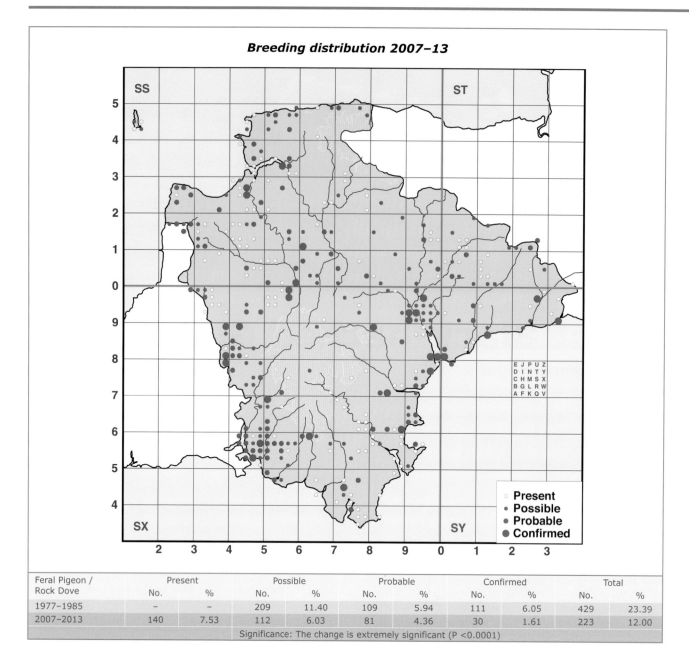

**Breeding distribution 2007–13**

| Feral Pigeon / Rock Dove | Present | | Possible | | Probable | | Confirmed | | Total | |
|---|---|---|---|---|---|---|---|---|---|---|
| | No. | % | No. | % | No. | % | No. | % | No. | % |
| 1977–1985 | – | – | 209 | 11.40 | 109 | 5.94 | 111 | 6.05 | 429 | 23.39 |
| 2007–2013 | 140 | 7.53 | 112 | 6.03 | 81 | 4.36 | 30 | 1.61 | 223 | 12.00 |
| Significance: The change is extremely significant (P <0.0001) | | | | | | | | | | |

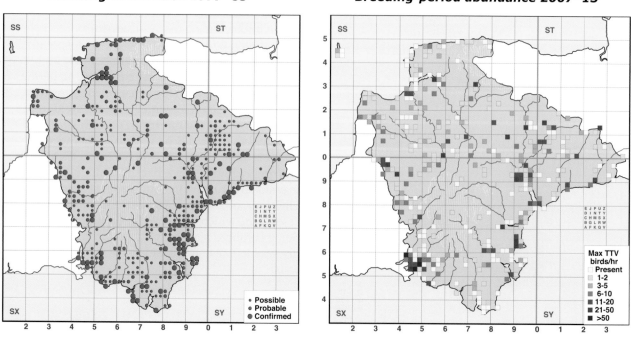

**Breeding distribution 1977–85**

**Breeding-period abundance 2007–13**

# Feral Pigeon/Rock Dove

*Columba livia*

FERAL PIGEONS are distant descendants of the Rock Dove. Pure-bred Rock Doves no longer occur in Devon (Moore 1969), if anywhere in the UK. Feral Pigeons are widespread and locally abundant in the county, with higher densities occurring mainly in urban and industrial centres. Birds are frequently recorded breeding along coastal cliffs, whilst inland nesting and roosting occurs communally in or on buildings, including many farmsteads. Transient individuals or flocks can be recorded in flight virtually anywhere, although they are often indistinguishable from racing pigeons.

### Winter-period abundance 2007–13

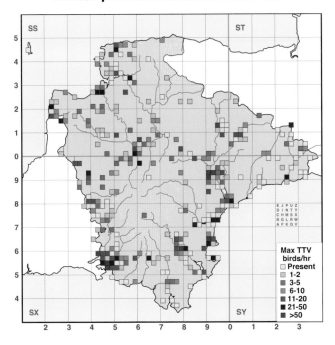

Max TTV
birds/hr
☐ Present
◻ 1-2
▨ 3-5
▨ 6-10
■ 11-20
■ 21-50
■ >50

The species is absent from many upland areas of Devon and is also thinly distributed inland. The Atlas breeding-period map shows that most of the confirmed breeding records came from villages, towns or cities. There were also almost contiguous breeding records from along both coasts, but many of these were probably associated with coastal settlements.

The *Devon Tetrad Atlas 1977–85* shows that Feral Pigeons were recorded in 23% of tetrads, whereas the present survey suggests a significant decline, with presence in only 12% of tetrads. Comparison of breeding maps for the two Atlases shows that much of this decline appears to have been driven by losses from the southern half of the county. A possible cause is that people are now discouraged from feeding Feral Pigeons in towns, so there may be less food available. Farmers generally tolerate small numbers around their buildings but will control them if they become too numerous; there is increased attention to hygiene in farm buildings, particularly dairies, and this may also have resulted in local declines. Feral Pigeons were amongst those species that fed on traditional winter stubbles and increased autumn ploughing will have reduced this food source.

Winter-period distribution and density appear very similar to those during the breeding period, which is unsurprising as Feral Pigeons are highly sedentary throughout their range (Wernham *et al.* 2002).

*Text: Simon Geary / Photo: Paul Sterry/NPL*

Balmer *et al.* 2013: 434; Sitters 1988: 124; Tyler 2010: 388

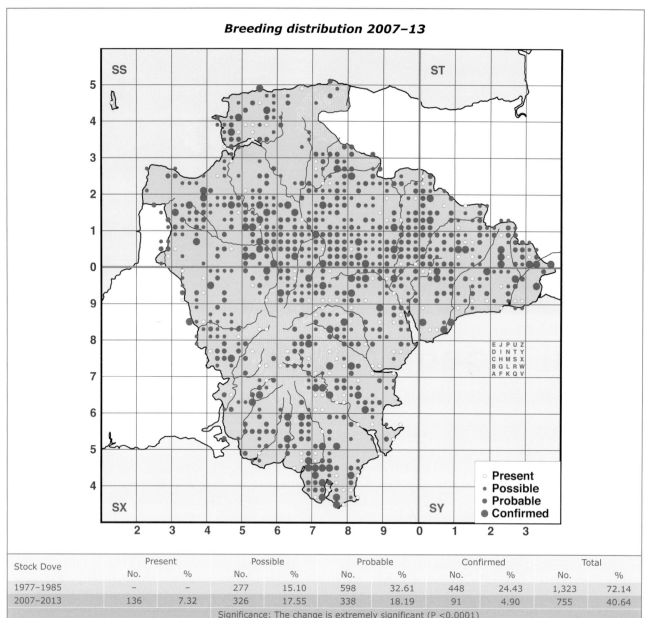

### Breeding distribution 2007–13

| Stock Dove | Present | | Possible | | Probable | | Confirmed | | Total | |
|---|---|---|---|---|---|---|---|---|---|---|
| | No. | % | No. | % | No. | % | No. | % | No. | % |
| 1977–1985 | – | – | 277 | 15.10 | 598 | 32.61 | 448 | 24.43 | 1,323 | 72.14 |
| 2007–2013 | 136 | 7.32 | 326 | 17.55 | 338 | 18.19 | 91 | 4.90 | 755 | 40.64 |
| Significance: The change is extremely significant (P <0.0001) | | | | | | | | | | |

### Breeding distribution 1977–85

### Breeding-period abundance 2007–13

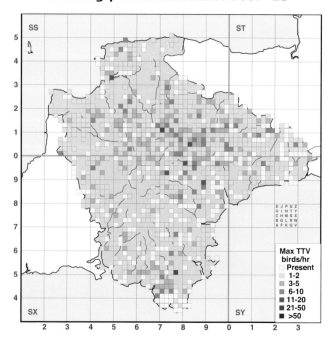

# Stock Dove
## Columba oenas

Amber listed

THE STOCK Dove is a bird of arable or mixed farmland in combination with trees or woodland, including older trees with cavities for nesting. Nestboxes and barns are also used readily. It is no surprise, therefore, that distribution is concentrated in more arable areas of the county, especially Mid Devon and parts of the South Hams and East Devon. It is absent from the higher areas of Dartmoor and Exmoor.

There has been a massive decline in breeding records of Stock Doves since the *Devon Tetrad Atlas 1977–85*, which found breeding evidence in 72% of

### Winter-period abundance 2007–13

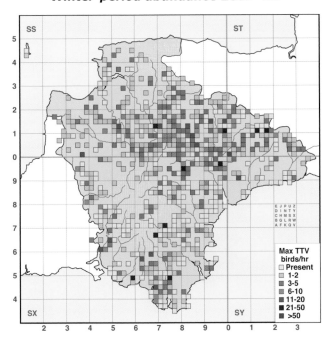

Max TTV birds/hr
- ☐ Present
- 1-2
- 3-5
- 6-10
- 11-20
- 21-50
- >50

tetrads as against 41% for the current survey. Although the core distribution appears not to have changed between Atlases, there are some districts where the species appears to have declined particularly dramatically, for example West Devon, Torridge and North Devon – regions where there has also been a significant decline in mixed and arable cropping. Generally across the county, Stock Dove abundance has fallen and confirmed breeding records are much scarcer than during the 1977–85 survey. The apparent decline in Devon contrasts with the generally stable or slightly increasing national and regional breeding trends for this species demonstrated in the Breeding Bird Survey (BBS) in which, for South West England, the smoothed figure for 1995–2013 was a 20% increase (Baillie *et al.* 2014).

Stock Doves can also be elusive and difficult to record as breeding birds, so without further survey work it is not easy to be sure whether the decline is as severe as suggested. *Bird Atlas 2007–11* also indicates a general reduction in breeding abundance for the species in the South West. It may be that differences in atlas methodology and coverage may explain at least some of the discrepancy between this and the BBS. Although it seems that the species remains widespread in Devon, its long-term status must not be taken for granted.

Winter distribution and density are very similar to those found during the breeding season, which is not surprising as the British population is considered to be sedentary (Wernham *et al.* 2002).

*Text: Simon Geary / Photo: Charlie Fleming*
*Stock Dove sponsored by Peter Robinson*

Balmer *et al.* 2013: 436; Sitters 1988: 126; Tyler 2010: 389

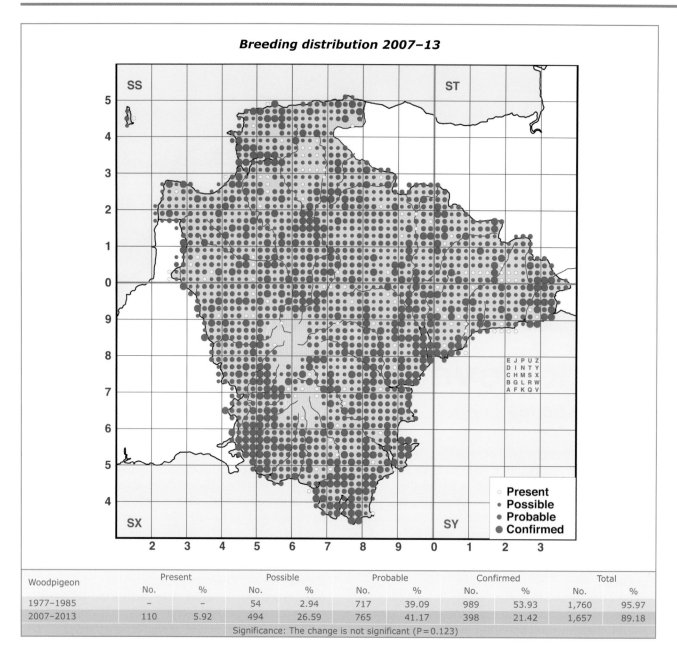

## Breeding distribution 2007–13

| Woodpigeon | Present | | Possible | | Probable | | Confirmed | | Total | |
|---|---|---|---|---|---|---|---|---|---|---|
| | No. | % | No. | % | No. | % | No. | % | No. | % |
| 1977–1985 | – | – | 54 | 2.94 | 717 | 39.09 | 989 | 53.93 | 1,760 | 95.97 |
| 2007–2013 | 110 | 5.92 | 494 | 26.59 | 765 | 41.17 | 398 | 21.42 | 1,657 | 89.18 |
| Significance: The change is not significant (P = 0.123) | | | | | | | | | | |

## Breeding distribution 1977–85

## Breeding-period abundance 2007–13

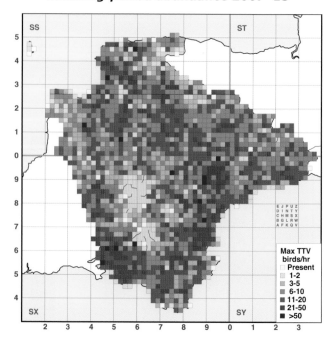

# Woodpigeon
*Columba palumbus*

THERE IS no doubt that the Woodpigeon has become an even more ubiquitous species in recent decades. Nationally, it is the species most frequently recorded by the BTO Breeding Bird Survey (BBS), being twice as numerous as Blackbird, the next most recorded species (Harris *et al.* 2015). Traditionally a bird of arable farmland, Woodpigeons are now adapted to many environments, including urban centres. Their poorly constructed nests require some shelter, and the species is thus absent from the high moors during the breeding season. Nesting birds are quite tolerant of high levels of human disturbance and can frequently be found in urban areas and in planted amenity woodland next to busy roads.

Both the *Devon Tetrad Atlas 1977–85* and the current survey found Woodpigeons to be widespread, occurring in slightly more than 95% of tetrads during the breeding season. Overall distribution appears not to have changed between Atlases but, as with a number of other species, the number of tetrads with confirmed breeding appears to have declined. This is possibly due to differences in survey methodology and coverage. According to BBS records there was a 43% increase in South West England between 1995 and 2013 (Harris *et al.* 2014), suggesting that confirmed breeding in Devon should be more widespread than this survey has recorded, which in turn tends to confirm that differences in survey method between the two Devon Atlases may account for the apparent change.

## Winter-period abundance 2007–13

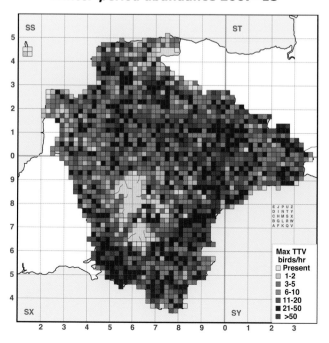

Max TTV birds/hr
- ☐ Present
- 1-2
- 3-5
- 6-10
- 11-20
- 21-50
- >50

Winter distribution is very similar to that in the breeding season, which is not surprising as the British population is largely sedentary, although considerable numbers of birds can move small distances, particularly in their first year (Wernham *et al.* 2002). Winter density is often greater than breeding density. The reasons for this are unclear, but several possibilities include an influx of birds during late autumn – for example, 126,000 moving south-west at Haldon in four hours on 6 November 2011 and two counts of more than 25,000 passing through south coast sites in late October and early November 2012 (*DBRs*) which then overwinter – or that winter flocks are larger and more conspicuous to surveyors. However, if the latter was the sole reason then some tetrads would be expected to lose birds and the winter density map would be expected to have a more dappled appearance.

It seems that the future of the Woodpigeon in Devon is not under threat and its adaptation to human environments should ensure that it continues to thrive.

*Text: Simon Geary / Photo: Neil Bygrave*
*Woodpigeon sponsored by Chris Skinner*

Balmer *et al.* 2013: 438; Sitters 1988: 128; Tyler 2010: 391

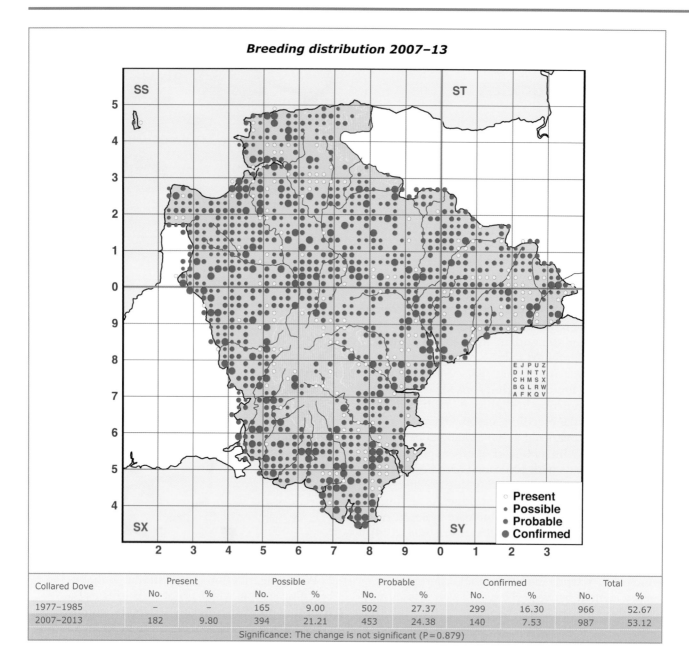

### Breeding distribution 2007–13

| Collared Dove | Present | | Possible | | Probable | | Confirmed | | Total | |
|---|---|---|---|---|---|---|---|---|---|---|
| | No. | % | No. | % | No. | % | No. | % | No. | % |
| 1977–1985 | – | – | 165 | 9.00 | 502 | 27.37 | 299 | 16.30 | 966 | 52.67 |
| 2007–2013 | 182 | 9.80 | 394 | 21.21 | 453 | 24.38 | 140 | 7.53 | 987 | 53.12 |
| Significance: The change is not significant (P=0.879) | | | | | | | | | | |

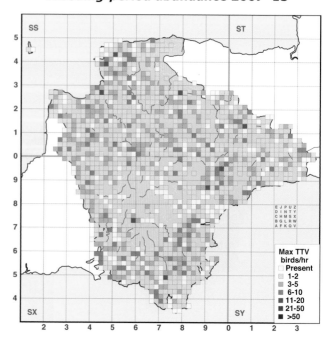

### Breeding distribution 1977–85

### Breeding-period abundance 2007–13

# Collared Dove
## Streptopelia decaocto

Very much a bird of human habitation, the Collared Dove has now become a common and familiar resident of Devon's villages, towns and cities. Previously found in Turkey and Asia Minor (now the Middle East), the species underwent a rapid north-westward expansion across Europe in the 1930s and reached Britain in the mid-1950s. Collared Doves were first recorded in Devon in Plymouth in 1960, when they probably bred, and breeding was first confirmed in at least four sites in 1962. Numbers increased and they spread rapidly; in 1966 there were around 200 in Budleigh Salterton and by the end of the following year Collared Doves were present in most of the main towns and villages (Tyler 2010). By the time of the *Devon Tetrad Atlas 1977–85* it was estimated there were 3,500–5,000 pairs breeding in Devon and a similar calculation, based on the current survey, would suggest a further increase.

Collared Doves have continued to expand their range and are now breeding to the west of Okehampton, north of Hatherleigh, around Witheridge and north of Barnstaple. However, the species is still absent from much of upland Dartmoor and Exmoor. Some of the villages on Dartmoor did not record Collared Doves until the 1990s or even later (Smaldon 2005). Their distribution in the *Devon Tetrad Atlas 1977–85* shows preponderance in areas of lowland arable farming, and few bred above 300 metres. Surprisingly, and despite currently being more widespread, this striking bird was recorded less often as a confirmed or probable breeder.

Collared Doves appear to have become scarcer between Exeter and Sidmouth, east of Barnstaple, around Totnes and especially around Torbay. Although the species was first seen on Lundy in May 1961, breeding was only confirmed there for the first time in 1998 (Davis & Jones 2007).

Collared Doves breed almost throughout the year. A pair in Stoke Canon made five nesting attempts in 2008. The first eggs were laid in early January and young of the final brood were still in the nest in late December (Jarvis 2009). Nationally, the number of young Collared Doves fledging per breeding attempt has increased significantly over the last four decades (BTO BirdTrends 2014), although there are recent signs of a decline. *Bird Atlas 2007–11* shows an increase in relative abundance in the breeding season in Devon.

A regular pattern of early summer arrivals on Lundy (Davis & Jones 2007) shows that movements are not always local and that there is substantial dispersal; birds ringed on Lundy have been recovered in Ireland and Wales.

*Text: A W G John / Photo: John Clark*
*Collared Dove sponsored by Stella Beavan*

Balmer *et al.* 2013: 440; Sitters 1988: 130; Tyler 2010: 393

### Winter-period abundance 2007–13

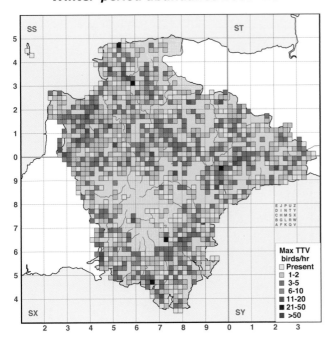

Max TTV birds/hr
☐ Present
☐ 1-2
▨ 3-5
▨ 6-10
■ 11-20
■ 21-50
■ >50

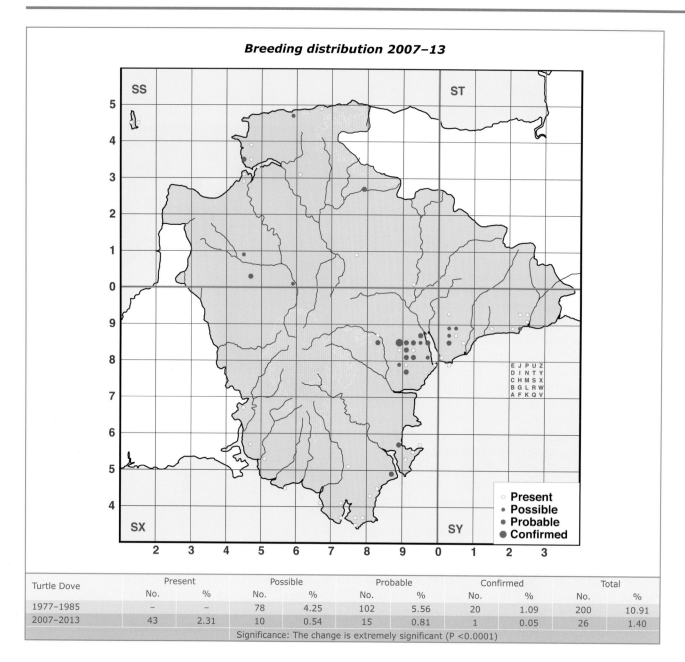

**Breeding distribution 2007–13**

| Turtle Dove | Present | | Possible | | Probable | | Confirmed | | Total | |
|---|---|---|---|---|---|---|---|---|---|---|
| | No. | % | No. | % | No. | % | No. | % | No. | % |
| 1977–1985 | – | – | 78 | 4.25 | 102 | 5.56 | 20 | 1.09 | 200 | 10.91 |
| 2007–2013 | 43 | 2.31 | 10 | 0.54 | 15 | 0.81 | 1 | 0.05 | 26 | 1.40 |
| Significance: The change is extremely significant (P <0.0001) | | | | | | | | | | |

**Breeding distribution 1977–85**

**Breeding-period abundance 2007–13**

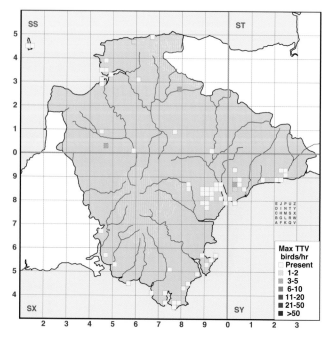

# Turtle Dove
*Streptopelia turtur*

**Red listed**

TURTLE DOVES are summer visitors, wintering in the Sahelian zone of sub-Saharan Africa and returning from mid-April. They are birds of mixed farmland habitat with tall hedges, scrub or woodland edges for nesting; they feed on the ground in weedy areas or where there is spilt grain or stubble.

There has been a dramatic decline since the *Devon Tetrad Atlas 1977–85*, with the number of tetrads for which breeding evidence was recorded falling from 200 (just under 11%) in the earlier survey to only 26 (1.4%) in the current Atlas. The seriousness of this decline is underlined by the almost complete absence of breeding birds, with breeding confirmed in just a single tetrad during 2007–2013. Probable and possible breeding was reported from 15 and 10 tetrads respectively, and 'presence only' in a further 43 tetrads, with many, if not most, of the latter records likely to refer to migrants.

The *Devon Tetrad Atlas 1977–85* shows that the species was then widespread in the east of the county, from Haldon, through the East Devon Pebblebeds and across into the Blackdown Hills to the Somerset border; it is here that most losses have occurred. Overall, distribution during the current survey was broadly similar to that shown by the earlier Atlas, with concentrations around the Taw/Torridge Estuary and the North Devon coast, and scattered occurrences in Mid Devon and in southern coastal areas. Breeding evidence came mostly from the Haldon area and around the East Devon Pebblebeds.

Nationally, Turtle Doves have also declined sharply, with a contraction in range away from the north, west and south-west, and with densities falling within their remaining breeding range (*Bird Atlas 2007–11*). Across the UK, the breeding population fell by 95% between 1970 and 2011 (*State of the UK's Birds 2013*) leaving the species concentrated in East Anglia and the south-east, perhaps favouring the warmer, drier conditions of this part of Britain.

The reasons for the reduction in the numbers of Turtle Doves is not fully understood, but loss of breeding habitat, including a supply of seed-rich food sources, hunting in southern Europe during migration and changes to the African wintering habitat are each possible contributing factors. In Devon, habitat loss in the farmed landscape, particularly in East Devon, may be contributing to this decline. If the national and regional trend continues, Turtle Doves may soon vanish altogether from Devon.

*Text: Helen Booker / Photo: John Clark*
*Turtle Dove sponsored by Jon Valters*

Balmer *et al.* 2013: 442; Sitters 1988: 132; Tyler 2010: 395

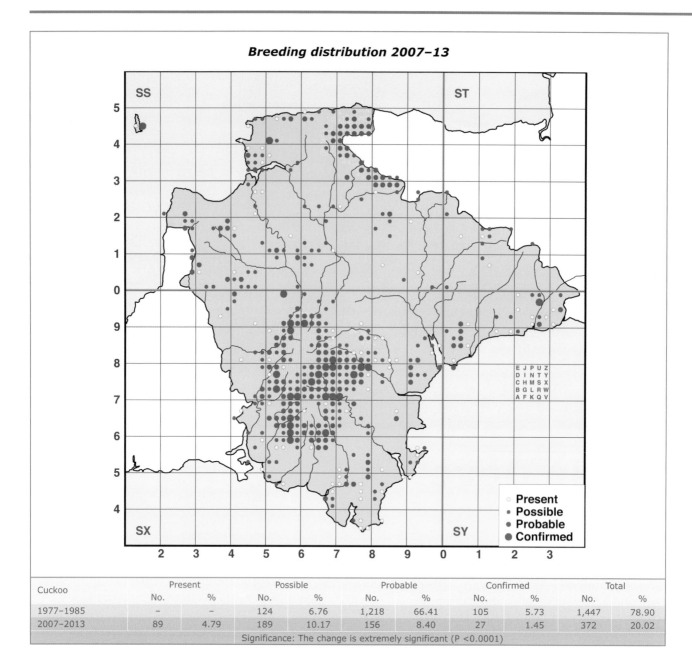

### Breeding distribution 2007–13

| Cuckoo | Present | | Possible | | Probable | | Confirmed | | Total | |
|---|---|---|---|---|---|---|---|---|---|---|
| | No. | % | No. | % | No. | % | No. | % | No. | % |
| 1977–1985 | – | – | 124 | 6.76 | 1,218 | 66.41 | 105 | 5.73 | 1,447 | 78.90 |
| 2007–2013 | 89 | 4.79 | 189 | 10.17 | 156 | 8.40 | 27 | 1.45 | 372 | 20.02 |
| Significance: The change is extremely significant (P <0.0001) | | | | | | | | | | |

### Breeding distribution 1977–85

### Breeding-period abundance 2007–13

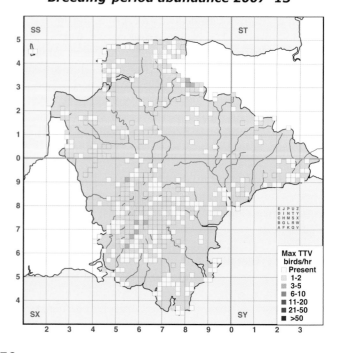

# Cuckoo
*Cuculus canorus*

HISTORICALLY, DEVON's breeding Cuckoos were widespread birds found in agricultural, reedbed, woodland and moorland habitats. Individual females specialize in a single habitat and host species and use favoured perches to locate nests to parasitize. Males range more widely and, although obvious from their well-known and distinctive call, their mobility makes accurate mapping of territories difficult. Locating nests parasitized by Cuckoos in order to confirm breeding is equally challenging.

Comparison of data from the present survey with the *Devon Tetrad Atlas 1977–85* shows that the Cuckoo has seen one of the largest 'between Atlas' declines of any bird in Devon. Sadly this mirrors the situation throughout southern Britain (*Bird Atlas 2007–11*). Cuckoos were recorded in only 20% of tetrads during 2007–13, representing losses from 1,075 tetrads or two-thirds of the total during 1977–85. It is clear that the species has almost totally disappeared from the county's agricultural lowlands and is now only common in the uplands of Dartmoor and Exmoor. Reasons for this steep and rapid decline are unknown and may be attributable to multiple causes owing to the species' complex ecology. However, reduced availability of large caterpillars (the favoured prey of Cuckoos), which have declined significantly in lowland agricultural areas (Denerley 2013), is likely to be significant. Earlier breeding of host species due to climate change may adversely affect Cuckoos if they do not also arrive earlier in spring to match this advance. It is also striking that the decline in the Cuckoo closely matches that of the Meadow pipit, their main host species in Devon. Satellite-tracking of UK breeding birds has shown that 'our' Cuckoos spend only 15% of their annual cycle here, meaning that conditions in the Central African wintering quarters, and along migration routes through (or over) multiple countries, are likely to play an important role in explaining the decline. For example, parts of West Africa are now known to be important refuelling areas prior to crossing of the Sahara in spring and so habitat loss and degradation in these areas could have major impacts.

Four male Cuckoos satellite-tagged on Dartmoor in May 2013, as part of the ongoing national project led by the BTO, contributed to enormous advances in our knowledge of Cuckoo movements, both locally on the breeding grounds and throughout the species' range. All four of the Dartmoor birds had already left the UK before the end of June 2013, with one reaching wintering grounds in the Congo basin by October that year. The wider project suggests that Devon's Cuckoos share migration behaviour with Cuckoos from southern and eastern England, with most migrating along a western route to Africa via Iberia. This route may have lower survival rates than the more easterly route favoured by Cuckoos breeding in Wales and Scotland, where numbers remain strong. Work to diagnose the causes of the Cuckoo's decline in England and to understand more about its behavioural ecology on Dartmoor continues through the BTO satellite-tracking project, and through research conducted by the University of Exeter and the RSPB.

*Text: Malcolm Burgess / Photos: Dave Scott*
*Cuckoo sponsored by Dartmoor National Park Authority*

Balmer *et al.* 2013: 446; Sitters 1988: 134; Tyler 2010: 397

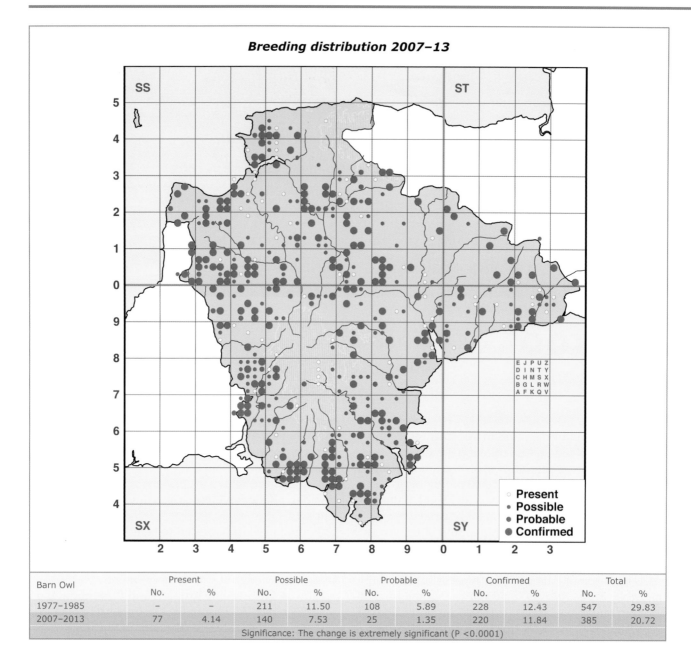

**Breeding distribution 2007–13**

| Barn Owl | Present | | Possible | | Probable | | Confirmed | | Total | |
|---|---|---|---|---|---|---|---|---|---|---|
| | No. | % | No. | % | No. | % | No. | % | No. | % |
| 1977–1985 | – | – | 211 | 11.50 | 108 | 5.89 | 228 | 12.43 | 547 | 29.83 |
| 2007–2013 | 77 | 4.14 | 140 | 7.53 | 25 | 1.35 | 220 | 11.84 | 385 | 20.72 |
| | Significance: The change is extremely significant (P <0.0001) | | | | | | | | | |

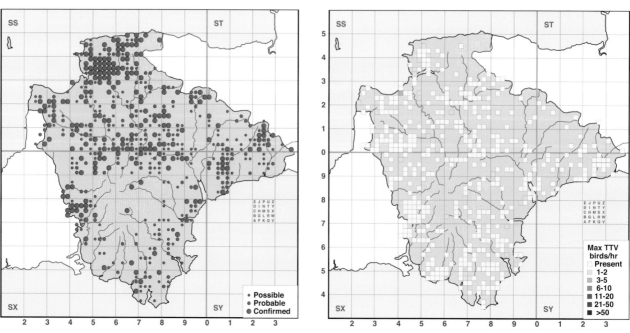

**Breeding distribution 1977–85**

**Breeding-period abundance 2007–13**

# Barn Owl
## *Tyto alba*

**B**ARN OWLS are one of the iconic birds of the British countryside, often breeding in old farm buildings and feeding in areas of rough grassland close to habitations. They are essentially birds of open country with hedgerows and small patches of trees, combined with old hedgerow trees with cavities in which they can nest and areas of vole-rich rough grassland where they can hunt. Their abundance varies according to the populations of their prey; early 2013, as well as being very cold, was also a poor vole year; few owls bred and those that did raised few young; a number of adults were found dead or moribund through starvation (*DBR*). Intensive studies by the Barn Owl Trust, which is based in Devon, mean that we have a fairly good picture of the status and breeding success of Barn Owls within the county. Numerous farms now have Barn Owl nestboxes, and many chicks are ringed at the nest. Breeding starts early, but in good vole years a second brood may be raised once the first has fledged.

Barn Owls are widespread in Devon, although largely absent from the high ground of Dartmoor and Exmoor. Ringing recoveries show that most birds are sedentary, with only short-distance dispersal of the young (Barn Owl Trust 2015). The present survey shows the highest concentrations in the coastal strip east of Plymouth, while the *Devon Tetrad Atlas 1977–85* had a major concentration in North Devon. One wonders if these concentrations may represent areas where Barn Owl specialists were particularly active, rather than reflecting real

'patches' of birds. In the present Atlas, Barn Owls were recorded in all breeding categories from 385 tetrads, while in the 1977–85 survey they were found in 547 tetrads. *Bird Atlas 2007–11* shows a slight increase in England, but a substantial expansion of range in Scotland and a strong decline in Ireland.

Changes in farming practices have reduced the amount of rough grassland available for hunting; modern rodenticides may also affect Barn Owls (and other owls) and the prevalence of rough grassland along motorways and arterial roads means that road casualties are high because Barn Owls find good hunting areas there but are vulnerable to the strong wind currents generated by heavy goods vehicles. These adverse factors seem to have been largely counterbalanced by the provision of nestboxes and, at least until 2000, the release of captive-bred birds (Toms 2014).

Barn Owls are adversely affected by hard winters and those of 2009/10 and 2010/11, together with the cold spring of 2013, have all contributed to a reduction in numbers. This is echoed nationally, with a significant downturn in the UK population index since 2009 (BTO BirdTrends 2014). Better weather conditions and an ample food supply could lead to a rapid recovery in the population.

*Text: J M Lock / Photo: Steve Hatch*
*Barn Owl sponsored by Chris Wright*

Balmer *et al.* 2013: 448; Sitters 1988: 136; Tyler 2010: 400

### Winter-period abundance 2007–13

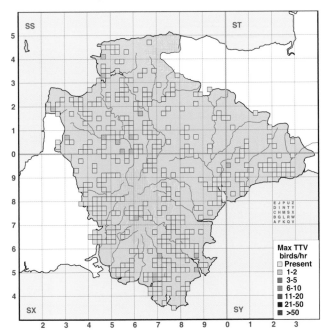

Max TTV birds/hr
- ☐ Present
- 1-2
- 3-5
- 6-10
- 11-20
- 21-50
- >50

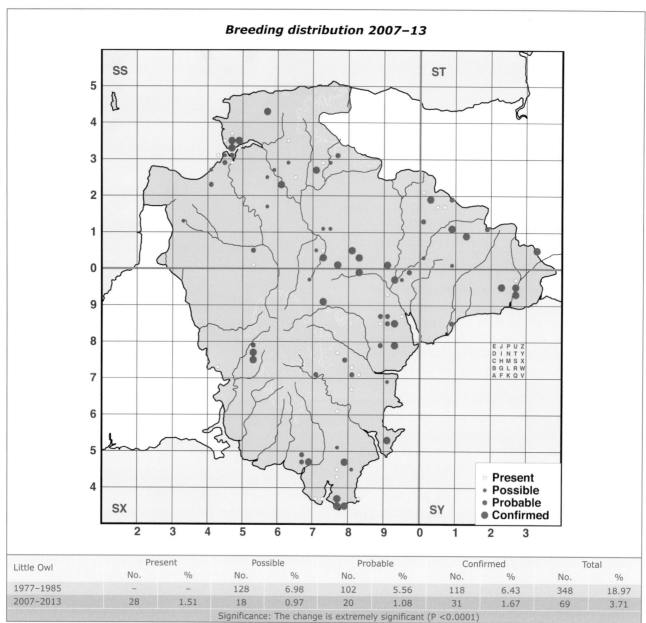

## Breeding distribution 2007–13

| Little Owl | Present | | Possible | | Probable | | Confirmed | | Total | |
|---|---|---|---|---|---|---|---|---|---|---|
| | No. | % | No. | % | No. | % | No. | % | No. | % |
| 1977–1985 | – | – | 128 | 6.98 | 102 | 5.56 | 118 | 6.43 | 348 | 18.97 |
| 2007–2013 | 28 | 1.51 | 18 | 0.97 | 20 | 1.08 | 31 | 1.67 | 69 | 3.71 |
| Significance: The change is extremely significant (P <0.0001) | | | | | | | | | | |

## Breeding distribution 1977–85

## Breeding-period abundance 2007–13

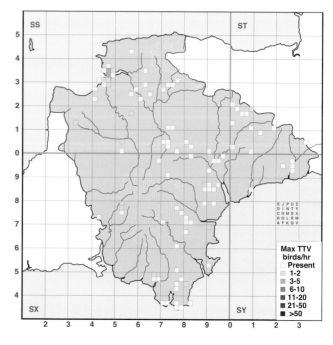

# Little Owl
## *Athene noctua*

LITTLE OWLS are native to continental Europe and the British population originates from introductions made in Kent and Northamptonshire in the second half of the 19th century (Toms 2014). Since its introduction it has spread throughout England, but is scarce in Wales and almost absent from Scotland. It has not reached Ireland. It is a bird of open country with hedges and isolated large trees, in the hollows of which it often nests, although it may also nest in old buildings and in the spaces between stored straw bales. It also frequents farm buildings where its small dumpy form may often be seen silhouetted on a roof ridge at dusk. It feeds largely on insects but also takes small mammals and, on occasion, small birds, and mainly hunts from a perch.

The *Devon Tetrad Atlas 1977–85* recorded Little Owls in 19% of tetrads, with concentrations in North Devon, the upper Exe Valley, East Devon and in the Haldon area west of the Exe Estuary. Breeding was confirmed in 118 tetrads and may have occurred in a further 230. In the present survey, breeding was confirmed in only 31 tetrads and possible/probable breeding in a further 38. The clear areas of concentration seen in the 1977–85 survey have disappeared, although there are scattered records of confirmed breeding in all of them. Confirming breeding in this species is not easy and even where it is known to breed, daylight sightings can be very uncommon indeed. Birds can sometimes be seen at dusk and be heard calling in the evenings, but actually finding a nest is very difficult and proof of

breeding may only come from seeing newly fledged young.

The winter distribution mirrors that in the breeding season, although there were no winter records from some areas in the South Hams and Mid Devon that were occupied in the breeding season. In total there were fewer tetrad records in winter, perhaps because the species is harder to locate at this time of year.

The decline in Devon is mirrored in *Bird Atlas 2007–11*, with an overall 11% decline country-wide, most of which has occurred in Cornwall, Devon and Wales, where declines have been much greater. *Bird Atlas 2007–11* suggests a link with changes in farming practices; in Devon it is possible that the widespread conversion of old mixed grass pasture into ryegrass monoculture may have depressed the numbers of insects such as craneflies (Tipulidae).

*Text: J M Lock / Photo: Andrew Cunningham*
*Little Owl sponsored by Mike & Lesley Lock*

Balmer *et al.* 2013: 452; Sitters 1988: 138; Tyler 2010: 404

### Winter-period abundance 2007–13

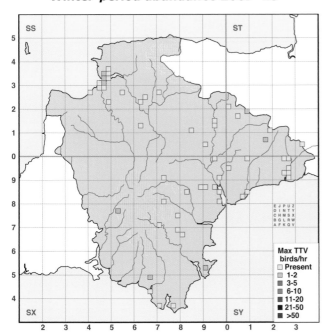

Max TTV birds/hr
- □ Present
- 1-2
- 3-5
- 6-10
- 11-20
- 21-50
- >50

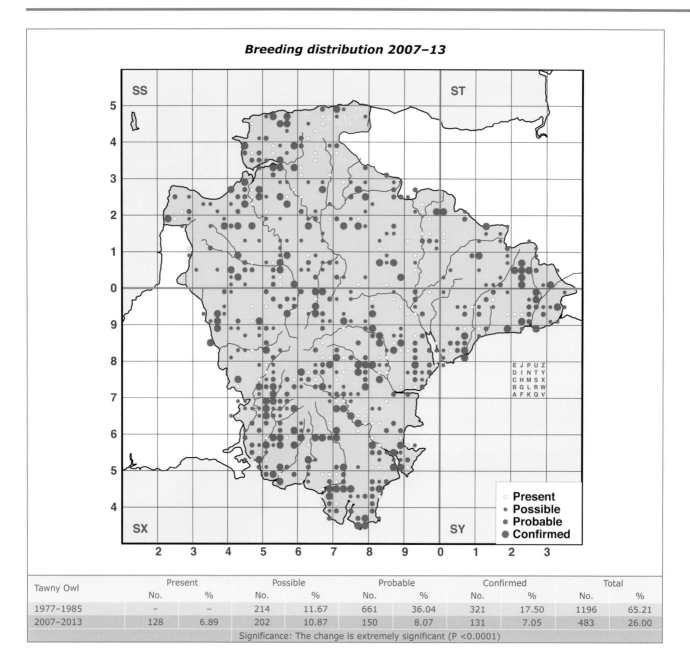

**Breeding distribution 2007–13**

| Tawny Owl | Present | | Possible | | Probable | | Confirmed | | Total | |
|---|---|---|---|---|---|---|---|---|---|---|
| | No. | % | No. | % | No. | % | No. | % | No. | % |
| 1977–1985 | – | – | 214 | 11.67 | 661 | 36.04 | 321 | 17.50 | 1196 | 65.21 |
| 2007–2013 | 128 | 6.89 | 202 | 10.87 | 150 | 8.07 | 131 | 7.05 | 483 | 26.00 |
| Significance: The change is extremely significant (P <0.0001) | | | | | | | | | | |

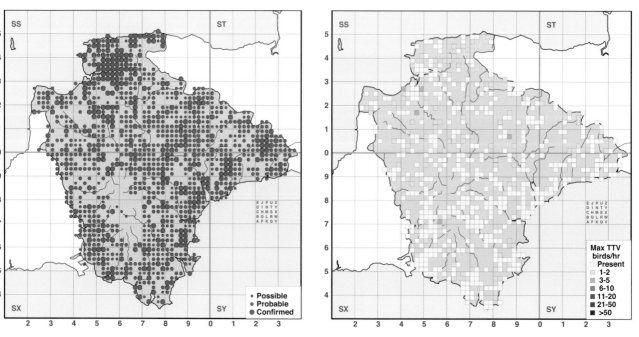

**Breeding distribution 1977–85**

**Breeding-period abundance 2007–13**

# Tawny Owl
## *Strix aluco*

THE HOOTING of the Tawny Owl is still one of the characteristic sounds of autumn and winter nights in Devon. 'Tawnies' are woodland birds, preferring deciduous communities and hunting both by quartering open grasslands nearby and beneath the woodland canopy, where they may hunt from a perch. They will live within urban areas as long as there are sufficient trees to provide daytime cover and hollows for nesting. They take readily to large nestboxes, but nest in buildings much less often than Barn Owls.

Tawnies occur throughout Britain but are absent from Ireland and the Isle of Wight, where Long-eared Owls, with which they appear to compete, are much more common (Toms 2014). They are also absent from the highest parts of Scotland, but are the commonest British owl. They feed largely on small mammals up to the size of Common Rats but will also take small birds and invertebrates. They are largely sedentary, with young rarely dispersing more than 20 kilometres from the breeding site.

The present survey shows Tawny Owls to be widely scattered throughout Devon, with no obvious concentrations, although they are absent from the highest ground of Dartmoor and Exmoor, and very sparse in eastern Mid Devon. This is in distinct contrast to the *Devon Tetrad Atlas 1977–85* which shows a very marked cluster of tetrads with confirmed breeding in North Devon, east of the Taw/Torridge Estuary. As with the Barn Owl, one

wonders if this is an artefact resulting from different survey methodology or particularly active owl watchers in that area in the earlier survey! Overall, however, taking all breeding categories together, Tawny Owls were recorded from 483 tetrads in the present survey, less than half that (1,196) in the 1977–85 survey. Confirmed breeding took place in 131, compared with 321 in 1977-85. *Bird Atlas 2007–11* found a slight (6%) nationwide decline – without a clear geographical pattern and possibly not significant bearing in mind the difficulty of censusing a nocturnal bird. The fact that no steep decline has been recorded nationally lends weight to the notion that the apparent losses in Devon may be largely to do with differences in atlas methodology and/or coverage.

However, other possible reasons for losses in Devon include changes in agricultural practices, loss of mature hedgerow trees – particularly elms with their large potential nesting cavities – increased mortality on roads and the increased use of modern rodenticides, although no link has been demonstrated between these and owl mortality (*Bird Atlas 2007–11*).

*Text: J M Lock / Photos: Steve Hatch (top) & Debbie Thomas*
*Tawny Owl sponsored by Kevin & Donna Cox*

Balmer *et al.* 2013: 456; Sitters 1988: 140; Tyler 2010: 406

### Winter-period abundance 2007–13

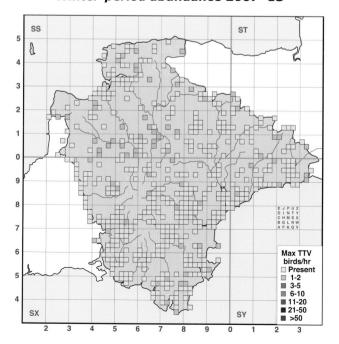

Max TTV birds/hr
- ☐ Present
- ☐ 1-2
- ▨ 3-5
- ▨ 6-10
- ■ 11-20
- ■ 21-50
- ■ >50

# Long-eared Owl

*Asio otus*

LONG-EARED OWLS are mainly scarce winter visitors to Devon, with fewer than ten records in most years (*DBRs*), often of apparent migrants at coastal sites. There are also a few confirmed breeding records. The species appears to have difficulty in competing with the larger Tawny Owl, so that it is relatively common in Ireland and the Isle of Wight, where there are no Tawnies (Toms 2014). In Devon, as in much of its British range, it is a bird of mature conifer plantations, feeding both within the woodland and also in open areas of rough grassland nearby, where its small mammal prey can be found. It is the most nocturnal of our owls. The nest is usually the old nest of a corvid or other large bird; in some areas dog-baskets have been provided and used (Toms 2014).

Breeding records in Devon are rare and during the Atlas period there was only a single record of confirmed breeding, which came from the Dartmoor conifer plantations. Confirmed breeding occurred just prior to the Atlas period, when two young were fledged from a nest on Aylesbeare Common, this being the first such record for 20 years (*DBR* 2007). The *Devon Tetrad Atlas 1977–85* recorded confirmed breeding at two sites, both in 1985, one on the East Devon Commons and the other in Eggesford Forest. As S.G. Madge wrote in the 1977–85 Atlas, this is a species likely to be under-recorded, as the best way to find breeding birds is to listen for the territorial call – and few venture into conifer plantations during cold February nights!

*Text: J M Lock / Photo: Andrew Cunningham*
*Long-eared Owl sponsored by Glendinning*

**Glendinning**
QUARRY & CONCRETE PRODUCTS

Balmer *et al.* 2013: 456; Sitters 1988: 301; Tyler 2010: 408

## Breeding-period abundance 2007–13

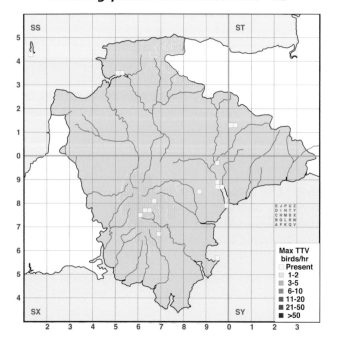

## Winter-period abundance 2007–13

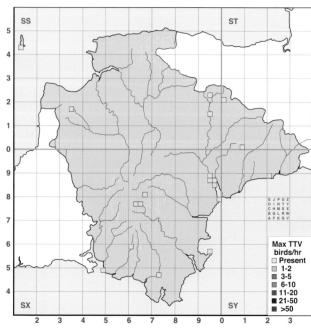

# Short-eared Owl

*Asio flammeus*

Amber listed

SHORT-EARED OWLS are winter visitors and passage migrants to Devon, being seen mainly in the autumn at coastal locations, as well as on the moors. Usually there are 20–25 records in a year but 2011 was exceptional, with 58 (*DBR*). Breeding has been suspected on occasion but not proved since 1943 when three pairs nested on Braunton Burrows (Tyler 2010).

Birds of open country, nesting on the ground and needing rough grass rich in voles for feeding, Short-eared Owls are particularly associated with the early stages of young conifer plantations, before the canopy closes. The decline of almost 50% shown by *Bird Atlas 2007–2011* since the earlier Atlases may be due to the maturation of the many plantations that were planted in the 1950s and 1960s.

The winter distribution is concentrated around the coasts and on Dartmoor and Exmoor; this may reflect both the species' preference for open country and also the prevalence of rough grassland, with voles, in these areas. Many of the records probably relate to passage birds. The majority of the summer records also probably refer to late passage birds, which are often seen in April and May. Although occasional birds are seen in summer, they are probably summering non-breeders or failed breeders dispersing early; breeding on Devon's moors is now extremely unlikely given the current levels of disturbance by walkers and their dogs.

*Text: J M Lock / Photo: Paul Sterry/NPL*
*Short-eared Owl sponsored by Estelle Skinner*

Balmer *et al.* 2013: 458; Sitters 1988: 301; Tyler 2010: 410

### Breeding-period abundance 2007–13

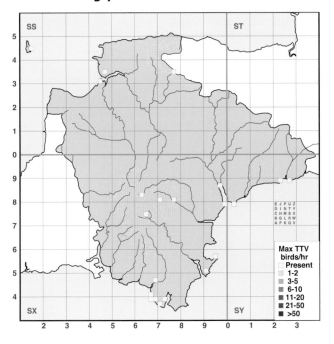

### Winter-period abundance 2007–13

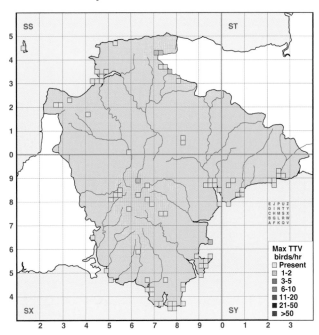

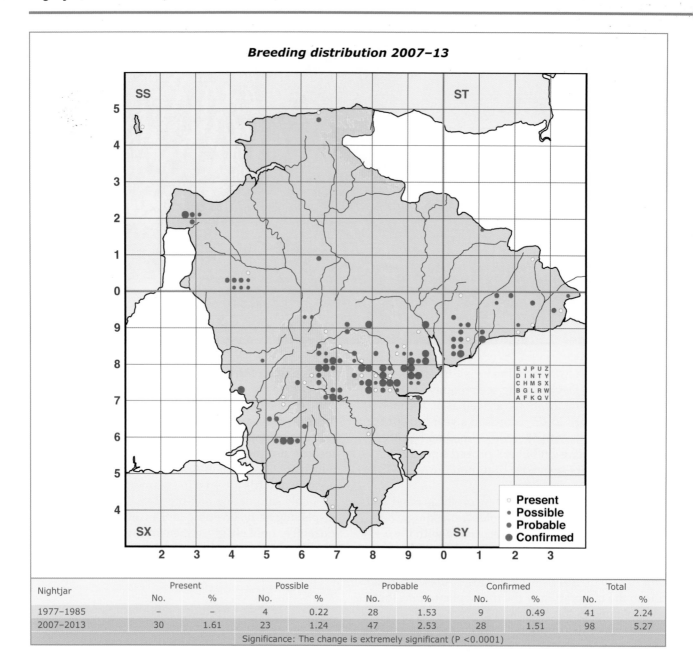

### Breeding distribution 2007–13

| Nightjar | Present | | Possible | | Probable | | Confirmed | | Total | |
|---|---|---|---|---|---|---|---|---|---|---|
| | No. | % | No. | % | No. | % | No. | % | No. | % |
| 1977–1985 | – | – | 4 | 0.22 | 28 | 1.53 | 9 | 0.49 | 41 | 2.24 |
| 2007–2013 | 30 | 1.61 | 23 | 1.24 | 47 | 2.53 | 28 | 1.51 | 98 | 5.27 |
| Significance: The change is extremely significant (P <0.0001) | | | | | | | | | | |

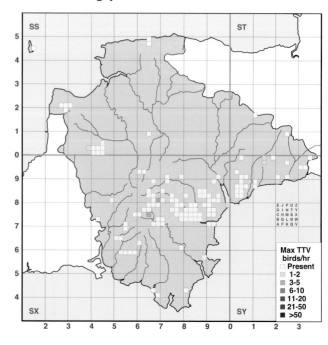

### Breeding distribution 1977–85

### Breeding-period abundance 2007–13

# Nightjar
*Caprimulgus europaeus*

Amber listed

THE NIGHTJAR is a bird of open woodland or heathland, particularly early successional birch and Scots Pine and young conifer plantations. In Devon they are found mainly in heathland and in young or clear-felled conifer plantations, most of which are found on Dartmoor, in Haldon Forest and on the Pebblebed Heaths of East Devon. Although Nightjars actually nest in these open woodland habitats, they forage more widely, including over mature woodland, and so require a well-wooded and connected landscape around breeding sites.

Data from the current survey show that Nightjars have extended their Devon range since the *Devon Tetrad Atlas 1977–85* and are now present in 5% of tetrads, a highly significant increase. The newly occupied tetrads are almost all within Dartmoor and its fringes, in Haldon Forest and in heathland around Chudleigh Knighton. The breeding populations on the Pebblebed Heaths were present during the 1977-85 survey and these tetrads are all still occupied. Both Haldon Forest and Chudleigh Knighton have seen large-scale heathland restoration from former conifer plantations and improvement in the condition of already existing heathland, much of which has been carried out specifically to benefit Nightjars. This management has clearly been very effective. On Dartmoor, Nightjars have also benefited from heathland restoration at the moorland edge, particularly around East Dartmoor

NNR (Trendlebere Down), around Lee Moor and in open areas created through felling within conifer plantations, such as at Fernworthy Forest. Losses from a few tetrads in North Devon probably reflect changes in the woodland age as the birds located during the 1977–85 survey were in very young or recently clear-felled conifer plantations which have since matured.

Nationally, population trends for Nightjar are similar to those in Devon and there have been increases in young upland conifer plantations in particular (Conway 2009). Clear-felling of larch plantations because of infection with *Phytophthora ramorum* (a fungal disease to which larch is particularly susceptible) may increase available habitat still further.

This migratory species does not appear to be under any threat outside its breeding areas and so if the total available area of suitable habitat across Devon remains, and if increasing pressure of disturbance on heathland situated close to human settlements is appropriately managed, then the future for Nightjars in Devon looks secure. Many occupied areas in Devon are owned by conservation organizations or by landowners who manage heathland with Nightjars in mind.

*Text: Malcolm Burgess / Photo: Jon Avon*
*Nightjar sponsored in memory of C. Hamlet*

Balmer *et al.* 2013: 461; Sitters 1988: 142; Tyler 2010: 411

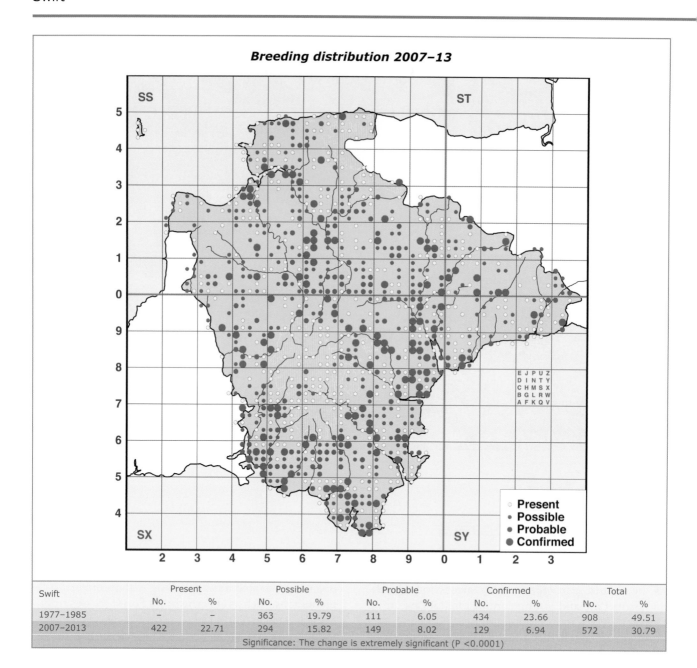

## Breeding distribution 2007–13

- ○ Present
- ● Possible
- ● Probable
- ● Confirmed

| Swift | Present | | Possible | | Probable | | Confirmed | | Total | |
|---|---|---|---|---|---|---|---|---|---|---|
| | No. | % | No. | % | No. | % | No. | % | No. | % |
| 1977–1985 | – | – | 363 | 19.79 | 111 | 6.05 | 434 | 23.66 | 908 | 49.51 |
| 2007–2013 | 422 | 22.71 | 294 | 15.82 | 149 | 8.02 | 129 | 6.94 | 572 | 30.79 |
| | | | | | | | | Significance: The change is extremely significant (P <0.0001) | | |

## Breeding distribution 1977–85

- ● Possible
- ● Probable
- ● Confirmed

## Breeding-period abundance 2007–13

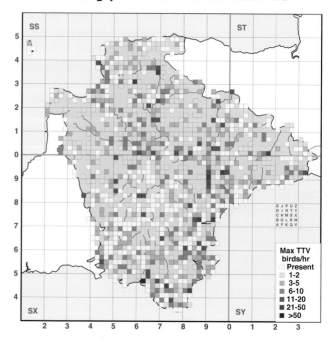

Max TTV
birds/hr
- ☐ Present
- 1-2
- 3-5
- 6-10
- 11-20
- 21-50
- >50

# Swift
*Apus apus*

Amber listed

THE SIGHT and sound of parties of screaming Swifts hurtling across the rooftops is redolent of warm summer evenings in our villages, towns and cities. Sadly, this is a memory that for many of us is increasingly confined to years gone by, for the Swift is a species in trouble. The UK population trend has been in continuous decline since the national Breeding Bird Survey came into being, showing a 39% fall between 1995 and 2011, and resulting in Swift being added to the 'amber' list of birds of conservation concern (BTO BirdTrends 2014).

Fieldwork for the *Devon Tetrad Atlas 1977–1985* resulted in probable or confirmed breeding in 545 tetrads (with breeding confirmed in 434 of these). The corresponding statistic for the current Atlas is 278 (149 probable and 129 confirmed), pointing towards a substantial decline, even when the possible effects of differences in coverage and methodology between the two surveys are taken into account. A side-by-side comparison of maps from the two Devon breeding Atlases suggests that while Swifts remain widespread in the county, they have become much more thinly distributed. The breeding abundance map shows that counts of more than ten Swifts were made in only 59 tetrads, indicating generally low population densities. While this might be expected for a largely rural county, there is clear evidence that the changes observed in Devon are consistent with UK-wide declines in Swift abundance.

*Bird Atlas 2007–11* shows that the actual distribution of Swifts in the UK has changed little since the *Breeding Atlas 1968–72* but that abundance has fallen markedly. While changes to the design and construction of new buildings and the refurbishment of older ones may be making our built-up areas less welcoming for Swifts, factors affecting the abundance of insects and the possible effects of climate change throughout their migration flyway also need to be taken into account. The sheer geographical extent of this flyway was glimpsed through a BTO project in 2010 and 2011, in which a British-breeding Swift tagged with a geolocator was tracked to its wintering quarters over Mozambique, on the edge of the Indian Ocean (BTO 2012).

Here in Devon, we can give Swifts a helping hand by trying to ensure that building construction and repairs do not exclude Swifts, and by erecting nestboxes. While the effectiveness of nestboxes was mentioned in the Swift species account for the *Devon Tetrad Atlas 1977–85*, some 25 years later their use is sadly still not as widespread as it ought to be in the county.

*Text: Tim Davis & Tim Jones*
*Photos: Paul Sterry/NPL & (inset) Robert Hurrell*
*Swift sponsored by Linda Tilbury*

Balmer *et al.* 2013: 462; Sitters 1988: 144; Tyler 2010: 414

# Hoopoe
## *Upupa epops*

HOOPOES, WITH their black and white wings, pink body and spiky pink crest, are unmistakable exotic visitors from Europe and as such are often reported by members of the public when found. They are near-annual visitors to Devon, mostly during the spring, from March to April (the earliest during the Atlas years was 14 March 2010; *DBR*) when birds overshoot their breeding grounds in central and southern Europe where they nest in dry, open habitats. Smaller numbers continue to arrive later in the spring and early summer, exceptionally into July (e.g. at Tiverton on 19 July 2011; *DBR*).

Hoopoes were recorded in 54 tetrads during the Atlas period and this corresponds to about 46 individuals, of which an extraordinary 18 were seen in private gardens (*DBRs*). Records were scattered, with a bias towards the southern and eastern parts of the county, perhaps reflecting the distribution of shorter areas of heathland and coastal grassland, both being suitable feeding areas for the species. Coastal records included Lundy (where single birds were present in March/April 2011 and May 2013) and various scattered locations along the south coast, but there were also reports as far inland as Mid Devon where a bird was seen in Crediton in June 2011 (*DBRs*). The *Devon Tetrad Atlas 1977–1985* gave details of possible breeding near Chittlehampton (SS62T) in 1984 but there have been no subsequent breeding records.

There were only a handful of autumn records during the Atlas period: two in late August 2012 and single birds in September and October 2009 (*DBRs*). A ringed Hoopoe seen in Tiverton in December 2010 was believed to have escaped from captivity (*DBR*).

*Text: Helen Booker / Photo: Paul Sterry/NPL*

*Hoopoe sponsored by NHBS*

Everything for wildlife, science & environment

Balmer *et al.* 2013: 463; Sitters 1988: 301; Tyler 2010: 421

### Breeding-period abundance 2007–13

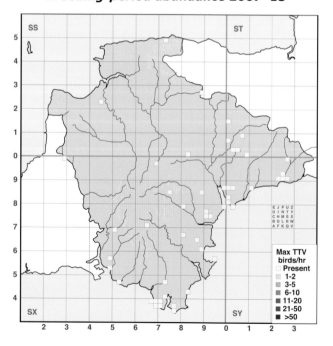

### Winter-period abundance 2007–13

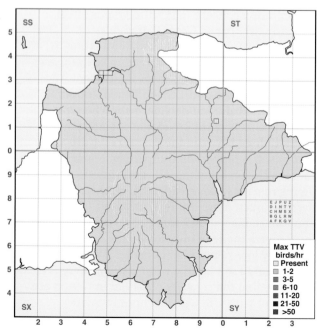

# Wryneck
## *Jynx torquilla*

KNOWN FOR its cryptic plumage and its ability to twist its neck in a snake-like manner when threatened, the Wryneck formerly bred in Devon, with the last breeding record in 1954 (Moore 1969), but it is now seen only as a passage migrant. During the Atlas years there were records for 69 tetrads during the breeding period (March–September) and 19 in the winter period (October–February), spanning both spring and autumn passage. Spring records were relatively widespread, coming from both coastal and inland locations. The earliest was at Mary Tavy on 3 April 2011; a migrant at Bolt Tail (South Hams) on 25 April 2008 was heard to sing twice (*DBRs*).

The autumn records (mainly August/September) show a stronger bias towards coastal tetrads, with nearly all records that technically fall in the Atlas 'winter' period being along the south coast and relating to migrants in October, with the exception of a late straggler at Labrador Bay on 19 November 2010 (*DBR*).

*Text: Helen Booker / Photo: Paul Sterry/NPL*

Balmer *et al.* 2013: 472; Sitters 1988: not treated; Tyler 2010: 423

### Breeding-period abundance 2007–13

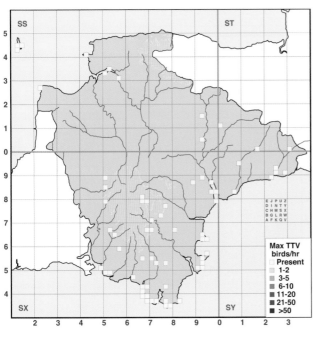

### Winter-period abundance 2007–13

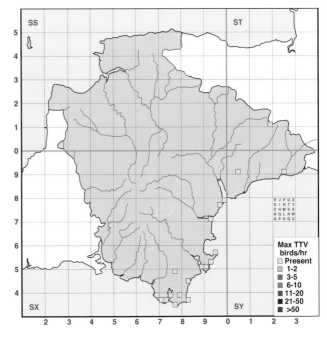

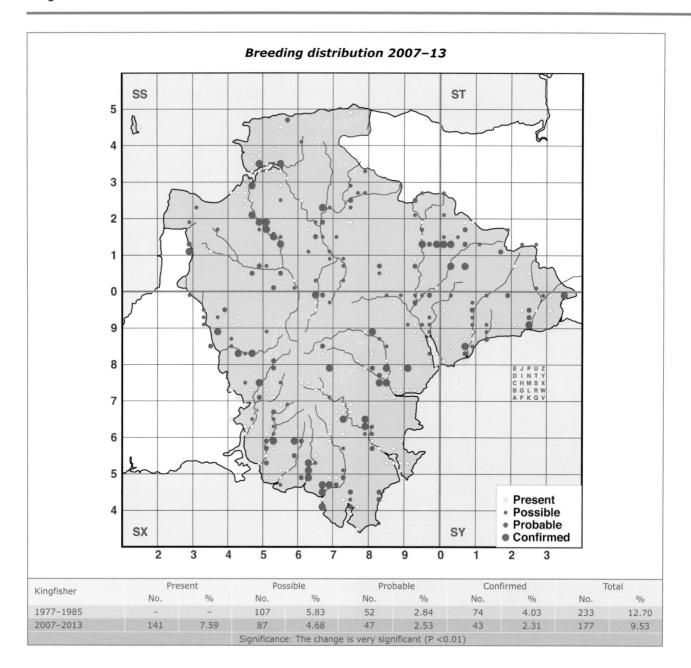

## Breeding distribution 2007–13

| Kingfisher | Present | | Possible | | Probable | | Confirmed | | Total | |
|---|---|---|---|---|---|---|---|---|---|---|
| | No. | % | No. | % | No. | % | No. | % | No. | % |
| 1977–1985 | – | – | 107 | 5.83 | 52 | 2.84 | 74 | 4.03 | 233 | 12.70 |
| 2007–2013 | 141 | 7.59 | 87 | 4.68 | 47 | 2.53 | 43 | 2.31 | 177 | 9.53 |
| Significance: The change is very significant (P <0.01) | | | | | | | | | | |

## Breeding distribution 1977–85

## Breeding-period abundance 2007–13

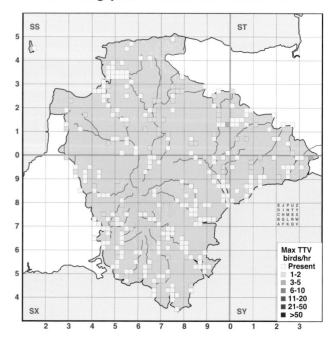

# Kingfisher
*Alcedo atthis*

**Amber listed**

KINGFISHERS ARE popular and strikingly colourful resident birds, easily spotted by the vivid blue flash on their back as they fly along watercourses. They occupy rivers, canals and estuaries where there is a rich supply of small fish. They need steep banks in which to excavate tunnels for nesting and have a protracted breeding season with at least two broods in a year.

The species is fairly widespread in Devon, having been recorded from 318 tetrads, just under 14% of the total. Kingfishers are found along rivers throughout the county and the 2007–13 map indicates their overall distribution to be very similar to that in the *Devon Tetrad Atlas 1977–85*. However,

### Winter-period abundance 2007–13

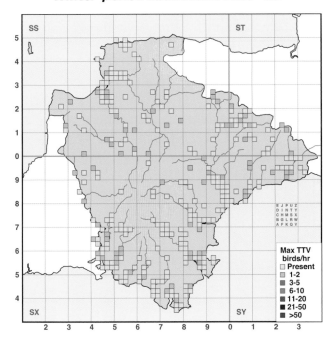

the current map also shows that the species is occupying sites further upstream into Dartmoor and Exmoor, although it continues to be absent from the high moors. Aside from this small range expansion, the only notable difference in the breeding maps between the two Atlases relates to breeding status, with 74 confirmed breeding records reported in the 1977–85 survey compared with 43 during the current survey. However, with 47 tetrads supporting probable breeding, 87 possible breeding and birds present in a further 141 tetrads, it is likely that many of these would also have yielded confirmed breeding records.

The higher overall tetrad occupancy for 2007–2013 is encouraging. Historically across the country, Kingfisher populations have fluctuated in response to severe winters and loss of habitat quality through industrialization, river pollution and water abstraction (Brown & Grice 2005). Between the two most recent national Atlases there was a mixed picture of gains and losses across the country (*Bird Atlas 2007–11*) which most likely reflect local changes in the quality of habitat.

Winter-period distribution (October–February) in Devon is very similar to that in summer, with 300 tetrads (16.2%) occupied. The slightly higher number of occupied tetrads in winter may reflect the dispersal of juveniles and/or a shift away from higher ground, although this is not particularly obvious from the maps. The most densely occupied area in the county is the Grand Western Canal which supported seven and six birds respectively in January and November 2012 (*DBR*).

*Text: Helen Booker / Photo: Steve Hatch*
*Kingfisher sponsored by Betty Smith*

Balmer *et al.* 2013: 464; Sitters 1988: 146; Tyler 2010: 417

## Breeding distribution 2007–13

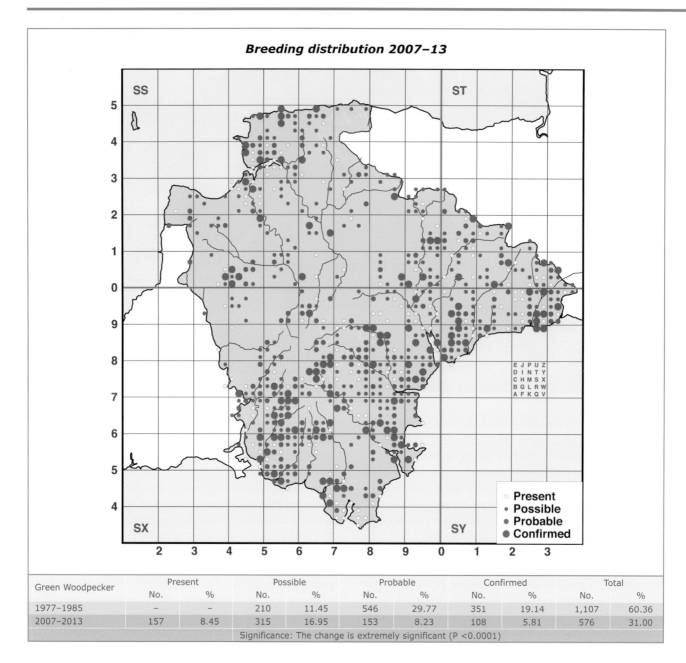

| Green Woodpecker | Present | | Possible | | Probable | | Confirmed | | Total | |
|---|---|---|---|---|---|---|---|---|---|---|
| | No. | % | No. | % | No. | % | No. | % | No. | % |
| 1977–1985 | – | – | 210 | 11.45 | 546 | 29.77 | 351 | 19.14 | 1,107 | 60.36 |
| 2007–2013 | 157 | 8.45 | 315 | 16.95 | 153 | 8.23 | 108 | 5.81 | 576 | 31.00 |
| Significance: The change is extremely significant (P <0.0001) | | | | | | | | | | |

## Breeding distribution 1977–85

## Breeding-period abundance 2007–13

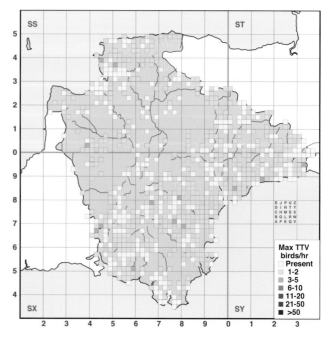

# Green Woodpecker

*Picus viridis*

GREEN WOODPECKERS are resident birds of pasture and open woodlands. They nest in holes in mature trees and require short grass rich in invertebrates, especially ants and their eggs and pupae, which form the Green Woodpecker's main diet, though birds sometimes also forage for beetles on old tree limbs. Close-cropped unimproved grasslands, coastal grassland and even gardens can all provide suitable foraging sites.

The breeding distribution and abundance maps show that Green Woodpeckers are widespread, present in all except one 10-km square, with breeding confirmed in most. They are most densely distributed in the southern half of the county, with the most obvious gaps being in Mid Devon and on the high moors of Dartmoor.

Despite being widespread, their population has declined very significantly in the county since the *Devon Tetrad Atlas 1977–85*, with a drop in the proportion of tetrads for which breeding evidence was recorded from 60% to 31%. There is little discernable pattern to the widespread reduction, though it is perhaps most marked in both North and Mid Devon. The species' reliance on a combination of old trees and invertebrate-rich grassland in close proximity leaves them vulnerable to losses in either of these habitats. Intensification of grassland management, with extensive loss of short unimproved pastures, particularly in North Devon

where the dominance of improved grassland (see Figure 11 on p. 42), may be affecting this species adversely.

As Green Woodpeckers are sedentary, there is very little difference between the pattern of distribution for the breeding and winter periods, though the overall number of tetrads occupied was lower in winter (29%) than in summer (39%). Winter densities, however, appear slightly higher, with several locations holding three to five birds per tetrad.

Although the UK population showed an increase of 115% between 1970 and 2010 (SUKB 2012), a comparison of the last two national Atlases shows that increases occurred largely on the eastern side of the country, with declines across much of the west (*Bird Atlas 2007–11*). The losses in Devon are in line with these regional contrasts.

*Text: Helen Booker / Photo: Dave Scott*

Balmer *et al.* 2013: 466; Sitters 1988: 148; Tyler 2010: 425

### Winter-period abundance 2007–13

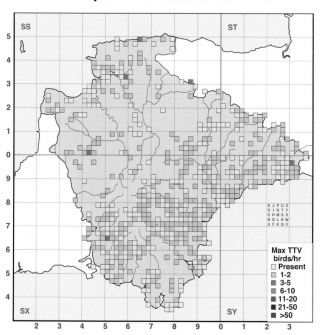

Max TTV birds/hr
- ☐ Present
- 1-2
- 3-5
- 6-10
- 11-20
- 21-50
- >50

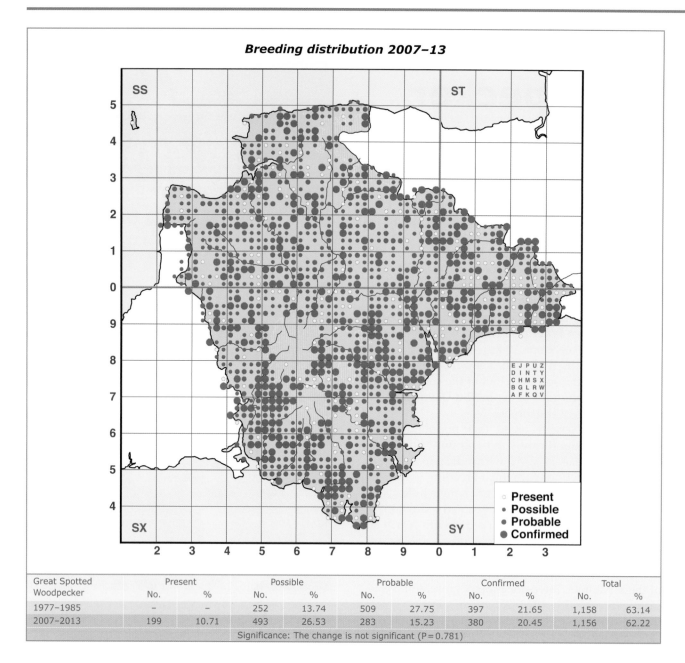

**Breeding distribution 2007–13**

| Great Spotted Woodpecker | Present | | Possible | | Probable | | Confirmed | | Total | |
|---|---|---|---|---|---|---|---|---|---|---|
| | No. | % | No. | % | No. | % | No. | % | No. | % |
| 1977–1985 | – | – | 252 | 13.74 | 509 | 27.75 | 397 | 21.65 | 1,158 | 63.14 |
| 2007–2013 | 199 | 10.71 | 493 | 26.53 | 283 | 15.23 | 380 | 20.45 | 1,156 | 62.22 |
| Significance: The change is not significant (P=0.781) | | | | | | | | | | |

**Breeding distribution 1977–85**

**Breeding-period abundance 2007–13**

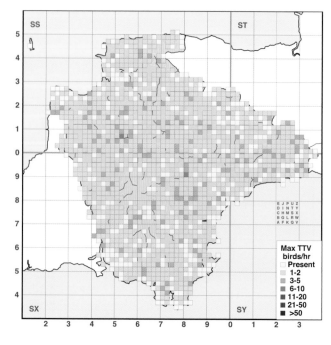

# Great Spotted Woodpecker

*Dendrocopos major*

GREAT SPOTTED Woodpecker is primarily a bird of broad-leaved woodland but is common in all habitats that contain mature broad-leaved trees, including mixed woodlands, small woodlands and urban areas. Nowadays, the species is also commonly seen on bird feeders in both urban and rural areas.

Great Spotted Woodpeckers are found throughout Devon and were recorded in 62% of tetrads during the current survey. Distribution in Devon reflects the well-wooded nature of the county; they are absent only from the treeless areas of Dartmoor and Exmoor and more extensive areas of open farmland. Distribution and abundance are much the same in both summer and winter periods, reflecting the species' year-round site faithfulness.

Nationally, Great Spotted Woodpeckers have seen a large population increase: 405% during 1967–2011 (BTO BirdTrends 2014). However, comparison of data from the current survey with that from the *Devon Tetrad Atlas 1977–85* shows almost no change, probably because Devon's population was already high, with so much of the county containing broadleaf woodland.

It is still not fully understood why Great Spotted Woodpeckers have increased nationally so much in recent decades. When the rise in numbers was first observed, it was thought that they had benefited from the dead and dying elm trees available in the 1970s and 1980s after Dutch Elm Disease (Smith 1997), and

perhaps to a lesser extent from dead wood available after major storms in 1987 and 1990. But the rise in numbers has continued since and is perhaps instead connected to the species increased presence in urban and suburban habitats. Here they exploit supplementary food (especially fat and peanuts) provided in gardens, and this is known to give them advantages when it comes to breeding, enabling them to breed earlier and have higher nesting success (Smith & Smith 2013). Reduced nest-site competition with Starlings, which have declined as breeding birds in Britain, has also been suggested, as Great Spotted Woodpeckers often re-use the same nest holes each year.

*Text: Malcolm Burgess / Photo: Barry Bowden*
*Great Spotted Woodpecker sponsored by Valerie Shapley*

Balmer *et al.* 2013: 468; Sitters 1988: 150; Tyler 2010: 427

## Winter-period abundance 2007–13

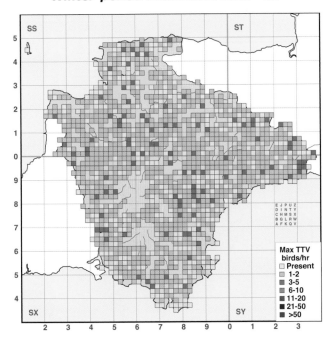

Max TTV birds/hr
- ☐ Present
- 1-2
- 3-5
- 6-10
- 11-20
- 21-50
- >50

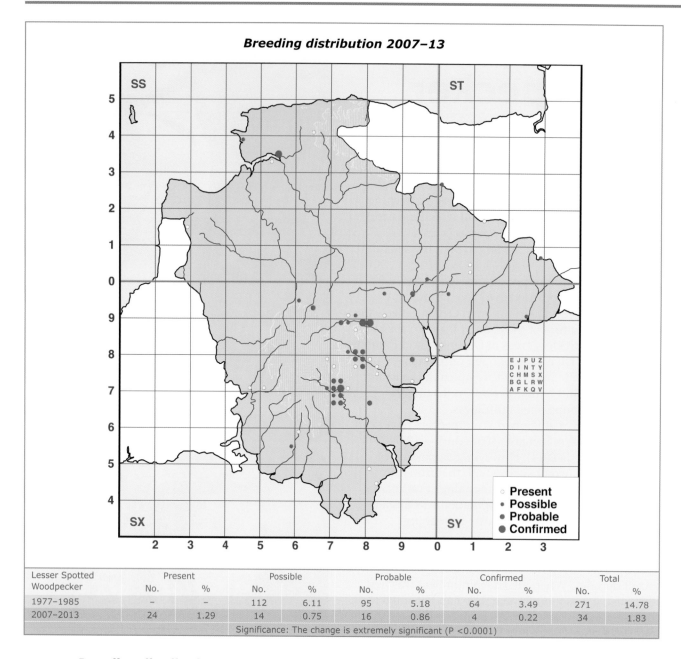

**Breeding distribution 2007–13**

| Lesser Spotted Woodpecker | Present | | Possible | | Probable | | Confirmed | | Total | |
|---|---|---|---|---|---|---|---|---|---|---|
| | No. | % | No. | % | No. | % | No. | % | No. | % |
| 1977–1985 | – | – | 112 | 6.11 | 95 | 5.18 | 64 | 3.49 | 271 | 14.78 |
| 2007–2013 | 24 | 1.29 | 14 | 0.75 | 16 | 0.86 | 4 | 0.22 | 34 | 1.83 |
| Significance: The change is extremely significant (P <0.0001) | | | | | | | | | | |

**Breeding distribution 1977–85**

**Breeding-period abundance 2007–13**

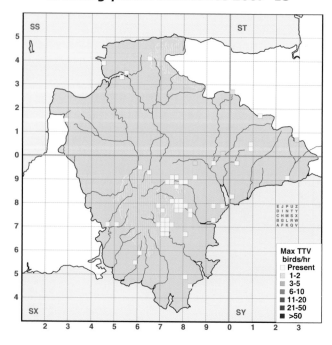

# Lesser Spotted Woodpecker
## *Dendrocopos minor*

**Red listed**

THE LESSER Spotted Woodpecker is a specialist woodland bird, almost exclusively found in mature broad-leaved woodland and old orchards, and only persists in well-wooded and connected landscapes. Lesser Spotted Woodpeckers have very large territories (typically 12 hectares; *BWP*) and are very difficult birds to see, especially once leaves have opened in spring. Both of these factors make the species difficult to find and they are probably under-recorded. Most records during this survey came from a small number of well-known woodlands where birdwatchers can expect to find them.

The current survey indicates that the species' Devon range is small and contracting. They were found in less than 2% of tetrads and have apparently been lost from 237 tetrads since the *Devon Tetrad Atlas 1977–85*. The new maps indicate losses across

nearly all of Devon, except for the well-wooded river valleys of the Dart, Bovey and Teign on the edges of Dartmoor, and Arlington in North Devon. The breeding map gives the impression that they favour riparian habitat. This huge contraction in range appears not to be related to a loss of woodland habitat or quality, since it seems unlikely that woodlands from where they have been lost have changed much in terms of suitability since the 1977–85 survey. Winter records are similarly sparse right across the county but do indicate presence in a few tetrads where breeding was possibly overlooked.

There has also been a very marked national decline, the causes of which are currently unknown, though recent RSPB research found low breeding success (Charman *et al.* 2012). This work also found that, as in other parts of the European range, females do not attend nests towards the end of the nestling stage prior to fledging. A consequence of this unusual ecology is that the male has to make up the shortfall in food provision just when the young are at their most demanding. It is possible that availability of food is lower than in past decades, perhaps below a critical threshold, resulting in the male alone being unable to find and provide enough for the young. Woodland fragmentation and landscape-scale availability of woodland is also likely to play a role in the observed contraction in distribution (Charman *et al.* 2010), but this is unlikely to affect Lesser Spotted Woodpeckers in Devon as the distribution of woodland and its connectivity in the landscape has changed little in recent decades. In Devon a loss of old orchards may play a role; in areas of Herefordshire where old orchards have survived, the species still does well.

*Text: Malcolm Burgess / Photo: Steve Young/NPL*
*Lesser Spotted Woodpecker sponsored by Kevin & Donna Cox*

Balmer *et al.* 2013: 470; Sitters 1988: 152; Tyler 2010: 428

### Winter-period abundance 2007–13

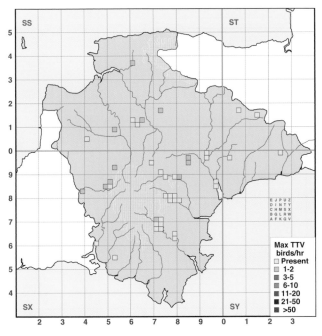

Max TTV birds/hr
□ Present
☐ 1-2
■ 3-5
■ 6-10
■ 11-20
■ 21-50
■ >50

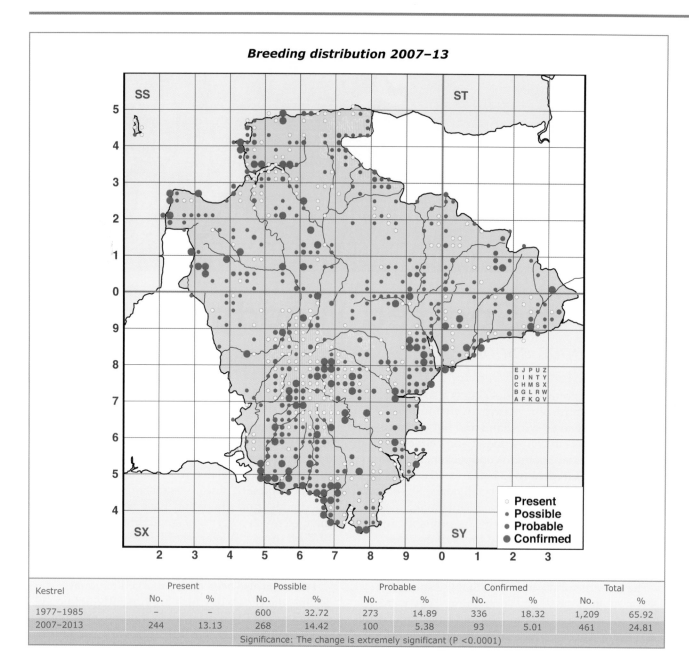

### Breeding distribution 2007–13

| Kestrel | Present | | Possible | | Probable | | Confirmed | | Total | |
|---|---|---|---|---|---|---|---|---|---|---|
| | No. | % | No. | % | No. | % | No. | % | No. | % |
| 1977–1985 | – | – | 600 | 32.72 | 273 | 14.89 | 336 | 18.32 | 1,209 | 65.92 |
| 2007–2013 | 244 | 13.13 | 268 | 14.42 | 100 | 5.38 | 93 | 5.01 | 461 | 24.81 |
| Significance: The change is extremely significant (P <0.0001) | | | | | | | | | | |

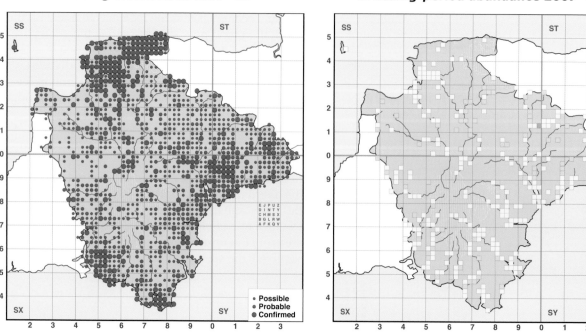

### Breeding distribution 1977–85

### Breeding-period abundance 2007–13

# Kestrel
## *Falco tinnunculus*

Amber listed

THE KESTREL is Devon's most abundant falcon. It is a year-round resident with an estimated UK population of 46,000 pairs (Musgrove *et al.* 2013). It is most frequently associated with rough grassland, the favoured habitat of small mammals, where it is often seen hunting by hovering to detect its prey. Extensive areas of this habitat are present on Dartmoor and Exmoor, around the coasts and in smaller pockets throughout the county, such as corridors along some major roads. Devon holds much suitable habitat for this species, which is borne out by the widespread distribution indicated by the breeding-period (March–September) map. Kestrels were recorded in just about all 10-km squares, while at the tetrad level they were found in just over one-third (37.9%). The distribution for October–February is much the same, governed by areas which still provide suitable hunting habitat; birds were present in 42.5% of tetrads.

### Winter-period abundance 2007–13

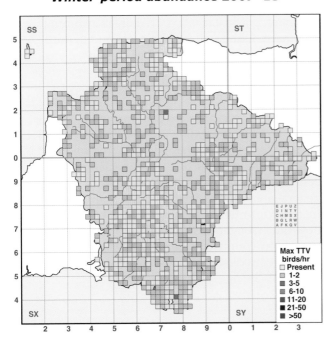

Max TTV birds/hr
☐ Present
▨ 1-2
▨ 3-5
▨ 6-10
■ 11-20
■ 21-50
■ >50

Compared with the *Devon Tetrad Atlas 1977–85*, there has been a highly significant decline of almost two-thirds in tetrads yielding breeding evidence, from 65.9% to just 24.8% of tetrads. Some of the observed differences may have arisen from either observer bias or differences in methodology, or both. For instance, the earlier Atlas showed confirmed breeding for nearly all tetrads in SS64, SS74 and SS53 (Exmoor and North Devon), a surprising pattern, especially in view of the fact that the neighbouring 10-km square (SS73), also containing much Exmoor rough grassland, appears far less populated. This trend was echoed in two East Devon 10-km squares (SY08 and SY09). The present Atlas shows a considerable decline in these North Devon/Exmoor and East Devon squares, with breeding evidence now more thinly distributed across the county. Confirmed breeding on Dartmoor appears to have increased and the South Hams coast remains a stronghold.

*Bird Atlas 2007–11* shows little change in Devon, with perhaps a slight increase compared to the *Breeding Atlas 1988–91*; these data may be less liable to bias than the tetrad-level comparisons made above. Despite the confusion, it is highly likely that the decline of the Kestrel in Devon is real. Possible reasons include the effects of agricultural intensification on farmland habitats and their populations of small mammals (BTO BirdTrends 2014), along with the increased use of Second Generation Anticoagulant Rodenticides, although it is difficult to see how this would have affected Exmoor so greatly. Because of the decline, the RSPB have commissioned a nation-wide project to investigate the causes.

*Text: Mark Darlaston / Photo: Dave Norman*
*Kestrel sponsored by Arthur Livett*

Balmer *et al.* 2013: 316; Sitters 1988: 74; Tyler 2010: 211

# Merlin
*Falco columbarius*

THE MERLIN is not only Devon's smallest falcon, but also the rarest breeder, with a very small population (rarely more than a single pair). The county lies at the south-western edge of the UK breeding range and Merlins are mainly passage migrants in both spring and, particularly, autumn, while some overwinter.

When breeding, this species has a strong association with mature Ling-dominated upland heath, which can still be found extensively on Exmoor. Such habitat is more impoverished on Dartmoor and there have been no documented records with breeding evidence (such as pairs, nests or recently fledged young) since 1966 (Smaldon 2005). Dartmoor may now be unsuitable due to a combination of factors such as habitat degradation, its more southerly location and perhaps disturbance,

although individual Merlins occasionally summer there.

The rarity of the Merlin as a breeding species in Devon means that no breeding-period map is provided. During the current survey there were just two tetrads for which breeding was confirmed and two further tetrads with evidence of possible breeding. All were in a tight cluster, which probably relates to a single pair's range during the seven years of the Atlas. During March to September, Merlins were present in a further 91 tetrads throughout Devon, mainly along the coasts, and on Exmoor and Dartmoor. These relate to birds on migration, as well as late wintering birds that may still be present into March or April. During the winter period (October to February) the species showed a wider distribution and was recorded in 234 tetrads (12.6%). This period includes the peak migration of Merlin through Devon in October, when they were noted particularly at coastal locations. Some birds remain to winter, particularly favoured areas including Dartmoor, Exmoor, the Culm grassland of north-west Devon (especially Bursdon Moor), the East Devon Commons, around major estuaries such as the Exe, and on the coast. Ringing recoveries show that some migrants belong to the Icelandic subspecies *F. c. subaesalon* (Langman *et al.* 2007).

As the Devon breeding population is so small, it is difficult to tell if there has been much change since the *Devon Tetrad Atlas 1977–85*, especially as confirmed breeding was restricted to the same general area in both Atlases, albeit from 20 rather than just four tetrads. It must, however, be uncertain how much longer this delightful falcon will remain among the county's breeding species, particularly given the predicted impacts of climate change.

*Text: Mark Darlaston / Photo: Steve Waite*
*Merlin sponsored by Leonard Hurrell & Alastair Henderson*

Balmer *et al.* 2013: 318; Sitters 1988: 294; Tyler 2010: 213

### Winter-period abundance 2007–13

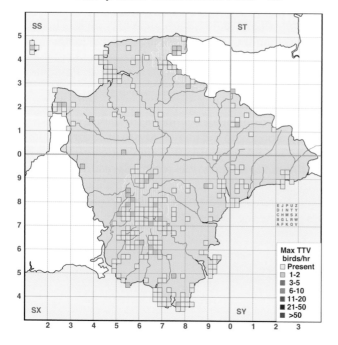

Max TTV
birds/hr
☐ Present
1–2
3–5
6–10
11–20
21–50
>50

# Hobby
*Falco subbuteo*

HOBBIES ARE summer visitors to Devon, usually arriving in late April/May and departing in September/October. These small falcons are masters of the air, capable of catching fast-moving dragonflies and hirundines, as well as an array of other flying invertebrates and small birds. For nesting they require the old nest of other birds (often Carrion Crow, Raven or Buzzard), usually in a stand of trees or plantation. Devon potentially holds much suitable habitat for this species, from rolling farmland interspersed with woodland to areas of heath with plantations in both upland and lowland areas.

### Breeding distribution 2007-13

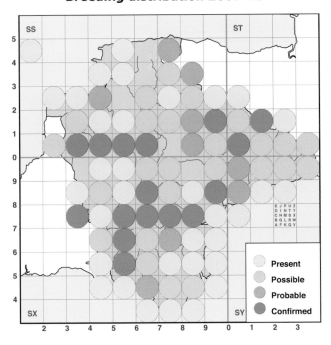

The current Atlas surveys found Hobbies to be fairly widespread in Devon, present in 371 tetrads (20.0%) and more than 90% of 10-km squares. This is a difficult species for which to prove breeding, with confirmed records from only 17 tetrads and probable/possible registrations from a further 88 tetrads. The 'possible' category is greatly influenced by observers' interpretation of suitable habitat; in some tetrads Hobbies were recorded as present (when often in suitable habitat), while in contrast, others assigned as 'in suitable habitat' may well have been migrants.

No data were published in the *Devon Tetrad Atlas 1977–85* and hence comparison is not possible, but the species has almost certainly increased in Devon, as it has nationally, with the British population now estimated at 2,800 pairs (Musgrove *et al.* 2013). In Devon the species was once thought to be strongly associated with heathland, but we now know that it is far more cosmopolitan in its habitat choice. One observation from the present Atlas is the apparent lack of confirmed breeding evidence from East Devon, often perceived as a Devon stronghold, perhaps further highlighting the difficulties in obtaining proof of breeding for this species.

While most Hobbies have left Devon by the end of September, late migrants were present in 23 tetrads in October, with very late single birds on Dartmoor and Lundy in early November.

*Text: Mark Darlaston / Photo: Paul Sterry/NPL*
*Hobby sponsored by Jane Emberson & Robert Powell*

Balmer *et al.* 2013: 320; Sitters 1988: 295; Tyler 2010: 216

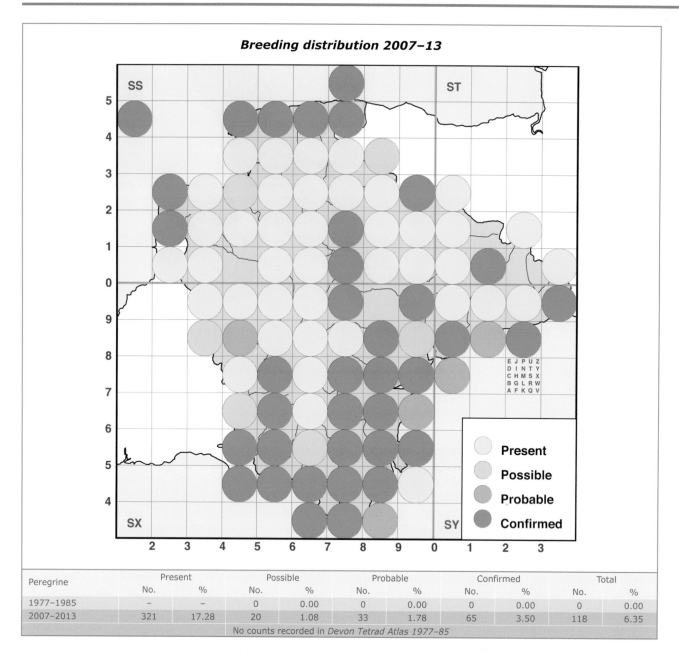

**Breeding distribution 2007–13**

Legend:
- Present
- Possible
- Probable
- Confirmed

| Peregrine | Present | | Possible | | Probable | | Confirmed | | Total | |
|---|---|---|---|---|---|---|---|---|---|---|
| | No. | % | No. | % | No. | % | No. | % | No. | % |
| 1977–1985 | – | – | 0 | 0.00 | 0 | 0.00 | 0 | 0.00 | 0 | 0.00 |
| 2007–2013 | 321 | 17.28 | 20 | 1.08 | 33 | 1.78 | 65 | 3.50 | 118 | 6.35 |
| | No counts recorded in *Devon Tetrad Atlas 1977–85* | | | | | | | | | |

# Peregrine
## Falco peregrinus

LUNDY IS the earliest documented UK breeding site for Peregrine, dating as far back as 1243 (Ratcliffe 1993), giving the species a distinguished historical link with the county. However, Peregrines were twice nearly eliminated; first during the 1940s under government order during the Second World War in an attempt to protect messenger pigeons and then as a result of the disastrous effects of organochlorine pesticides in the 1950s and 1960s. These days we are fortunate that this magnificent falcon has once again become a regular sight in Devon.

Devon contains much suitable breeding habitat, particularly along its two coastlines, both with extensive sea-cliffs. Although the south coast is longer, Lundy effectively adds a further eight-mile section to the north coast. In addition, inland quarries and man-made structures can also provide suitable ledges for nesting, while old Ravens' nests are sometimes favoured. Peregrines also use purpose-built artificial nest sites, such as the nest-tray installed by Devon Birds on the now famous Church of St Michael & All Angels in Exeter and, elsewhere, a nest-tray on a pylon (N. Dixon pers. comm.).

Sadly, continuing persecution remains a threat to Devon's Peregrines, so the 10-km square map only is shown so as not to draw attention to breeding sites, where birds often remain throughout the year. Peregrines range over much of Devon and were seen in or over 439 (23.6%) tetrads during the breeding period (March–September). Breeding evidence was recorded for 118 tetrads (6.4%) and confirmed in 65 tetrads (3.5%). Although Peregrines are easily detected, the Atlas methodology did not lend itself to an accurate assessment of Devon's population. Data collected during both the 2002 and 2014 BTO national Peregrine surveys show that breeding occurred in a number of coastal tetrads in those years, although no breeding evidence was recorded during the Atlas period. Furthermore, Peregrines have large territories which may span a number of tetrads (particularly inland) and pairs and family parties can be registered in tetrads adjoining the actual breeding site.

There are no comparable data available from the *Devon Tetrad Atlas 1977–85* but data from the 1991 and 2002 national surveys show that the county's population rose from around 47 pairs in 1991 (Ratcliffe 1993) to 87 pairs in 2002 (Darlaston & Johnson 2003). The UK population is currently estimated at 1,500 pairs (Musgrove *et al.* 2013), though this will be revised following analysis of results from the 2014 national survey.

During the winter period Peregrines were present in 439 tetrads (23.6%), with a similarly widespread distribution to the breeding period, with coastal areas, estuaries and Dartmoor being particularly favoured.

*Text: Mark Darlaston*
*Photos: Barry Bowden & (opposite) Mark Darlaston*
*Peregrine sponsored by Plymouth Branch of Devon Birds*

Balmer *et al.* 2013: 322; Sitters 1988: 296; Tyler 2010: 219

# Golden Oriole

*Oriolus oriolus*

**Red listed**

THE SIGHTING of a male Golden Oriole in full plumage is a birdwatcher's dream. Unfortunately these birds are only very scarce migrants in Devon, although there are records every year, almost all in spring and mostly on the south coast or on Lundy. Few are breeding-plumaged males. Golden Orioles were recorded in 11 tetrads during the Atlas years, mainly on the south coast and all in April and May (earliest 10 April 2011; latest 30 May 2012; *DBRs*). These are assumed to be migrants heading for Scandinavia or overshooting from breeding grounds further south in continental Europe. There were five records in 2008, five in 2011, about ten in 2012 and three in 2013. One was heard singing at Berry Head on 29 April 2011 (*DBR*). There is a very small breeding population in eastern England (*Bird Atlas 2007–2011*) but the last Devon breeding record was over 60 years ago (Tyler 2010).

*Text: J M Lock*

Balmer *et al.* 2013: 473; Sitters 1988: not treated; Tyler 2010: 431

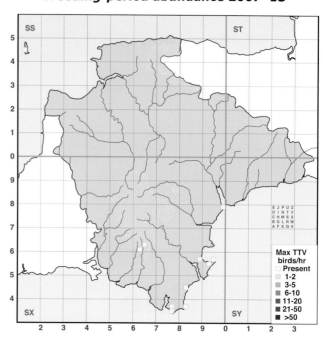

*Breeding-period abundance 2007–13*

Max TTV birds/hr
- Present
- 1-2
- 3-5
- 6-10
- 11-20
- 21-50
- >50

# Red-backed Shrike

*Lanius collurio*

**Red listed**

HISTORICALLY, RED-BACKED Shrikes, although not common, were present throughout Devon. They were lost from north Devon in the 1950s, and the last breeding was recorded on the Pebblebed Heaths of East Devon in the late 1960s and on Dartmoor in 1970 (Tyler 2010). They occupied habitats consisting of scrub associated with extensively managed grassland, including heathland, young conifer plantations and marginal farmland. For many decades, Red-backed Shrike has been an exceptionally rare bird in the UK, breeding infrequently and in very small numbers since the 1970s. Declines in large invertebrates resulting from agricultural intensification, along with persecution from egg collectors as they became rarer, probably contributed most to declines. However, as a migratory bird wintering in sub-Saharan Africa, they are also vulnerable to many other factors across their annual cycle.

Since their last breeding in Devon in 1970, Red-backed Shrikes have rarely been recorded in the county, although single birds have appeared in suitable breeding habitat intermittently over the years. In 2008 and 2009, three territory-holding males were recorded at one locality on Dartmoor. No female was observed until 2010 when two nesting attempts were made, one of which was successful, making these the first Red-backed Shrike fledglings in the UK for 18 years. Since then, one or two pairs have attempted to breed annually, with success in some but not all years. The location is kept confidential and is intensively wardened each breeding season. Single birds have occasionally been recorded on Dartmoor some distance from the known territories, including a female captured and ringed in late May 2012. Despite continuous presence during the current Atlas period, it remains to be seen whether the species can persist as a breeding bird and become permanently re-established in Devon.

*Text: J M Lock*
*Red-backed Shrike sponsored by Mike Glover & Gill Pope*

Balmer *et al.* 2013: 474; Sitters 1988: not treated; Tyler 2010: 433

# Great Grey Shrike

*Lanius excubitor*

GREAT GREY Shrike is a very scarce winter visitor to Devon from continental European breeding grounds. Most occur on extensive areas of scrubby heath or moorland, offering a combination of generally open terrain, abundant perches and a variety of small-bird and invertebrate prey.

Winter-period (October–February) records came from the perhaps surprisingly high total of 45 tetrads in nineteen 10-km squares, with notable clusters on Dartmoor, the East Devon Commons and, to a lesser

### Winter-period abundance 2007–13

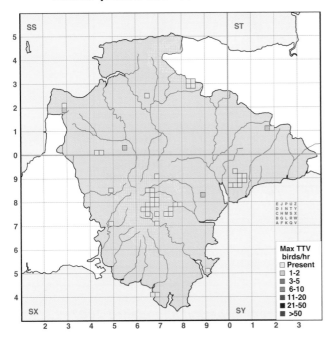

Max TTV birds/hr
- ☐ Present
- 1-2
- 3-5
- 6-10
- 11-20
- 21-50
- >50

extent, Exmoor. The number of occupied tetrads probably gives an exaggerated impression of the number of birds occurring, since individuals may be quite wide-ranging. The *Devon Bird Reports* confirm that the great majority of records were of single birds, but two were on the East Devon Commons in October/November 2010 and January 2011. The latter year was particularly good, with records of up to 11 different individuals at 17 sites.

The *Winter Atlas 1981–1984* shows ten occupied 10-km squares, with a similar scatter to the current Atlas. The lower number of squares occupied in the earlier Atlas is perhaps explained by that survey's shorter duration, as well as the notable influx of 2011, though Tyler (2010) presented data showing that the numbers reported during the 1970s and 1980s were generally higher than in recent years.

Fourteen tetrads (in twelve 10-km squares) were occupied during the Atlas breeding period (March–September), though all of these records are attributable either to early-arriving/late-departing wintering birds (the majority of cases) or to autumn/spring passage migrants; for example, a bird that overwintered in the Bellever area of Dartmoor in 2009/10 was last seen on 22 April (*DBRs*). Only two tetrads were occupied in the breeding period but not in the wintering period.

*Text: Tim Jones & Tim Davis / Photo: Brian Gibbs*
*Great Grey Shrike sponsored by*
*East Devon Branch of Devon Birds*

Balmer *et al.* 2013: 475; Sitters 1988: not treated; Tyler 2010: 435

# Chough

*Pyrrhocorax pyrrhocorax*

THE CHOUGH, a specialized insectivore that has very specific habitat requirements, is the rarest member of the crow family in Britain. It has locally recolonized breeding sites in west Cornwall since 2001 and although still a vagrant in Devon, single birds are occasionally recorded along the coast and on Lundy.

Records of non-breeding birds occurred at four widely separated coastal locations during the Atlas years, in North, South and East Devon, and on Lundy. One winter-period record, on Lundy,

involved a long-staying individual between October 2012 and March 2013. With further expansion of the Cornish population and careful management of cliff-top grassland with Choughs in mind, there is a realistic chance that this iconic species, which was a Devon breeding bird until 1910 (Tyler 2010), could nest once again in the county.

*Text: Simon Geary*
*Chough sponsored by Norman Cowling*

Balmer *et al.* 2013: 476; Sitters 1988: not treated; Tyler 2010: 439

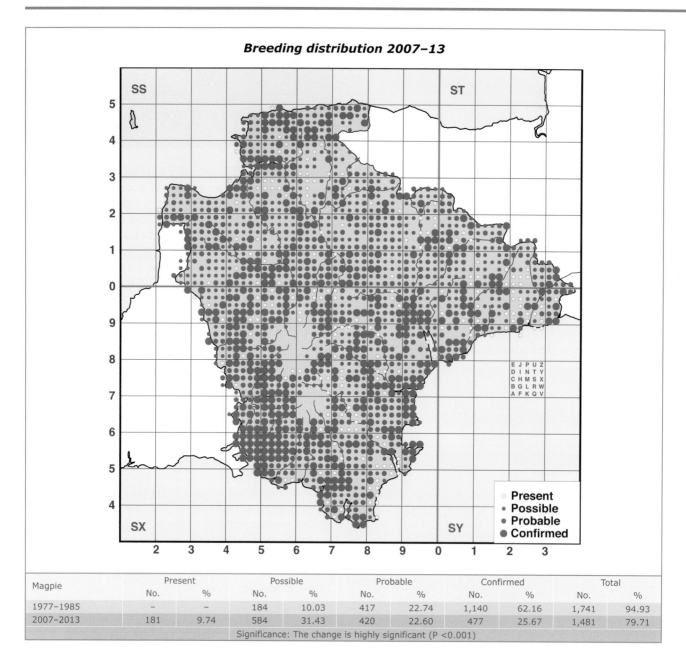

### Breeding distribution 2007–13

| Magpie | Present | | Possible | | Probable | | Confirmed | | Total | |
|---|---|---|---|---|---|---|---|---|---|---|
| | No. | % | No. | % | No. | % | No. | % | No. | % |
| 1977–1985 | – | – | 184 | 10.03 | 417 | 22.74 | 1,140 | 62.16 | 1,741 | 94.93 |
| 2007–2013 | 181 | 9.74 | 584 | 31.43 | 420 | 22.60 | 477 | 25.67 | 1,481 | 79.71 |
| Significance: The change is highly significant (P <0.001) | | | | | | | | | | |

### Breeding distribution 1977–85

### Breeding-period abundance 2007–13

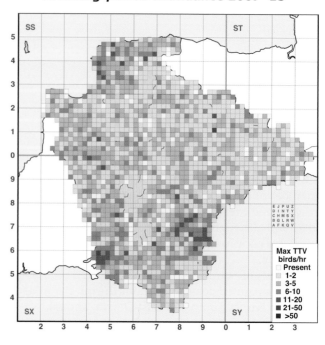

# Magpie
## *Pica pica*

THE MAGPIE is a highly adaptable species with a diverse diet and is found in most habitats containing suitably tall shrubs or trees for nesting. It can be especially abundant in towns and cities.

The breeding-period maps show a widespread distribution, with confirmed breeding in every 10-km square except a few coastal ones that contain little land area, for example Start Point. Magpies were present in most lowland tetrads with generally higher densities (more than 11–20 birds/hour) in Plymouth (Geary 1993, 2001, 2002), Teignbridge, Exeter and the coastal strip of North Devon. Lower densities (six to ten birds/hour) occurred across much of Dartmoor and Exmoor and in other largely rural areas, particularly East Devon, Mid Devon and Torridge districts, while Magpies were absent from the treeless regions of Dartmoor and Exmoor. Comparison of breeding evidence by tetrad for the *Devon Tetrad Atlas 1977–85* and the present Atlas reveals broadly similar patterns of distribution. However, there was a notable lack of breeding evidence from 71 lowland tetrads during the current survey compared with just eight such tetrads for the 1977–85 Atlas. Furthermore there was a significant decline in the proportion of tetrads for which breeding was confirmed (26% versus 62%).

Magpies were recorded year round in most tetrads and so some breeding pairs of this surprisingly secretive species – when nesting – may have been overlooked. Nests are best detected before leaf break and then re-checked for occupancy later in spring; an additional fieldwork effort that may not have been practical for combining with the TTV-based approach of the current Atlas. However, even allowing for differences in survey method, the change at county level is very marked and a genuine population decline cannot be ruled out. Although this would contradict the UK population trend since 1994, it would reflect the South West England population decline of 7% since 1995 (Risely *et al.* 2013).

As for Carrion Crow, tetrads in the far south-west of the county (i.e. between the rivers Yealm and Tamar, and from Plymouth north to Tavistock) constitute an exception to this wider Devon trend, showing little apparent change between Atlases. During the inter-Atlas period, a detailed survey of breeding Magpies in central Plymouth confirmed breeding within every 1-km square and therefore within the corresponding tetrads (Geary 2001). That survey, combined with the results of the two Atlases, indicates a relatively stable population in Plymouth since the late 1970s.

The winter-period map shows a similar distribution of population density to the breeding map. This is perhaps unsurprising as this species is highly sedentary in the UK (Wernham *et al.* 2002).

*Text: Simon Geary / Photo: Adrian Davey*

Balmer *et al.* 2013: 478; Sitters 1988: 250; Tyler 2010: 439

### Winter-period abundance 2007–13

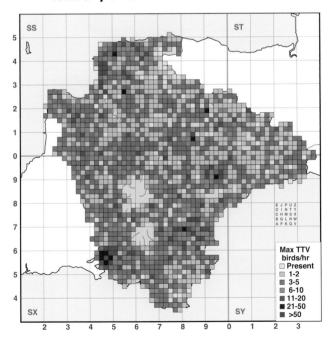

Max TTV birds/hr
- ☐ Present
- 1-2
- 3-5
- 6-10
- 11-20
- 21-50
- >50

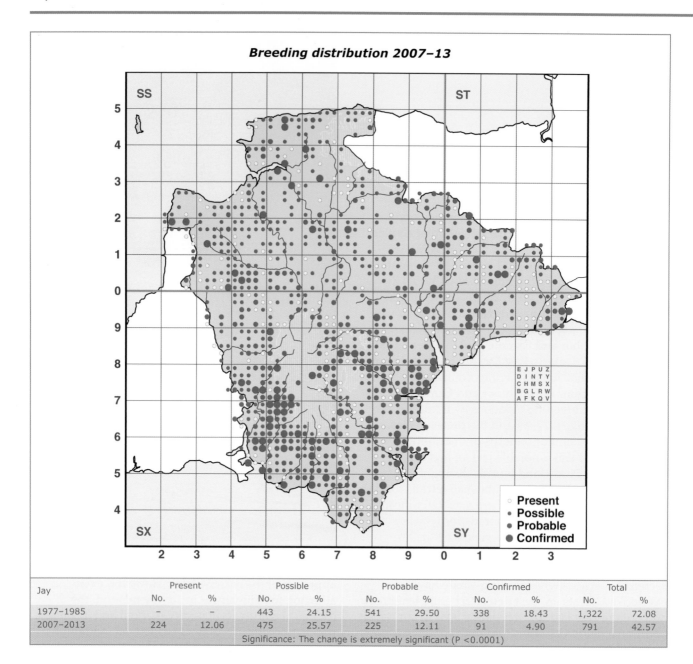

**Breeding distribution 2007–13**

| Jay | Present | | Possible | | Probable | | Confirmed | | Total | |
|---|---|---|---|---|---|---|---|---|---|---|
| | No. | % | No. | % | No. | % | No. | % | No. | % |
| 1977–1985 | – | – | 443 | 24.15 | 541 | 29.50 | 338 | 18.43 | 1,322 | 72.08 |
| 2007–2013 | 224 | 12.06 | 475 | 25.57 | 225 | 12.11 | 91 | 4.90 | 791 | 42.57 |
| | Significance: The change is extremely significant (P <0.0001) | | | | | | | | | |

**Breeding distribution 1977–85**

**Breeding-period abundance 2007–13**

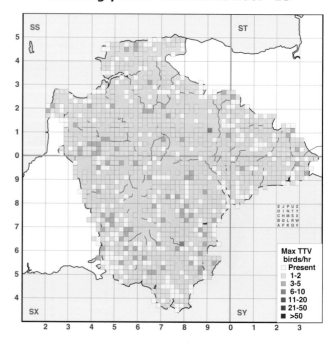

# Jay
## *Garrulus glandarius*

NORMALLY SHY woodland birds, Jays are most conspicuous in autumn when they collect large numbers of acorns (several thousand per bird) and bury them for use as a winter food store. The gathering of acorns in autumn is so important to Jays, normally sedentary birds, that failure of the acorn crop can result in parties of Jays moving considerable distances in search of acorns, as happened in Devon and right across southern England in October 1983 (John & Roskell 1985). During the Atlas years a small influx occurred in October 2012; nine double-digit counts were recorded, the highest being 21 (*DBR*).

During the *Devon Tetrad Atlas 1977–85*, Jays were recorded in 72% of tetrads; breeding was confirmed in 338 tetrads and probable in 541. The Devon population at that time was estimated to be 3,000–4,000 pairs. However, since then they appear to have suffered a serious decline in the county; in 2007–13 there were breeding registrations from only 43% of tetrads, including confirmed breeding in only 91 tetrads and probable breeding in just 225. Comparison of the tetrad maps for the two time periods shows a stark contrast that is hard to believe. Records are particularly sparse in north and north-east Devon, east of the Exe and in the South Hams. The breeding abundance change map in *Bird Atlas 2007–11* shows there have been decreases in the relative abundance of Jays in many parts of Devon since the *Breeding Atlas 1988–91*. Nationally, the Jay population is stable in woodland, but is increasing in farmland (BTO BirdTrends 2014); Breeding Bird Survey results show a 15% increase since 1995. The breeding abundance map indicates that densities were highest in the areas around Hatherleigh, west of Winkleigh, Moretonhampstead, Newton Abbot and south-west of Totnes.

As would be expected for a sedentary species, winter distribution is much the same as that in summer. However, Jays seem to be particularly scarce in areas around Barnstaple and Tiverton in winter.

*Text: A W G John / Photo: Adrian Davey*

Balmer *et al.* 2013: 480; Sitters 1988: 248; Tyler 2010: 441

### Winter-period abundance 2007–13

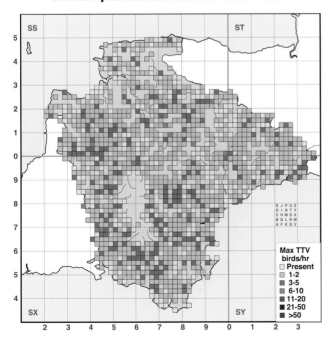

Max TTV birds/hr
- ☐ Present
- ☐ 1-2
- ■ 3-5
- ■ 6-10
- ■ 11-20
- ■ 21-50
- ■ >50

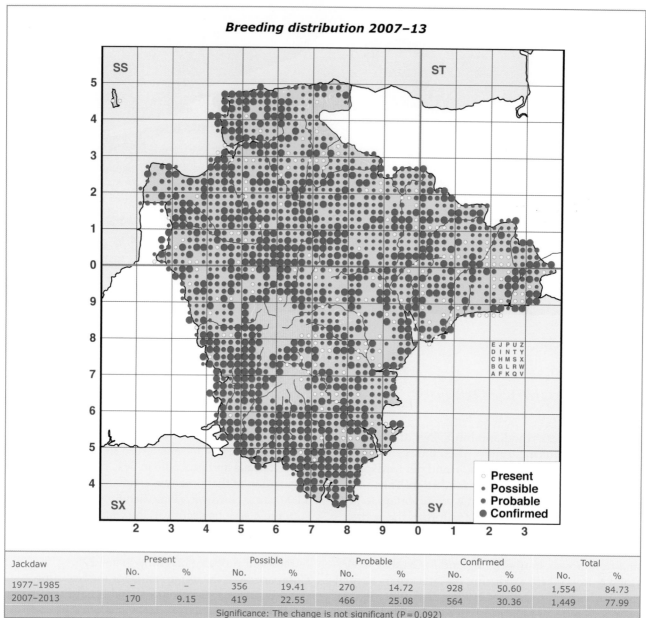

**Breeding distribution 2007–13**

| Jackdaw | Present | | Possible | | Probable | | Confirmed | | Total | |
|---|---|---|---|---|---|---|---|---|---|---|
| | No. | % | No. | % | No. | % | No. | % | No. | % |
| 1977–1985 | – | – | 356 | 19.41 | 270 | 14.72 | 928 | 50.60 | 1,554 | 84.73 |
| 2007–2013 | 170 | 9.15 | 419 | 22.55 | 466 | 25.08 | 564 | 30.36 | 1,449 | 77.99 |
| Significance: The change is not significant (P = 0.092) | | | | | | | | | | |

**Breeding distribution 1977–85**

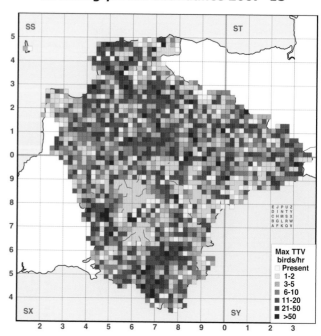

**Breeding-period abundance 2007–13**

# Jackdaw
## Corvus monedula

THE JACKDAW, like other members of the Corvidae, is a highly adaptable species with a diverse diet and is found across lowland farmland, often associating with Rooks outside the breeding season. Nesting is now particularly associated with buildings, where any cavity, such as a chimney, will be attractive.

The breeding-period maps show a widespread distribution; Jackdaws are present in most lowland tetrads but abundance is variable, with generally higher densities (more than 11–20 birds/hour) in areas of the South Hams, West Devon and North Devon. Lower densities (up to ten birds/hour) occur in rural areas of the county, particularly East Devon

### Winter-period abundance 2007–13

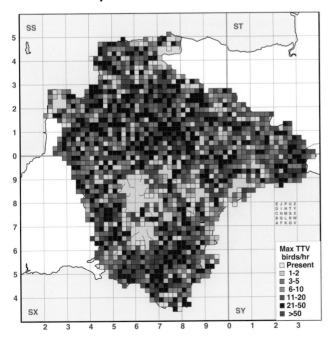

Max TTV birds/hr
- ☐ Present
- ☐ 1-2
- ◼ 3-5
- ◼ 6-10
- ◼ 11-20
- ◼ 21-50
- ◼ >50

and West Devon districts. The species is absent from the higher moorland of Dartmoor and Exmoor. The *Devon Tetrad Atlas 1977–85* confirmed breeding in 50% of tetrads, compared to 30% during the current survey. As stated in the earlier Atlas, records of possible breeding are widespread and of limited value as many probably represent birds foraging or in flight and bear little relationship to the location of actual nest sites.

Comparative analysis of breeding evidence by tetrad between the two Devon Atlases shows a similar pattern of distribution but also a slight, but statistically insignificant decline in confirmed breeding records across many lowland tetrads. This is especially evident along the coast where Jackdaws were confirmed to be breeding in all tetrads during 1977–85. It is likely that differences in survey methodology may explain the apparent small decline in confirmed breeding records, which contrasts with the increasing population trend for the UK as a whole and in South West England since 1995 (Risely *et al.* 2013).

The winter-period map shows a similar distribution to the breeding map. This is perhaps unsurprising as this species is largely sedentary in the UK (Wernham *et al.* 2002). Whilst the absence of the species from suboptimal foraging habitats such as moorland and heath is easily explained, the lack of records from some tetrads in, for example, the Teign Valley and Hartland are more difficult to understand and could be related to changes in land use.

*Text: Simon Geary / Photo: Steve Hatch*
*Jackdaw sponsored by Kevin & Donna Cox*

Balmer *et al.* 2013: 482; Sitters 1988: 252; Tyler 2010: 443

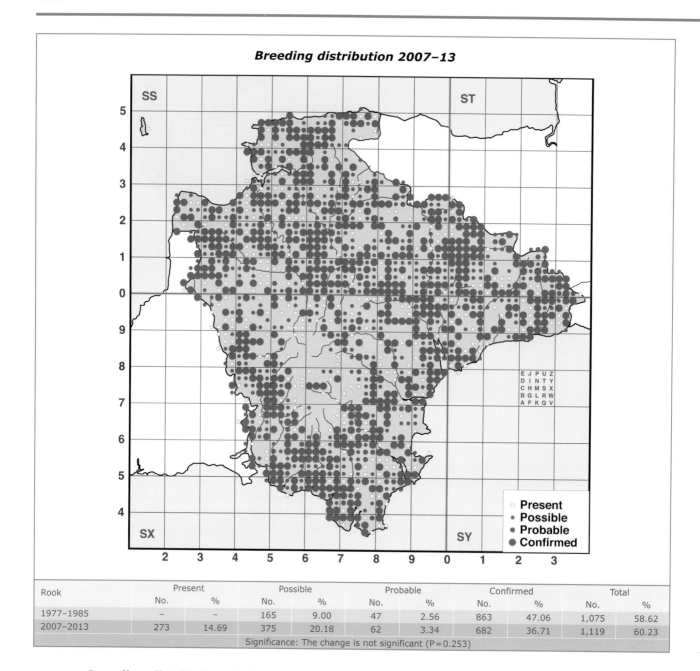

**Breeding distribution 2007–13**

| Rook | Present | | Possible | | Probable | | Confirmed | | Total | |
|------|------|-----|------|-----|------|-----|------|-----|------|-----|
| | No. | % | No. | % | No. | % | No. | % | No. | % |
| 1977–1985 | – | – | 165 | 9.00 | 47 | 2.56 | 863 | 47.06 | 1,075 | 58.62 |
| 2007–2013 | 273 | 14.69 | 375 | 20.18 | 62 | 3.34 | 682 | 36.71 | 1,119 | 60.23 |
| Significance: The change is not significant (P=0.253) | | | | | | | | | | |

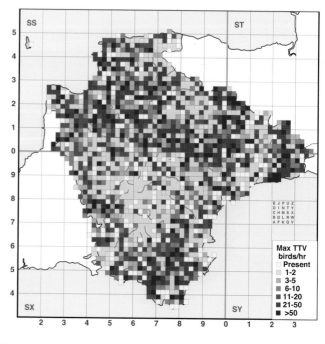

**Breeding distribution 1977–85**

**Breeding-period abundance 2007–13**

# Rook
*Corvus frugilegus*

THE ROOK is mainly a species of lowland, mixed farmland and favours areas where there are copses suitable for colonial nesting, together with disturbed ground and open grasslands for feeding. This survey shows that it occurs in most lowland tetrads, with lower densities (six to ten birds) recorded on the moorland edges, the Culm Measures, some parts of Mid Devon and Teignbridge. However it also occurs in more upland areas and there are 70 rookeries on Dartmoor with

one, at Princetown, being the highest in the county at 442 metres (Smaldon 2005).

The breeding-period maps show a widespread distribution, with confirmed breeding in every 10-km square except a few which are coastal and cover little land area or otherwise lack suitable nesting or foraging habitat, such as high moorland and urban centres.

While most Devon rookeries are in trees, there are some pre-Atlas records of pylons being used and this may be learned behaviour. The 1975 BTO Rookery Survey did not record any such nests in the county but in 1980 there were ten in three locations (Hayman 1981). In 2004, five nests were built on pylons at Huxham (Jarvis 2004).

Comparison of data from the current Atlas with that from the *Devon Tetrad Atlas 1977–85* suggests that there has been little change in overall status, with breeding evidence found in approximately 60% of tetrads during both surveys. The UK population showed a significant 17% decline between 1995 and 2011 (Risely *et al.* 2013), so it is good to see the species' range in Devon being maintained.

Rooks are sedentary in the UK (Wernham *et al.* 2002) and hence the winter-period map shows a generally similar distribution to that for the breeding-period map. However, there is a clear zone of higher winter abundance stretching from North Devon through Mid Devon into East Devon.

*Text: Simon Geary / Photo: Roy Churchill*

Balmer *et al.* 2013: 484; Sitters 1988: 254; Tyler 2010: 445

### Winter-period abundance 2007–13

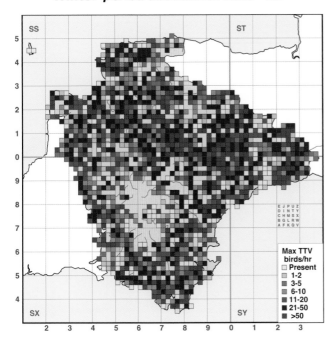

Max TTV birds/hr
- ☐ Present
- 1-2
- 3-5
- 6-10
- 11-20
- 21-50
- >50

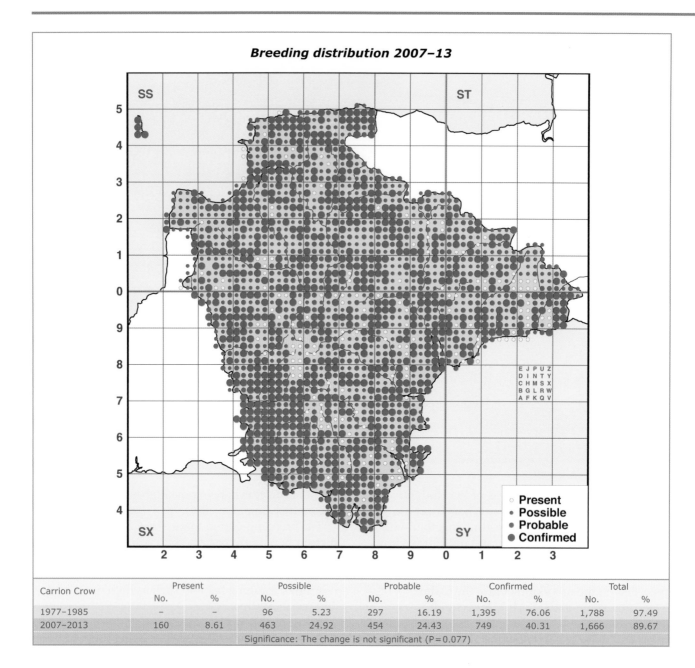

**Breeding distribution 2007–13**

| Carrion Crow | Present | | Possible | | Probable | | Confirmed | | Total | |
|---|---|---|---|---|---|---|---|---|---|---|
| | No. | % | No. | % | No. | % | No. | % | No. | % |
| 1977–1985 | – | – | 96 | 5.23 | 297 | 16.19 | 1,395 | 76.06 | 1,788 | 97.49 |
| 2007–2013 | 160 | 8.61 | 463 | 24.92 | 454 | 24.43 | 749 | 40.31 | 1,666 | 89.67 |
| Significance: The change is not significant (P = 0.077) | | | | | | | | | | |

**Breeding distribution 1977–85**

**Breeding-period abundance 2007–13**

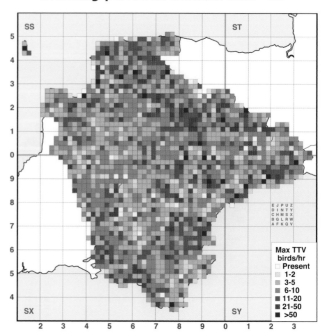

# Carrion Crow
## *Corvus corone*

THE CARRION Crow, well known for its raucous call, is a highly adaptable species with a diverse diet. It is found in all habitats – including intertidal areas, high moorland and city centres – nesting wherever there are suitable trees.

The breeding-period maps show that the species is widespread, with confirmed breeding in every 10-km square except a few that are coastal and hold little land area, such as Bolt Head. Crows were present in every tetrad during the breeding season, with generally higher densities (greater than 11–20 birds) in parts of Mid and North Devon and the Plymouth area, and lower densities (six to ten birds) in many rural areas, particularly across a swathe of land between the South Hams, across Dartmoor into West Devon and Torridge District. Bird density is not a reliable indicator of breeding density for this species because of the variable, sometimes large, numbers of non-breeding birds within the population.

Comparative analysis of breeding evidence by tetrad between the *Devon Tetrad Atlas 1977–85* and the current survey shows some similarities, such as a lack of confirmed breeding on much of the high moorland of Dartmoor and Exmoor. However, the most significant change is an apparent decline in confirmed breeding records across many lowland tetrads, with the exception of most tetrads in the far south-west of the county, between the rivers Erme and Tamar, and north to Tavistock. The 1977–85 survey had confirmed breeding records for the species in 76% of tetrads, as against 40% during

### Winter-period abundance 2007–13

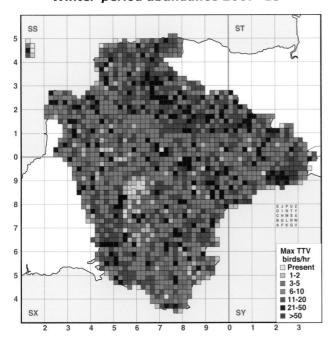

Max TTV birds/hr
☐ Present
☐ 1-2
☐ 3-5
☐ 6-10
☐ 11-20
☐ 21-50
☐ >50

2007–13. The nests of this species are best detected before leaf break, with a later check for occupancy, and differing methodologies may explain some of the apparent change in confirmed breeding between Atlases. The three breeding categories taken together perhaps provide a more valid comparison and indicate no significant difference overall between the two surveys.

During the inter-atlas period, a detailed survey of Carrion Crows in central Plymouth confirmed breeding within every 1-km square, and so within the corresponding Atlas tetrads (Geary 2001). The results of that survey indicate a relatively stable population in the Plymouth area since the late 1970s, which lies within the apparently most stable populated area in the county.

Other than a limited winter movement from the highest moorland tetrads, the winter-period map shows a similar distribution of population density to the breeding map. This is perhaps unsurprising as the species is highly sedentary in the UK (Wernham *et al.* 2002).

*Text: Simon Geary / Photos: Neil Bygrave (top) & Dave Scott*
*Carrion Crow sponsored by*
*Brent Birders – of South Brent Parish*

Balmer *et al.* 2013: 486; Sitters 1988: 256; Tyler 2010: 447

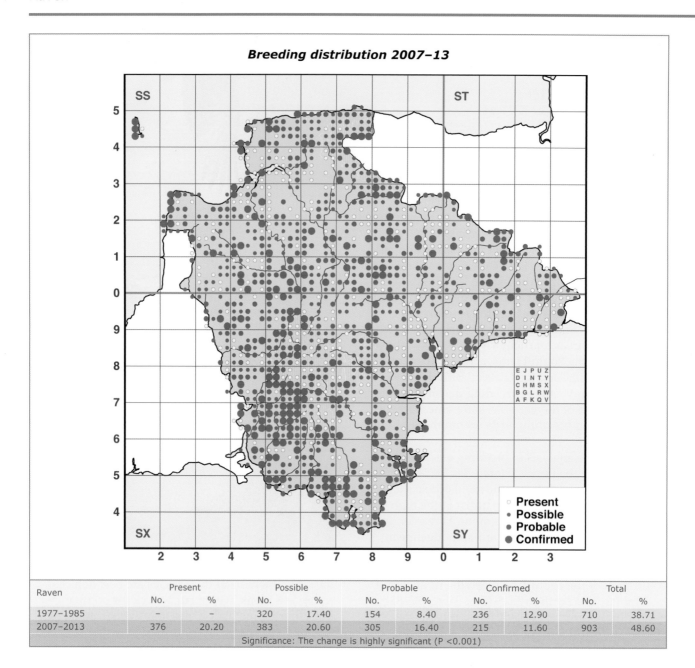

### Breeding distribution 2007–13

| Raven | Present | | Possible | | Probable | | Confirmed | | Total | |
|---|---|---|---|---|---|---|---|---|---|---|
| | No. | % | No. | % | No. | % | No. | % | No. | % |
| 1977–1985 | – | – | 320 | 17.40 | 154 | 8.40 | 236 | 12.90 | 710 | 38.71 |
| 2007–2013 | 376 | 20.20 | 383 | 20.60 | 305 | 16.40 | 215 | 11.60 | 903 | 48.60 |
| | Significance: The change is highly significant (P <0.001) | | | | | | | | | |

### Breeding distribution 1977–85

### Breeding-period abundance 2007–13

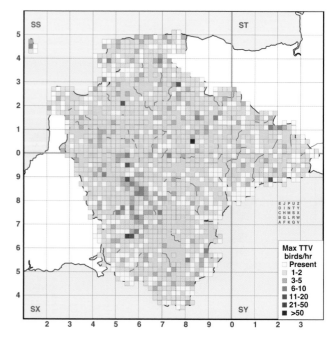

# Raven
*Corvus corax*

Tｈᴇ ᴄʜᴀʀᴀᴄᴛᴇʀɪsᴛɪᴄ, far-carrying, guttural *'cronk'* of Ravens draws attention to them at all times of year. Combined with a penchant for spectacular aerial acrobatics, particularly from early winter to early spring, this is a species that is not easily overlooked. Favoured nesting sites include cliffs, quarries and, especially, mature trees, and traditional sites may be in continuous use over many decades.

Perhaps most closely associated in the past with our wilder coasts and uplands, the Atlas maps show that Ravens are now virtually ubiquitous in Devon.

### Winter-period abundance 2007–13

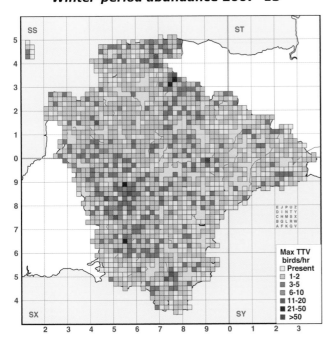

Max TTV
birds/hr
☐ Present
1-2
3-5
6-10
11-20
21-50
>50

Breeding was confirmed or probable in more than 95% of the county's 10-km squares, while breeding-period presence was recorded in more than two-thirds of all tetrads. During Atlas winter periods, Ravens were even more widely recorded, occurring in more than three-quarters of all tetrads.

A comparison of breeding-season statistics and maps for the present Atlas years with those for the *Devon Tetrad Atlas 1977–85* shows that while breeding was confirmed in slightly more tetrads in the earlier survey, the species' range has expanded noticeably. In particular, much of East and Mid Devon has been colonized. The apparent decrease in cases of confirmed breeding, especially in the north of the county, is perhaps more likely to reflect differences in coverage than real change in the species' status, though increased use of control measures by sheep farmers and perhaps increased recreational disturbance in some areas cannot be excluded as possible factors.

The range expansion eastwards in Devon is very much in line with the improved fortunes of Ravens nationally in response to generally reduced persecution. *Bird Atlas 2007–11* shows a dramatic eastward spread across England since the *Breeding Atlas 1968–72* and the *Winter Atlas 1981–84*. In spite of this notable national change, Devon (especially Dartmoor and Exmoor) continues to be the most important county for Ravens in England given the extent and density of its population.

*Text: Tim Davis & Tim Jones / Photo: Tom Bedford*
*Raven sponsored by Jim & Kath Braven*

Balmer *et al.* 2013: 490; Sitters 1988: 258; Tyler 2010: 450

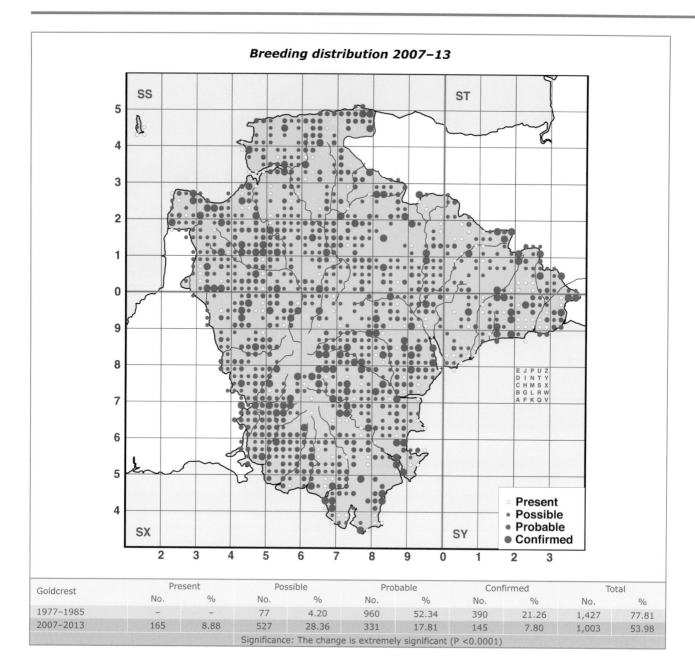

## Breeding distribution 2007–13

| Goldcrest | Present | | Possible | | Probable | | Confirmed | | Total | |
|---|---|---|---|---|---|---|---|---|---|---|
| | No. | % | No. | % | No. | % | No. | % | No. | % |
| 1977–1985 | – | – | 77 | 4.20 | 960 | 52.34 | 390 | 21.26 | 1,427 | 77.81 |
| 2007–2013 | 165 | 8.88 | 527 | 28.36 | 331 | 17.81 | 145 | 7.80 | 1,003 | 53.98 |
| Significance: The change is extremely significant (P <0.0001) | | | | | | | | | | |

## Breeding distribution 1977–85

## Breeding-period abundance 2007–13

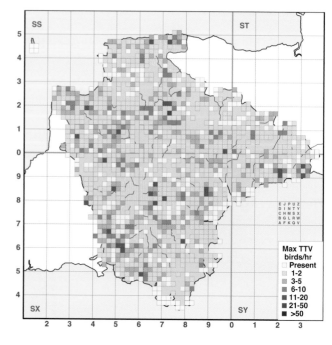

# Goldcrest
## *Regulus regulus*

THE TINY Goldcrest is a bird that can be easily overlooked as it flits through trees and shrubs. Its preferred habitats are dense stands of conifers, mixed woodlands, Sessile Oak woods interspersed with Holly and churchyards where Yew is growing. After breeding it ventures into gardens and during autumn and winter is frequently found in family parties, within flocks of foraging tits and Treecreepers. The thin but penetrating '*see-see-see-see*' calls are a familiar sound in woodlands – but may be inaudible to the older birdwatcher!

With the exception of the high moors of Dartmoor and Exmoor, the species is widely distributed across Devon and was recorded in all 10-km squares during the current Atlas period. Breeding evidence was recorded in 54% of tetrads compared with 78% during the *Devon Tetrad Atlas 1977–1985*. Comparison of the breeding status dot-maps for the two Atlases shows a significant reduction in the number of tetrads in which breeding was confirmed in the present survey: 144 tetrads versus 390 tetrads in 1977-85, while probable breeding fell from 960 to 331 tetrads.

If taken at face value, the apparent losses in Devon are apparently greater than the 15% national decline between 1995 and 2010 reported in *Bird Atlas 2007–11*, while BTO BirdTrends (2014) show a modest recovery since 2010, assessing the population in England as "fluctuating, with no long-term trend". It therefore seems possible that while there may well have been genuine losses (perhaps associated with the cold winters during the Atlas period, see below), these are exaggerated by differences of methodology and coverage between the two Atlases. Without specially targeted effort, Goldcrest is not an easy species for which to prove breeding.

Goldcrests were found in 66% of tetrads during the winter-period TTVs (November–February), broadly comparable with the 63% of tetrads occupied during the breeding-period TTVs (April–July). In winter and during passage periods – particularly autumn passage peaking in September/October – locally bred birds are joined by large numbers of migrants from the north of Britain and continental Europe. Large influxes may occur, particularly on Lundy (e.g. a fall of 500 on 17 October 2008; *DBR*). However, severe winter weather in 2009 and 2010 significantly depressed numbers recorded at coastal migration watchpoints in subsequent autumns, with counts remaining on the low side until autumn 2012 (*DBR*). It is highly likely that the same freezing conditions adversely affected local breeding numbers, though perhaps the impacts were greater further north.

*Text: Mike Tyler / Photo: John Clark*
*Goldcrest sponsored by Margaret Phillips*

Balmer *et al.* 2013: 492; Sitters 1988: 226; Tyler 2010: 452

### Winter-period abundance 2007–13

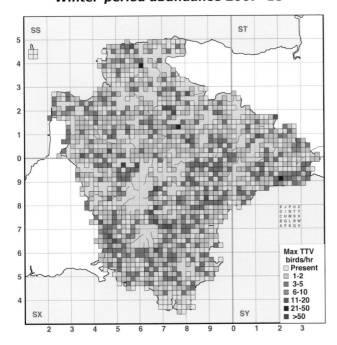

Max TTV birds/hr
- ☐ Present
- 1-2
- 3-5
- 6-10
- 11-20
- 21-50
- >50

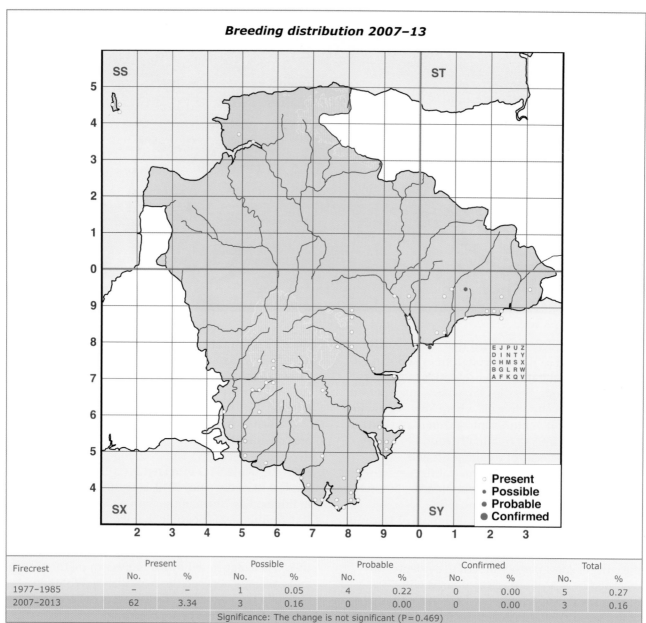

## Breeding distribution 2007–13

| Firecrest | Present | | Possible | | Probable | | Confirmed | | Total | |
|---|---|---|---|---|---|---|---|---|---|---|
| | No. | % | No. | % | No. | % | No. | % | No. | % |
| 1977–1985 | – | – | 1 | 0.05 | 4 | 0.22 | 0 | 0.00 | 5 | 0.27 |
| 2007–2013 | 62 | 3.34 | 3 | 0.16 | 0 | 0.00 | 0 | 0.00 | 3 | 0.16 |
| Significance: The change is not significant (P = 0.469) | | | | | | | | | | |

## Breeding distribution 1977–85

## Breeding-period abundance 2007–13

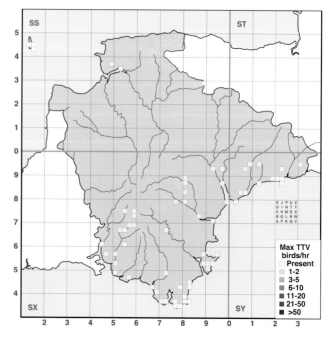

# Firecrest
## *Regulus ignicapilla*

THE DIMINUTIVE Firecrest is a regular passage migrant (particularly in autumn) and winter visitor to Devon. Its preferred habitat includes stands of conifers, but also both mixed and deciduous woodlands with a shrubby understorey. During autumn and winter it frequently consorts with flocks of foraging Goldcrests, tits and Treecreepers and occurs in a wider range of habitats, including coastal scrub and gardens.

The *Devon Tetrad Atlas 1977–85* reports breeding evidence for five tetrads (four probable, one possible). There were sporadic indications of likely breeding in the years between the two Devon Atlases, but breeding was not confirmed (Tyler 2010).

### Winter-period abundance 2007–13

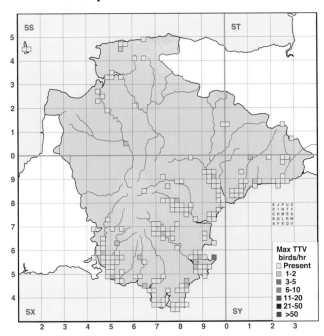

Max TTV
birds/hr
☐ Present
☐ 1-2
■ 3-5
■ 6-10
■ 11-20
■ 21-50
■ >50

During the current survey Firecrests were recorded in fifty-two 10-km squares, mainly in the south and east of the county where the species appears to be widely distributed, though it is important to bear in mind that the breeding-period map (March–September) will include a proportion of spring and early-autumn passage migrants. There were possible breeding records in three tetrads: two in south-east Devon and one on Exmoor. *Bird Atlas 2007–11* maps a considerable expansion in the UK breeding distribution since the *Breeding Atlas 1968–72* and Firecrests are now firmly established as breeding birds in some parts of the country.[1]

The winter-period map (October–February) shows records for 160 tetrads, again mainly in the south of the county. Many of these will inevitably have been migrants, given that autumn passage continues throughout October and much of November. The highest count during the Atlas period was of 14 at West Hill (about ten kilometres east of Exeter) on 30 October 2011 (*DBR*).

Severe winters will take their toll of this tiny bird which, although established, is likely to continue to fluctuate (Mead 2000). *Bird Atlas 2007–11* refers to population growth in Britain, particularly of breeding birds, and this is beginning to be seen in Devon when one compares the number of Firecrests in summer to that of the 1977–85 survey. Warmer winters may well help to establish the Firecrest as a regular breeder in Devon.

*Text: Mike Tyler / Photo: Mike Langman*
*Firecrest sponsored by David Jenks*

Balmer *et al.* 2013: 494; Sitters 1988: 302; Tyler 2010: 455

[1]Breeding was confirmed in Devon when several pairs nested in the Dart Valley in 2014, a year after the close of the Atlas period.

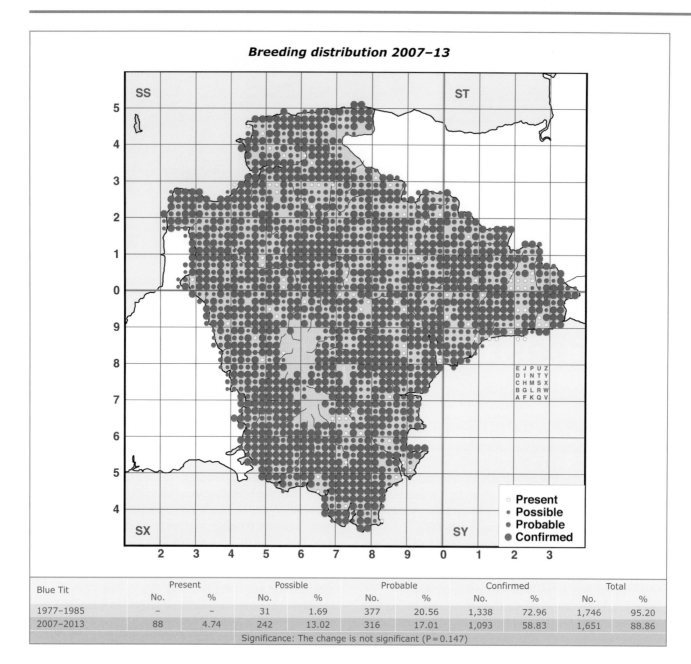

**Breeding distribution 2007–13**

| Blue Tit | Present | | Possible | | Probable | | Confirmed | | Total | |
|---|---|---|---|---|---|---|---|---|---|---|
| | No. | % | No. | % | No. | % | No. | % | No. | % |
| 1977–1985 | – | – | 31 | 1.69 | 377 | 20.56 | 1,338 | 72.96 | 1,746 | 95.20 |
| 2007–2013 | 88 | 4.74 | 242 | 13.02 | 316 | 17.01 | 1,093 | 58.83 | 1,651 | 88.86 |
| Significance: The change is not significant (P=0.147) | | | | | | | | | | |

**Breeding distribution 1977–85**          **Breeding-period abundance 2007–13**

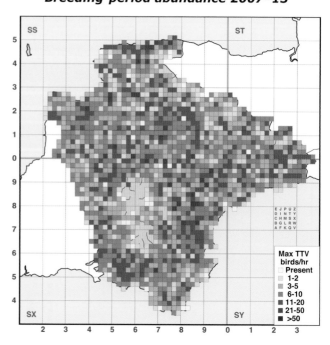

# Blue Tit
## *Cyanistes caeruleus*

THE BLUE Tit is ubiquitous, occurring in all except completely treeless habitats, but is most abundant in broad-leaved woodlands. It is especially common in urban and suburban habitats, though productivity is lower compared to that in broad-leaved woodland.

In Devon the Atlas survey confirmed that Blue Tit is found in virtually all tetrads (89%) and is only absent from treeless areas of Dartmoor and Exmoor. The species is sedentary and hence there is no difference between the summer and winter distributions. The few gaps in distribution in this survey, and a small decline in the proportion of occupied tetrads since the *Devon Tetrad Atlas 1977–85*, almost certainly result from under-reporting. The effects of harsh winter weather and high rainfall during the breeding season in some years of the survey may also account for the small decline.

Blue Tits are hole-nesters and readily use nestboxes. Consequently they are very well monitored by Devon nestbox schemes, and long-term trends in occupancy rates and productivity are well known. These data show that the abundance of Blue Tits in Devon has increased over recent decades.

At East Dartmoor National Nature Reserve (NNR), where nests have been closely monitored since 1955, the annual occupancy rate of nestboxes has increased significantly since the 1950s and continues to rise. Average clutch size has, however, declined over the same period, possibly due to increased competition with other Blue Tits as density has increased and territories have consequently become smaller. The number of birds fledged per breeding attempt has remained stable once lower clutch sizes are accounted for, although because there are more pairs nesting the total number of young fledged in the NNR has increased. Nest success is lower in years with higher rainfall in May, when young are in the nest (Burgess 2014).

Breeding Blue Tits are especially reliant on the short seasonal peak in caterpillar abundance, and need to time their breeding so that the peak demands of their nestlings at about 12 days old coincide with the peak in caterpillar availability. Spring has advanced in recent decades, and Blue Tits in East Dartmoor NNR have advanced timing of breeding by laying eggs earlier so that peak chick food demand still matches peak caterpillar availability (pers. obs.).

Thousands of adults and young are ringed in Devon each year, showing that Blue Tits are sedentary throughout the year, with very few birds moving more than a few kilometres from where they were hatched or first captured. Intensive nestbox ringing shows strong fidelity by females to the same nestbox each year.

*Text: Malcolm Burgess / Photo: Neil Bygrave*
*Blue Tit sponsored by Lizzie & Roger Little*

Balmer *et al.* 2013: 496; Sitters 1988: 240; Tyler 2010: 456

### Winter-period abundance 2007–13

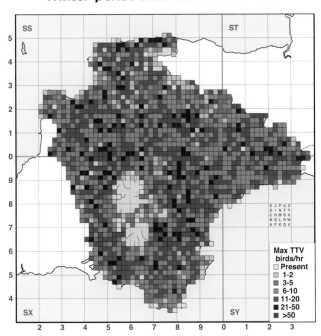

Max TTV birds/hr
- □ Present
- 1-2
- 3-5
- 6-10
- 11-20
- 21-50
- >50

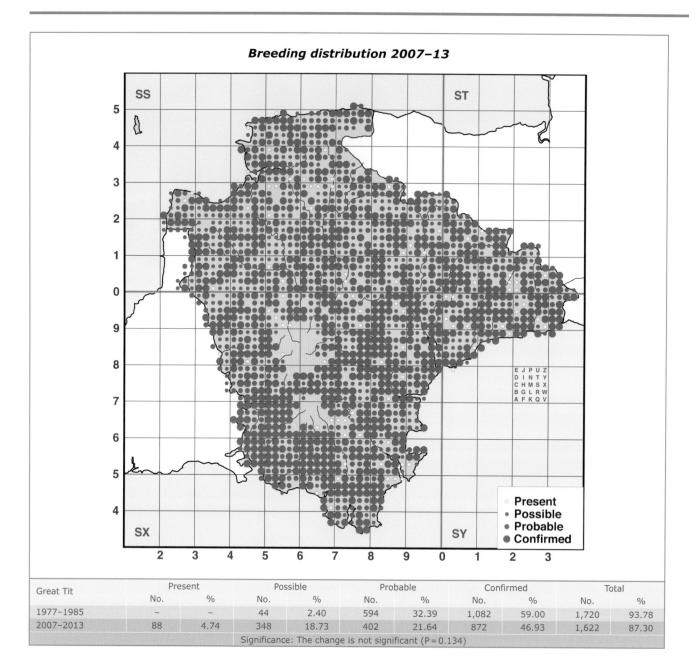

### Breeding distribution 2007–13

| Great Tit | Present | | Possible | | Probable | | Confirmed | | Total | |
|---|---|---|---|---|---|---|---|---|---|---|
| | No. | % | No. | % | No. | % | No. | % | No. | % |
| 1977–1985 | – | – | 44 | 2.40 | 594 | 32.39 | 1,082 | 59.00 | 1,720 | 93.78 |
| 2007–2013 | 88 | 4.74 | 348 | 18.73 | 402 | 21.64 | 872 | 46.93 | 1,622 | 87.30 |
| Significance: The change is not significant (P = 0.134) | | | | | | | | | | |

### Breeding distribution 1977–85

### Breeding-period abundance 2007–13

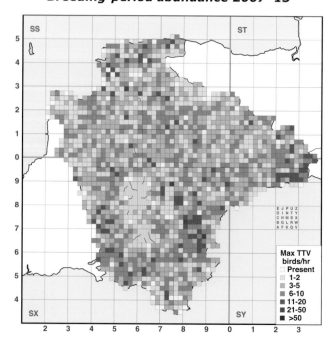

# Great Tit
## *Parus major*

Great Tits are a ubiquitous and essentially sedentary species found in all but treeless habitats, occurring most abundantly in broad-leaved woodlands. They are common in urban and suburban habitats and are a virtually year-round presence on garden bird feeders.

In Devon, Great Tits are found in almost all tetrads (92%). This distribution shows little change since the *Devon Tetrad Atlas 1977–85*, though the current survey recorded a higher proportion of tetrads with probable rather than confirmed breeding. Although this could be due to under-reporting of such a ubiquitous species, it could also be that abundance was lower in 2007–13, reducing detectability. Reduced abundance could result from lower winter survival due to the two harsh winters that occurred during the Atlas years, or fewer recruits resulting from reduced nest success in years of high rainfall in May, when young are in the nest (Burgess 2014). Great Tit populations also fluctuate in relation to beech mast crops (Perrins 1965), which were low in some years of this survey, although mature stands of beech are found only locally in Devon and so beech mast availability would be unlikely to make a significant overall difference. Nationally, over the same time period, the species has undergone a small expansion in range and quite large increases in abundance, which suggests that under-reporting for the current Atlas explains the small apparent decline and contrast with the national trend.

Great Tits are hole-nesters and readily use nestboxes, although they prefer a slightly larger entrance hole than Blue Tits and so may sometimes be inadvertently excluded by nestbox schemes. They are also less abundant than Blue Tits and thus monitored in smaller numbers, but their demographic trends are still very well known. Great Tit nest success is reliant on the short seasonal peak in caterpillar abundance, and breeding needs to be timed such that the peak demands of nestlings coincide with the peak in caterpillar availability (Cholewa & Wesołowski 2011). Great Tits can manage a second brood in favourable springs, suggesting less of a reliance on the caterpillar peak, although second broods tend not to be successful.

Many adults and young are ringed in Devon each year, and this shows that Great Tits are highly sedentary throughout the year, with few birds moving more than a few kilometres.

*Text: Malcolm Burgess / Photo: Andrew Cunningham*
*Great Tit sponsored by Sunflower Ecology*

**Ecological Consultancy**

Balmer *et al.* 2013: 498; Sitters 1988: 242; Tyler 2010: 458

### Winter-period abundance 2007–13

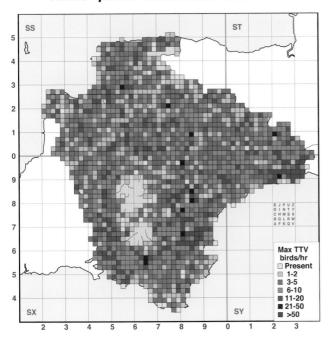

Max TTV birds/hr
- ☐ Present
- 1-2
- 3-5
- 6-10
- 11-20
- 21-50
- >50

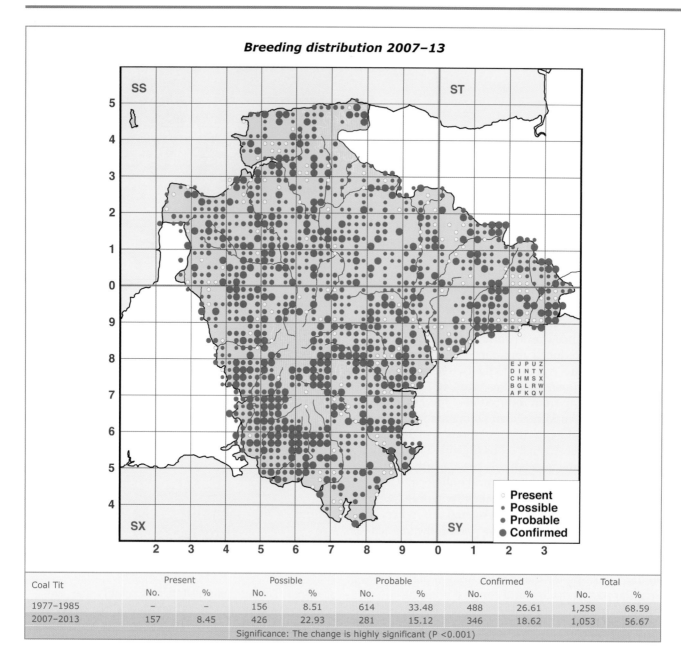

## Breeding distribution 2007–13

| Coal Tit | Present | | Possible | | Probable | | Confirmed | | Total | |
|---|---|---|---|---|---|---|---|---|---|---|
| | No. | % | No. | % | No. | % | No. | % | No. | % |
| 1977–1985 | – | – | 156 | 8.51 | 614 | 33.48 | 488 | 26.61 | 1,258 | 68.59 |
| 2007–2013 | 157 | 8.45 | 426 | 22.93 | 281 | 15.12 | 346 | 18.62 | 1,053 | 56.67 |
| | Significance: The change is highly significant (P <0.001) | | | | | | | | | |

## Breeding distribution 1977–85

## Breeding-period abundance 2007–13

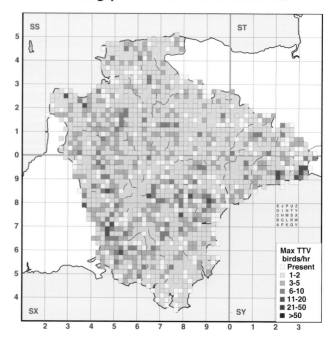

# Coal Tit
## *Periparus ater*

COAL TITS are primarily birds of coniferous woodland, but are also found in broad-leaved woodlands and in town and city gardens where they commonly visit bird feeders. The Devon breeding population belongs to the British subspecies *P. a. britannicus* (Langman *et al.* 2007). Birds from continental Europe belonging to the subspecies *P. a. ater* are occasionally recorded in the county, mainly from south coast headlands.

Breeding was confirmed in 57% of tetrads during the current survey, but it is probable that Coal Tits were under-recorded because their high-pitched call and tendency to feed high in the woodland canopy can make them hard to find. The large number of possible and probable breeding records also suggests under-recording of confirmed breeding. Fewer tetrads were occupied when compared to the *Devon*

*Tetrad Atlas 1977–85*, with the 205 'lost' tetrads being spread across Devon, especially in the north. However, many of these apparent gaps in breeding distribution were occupied during the winter period, and though Coal Tits move locally with other tit species in winter flocks, they are generally very sedentary and probably also breed in the tetrads concerned. Overall distribution in Devon has changed very little; the species is found right across the county except in treeless areas of Dartmoor and Exmoor.

Part of the recorded decline in occupied tetrads may be related to the two consecutive cold winters during the survey. Coal Tits are primarily insectivores but switch to tree seeds, such as those from conifers and beech, in colder weather. It might be expected that harsh winters would exert a particular toll on such a small bird, but Coal Tits cache food for consuming during cold periods and are therefore relatively resilient. Survival may be aided by garden feeding, especially provision of high-quality food items such as sunflower seeds and peanuts. Behaviour at garden feeders is different from other tits; Coal Tits make brief visits, taking food and flying off with it to cache rather than consuming it on the feeder. Ringing clearly shows the importance of supplementary garden feeding, with a relatively small number of individuals visiting the same feeders every day during the winter, ferrying food seemingly all day long. Ringing also clearly shows high year-round site fidelity (Wernham *et al.* 2002).

*Text: Malcolm Burgess / Photo: Carole Bowden*
*Coal Tit sponsored by Susan Nethercott*

Balmer *et al.* 2013: 502; Sitters 1988: 238; Tyler 2010: 461

### Winter-period abundance 2007–13

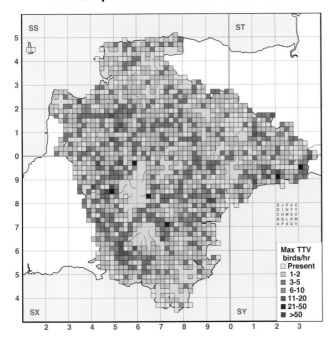

Max TTV birds/hr
- □ Present
- 1-2
- 3-5
- 6-10
- 11-20
- 21-50
- >50

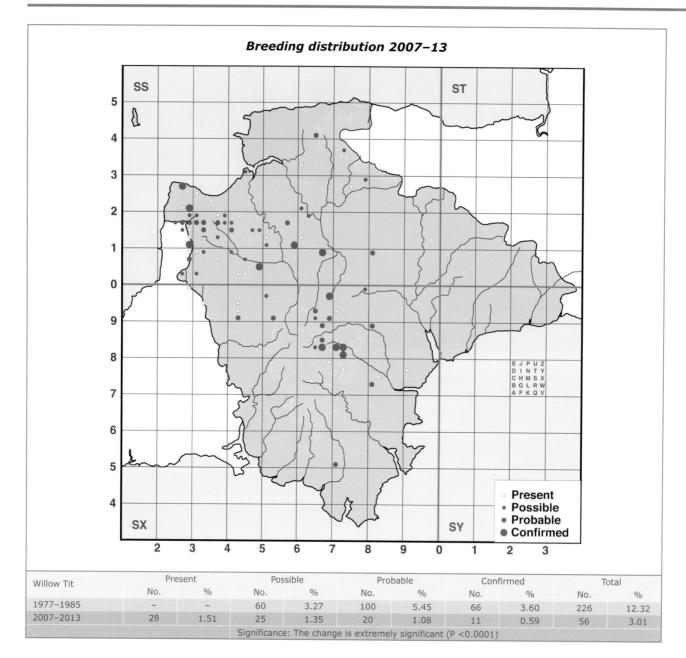

### Breeding distribution 2007–13

| Willow Tit | Present | | Possible | | Probable | | Confirmed | | Total | |
|---|---|---|---|---|---|---|---|---|---|---|
| | No. | % | No. | % | No. | % | No. | % | No. | % |
| 1977–1985 | – | – | 60 | 3.27 | 100 | 5.45 | 66 | 3.60 | 226 | 12.32 |
| 2007–2013 | 28 | 1.51 | 25 | 1.35 | 20 | 1.08 | 11 | 0.59 | 56 | 3.01 |
| Significance: The change is extremely significant (P <0.0001) | | | | | | | | | | |

### Breeding distribution 1977–85

### Breeding-period abundance 2007–13

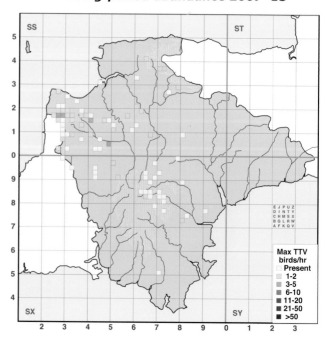

# Willow Tit
## Poecile montana

**Red listed**

THE WILLOW Tit inhabits areas of scrubby wet woodland, an association linked to its absolute requirement for rotten wood within which it can make its nest hole (*BWP*). Only very rarely will it use an existing tree hole or nestbox; the latter only if specially designed (Last & Burgess 2015).

Willow Tits are highly sedentary and will stay in the same area throughout the year. Once a Willow Tit has settled in its territory, it is likely to remain there for the rest of its life (*BWP*). Movements of Willow Tits are most commonly observed post-fledging and just prior to the start of the breeding season. It is possible that this sedentary characteristic, whereby all needs have to be covered by the territory throughout the year, explains the large territory size required; this averages five hectares, or larger if there are patches of unsuitable habitat within it (Lüdescher 1973). Gaps in woodland cover generally operate as natural territory boundaries. Only if weather conditions become very severe in winter will Willow Tits move from their territory. Like most tit species, they live off insects in the summer months and switch to seeds in the winter.

In the *Devon Tetrad Atlas 1977–85*, Willow Tits were found to be present in 226 tetrads during the breeding season. The current Atlas shows a collapse in range, with records from only 55 tetrads during the breeding season and a reduction in the number of tetrads for which breeding was confirmed or probable from 166 to just 31. The losses in Devon mirror a national decline, with an estimated

population decline of 79% between 1995 and 2010 (*Bird Atlas 2007–11*). The species has disappeared entirely from East Devon and almost entirely from North Devon, as well as from much of the remaining core area to the north and west of Dartmoor. Conversely, there appears to have been a small expansion in range on Dartmoor's north-eastern fringes, with presence (including four instances of confirmed breeding) recorded in ten tetrads in SX68 and SX78 against just one in 1977–85. As might be expected for a highly sedentary species, the distribution in winter is very similar to that during the breeding period.

The reasons for the decline, both nationally and within the county, are not well understood, especially as seemingly suitable habitat appears to be unoccupied (*Bird Atlas 2007–11*). Factors such as competition from other tit species for nest holes, predation by Great Spotted Woodpeckers or unsuitable woodland structure have all been investigated but no firm links have yet been made (Lewis *et al.* 2009). It is possible that all these factors, together with fragmentation of wet woodlands and a loss of suitable dead wood, have a role to play.

The challenge of separating Willow and Marsh Tits may have led to a few errors in recording, but every effort has been made to eliminate these.

*Text: Naomi Barker / Photo: Paul Sterry/NPL*
*Willow Tit sponsored by Ian Taylor (Bishops Tawton)*

Balmer *et al.* 2013: 504; Sitters 1988: 236; Tyler 2010: 463

### Winter-period abundance 2007–13

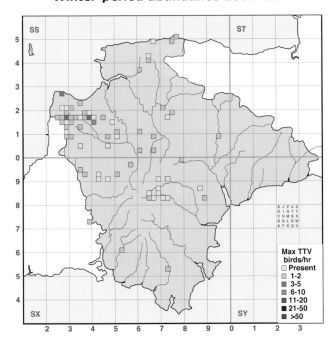

Max TTV birds/hr
☐ Present
▨ 1-2
▨ 3-5
■ 6-10
■ 11-20
■ 21-50
■ >50

## Breeding distribution 2007–13

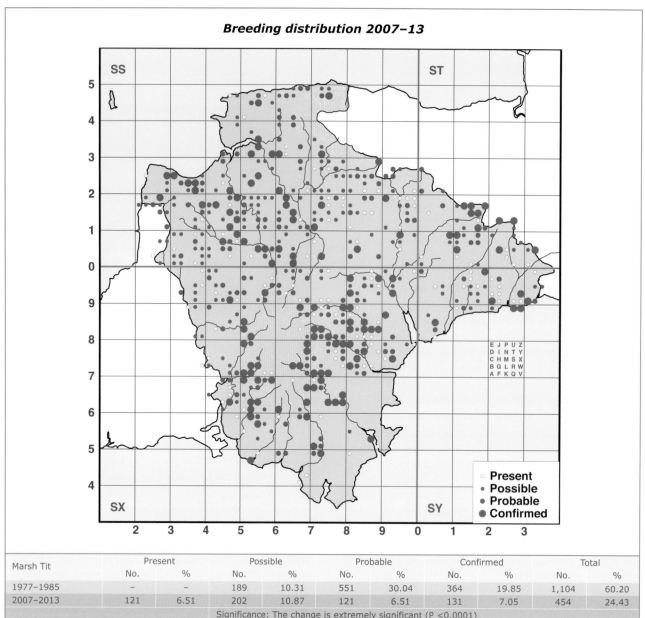

| Marsh Tit | Present | | Possible | | Probable | | Confirmed | | Total | |
|---|---|---|---|---|---|---|---|---|---|---|
| | No. | % | No. | % | No. | % | No. | % | No. | % |
| 1977–1985 | – | – | 189 | 10.31 | 551 | 30.04 | 364 | 19.85 | 1,104 | 60.20 |
| 2007–2013 | 121 | 6.51 | 202 | 10.87 | 121 | 6.51 | 131 | 7.05 | 454 | 24.43 |
| Significance: The change is extremely significant (P <0.0001) | | | | | | | | | | |

## Breeding distribution 1977–85

## Breeding-period abundance 2007–13

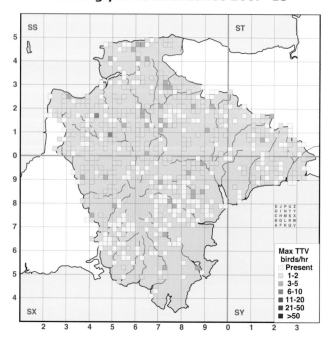

# Marsh Tit

*Poecile palustris*

**Red listed**

MARSH TITS rely on well-wooded landscapes and are only found within or near to well-connected areas of woodland (Broughton & Hinsley 2015), although this can include woodlands on the edges of towns and cities. They prefer taller mature trees with a closed canopy and usually require woods of at least ten hectares in size in which to breed (Hinsley *et al.* 1995). Marsh Tits are highly sedentary, rarely dispersing more than a few kilometres (Broughton *et al.* 2010), which is why the winter distribution map so closely matches the breeding map, although they do range further in winter than in summer.

Marsh Tits underwent a significant decline between the *Devon Tetrad Atlas 1977–85* and the current survey, having been lost from more than half (650) of the comparable tetrads occupied in 1977–85. While Marsh Tits were previously found across Devon, except in the treeless areas of Dartmoor and Exmoor, they are now much more thinly distributed, with a suggestion of significant contractions in the more populated southern and eastern parts of the county. The decline may be partly a consequence of loss of woodland connectivity during the inter-Atlas period. Mature, infrequently cut hedgerows containing trees allowed to grow to their full height are less common in Devon today than in the past. However, recent research shows that national Marsh Tit declines may not be related to either food availability or habitat quality, but suggests that

Marsh Tits might be out-competed by increasing populations of Blue and Great Tits, to which Marsh Tit is subordinate (Broughton & Hinsley 2015). That study shows a negative correlation between the productivity of Blue and Great Tits and Marsh Tit survival in the following year and postulates that this sets up a greater need for Marsh Tits to move in from surrounding areas to maintain breeding numbers; something that is potentially less possible nowadays due to a loss of woodland connectivity. Despite concerns that a lack of woodland management may have shaded out the important shrub layer (*Bird Atlas 2007–11*), research shows that woodland understory has actually increased substantially since the 1980s (Amar *et al.* 2010), leading to an apparent increase in habitat quality for Marsh Tits (Broughton & Hinsley 2015).

Abundance maps from TTVs show that Marsh Tits occur at low densities, which makes populations more susceptible to change over time. The changes found in Devon reflect the 22% contraction in national breeding range since 1968–72 (*Bird Atlas 2007–11*). The national change in winter distribution since the *Winter Atlas 1981–84* has, however, been small, a picture reflected in few losses or gains at the 10-km square level in Devon since 1981–84 (*Bird Atlas 2007–11*).

The identification of and separation of Marsh Tits and Willow Tits is fraught with difficulty, particularly for less experienced observers, and many of the published identification criteria have been shown to be "unreliable or highly subjective" (Broughton 2009), though call remains the best means of separation in the field. Considerable care has been taken in checking records and we believe that the maps provide a satisfactory picture of the distribution of the two species.

*Text: Malcolm Burgess / Photo: John Clark*
*Marsh Tit sponsored by John Bower MBE*

Balmer *et al.* 2013: 506; Sitters 1988: 234; Tyler 2010: 464

### Winter-period abundance 2007–13

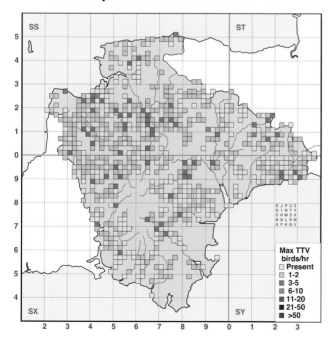

Max TTV birds/hr
- ☐ Present
- ☐ 1-2
- ☐ 3-5
- ☐ 6-10
- ☐ 11-20
- ■ 21-50
- ■ >50

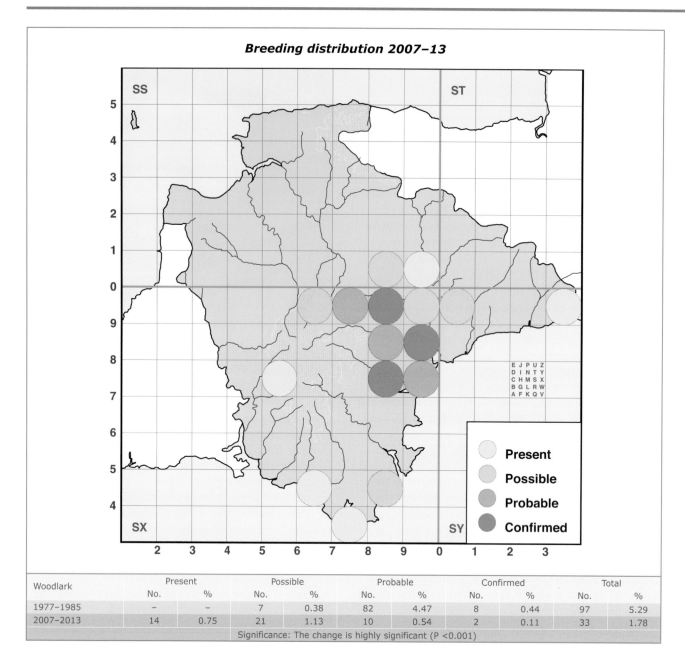

## Breeding distribution 2007–13

| Woodlark | Present | | Possible | | Probable | | Confirmed | | Total | |
|---|---|---|---|---|---|---|---|---|---|---|
| | No. | % | No. | % | No. | % | No. | % | No. | % |
| 1977–1985 | – | – | 7 | 0.38 | 82 | 4.47 | 8 | 0.44 | 97 | 5.29 |
| 2007–2013 | 14 | 0.75 | 21 | 1.13 | 10 | 0.54 | 2 | 0.11 | 33 | 1.78 |
| Significance: The change is highly significant (P <0.001) | | | | | | | | | | |

## Breeding distribution 1977–85

## Winter-period abundance 2007–13

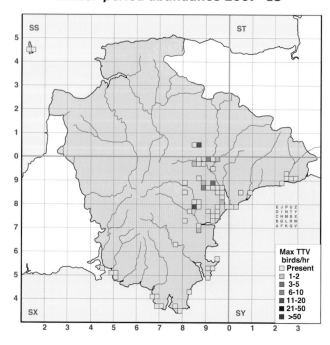

# Woodlark

*Lullula arborea*

OVER MUCH of Britain, Woodlarks are birds of open country with scattered trees, mainly on heathlands and their margins, but in Devon the majority occur in areas of low-intensity mixed farmland where they often breed in autumn- and spring-sown crops. The male usually sings in flight; the nest is on the ground, normally well concealed and very difficult to find. Woodlarks are Schedule 1 species and searching for nests requires a licence, so observers will have found confirmation of breeding difficult.

The species is now largely confined to an area to the west of Exeter, and within this breeding was only confirmed in two tetrads during the Atlas period, with 'probables' in ten and 'possibles' in a further 21 tetrads. These figures are similar to those found in detailed RSPB surveys which found 55 territories in 37 tetrads between 2002 and 2004 (Rylands 2005). In 2014 and 2015, intensive searches found eight and six nests respectively in growing autumn-sown crops (Josh Marshall, pers. comm.). At the time of writing, Woodlark is a rare breeding species in Devon, such that localities are no longer published in the *Devon Bird Report*.

Comparison with the *Devon Tetrad Atlas 1977–85* shows a major contraction in range as well as a decline in the number of breeding records from 97 in the 1977–1985 period to 33 in the present study. Woodlark has been lost as a breeding bird from many parts of Devon, including the East Devon

Commons, the Bere Alston area (where it bred in horticultural areas), North Devon and the area between the Dart and the Teign. This loss was balanced nationally by a considerable increase in eastern and southern England, now largely ceased. Habitat loss may be important, as may agricultural intensification leading to increased disturbance and nest loss, as well as the effects of hard winters – such as those in 2009 and 2010 – to which the species is known to be very susceptible. Sitters (1988) believed that the population probably did not exceed 30–40 pairs in any of the years of his survey, with as few as four in 1982 following a severe winter, and between 15 and 30 pairs in 1985. The number of pairs may now be in double figures. As the species has shown a considerable ability to bounce back after hard winters, and with habitat conservation measures in the core area, there is scope for recovery.

The winter map shows that most birds remain within the breeding areas; birds near the coast, where stubble fields are a preferred habitat, may be local but there is also immigration from further east; a colour-ringed bird from Suffolk was at Dawlish in February 1996. Stubble fields are not often surveyed in winter so birds may have been missed.

*Text: J M Lock, with thanks to Kevin Rylands & Josh Marshall*
*Photos: Paul Sterry/NPL & (right) Josh Marshall*
*Woodlark sponsored by Dr David Cabot*

Balmer *et al.* 2013: 510; Sitters 1988: 154; Tyler 2010: 469

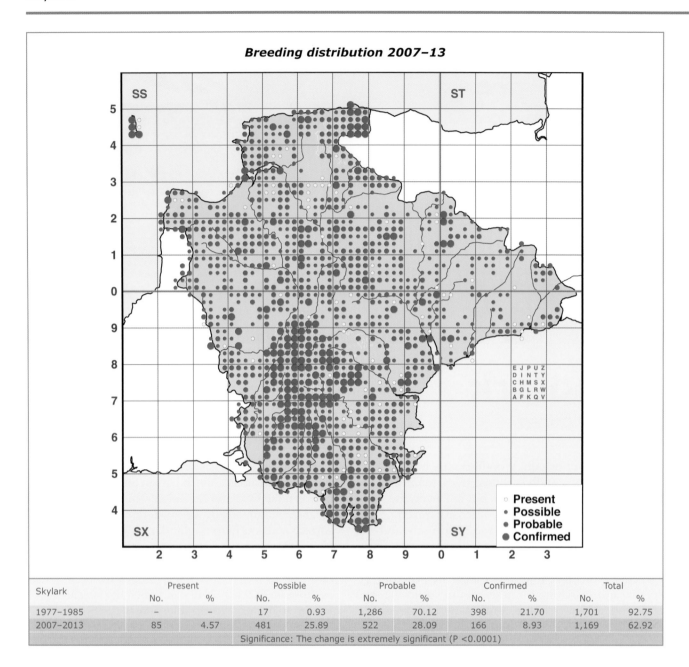

**Breeding distribution 2007–13**

| Skylark | Present | | Possible | | Probable | | Confirmed | | Total | |
|---|---|---|---|---|---|---|---|---|---|---|
| | No. | % | No. | % | No. | % | No. | % | No. | % |
| 1977–1985 | – | – | 17 | 0.93 | 1,286 | 70.12 | 398 | 21.70 | 1,701 | 92.75 |
| 2007–2013 | 85 | 4.57 | 481 | 25.89 | 522 | 28.09 | 166 | 8.93 | 1,169 | 62.92 |
| Significance: The change is extremely significant (P <0.0001) | | | | | | | | | | |

**Breeding distribution 1977–85**

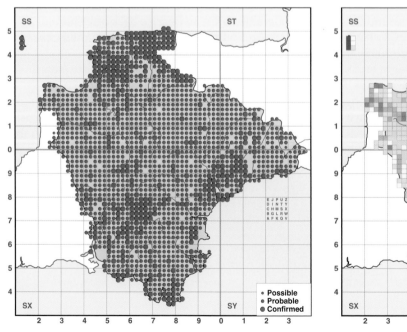

**Breeding-period abundance 2007–13**

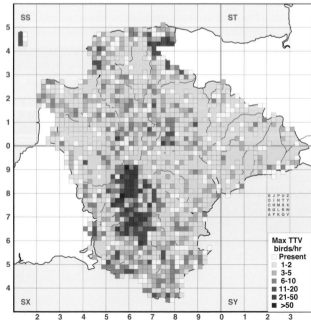

# Skylark
*Alauda arvensis*

**Red listed**

THE SKYLARK is a bird of open country, absent from densely wooded areas and from towns and cities. A survey of Dartmoor in 1979 revealed the highest breeding density of any upland area in Britain (Mudge *et al.* 1981). The species' well-known song-flight makes it independent of a perch and nests are built among grass or low crops. Skylarks are essentially omnivorous, with seeds and leaves forming a large part of the diet, particularly in winter, and insects making up the balance.

The breeding-period map shows marked concentrations on Dartmoor and Exmoor, with lower frequencies along the north and south coasts and in the South Hams, and a scattering of records elsewhere. This distribution reflects the link between Skylarks and open country with rough grassland, although some pairs breed in arable fields. The species' habit of alighting well away from the nest and running to it makes the nest hard to find and it is likely that most 'probables' and many 'possibles' represent actual breeding.

There has been a substantial decline in recent decades. The *Devon Tetrad Atlas 1977–85* showed the species present in 93% of tetrads, as against 63% in the current survey. The current map shows large areas, mainly farmland, where Skylarks are scarce or absent. This reflects the 80% decline nationwide (Mead 2000) which has been attributed to the change from spring-sown to autumn-sown crops, so that stubbles, with their reserves of spilled grain and weed seeds, are no longer available as winter food sources. In Devon, a further factor may be the prominence of cattle farming; maize is probably unsuitable for nesting, being either too sparse or too tall at the crucial period, and many grass leys are regularly reseeded as ryegrass monocultures, heavily fertilized, and cut three to five times for silage between May and August.

The winter map shows that birds leave the high moors, and that there is an increase in coastal areas, particularly in the south – a pattern also documented in the *Winter Atlas 1981–84*. Skylarks are essentially nomadic in winter, and in cold weather (especially snowy conditions) large influxes may occur and flocks can be found feeding in snow-free fields almost anywhere. Autumn movements involving hundreds or even thousands of birds are regularly reported, particularly in October on the south coast. Few Skylarks have been ringed in the county, and even fewer recovered, so it is not possible to say whether this is a local movement or whether Devon's moorland birds move further afield while wintering birds arrive from elsewhere. Some may be migrants from further east, including continental Europe, moving on to winter in Ireland or France (Wernham *et al.* 2002).

If present trends continue, breeding Skylarks will become largely confined to the moors and to areas of rough grassland mainly along the coast. The glorious song-flight will become less and less familiar in more intensively farmed areas.

*Text: J M Lock / Photo: Paul Sterry/NPL*
*Skylark sponsored in memory of Pauline Hartnell*

Balmer *et al.* 2013: 512; Sitters 1988: 156; Tyler 2010: 471

### Winter-period abundance 2007–13

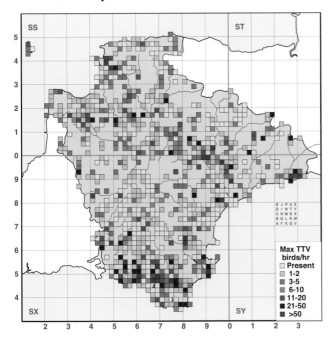

## Breeding distribution 2007–13

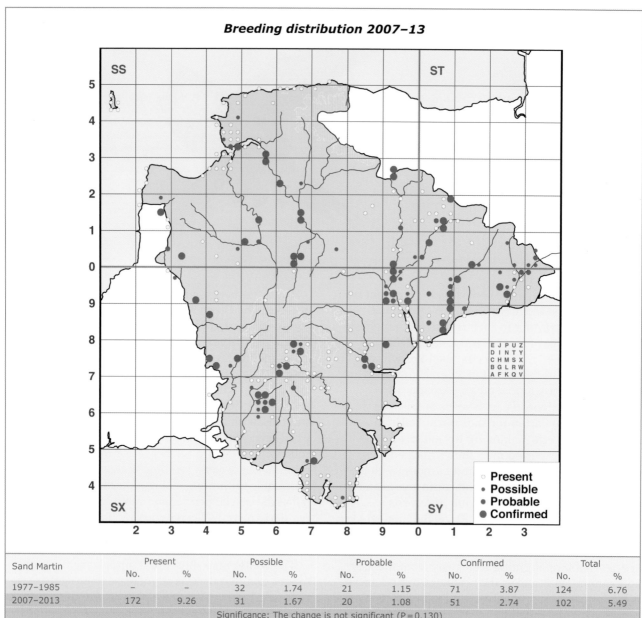

| Sand Martin | Present | | Possible | | Probable | | Confirmed | | Total | |
|---|---|---|---|---|---|---|---|---|---|---|
| | No. | % | No. | % | No. | % | No. | % | No. | % |
| 1977–1985 | – | – | 32 | 1.74 | 21 | 1.15 | 71 | 3.87 | 124 | 6.76 |
| 2007–2013 | 172 | 9.26 | 31 | 1.67 | 20 | 1.08 | 51 | 2.74 | 102 | 5.49 |
| | | | Significance: The change is not significant (P = 0.130) | | | | | | | |

## Breeding distribution 1977–85

## Breeding-period abundance 2007–13

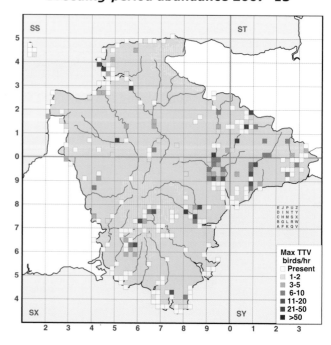

# Sand Martin
*Riparia riparia*

SAND MARTINS are summer visitors and passage migrants to Devon; they winter in sub-Saharan West Africa, where periodic droughts may cause population crashes. They are among the earliest migrants to arrive, with the first often being seen at the end of February or in early March on south coast estuaries. The major constraint on their breeding distribution is their need for vertical banks in which to excavate nesting burrows. Soft sandstones are scarce in Devon and many pairs breed in riverbanks, where they are vulnerable to summer flash floods. They will, however, use any vertical sandy bank, some of which may be temporary and become unsuitable when vegetation spreads. Near Ottery St Mary they use a sandy bank less than a metre high beside a busy car park. They will also use drainage holes in concrete banks of rivers and roads.

The present population is strongest along the East Devon rivers – Exe, Culm, Otter and Axe, with some also along the lower Dart, Avon, Plym, Tamar, Taw and Torridge. It has become evident that china clay workings can also be important nesting sites and there is a cluster of breeding records for the present Atlas period marking the area of such workings on south-east Dartmoor. Another, smaller, cluster exists in the Bovey Tracey area where there are also clay workings.

Comparison with the *Devon Tetrad Atlas 1975–85* suggests a slight decline, particularly in the east of the county, and recent *Devon Bird Reports* mention colonies of up to 40 pairs against over 100 in the 1990s. Breeding records are fewer along the Culm, Otter, Axe and Creedy and some coastal sites in the Thurlestone area seem to have been lost, possibly through coastal erosion. Conversely, there are more breeding records from the Lee Moor area of south-east Dartmoor where birds use the china clay workings. In Britain generally, *Bird Atlas 2007–11* shows a tendency towards losses in lowland south-east Britain and an increase in the north.

Possible, probable or confirmed breeding was recorded in 102 tetrads. Surveys of Sand Martins in the 1990s, mainly in East Devon, recorded over 100 pairs at some sites (Tyler 2010), although riverbank colonies are generally much smaller. If one assumes ten pairs per tetrad and uses only probable and confirmed tetrads, then the Devon breeding population during the Atlas period was in the region of 700 pairs. Ellicott (1975) estimated a population of 1,500–2,000 pairs in the county.

*Text: J M Lock / Photos: Steve Hatch & (inset) Dave Scott*
*Sand Martin sponsored by Peter Ellicott*

Balmer *et al.* 2013: 516; Sitters 1988: 158; Tyler 2010: 475

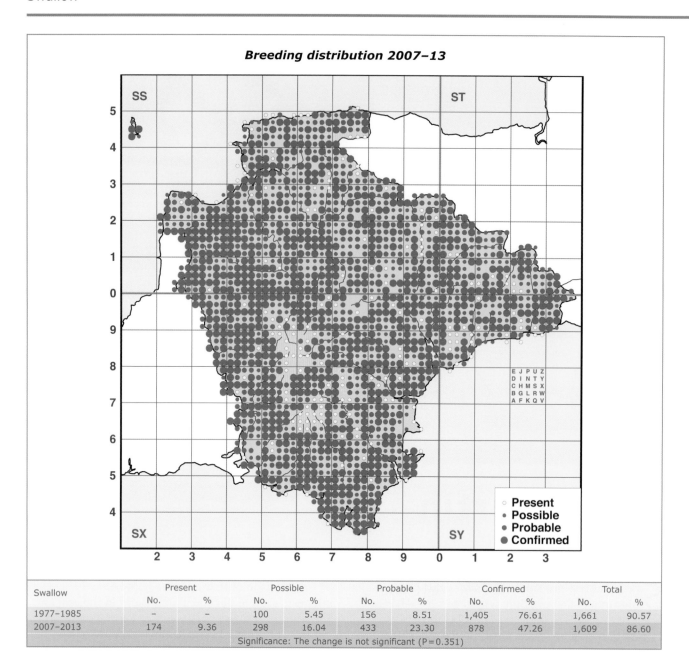

**Breeding distribution 2007–13**

| Swallow | Present | | Possible | | Probable | | Confirmed | | Total | |
|---|---|---|---|---|---|---|---|---|---|---|
| | No. | % | No. | % | No. | % | No. | % | No. | % |
| 1977–1985 | – | – | 100 | 5.45 | 156 | 8.51 | 1,405 | 76.61 | 1,661 | 90.57 |
| 2007–2013 | 174 | 9.36 | 298 | 16.04 | 433 | 23.30 | 878 | 47.26 | 1,609 | 86.60 |
| Significance: The change is not significant (P = 0.351) | | | | | | | | | | |

**Breeding distribution 1977–85**

**Breeding-period abundance 2007–13**

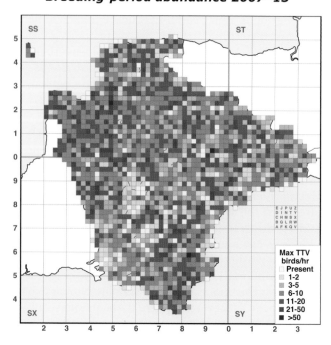

# Swallow
## Hirundo rustica

IF EVER there was a bird to fire the popular imagination, it must surely be the Swallow, exotic and iconic harbinger of the British summer and globetrotter extraordinaire – skimming Saharan dunes en route to Southern Hemisphere wintering grounds almost as far south in Africa as it is possible to go (Ellicott 2012). The fact that Swallows nest almost exclusively on or within buildings also forges a special bond between birds and people. Who (except those who erect net screens to prevent Swallows from nesting in church porches and the entrances to houses) can fail to be moved by the sight of Swallow chicks peering over the top of a perfect mud cup?

We are fortunate in Devon that Swallows are common breeding birds, absent only from parts of Dartmoor and Exmoor, and to a less obvious extent from the heavily urbanized areas of Plymouth and Torbay, as attested by the maps from the present Atlas. Indeed, breeding was confirmed in all but a handful of Devon's 10-km squares, the exceptions containing only fragments of coastline or tiny parts of the county along the border with Cornwall. Altogether, probable or confirmed breeding occurred in 1,311 tetrads. While this represents a decrease in comparison with the *Devon Tetrad Atlas 1977–85* (when breeding was probable or confirmed in 1,561 tetrads), with a particularly noticeable drop in the number of tetrads with confirmed breeding, it may well be that differences in coverage and methodology have contributed to an apparent change rather than a real decline. Certainly the overall range seems largely unchanged, though there are signs of colonization of more tetrads on both Dartmoor and Exmoor, perhaps resulting from climate change.

Swallow is an amber-listed species of conservation concern because of a long-term European population decline (PECBMS 2014). However, the national picture is rather more encouraging, with the Breeding Birds Survey index for England having risen sharply and almost continuously since the early 1990s to reach its highest-recorded level (BTO BirdTrends 2014). The indices for the rest of the UK have also shown significant increases, which tends to support the theory that an apparent decline in probable and confirmed breeding in Devon is due mainly to differences in Atlas methodology. *Bird Atlas 2007–11* shows that Swallow population densities are much higher in the South West than in central southern and south-east England, and highest of all in northern Britain and Ireland. While this may partly reflect the dominance of livestock rearing in northern and western Britain generally, other factors, including climate change across the species' huge range, are thought to be involved (BTO BirdTrends 2014).

The fact that Swallows were recorded in 171 tetrads during the Atlas winter-period attests to the species' status as one of our later-lingering summer migrants. While the main southward migration occurs in September and early October, stragglers are typically seen well into November, with some later still, as was the case when one was at Stoke Gabriel on 10 December 2012 (DBR).

*Text: Tim Jones & Tim Davis / Photo: Paul Sterry/NPL*
*Swallow sponsored by **DJEnvironmental***
*(Tim Davis & Tim Jones)*

Balmer *et al.* 2013: 518; Sitters 1988: 160; Tyler 2010: 477

### Winter-period abundance 2007–13

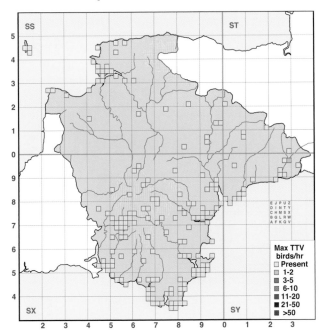

Max TTV birds/hr
□ Present
□ 1-2
▨ 3-5
▨ 6-10
■ 11-20
■ 21-50
■ >50

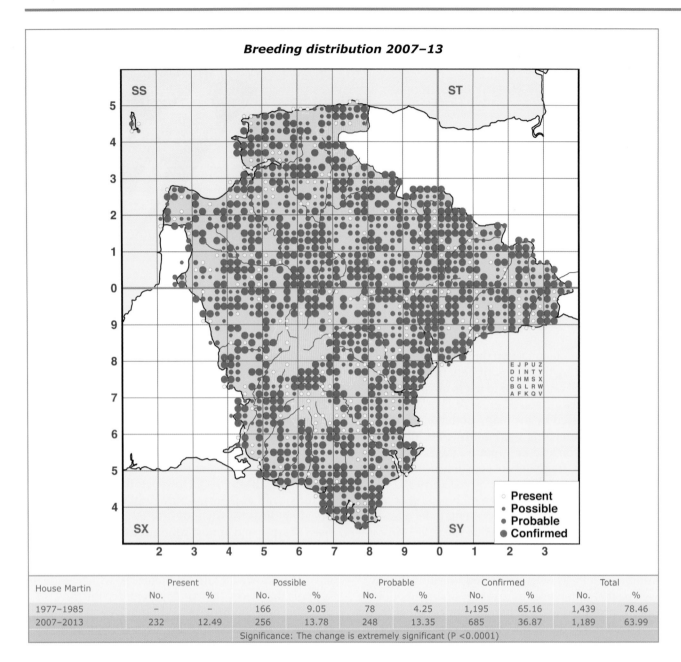

## Breeding distribution 2007–13

| House Martin | Present | | Possible | | Probable | | Confirmed | | Total | |
|---|---|---|---|---|---|---|---|---|---|---|
| | No. | % | No. | % | No. | % | No. | % | No. | % |
| 1977–1985 | – | – | 166 | 9.05 | 78 | 4.25 | 1,195 | 65.16 | 1,439 | 78.46 |
| 2007–2013 | 232 | 12.49 | 256 | 13.78 | 248 | 13.35 | 685 | 36.87 | 1,189 | 63.99 |
| Significance: The change is extremely significant (P <0.0001) | | | | | | | | | | |

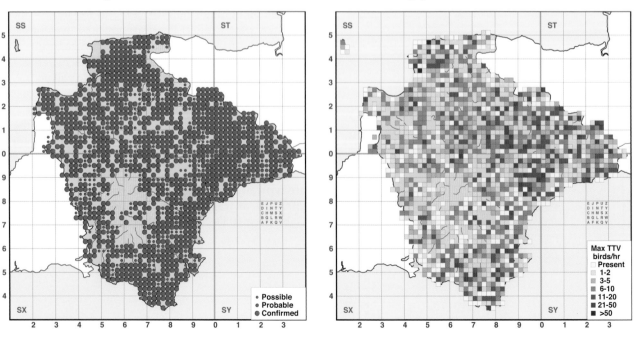

## Breeding distribution 1977–85

## Breeding-period abundance 2007–13

# House Martin
## *Delichon urbicum*

THE HOUSE Martin's association with man is well known, nesting as it does in colonies under the eaves of buildings in towns and villages. Other requirements include a good source of mud for nest building, and insect food; fields with cattle and hedges behind which insects accumulate in windy weather are also habitat factors that help this species. Much of its time is spent on the wing, and its twittering song is delivered both when flying and also from around the nest site.

House Martins are summer visitors to Devon and are widely distributed throughout the county; they are only absent where there are few buildings to provide nest sites. This can be seen from the breeding-period map, with few breeding records from the higher parts of Dartmoor and Exmoor away from villages and farms. The highest density of birds was recorded in the east and south of the county. Confirmed breeding was noted in 685 tetrads, compared with 1,195 tetrads during the *Devon Tetrad Atlas 1977–85*. This suggests a reduction in breeding tetrads of nearly 50%, but the present map shows more 'probable' nesting records, suggesting that observers may have taken a more cautious approach, but for such an obvious species, closely associated with man, one would expect relatively unbiased results. *Bird Atlas 2007–2011* does not show a decline in Devon at the 10-km square level; all were occupied and breeding was confirmed in all but three. *Bird Atlas 2007–2011* does, however, show a considerable decline in southern England since the *Breeding Atlas 1988–91* and the BTO began a survey in 2015 to investigate possible causes. No cliff-nesting House Martins were found during the Atlas survey.

The winter map has records for House Martins in 13 tetrads, but there was no evidence of birds overwintering. The latest date in all Atlas years occurred in the first week of November, on Lundy on 7 November 2009 (*DBR*).

*Text: Mike Tyler / Photo: Steve Hatch*
*House Martin sponsored by Heather Gitsham*

Balmer *et al.* 2013: 520; Sitters 1988: 162; Tyler 2010: 479

### Winter-period abundance 2007–13

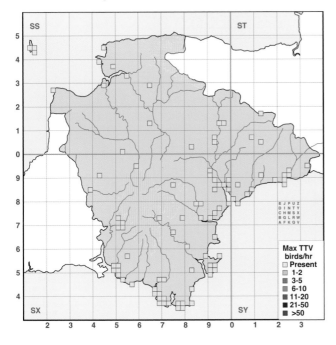

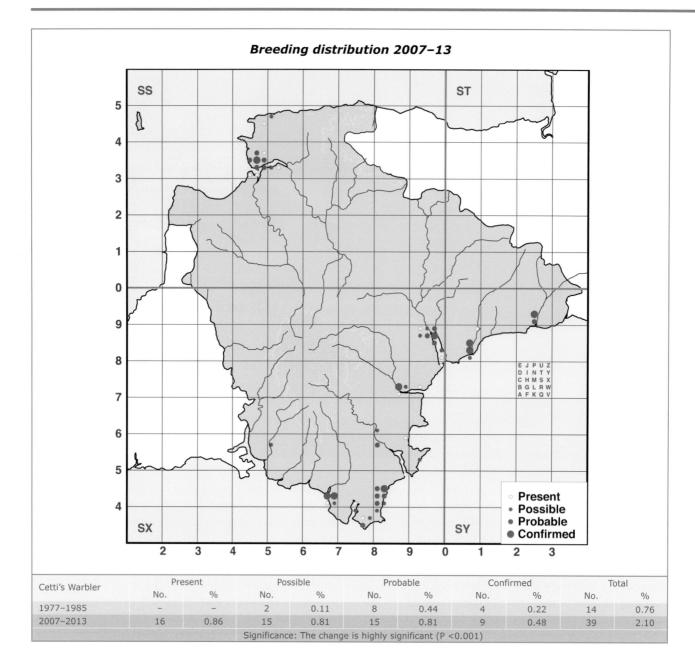

### Breeding distribution 2007–13

| Cetti's Warbler | Present | | Possible | | Probable | | Confirmed | | Total | |
|---|---|---|---|---|---|---|---|---|---|---|
| | No. | % | No. | % | No. | % | No. | % | No. | % |
| 1977–1985 | – | – | 2 | 0.11 | 8 | 0.44 | 4 | 0.22 | 14 | 0.76 |
| 2007–2013 | 16 | 0.86 | 15 | 0.81 | 15 | 0.81 | 9 | 0.48 | 39 | 2.10 |
| Significance: The change is highly significant (P <0.001) | | | | | | | | | | |

### Breeding distribution 1977–85

### Breeding-period abundance 2007–13

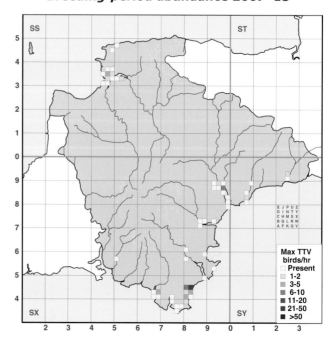

# Cetti's Warbler
## *Cettia cetti*

THE SPARROW-SIZED Cetti's Warbler has inconspicuous olive-grey plumage and a long rounded tail but is rarely seen, spending most of its time in thick cover (*BWP*). However, its distinctive song is one of the loudest in Europe and territorial males sing frequently, especially during territorial disputes (Scuffil 2005). It inhabits waterside and swamp vegetation and tends to select scrub and bramble within reedbeds, feeding on terrestrial or aquatic invertebrates (Wotton *et al.* 1998).

The first British breeding record was in Kent in 1973 (Wotton *et al.* 1998) but since then the population has spread north and west at a steady rate, with the most northerly records now in Tyneside, though the bulk of the population is still concentrated in southern and south-eastern Britain (*Bird Atlas 2007–11*).

The first records for Devon were of two birds trapped at Exe Estuary reedbeds in 1974, with further birds caught at Slapton and South Milton in 1975 (Tyler 2010). The first breeding record for Devon was at Lannacombe in 1975 during fieldwork for the *Devon Tetrad Atlas 1977–85*. During this period Cetti's Warblers were found in 14 tetrads, with five population clusters centred on the Exe, the Teign, Slapton to Prawle Point, the Avon and the Tamar. The current Atlas shows how some of the estuaries along Devon's south coast have been colonized by Cetti's Warblers since then, with populations present also on the Axe, the Otter and the Dart, as well as a significant population in North Devon on the Taw/Torridge Estuary. Altogether, the species was present in a total of 39 tetrads. It is likely that unless Cetti's Warblers start colonizing habitats away from water, they may now occupy all the suitable sites that Devon has to offer.

Cetti's Warblers are exclusively insectivorous (Limbrunner *et al.* 2001), yet unlike most other insectivorous birds they do not migrate to warmer regions in the winter. This renders them very vulnerable to harsh winter weather, and the series of cold winters between 2008/09 and 2010/11 had a significant impact on the county population. Ringers at Slapton trapped 47 new birds in 2011, compared with 68 in 2009 (Nik Ward pers. comm.), reflecting the first national decline witnessed since the species' arrival (*Bird Atlas 2007–2011*). However, as seen following declines in response to previous cold winters, numbers are able to recover rapidly.

*Text: Naomi Barker / Photo: Paul Sterry/NPL*
*Cetti's Warbler sponsored by Slapton Bird Observatory Ringing Group, Nik Ward & Keith Grant*

Balmer *et al.* 2013: 522; Sitters 1988: 202; Tyler 2010: 482

### Winter-period abundance 2007–13

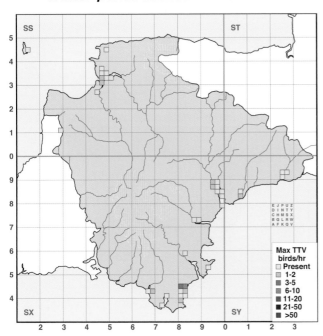

Max TTV birds/hr
- ☐ Present
- 1-2
- 3-5
- 6-10
- 11-20
- 21-50
- >50

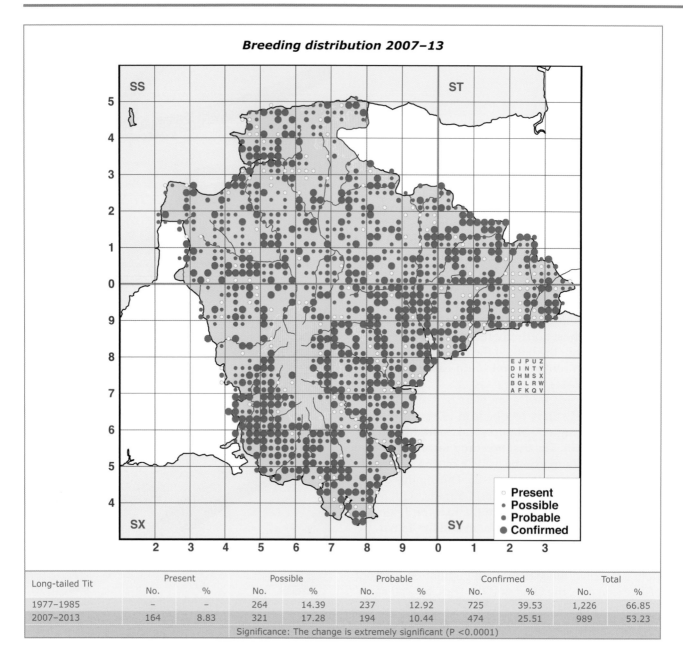

### Breeding distribution 2007–13

| Long-tailed Tit | Present | | Possible | | Probable | | Confirmed | | Total | |
|---|---|---|---|---|---|---|---|---|---|---|
| | No. | % | No. | % | No. | % | No. | % | No. | % |
| 1977–1985 | – | – | 264 | 14.39 | 237 | 12.92 | 725 | 39.53 | 1,226 | 66.85 |
| 2007–2013 | 164 | 8.83 | 321 | 17.28 | 194 | 10.44 | 474 | 25.51 | 989 | 53.23 |
| Significance: The change is extremely significant (P <0.0001) | | | | | | | | | | |

### Breeding distribution 1977–85

### Breeding-period abundance 2007–13

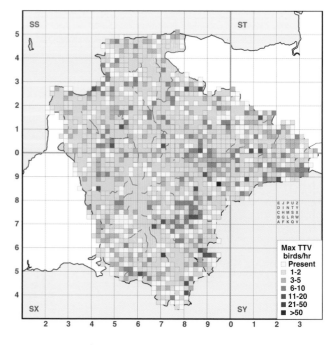

# Long-tailed Tit
## Aegithalos caudatus

THE LONG-TAILED Tit is a sedentary bird of scrub, hedgerow and woodlands. Its populations have a social structure that is unique amongst British birds, with roving flocks of related individuals remaining together from June until March of the following year. Each flock roosts communally, individuals huddling close together on a branch to conserve heat, enabling these tiny birds to survive the winter in this country. They are almost exclusively insectivorous, but are increasingly frequent visitors to garden bird tables in winter, where they feed on fatballs, suet and peanuts (Cannon 2000). Females move flocks in late winter to prevent inbreeding (*BWP*) and nest building takes place from late February through March. Long-tailed Tits are particularly evident at this time as each nest takes about three weeks to complete and the birds are not at all secretive whilst building. Conspicuous nests in the forks of tree branches are almost always predated, and those pairs choosing dense cover such as gorse are more likely to fledge young.

Long-tailed Tits are widely distributed throughout the county but noticeably absent from the exposed upland areas of Dartmoor and Exmoor. Since the *Devon Tetrad Atlas 1977–85* there has been a significant decline in the number of tetrads for which breeding evidence was recorded, from 67% to 53%. However, nationally, *Bird Atlas 2007–11* reported an increase in numbers over the 20 years to 2011 that may be due to milder winters.

The decline reported in this survey may be attributable in part to differences in methodology between the two Devon Atlases. Some tetrads that

were occupied during the winter period of the current survey appear to be lacking breeding birds, but this is unlikely to be the case as pairs always nest within the winter territory of the flock (*BWP*). The cold winters during the Atlas years, 2009 and 2010 in particular, may have had a significant impact on populations (see below).

Flocks can disperse during the autumn but movements are usually small, the vast majority of ringing recoveries being within 20 kilometres (Wernham *et al.* 2002). The winter-period distribution broadly mirrors that during the breeding period. Flocks range within a few kilometres of their roost site during the course of a day and return to the same roost each evening, unless disturbed, when they will choose another similar site nearby (pers. obs.).

Long-tailed Tits are highly susceptible to cold winters and especially to frosts that glaze branches and prevent access to the small invertebrates and insect eggs which form the bulk of their winter diet, so that populations can decline severely after very cold winters. Loss of connectivity between sites through the removal of large hedges and copses in open farmland may isolate populations, leading to slower recovery after such events.

*Text: John Walters*
*Photos: Dave Scott (top) & Margaret Phillips*
*Long-tailed Tit sponsored by David & Sandra Ingles*

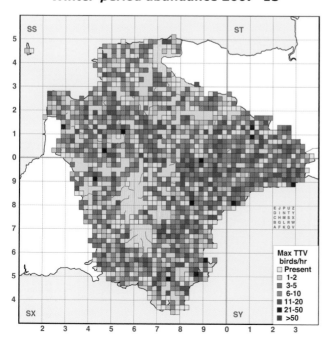

### Winter-period abundance 2007–13

Max TTV
birds/hr
□ Present
1-2
3-5
6-10
11-20
21-50
>50

Balmer *et al.* 2013: 524; Sitters 1988: 232; Tyler 2010: 484

# Bearded Tit
## *Panurus biarmicus*

Bearded Tits are exclusively birds of extensive reedbed habitats of which there are several suitable areas in coastal Devon. Bearded Tits were confirmed as breeding in Devon for the first time in 1981 (*Devon Tetrad Atlas 1977–85*) and since that time they have occasionally bred in very small numbers, although not in all years. During the current survey, breeding was confirmed at Bowling Green Marsh on the Exe Estuary in 2011. Overall during the Atlas breeding period (March–September) there were records from three tetrads on the Exe Estuary and one at Dawlish. During the winter period (October–February), they were present in six tetrads, around South Milton Ley, South Huish Marsh, Dawlish Warren and Colyton, all on the south coast.

*Text: Malcolm Burgess / Photo: Paul Sterry/NPL*

Balmer *et al.* 2013: 508; Sitters 1988: 302; Tyler 2010: 465

### Breeding distribution 2007–13

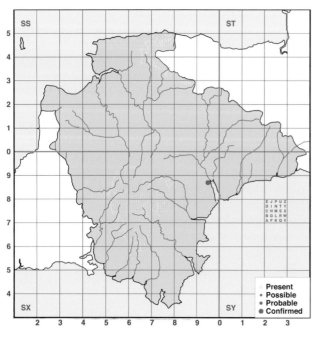

### Winter-period abundance 2007–13

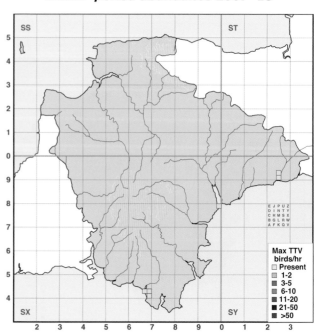

# Yellow-browed Warbler
## *Phylloscopus inornatus*

HISTORICALLY MUCH less frequent in Devon, with few records prior to 1978, numbers of Yellow-browed Warblers have increased substantially in recent decades (Tyler 2010). Records were annual during the current survey, occurring in 43 tetrads in the winter period (October–February) and in eight tetrads in the breeding period (March–September), though all of the latter can be safely attributed to migrants in September and a single late-wintering bird, as detailed below.

Autumn records fell between 19 September (2009) and 23 November (2010), with a peak in October, though one overwintered in the Clennon Valley in 2011/12. In addition, single birds were recorded at two south coastal sites in February/March 2008 and at four such sites in January/February 2012. The latter year saw a record number of autumn migrants involving 34 birds at 16 sites. Although these totals were eclipsed in autumn 2013, some of that year's migrants occurred just outside the close of the Atlas period (*DBRs*). Most of the autumn records were from Lundy and south coast headlands, but also – as shown in the October–February map – from a variety of other coastal sites and a handful of inland tetrads.

Perhaps surprisingly, Yellow-browed Warblers were located in only three 10-km squares in Britain and Ireland during the *Winter Atlas 1981–1984* (none of which was in Devon) but this had increased to 130 during *Bird Atlas 2007–11*, with most potentially overwintering birds located in south-west Britain. With numbers of autumn migrants continuing to increase in western Europe and predictions of generally milder winters in the decades ahead, there seems every likelihood that this species will become a more familiar component of Devon's avifauna.

*Text: Mike Tyler / Photo: Gary Thoburn*
*Yellow-browed Warbler sponsored by A K Searle*

Balmer *et al.* 2013: 550; Sitters 1988: not treated; Tyler 2010: 488

### Winter-period abundance 2007–13

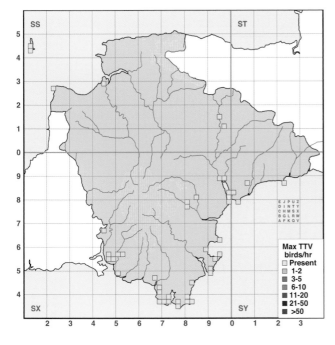

Max TTV birds/hr
☐ Present
1-2
3-5
6-10
11-20
21-50
>50

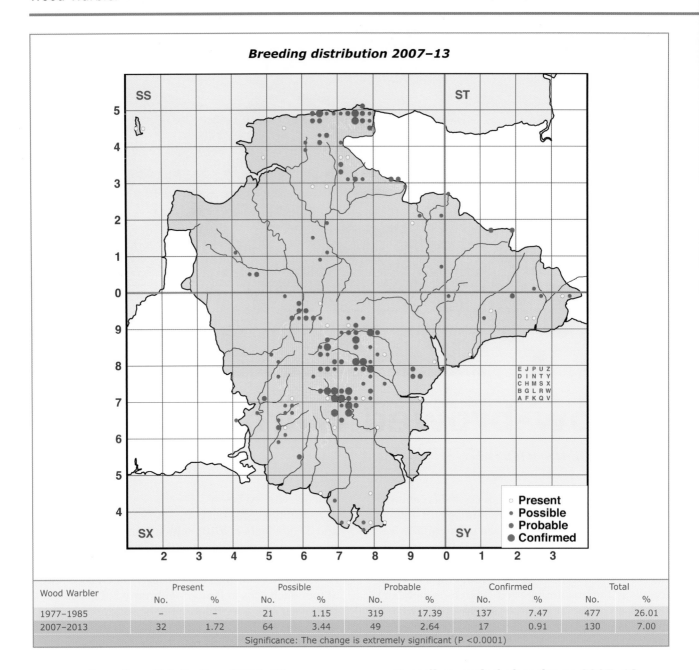

**Breeding distribution 2007–13**

| Wood Warbler | Present | | Possible | | Probable | | Confirmed | | Total | |
|---|---|---|---|---|---|---|---|---|---|---|
| | No. | % | No. | % | No. | % | No. | % | No. | % |
| 1977–1985 | – | – | 21 | 1.15 | 319 | 17.39 | 137 | 7.47 | 477 | 26.01 |
| 2007–2013 | 32 | 1.72 | 64 | 3.44 | 49 | 2.64 | 17 | 0.91 | 130 | 7.00 |
| Significance: The change is extremely significant (P <0.0001) | | | | | | | | | | |

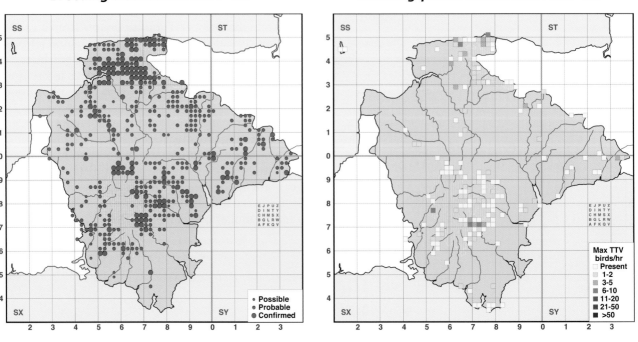

**Breeding distribution 1977–85**

**Breeding-period abundance 2007–13**

# Wood Warbler
## *Phylloscopus sibilatrix*

Red-listed

THE TRILLING song of a Wood Warbler, augmented by a far-carrying '*tew-tew-tew*', has long been a feature of Devon's oakwoods from late April to early June. To watch this bright lime-green warbler with its lemon-yellow breast and pure white underparts as it tumbles from branch to branch in search of insects is pure joy. That its days in Devon may be numbered as its seemingly inexorable decline continues is unthinkable, but such is the current outlook, albeit long-term, for one of Britain's fastest-disappearing migrants.

Wood Warblers are birds of mature broadleaf woodland – principally of Sessile Oak but also stands of Beech, Ash and even Sycamore – where they require a sparse understorey in which to nest and a dense canopy in which to feed (*BWP*). In Devon, their strongholds are the sessile oakwoods of Exmoor, particularly the 'hanging' oak woodland of the north coast, and the northern and eastern slopes of Dartmoor.

*Bird Atlas 2007–11* reports a 37% contraction in the species' range in Britain since the *Breeding Atlas 1988–91*, mainly around the margins of the core areas. In Devon this is reflected in the current Atlas breeding-period map which shows a very marked withdrawal from lowland wooded areas, especially in the north and east of the county, since the *Devon Tetrad Atlas 1977–85*. The figures are stark. In 1977–85, Wood Warblers were recorded in 477 (26%) of tetrads; this compares with 162 tetrads (less than 9%) for the current Atlas, with confirmed breeding in only 17 tetrads compared to 137 in 1977–85. For a species that is relatively easy to survey, given its restricted habitat, far-reaching song and relatively easy-to-find nest sites, there can be little doubt that these figures indicate the reality of the situation. More broadly, across continental Europe the species

declined by 35% between 1980 and 2012 (PECBMS 2014), while in Britain the Breeding Bird Survey has shown a 69% fall between 1995 and 2011 (BTO BirdTrends 2014), resulting in the Wood Warbler being 'red-listed' as a species of conservation concern in 2009.

Peter Goodfellow, in the *Devon Tetrad Atlas*, estimated the Devon population to be 1,200–1,600 pairs, 3–5% of the British population. With tetrad occupancy rates having fallen throughout the Wood Warbler's range in Britain since 1988–91 (*Bird Atlas 2007–11*), Devon's contribution to the national population may still hold good, though with greatly reduced numbers. Reduction in habitat quality may be a key factor, as shown by Mallord *et al.* (2012) who recommend the introduction of a moderate grazing regime to restore optimum nesting conditions. Loss of habitat arising from changes in land use, along with climate change, in the Wood Warbler's wintering area in the humid tropics of West Africa are likely contributory factors in the species' decline, and may also be affecting survival on migration (Ockendon 2012).

In his summation in the *Devon Tetrad Atlas*, Peter Goodfellow wrote: "To keep them, we must conserve the type of mature, broadleaf woodland which they require." Never have such words been more prophetic – but however much we maintain our oakwoods, the key is probably to understand and address what is going on in the wintering grounds and along the migration flyway.

*Text: Tim Jones & Tim Davis / Photo: Gray Clements*
*Wood Warbler sponsored by **DJEnvironmental***
*(Tim Davis & Tim Jones)*

Balmer *et al.* 2013: 526; Sitters 1988: 220; Tyler 2010: 492

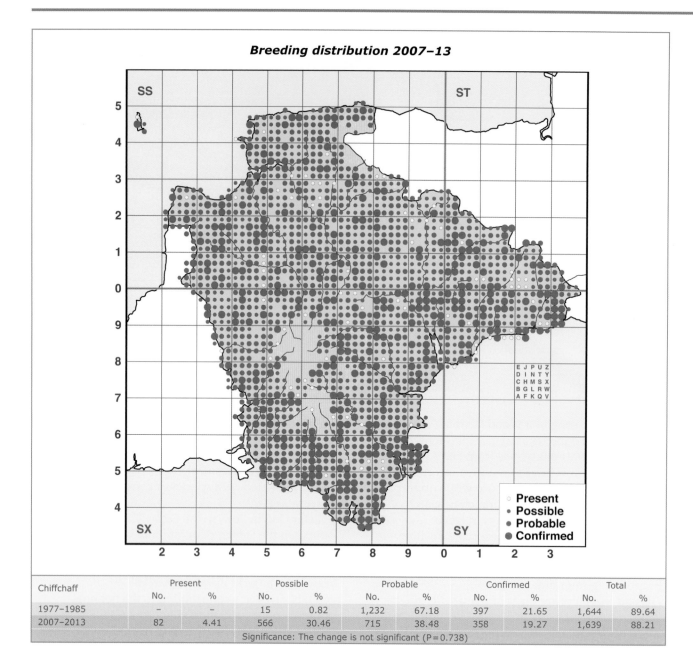

## Breeding distribution 2007–13

| Chiffchaff | Present | | Possible | | Probable | | Confirmed | | Total | |
|---|---|---|---|---|---|---|---|---|---|---|
| | No. | % | No. | % | No. | % | No. | % | No. | % |
| 1977–1985 | – | – | 15 | 0.82 | 1,232 | 67.18 | 397 | 21.65 | 1,644 | 89.64 |
| 2007–2013 | 82 | 4.41 | 566 | 30.46 | 715 | 38.48 | 358 | 19.27 | 1,639 | 88.21 |
| Significance: The change is not significant (P=0.738) | | | | | | | | | | |

## Breeding distribution 1977–85

## Breeding-period abundance 2007–13

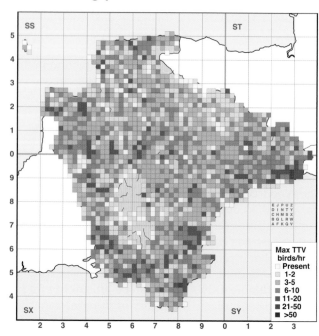

# Chiffchaff
## *Phylloscopus collybita*

THE CHIFFCHAFF'S capacity to breed in even the smallest copse, tall hedgerow or woodland, whether deciduous or evergreen, makes the species the most widely distributed and commonest warbler in Devon. Unlike the Willow Warbler, the Chiffchaff requires at least some mature trees in which to forage. It is absent only from tetrads on the open moorlands of Dartmoor and western Exmoor. The unmistakeable two-note song means that its presence is easily confirmed.

Chiffchaffs are one of the earliest spring migrants, regularly arriving in the first few days of March. During mild springs these birds will stop and sing before completing their migration. The uncharacteristically prolonged cold spring of 2013 was notable for many Chiffchaffs, often in poor condition, feeding on sheltered lawns; these birds were too busy feeding to sing. During mid-April and May it is likely that the majority of singing birds found represent 'probable' breeding.

There was an insignificantly small reduction in the number of tetrads occupied during the present survey in comparison with that found by the *Devon Tetrad Atlas 1977–85*. This mirrors the national picture of "little change" shown in *Bird Atlas 2007–2011*.

Most British Chiffchaffs are summer migrants, moving south during the autumn to the Mediterranean and North Africa, with some continuing on into western West Africa (Wernham *et al.* 2002). The Chiffchaff's autumn migration is hugely protracted, with birds still being noted during late October and even November, well within the period covered by the winter-period map.

### Winter-period abundance 2007–13

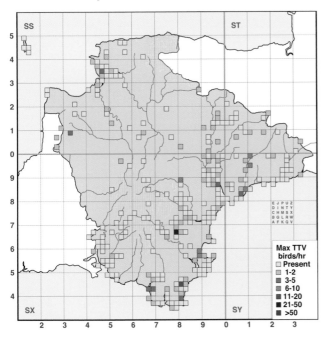

Max TTV birds/hr
- ☐ Present
- 1-2
- 3-5
- 6-10
- 11-20
- 21-50
- >50

Chiffchaffs have long been known to winter in the usually mild counties of South West England, but the number of 10-km squares occupied in winter increased by 85% and showed a northward shift between the *Winter Atlas 1981–84* and *Bird Atlas 2007–11*; a similar comparison in Devon shows a spread northwards away from the coast. Wintering birds probably come from a wide area of northern Europe, with some British-bred birds also (Wernham *et al.* 2002). They are mostly found close to invertebrate-rich locations such as coastal marshes or alongside watercourses, and even frost-prone inland sites, such as sewage treatment works, can sustain wintering Chiffchaffs, sometimes in good numbers. The closure of some open filter-bed sewage treatment works in villages and small towns over the last decade will almost certainly have reduced isolated wintering populations.

### 'Eastern' Chiffchaff
### *P. c. tristis / P. c. abietinus*

From November onwards small numbers of brown/grey and white Chiffchaffs appear among migrating and wintering Chiffchaffs in Devon. Many seem to fit the Siberian subspecies *P. c. tristis*, while others are considered to be Scandinavian Chiffchaff *P. c. abietinus* (DBR 2012: 137).

*Text: Mike Langman*
*Photos: Gary Thoburn (lower: Siberian Chiffchaff)*
*Chiffchaff sponsored by R Burridge & N C Ward*

Balmer *et al.* 2013: 528; Sitters 1988: 222; Tyler 2010: 495

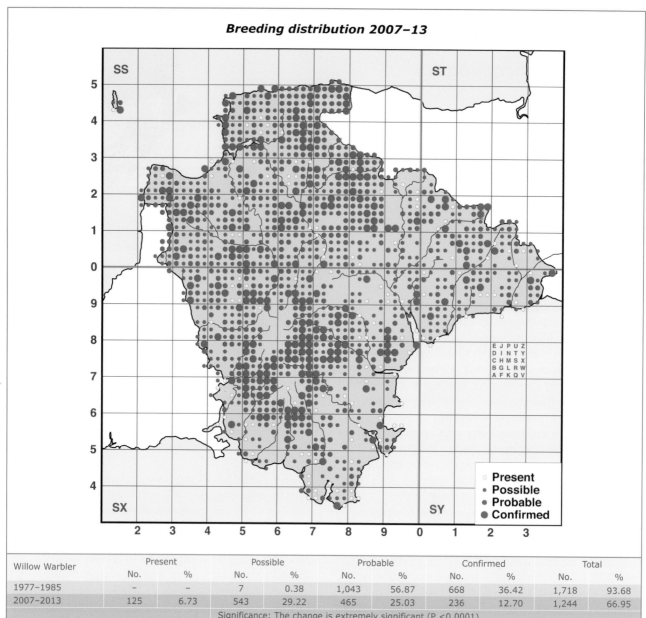

### Breeding distribution 2007–13

| Willow Warbler | Present | | Possible | | Probable | | Confirmed | | Total | |
|---|---|---|---|---|---|---|---|---|---|---|
| | No. | % | No. | % | No. | % | No. | % | No. | % |
| 1977–1985 | – | – | 7 | 0.38 | 1,043 | 56.87 | 668 | 36.42 | 1,718 | 93.68 |
| 2007–2013 | 125 | 6.73 | 543 | 29.22 | 465 | 25.03 | 236 | 12.70 | 1,244 | 66.95 |
| Significance: The change is extremely significant (P <0.0001) | | | | | | | | | | |

### Breeding distribution 1977–85

### Breeding-period abundance 2007–13

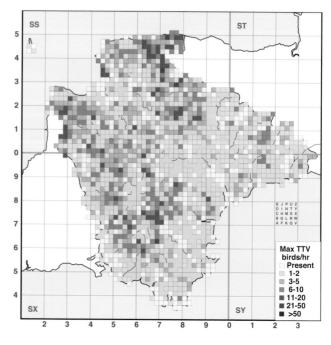

# Willow Warbler
*Phylloscopus trochilus*

A SURE sign of the arrival of spring is hearing the descending notes that make up the beautiful song of a Willow Warbler freshly arrived from its winter quarters in sub-Saharan Africa. Willow Warblers return to our shores from as early as the end of March but most passage occurs in the first two weeks of April. Males are soon busy setting up territories in suitable habitats, which range from open woodland with ground cover for nesting to open rough grassland with scattered trees and shrubs.

Although the breeding-period map shows that this species is still fairly widespread across Devon, the range has contracted greatly since the *Devon Tetrad Atlas 1977–85*, with the number of occupied tetrads falling by a third. This is in line with the national picture shown in *Bird Atlas 2007–11*; although Willow Warbler remains one of the most ubiquitous species in Britain and Ireland, relative abundance has declined over much of southern England and increased, albeit patchily, in northern England, Scotland and Ireland.

The reduction in occupied tetrads is fairly uniform across the county, though there are some noticeably heavy losses in South and East Devon. The species' range on and around the fringes of Dartmoor appears to have remained reasonably stable, as it has on much of Exmoor. Other notable clusters occur on the Hartland Culm Measures in the north-west of the county and on the East Devon Commons. In general, the most important remaining breeding areas appear to be associated with land where there has been least agricultural intensification.

The biggest losses appear to be in lowland farmed areas and are likely to be associated with changing agricultural practices, which have seen scrubby areas 'tidied up' and grassland managed mainly for silage, reducing the extent and quality of suitable breeding habitat. Pressures along migration routes and in the winter quarters may also be affecting the population, but it is a reduction in habitat quality on the breeding grounds, resulting in lower fledging success, which is driving the long-term declines (Fuller *et al.* 2005).

Although Willow Warblers winter in sub-Saharan Africa, there were a handful of winter records, which surely must refer to late-staying birds. The latest date recorded by Tyler (2010) is 21 December 2004, and there are no records of truly overwintering birds, as there are for some other warbler species.

Although the Willow Warbler is still a fairly widespread bird and may be encountered in many areas of Devon, its national distribution seems to be shifting gradually northwards, perhaps in response to climate change. However, this is a also a species that uses those little copses and thickets in field corners and woodland edges which are so liable to disappear through 'tidying up'. Eventually its Devon distribution may become restricted to the less intensively cultivated parts of the county.

*Text: Nik Ward / Photo: Carole Bowden*
*Willow Warbler sponsored by R Burridge & D Scott*

Balmer *et al.* 2013: 530; Sitters 1988: 224; Tyler 2010: 499

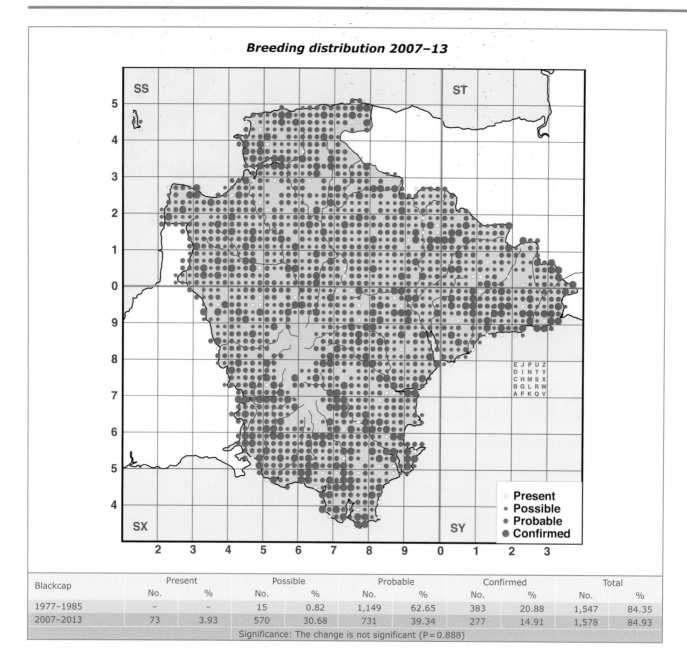

### Breeding distribution 2007–13

| Blackcap | Present | | Possible | | Probable | | Confirmed | | Total | |
|---|---|---|---|---|---|---|---|---|---|---|
| | No. | % | No. | % | No. | % | No. | % | No. | % |
| 1977–1985 | – | – | 15 | 0.82 | 1,149 | 62.65 | 383 | 20.88 | 1,547 | 84.35 |
| 2007–2013 | 73 | 3.93 | 570 | 30.68 | 731 | 39.34 | 277 | 14.91 | 1,578 | 84.93 |
| Significance: The change is not significant (P = 0.888) | | | | | | | | | | |

### Breeding distribution 1977–85

### Breeding-period abundance 2007–13

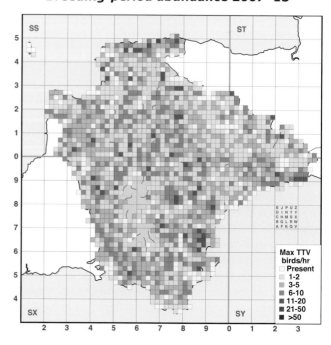

# Blackcap
## *Sylvia atricapilla*

THE RICH and melodious song of the Blackcap, from late March to July, draws attention to this otherwise rather inconspicuous bird that normally remains in thick scrub and bushes. Its favoured breeding habitats are mature deciduous woodland containing a thick scrub layer, overgrown hedgerows and larger gardens. Birds wintering in Britain favour gardens where supplementary food is regularly available from bird tables and feeders.

The breeding map shows Blackcaps to be widely distributed across the county, with the exception of the higher areas of Dartmoor and Exmoor where the species' preferred habitat is absent. Breeding was confirmed in 277 tetrads, widespread across Devon, probable in 731 and possible in 570, accounting for 85% of the county's tetrads altogether. The *Devon Tetrad Atlas 1977–85* shows confirmed breeding in 383 tetrads, which might suggest that there has been a reduction in the breeding population. It may also be true that surveyors have been more circumspect in their recording and, taking into account the high number of tetrads with evidence of probable and possible breeding, there has probably been little actual change between the two surveys. *Bird Atlas 2007–11* records a substantial westward and northward extension of range in Scotland and Ireland, as well as an increase in breeding density in much of lowland England. Breeding densities varied, with 21–50 birds located in one tetrad in North Devon, while most tetrads held three to ten pairs of birds during the breeding season.

The winter map shows birds present in 287 tetrads, 15% of the total, largely in South and East Devon, with a small concentration in the north-west of the county and fewer records from tetrads in Mid Devon. Wintering birds have been recorded in Devon since the 1860s (Tyler 2010) but have become much more abundant since the 1980s. *Bird Atlas 2007–11* found a 77% increase in winter birds compared with the *Winter Atlas 1981–84*. This has been attributed to generally milder winters (Balmer *et al.* 2013) and changing migration patterns of continental European birds (Berthold & Terrill 1988). Blackcaps are now much more frequent winter visitors to Devon gardens, although ringing studies have shown that most individuals move on quickly so that an apparently high garden population may be composed largely of transient birds (Jenks 1998). In both winter periods in 2013, numbers were well down on previous years, suggesting that the hard winters of 2010 and 2012 may have taken their toll.

*Text: Mike Tyler*
*Photos: Neil Bygrave & (below) Andrew Cunningham*
*Blackcap sponsored by Julia & George Harris*

Balmer *et al.* 2013: 532; Sitters 1988: 218; Tyler 2010: 502

### Winter-period abundance 2007–13

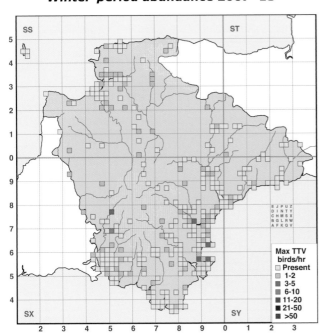

Max TTV birds/hr
- □ Present
- 1-2
- 3-5
- 6-10
- 11-20
- 21-50
- >50

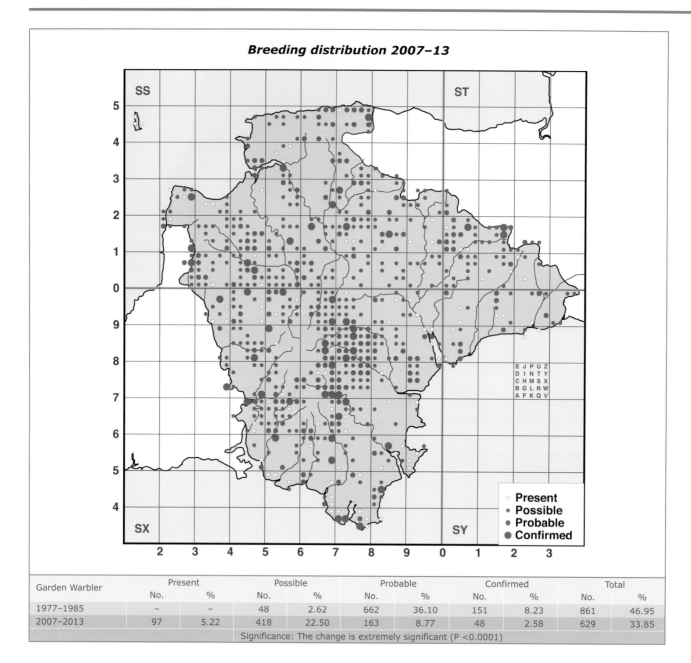

## Breeding distribution 2007–13

| Garden Warbler | Present | | Possible | | Probable | | Confirmed | | Total | |
|---|---|---|---|---|---|---|---|---|---|---|
| | No. | % | No. | % | No. | % | No. | % | No. | % |
| 1977–1985 | – | – | 48 | 2.62 | 662 | 36.10 | 151 | 8.23 | 861 | 46.95 |
| 2007–2013 | 97 | 5.22 | 418 | 22.50 | 163 | 8.77 | 48 | 2.58 | 629 | 33.85 |
| Significance: The change is extremely significant (P <0.0001) | | | | | | | | | | |

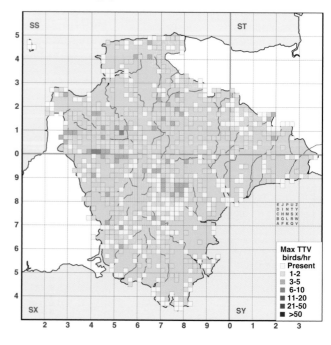

## Breeding distribution 1977–85

## Breeding-period abundance 2007–13

# Garden Warbler

*Sylvia borin*

THE GARDEN Warbler is a rather dull-plumaged species, which makes it difficult to locate as it moves quickly but discreetly through dense herbage. It often declares its presence with its attractive song which is hard to distinguish from, and often confused with, that of the Blackcap. Like the Blackcap, it breeds in overgrown hedgerows, scrub, areas of wet willow scrub, the edges of deciduous woodland and young conifer plantations. Despite its name, it rarely breeds in gardens.

Garden Warblers are widespread across Devon but records of confirmed breeding were mainly in the west of the county, with the highest densities close to Dartmoor where the species appears to be attracted to the higher fringes of wooded river valleys. Breeding was confirmed in 48 tetrads, a highly significant 68% reduction from the 151 tetrads recorded by the *Devon Tetrad Atlas 1977–85*. The breeding-period map shows a decline in East Devon but little change in breeding status and density in South Devon. Probable breeding records have also decreased significantly: 163 tetrads during the current survey compared to 662 tetrads for 1977–85. *Bird Atlas 2007–11* showed a northward expansion in range but a decline in abundance in southern England since the *Breeding Atlas 1988-91*; in Devon, although the species was lost from only a single 10-km square, all but one square showed either a decline in numbers or no change.

### Winter-period abundance 2007–13

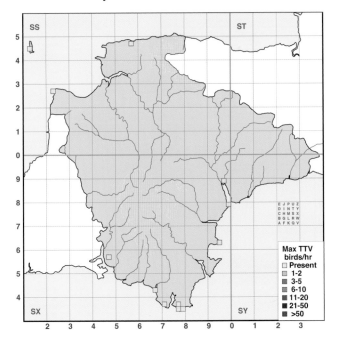

Max TTV birds/hr
- ☐ Present
- 1-2
- 3-5
- 6-10
- 11-20
- 21-50
- >50

The winter-period (October–February) map shows 12 occupied tetrads, all in coastal areas. Most of these refer to late passage migrants in October, though there were three later occurrences, one on Lundy on 4 November 2011, one at Combe Martin on 23 November 2007 and the other in a Plymouth garden on 3 December 2009 (*DBRs*). Since Garden Warblers do not normally overwinter in Britain, these are likely to represent stragglers on migration, although some individuals in earlier years – such as the one seen at Prawle between November 2006 and January 2007 – may have been true wintering birds.

Reasons for the Garden Warbler's decline remain uncertain; changes to its woodland understorey habitat through increased deer browsing, and possibly changes in land use (deforestation) and climate in the humid West African tropics where it winters, are possible factors (Balmer *et al.* 2013).

*Text: Mike Tyler*
*Photos: Paul Sterry/NPL & (inset) John Walters*
*Garden Warbler sponsored in memory of John Randall*

Balmer *et al.* 2013: 534; Sitters 1988: 216; Tyler 2010: 505

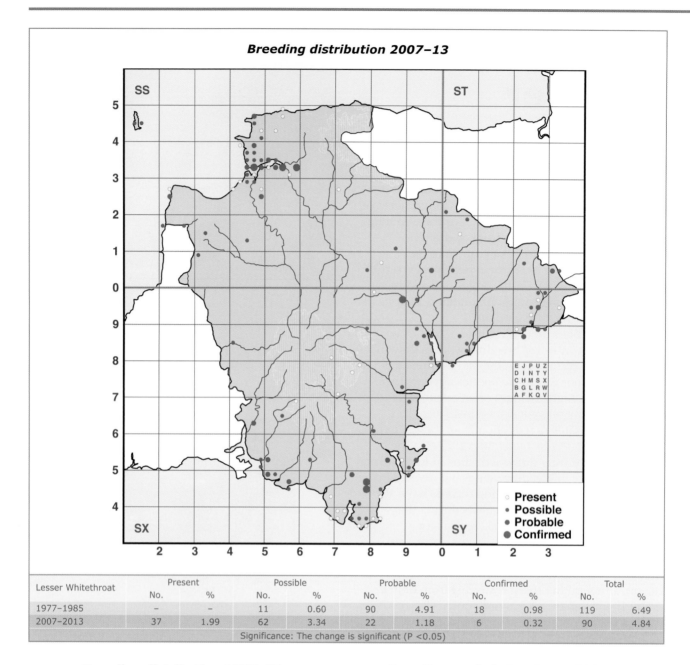

### Breeding distribution 2007–13

| Lesser Whitethroat | Present | | Possible | | Probable | | Confirmed | | Total | |
|---|---|---|---|---|---|---|---|---|---|---|
| | No. | % | No. | % | No. | % | No. | % | No. | % |
| 1977–1985 | – | – | 11 | 0.60 | 90 | 4.91 | 18 | 0.98 | 119 | 6.49 |
| 2007–2013 | 37 | 1.99 | 62 | 3.34 | 22 | 1.18 | 6 | 0.32 | 90 | 4.84 |
| Significance: The change is significant (P <0.05) | | | | | | | | | | |

### Breeding distribution 1977–85

### Breeding-period abundance 2007–13

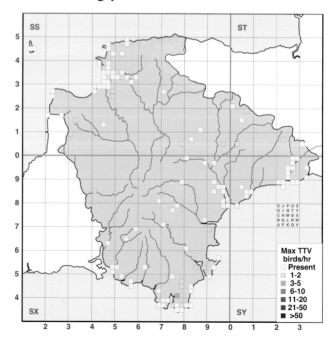

# Lesser Whitethroat

*Sylvia curruca*

DURING THE breeding season Lesser Whitethroats spend much of their time in the deep cover offered by mature hedgerows, scrub and young conifer plantations. This can make them difficult to locate – familiarity with the song is essential – especially given that their density is low in South West England, which is on the edge of the species' breeding range (*Bird Atlas 2007–11*). On migration they occur in more varied habitats. Many of the breeding season records come from coastal areas in both the north and the south of the county, but some of these may well refer to passage migrants. The species was not recorded from the high ground of Dartmoor or Exmoor.

*Bird Atlas 2007–11* shows that the UK breeding range of Lesser Whitethroat has expanded significantly northwards and westwards in recent decades, though the highest densities remain in central and eastern England. By comparison with the *Devon Tetrad Atlas 1977–85*, the number of tetrads for which evidence of breeding was obtained during the current survey fell by about a quarter and the change is marginally significant. Breeding was confirmed in only six tetrads compared to 18 for the earlier Atlas.

The winter-period map (October–February) shows records in six tetrads on the south coast and two in the north, including one on Lundy. These were probably straggling migrants, but birds have been present during eight winters since 1975, although not during this Atlas period (Tyler 2010).

There is no clear long-term trend in the UK breeding population, with Breeding Bird Survey and Constant Effort Site data providing conflicting signals, perhaps due in part to a northward shift in distribution (BTO BirdTrends 2014). Given that apparently suitable breeding habitat is widespread in Devon, the species' future status in the county is likely to be influenced mostly by factors affecting overall range, including habitat availability and quality along the migration route, which is unusual among British warblers in being south-easterly, with wintering occurring just south of the eastern Sahara (Wernham *et al.* 2002); here climate change may be critical.

Birds showing characteristics of the race *S. c. halimodendri*, the 'Siberian' or 'Central Asian' Lesser Whitethroat, have been recorded in Devon; the last wintered in 2006/07 (*DBR*), prior to the Atlas period.

### Winter-period abundance 2007–13

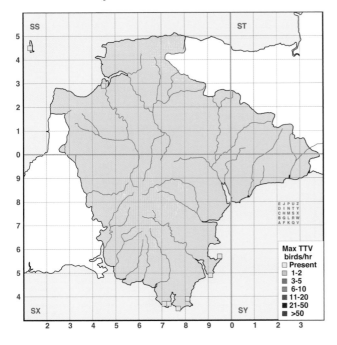

Max TTV birds/hr
- ☐ Present
- 1-2
- 3-5
- 6-10
- 11-20
- 21-50
- >50

*Text: Mike Tyler / Photo: Paul Sterry/NPL*

Balmer *et al.* 2013: 536; Sitters 1988: 212; Tyler 2010: 510

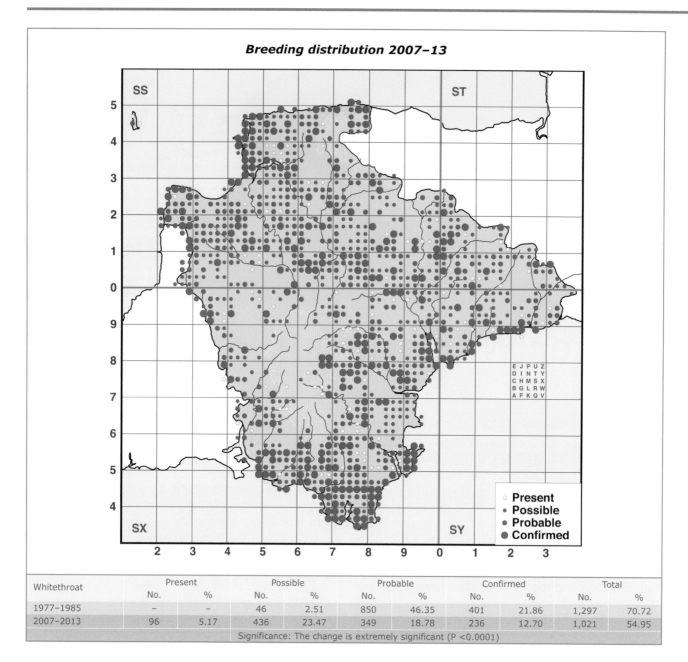

### Breeding distribution 2007–13

| Whitethroat | Present | | Possible | | Probable | | Confirmed | | Total | |
|---|---|---|---|---|---|---|---|---|---|---|
| | No. | % | No. | % | No. | % | No. | % | No. | % |
| 1977–1985 | – | – | 46 | 2.51 | 850 | 46.35 | 401 | 21.86 | 1,297 | 70.72 |
| 2007–2013 | 96 | 5.17 | 436 | 23.47 | 349 | 18.78 | 236 | 12.70 | 1,021 | 54.95 |
| Significance: The change is extremely significant (P <0.0001) | | | | | | | | | | |

### Breeding distribution 1977–85

### Breeding-period abundance 2007–13

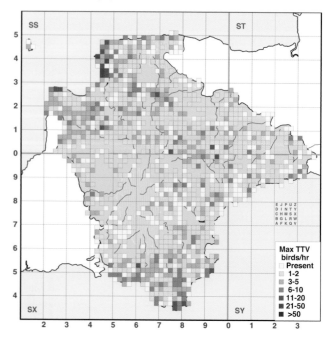

# Whitethroat
## Sylvia communis

THE WHITETHROAT is a rather skulking bird, though
territorial males give themselves away by a
rapidly uttered warble delivered from a prominent
perch or dancing song-flight. Preferred breeding
habitat includes open scrub, hedgerows, recently
coppiced broadleaf woodland and young conifer
plantations, while migrants can occur virtually
anywhere. During the Atlas years, the earliest spring
arrivals occurred between 5 & 14 April and the
maximum spring passage count was 160 at Start
Point on 1 May 2012 (*DBRs*).

The maps reveal a highly significant decline since
the *Devon Tetrad Atlas 1977–1985* when Whitethroats
were present in 71% of tetrads, compared with 55%
during the breeding period (March–September, also
embracing the whole of spring passage and peak
autumn passage) of the current survey. Even more
strikingly, the proportion of tetrads for which
probable or confirmed breeding was recorded fell
from 68% to 31%. BTO data show that the UK
population crashed by 70% in the late 1960s and that
declines continued until 1985, since when there has
been a shallow but sustained recovery. These
fluctuations are thought to be driven by conditions
in the Sahelian wintering grounds (*Bird Atlas
2007–11*, BTO BirdTrends 2014).

The improved fortunes of the UK population since
1985 appear at variance with the apparent significant
inter-Atlas decline in Devon. Possible explanations
include the fact that the national decline continued
throughout the 1977–85 Devon survey and so
numbers may have been relatively high at the start of

that period. It is also possible that differences in
methodology and coverage between the Atlases led to
a degree of under-recording in 2008–2013.
Nevertheless, there appear to have been genuine
losses, particularly in the hinterlands of both the north
and south coasts. Abundance is generally low across
inland parts of Mid and East Devon, while the species
is largely absent from the higher parts of the moors.

Return migration occurs mainly between late July
and mid-September (maximum count during the
Atlas period 150 at Prawle on 31 July 2011; *DBR*),
with stragglers remaining into October (the latest
dates during the Atlas years were all in the range
15–21 October; *DBRs*) accounting for nearly all of the
tetrads shown on the winter-period map. The
exception was one trapped and ringed in a
Kingsteignton garden on 17 January 2010 (*DBR* ) –
presumably a wintering individual, of which there
had been five previous Devon occurrences in earlier
decades (Tyler 2010).

*Text: Tim Jones & Tim Davis / Photo: Lee Collins*
*Whitethroat sponsored by Hilary Thomas*

Balmer *et al.* 2013: 538; Sitters 1988: 214; Tyler 2010: 511

### Winter-period abundance 2007–13

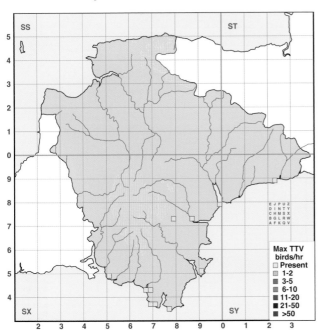

Max TTV
birds/hr
☐ Present
▨ 1-2
▨ 3-5
▨ 6-10
■ 11-20
■ 21-50
■ >50

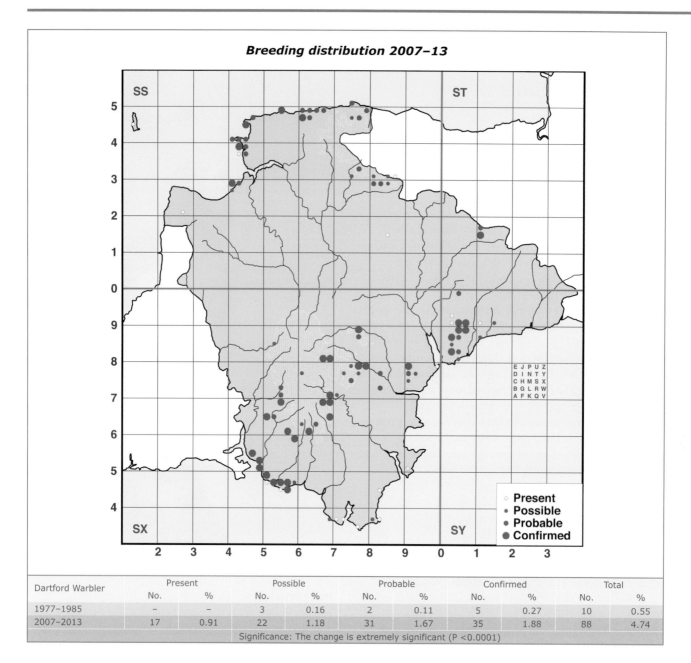

**Breeding distribution 2007–13**

| Dartford Warbler | Present | | Possible | | Probable | | Confirmed | | Total | |
|---|---|---|---|---|---|---|---|---|---|---|
| | No. | % | No. | % | No. | % | No. | % | No. | % |
| 1977–1985 | – | – | 3 | 0.16 | 2 | 0.11 | 5 | 0.27 | 10 | 0.55 |
| 2007–2013 | 17 | 0.91 | 22 | 1.18 | 31 | 1.67 | 35 | 1.88 | 88 | 4.74 |
| Significance: The change is extremely significant (P <0.0001) | | | | | | | | | | |

**Breeding distribution 1977–85**

**Breeding-period abundance 2007–13**

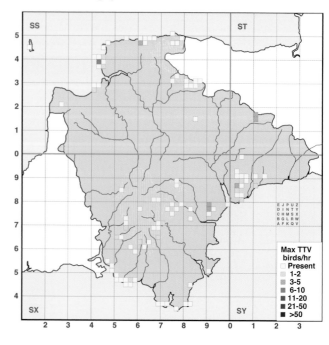

# Dartford Warbler

## *Sylvia undata*

**Amber listed**

DARTFORD WARBLERS are largely confined to the southern parts of Britain, which represents the northern edge of their European range. The species is dependent on heathlands and its distribution in Devon reflects the availability of lowland, upland and coastal heaths. Within these areas they require dense shrubs such as gorse and heather both for nesting and finding prey. The species is unusual in being a largely insectivorous resident, relying on spiders and other invertebrates all year round.

The breeding and wintering distribution maps show very little difference, with birds remaining on the heathlands through the winter. The species' dependence on invertebrate prey makes it vulnerable to prolonged periods of extreme cold. Thus the availability of high-quality heathland, with sufficient dense cover to promote the survival of invertebrates, is essential.

The period between the *Devon Tetrad Atlas 1977–85* and the present Atlas saw a major expansion in both numbers and range in the county, from a total of just ten occupied tetrads (0.55%) in the earlier Atlas period to 88 tetrads (4.7%) during the current survey. Previously confined to the East Devon Heaths and a small number of coastal locations, the species has extended its range east into the Blackdown Hills and west to the Haldon Heaths, Bovey Basin and east Dartmoor, as well as spreading along both the north

and south coasts and into Exmoor. However, the highest densities remain in the East Devon Heaths, Haldon Heaths and coastal areas. A run of mild winters combined with habitat availability or restoration has facilitated this substantial increase, reflected across southern Britain, with the last national survey reporting a 70% increase between 1994 and 2006 (Wotton *et al.* 2009).

However, the fortunes of the Dartford Warbler changed drastically in the very cold winters of 2009 and 2010 which featured prolonged snow and ice with sub-zero temperatures. Nationally, numbers reported in 2010 were reduced to 19% of the 2006 population estimate (*Bird Atlas 2007–11*). In Devon, numbers dropped dramatically, especially in upland areas, with just two reports from two Dartmoor sites in 2012, compared to 40 in 2008. The East Devon Heaths also experienced a steep drop in numbers but remained the stronghold, with 17 reports from nine sites in 2012 (*DBR*). Milder winters and continued provision of suitable quality habitat should allow the population to increase once again.

*Text: Helen Booker / Photos: Roy Churchill & (inset) Dave Scott*
*Dartford Warbler sponsored by Clinton Devon Estates*
*& the Pebblebed Heaths Conservation Trust*

Pebblebed Heaths
CONSERVATION TRUST

Balmer *et al.* 2013: 540; Sitters 1988: 210; Tyler 2010: 515

### Winter-period abundance 2007–13

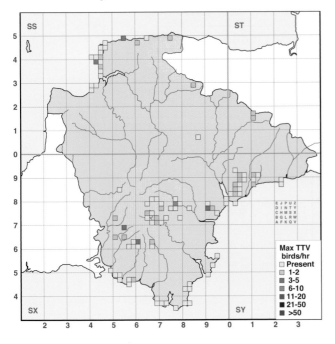

Max TTV birds/hr
- ☐ Present
- ☐ 1-2
- ▨ 3-5
- ▨ 6-10
- ■ 11-20
- ■ 21-50
- ■ >50

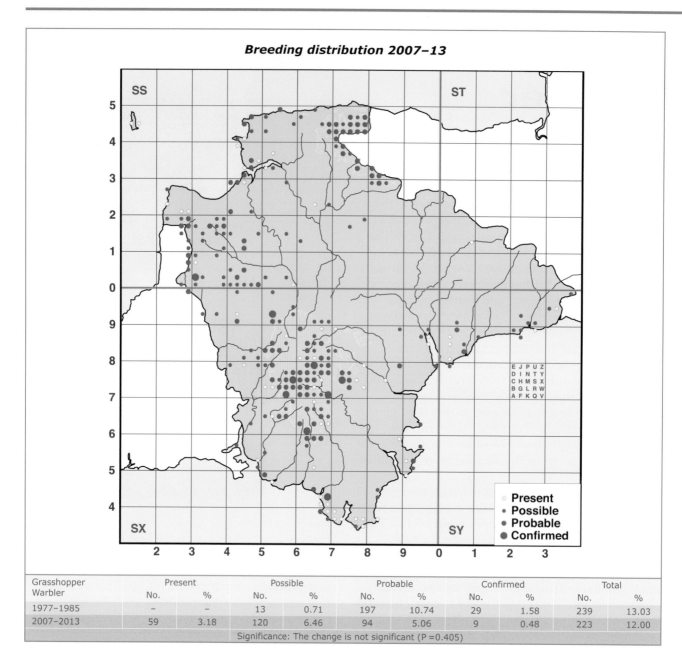

**Breeding distribution 2007–13**

| Grasshopper Warbler | Present | | Possible | | Probable | | Confirmed | | Total | |
|---|---|---|---|---|---|---|---|---|---|---|
| | No. | % | No. | % | No. | % | No. | % | No. | % |
| 1977–1985 | – | – | 13 | 0.71 | 197 | 10.74 | 29 | 1.58 | 239 | 13.03 |
| 2007–2013 | 59 | 3.18 | 120 | 6.46 | 94 | 5.06 | 9 | 0.48 | 223 | 12.00 |
| Significance: The change is not significant (P =0.405) | | | | | | | | | | |

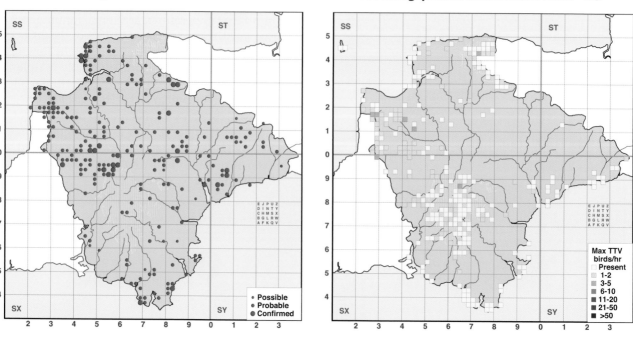

**Breeding distribution 1977–85**

**Breeding-period abundance 2007–13**

# Grasshopper Warbler

*Locustella naevia*

**Red listed**

THE DISTINCTIVE sound of a reeling song drifting over an open marshy valley early in the morning or late evening is usually the way in which a male Grasshopper Warbler gives itself away while remaining concealed from view. However, closer inspection of scattered clumps of bramble or small willows may reveal the song-post of this skulking, olive-brown streaky migrant. Proving breeding is another matter. The nest is well hidden in a tussock of coarse grass or sedge or low bush, often near or on the ground.

Grasshopper Warblers also take advantage of new conifer plantations, where the early stages provide a suitable tangle of vegetation with song-posts. As the crop matures, the forest no longer provides the open habitat that this species requires, and so populations within these managed plantings will ebb and flow. The *Devon Tetrad Atlas 1977–1985* shows that Grasshopper Warblers were scattered across Devon, with a concentration around north-west Dartmoor, extending further north-west through the Culm grasslands to Hartland. There was also a cluster of records along the coastline north of the Taw/Torridge Estuary between Croyde and Mortehoe. Additionally, there was a good scatter of records in East Devon, on and off the commons, and some across the South Hams.

Comparison between the 1977–1985 survey and the current Atlas shows no significant reduction in total numbers but a noticeable drop in the number of probable or confirmed breeding records, and a very obvious and remarkable shift in areas occupied, largely from lowland to upland areas, with highest densities on Dartmoor and Exmoor. This change may follow the reduction in livestock levels on upland areas, allowing suitable vegetation structure for this species to develop, providing ideal nesting and foraging areas. The intensification of farming practices in many lowland areas of Devon, particularly the drainage and 'improvement' of rough wet grasslands, has also undoubtedly led to the loss of much suitable habitat, perhaps reinforcing the shift to more upland areas, which may also be assisted by climate change. However, the secretive nature of this species makes it very hard to locate and, particularly, to prove breeding, so that slight differences in methodology and standards between the two surveys could have distorted the results either way.

*Bird Atlas 2007–11* showed that this species has declined in southern England but increased in Scotland and Ireland, so that overall there is little change. The drainage and 'improvement' of wet tussocky grasslands has probably been a contributory factor in the decline of this species in lowland areas. Most taller grassland is now very uniform and species-poor, and is usually cut several times during the breeding season for silage, so that most nesting attempts would be unlikely to succeed.

In addition to changes in their preferred breeding habitats, Grasshopper Warblers also face the rigours of migration to Africa south of the Sahara, where preferred wintering areas and habitats are poorly known (Wernham *et al.* 2002). Changes throughout the migratory flyway may affect population levels at least as much as those occurring in Britain.

*Text: Nik Ward / Photo: Paul Sterry/NPL*
*Grasshopper Warbler sponsored by Paul Madgett*

Balmer *et al.* 2013: 542; Sitters 1988: 204; Tyler 2010: 519

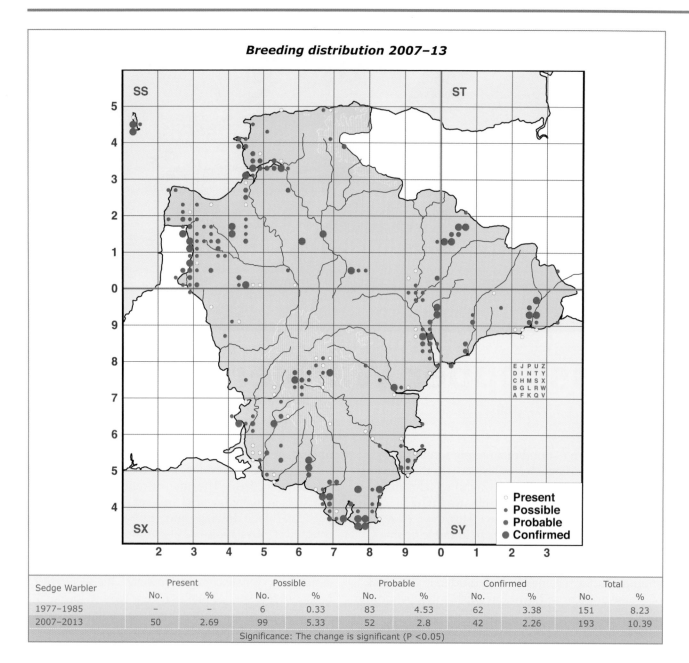

### Breeding distribution 2007–13

| Sedge Warbler | Present | | Possible | | Probable | | Confirmed | | Total | |
|---|---|---|---|---|---|---|---|---|---|---|
| | No. | % | No. | % | No. | % | No. | % | No. | % |
| 1977–1985 | – | – | 6 | 0.33 | 83 | 4.53 | 62 | 3.38 | 151 | 8.23 |
| 2007–2013 | 50 | 2.69 | 99 | 5.33 | 52 | 2.8 | 42 | 2.26 | 193 | 10.39 |
| Significance: The change is significant (P <0.05) | | | | | | | | | | |

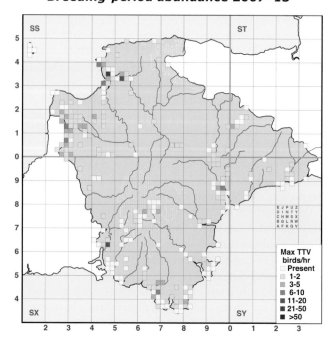

### Breeding distribution 1977–85

### Breeding-period abundance 2007–13

# Sedge Warbler
## *Acrocephalus schoenobaenus*

ALTHOUGH MOSTLY associated with wetland habitats, the Sedge Warbler is more of a generalist, setting up its territories to take in dry- to wet-zone habitats rather than pure stands of *Phragmites* reed. The fast chattering song interspersed with higher notes and phrases stolen from other species often draws attention, as does their song-flight between clumps of willow or bramble. The nest is usually well hidden in vegetation, allowing the adults to approach and leave undetected.

Sedge Warblers usually arrive in the first week of April (31 March being the earliest date during the Atlas years; *DBR* 2011) and are usually counted in single digits, although Lundy often records higher numbers in late April/early May, such as the 50 birds seen in early May 2012 (*DBR*). Autumn migration, between July and September, can see large numbers accumulating in the south coast reedbeds; 628 birds were ringed at South Milton Ley during August 2011 (*DBR*). There are sometimes a few late migrants recorded in October, the latest during the Atlas period being on 24 October 2012 in the Teign Estuary (*DBR*).

The Sedge Warbler has undergone expansion in its range since the *Devon Tetrad Atlas 1977–85*. There has been some colonization of Dartmoor which could be attributed to abandonment of land or, more certainly, to a reduction in grazing that has led to an increase in rough grassland and to scrub encroachment into marshy valleys that are the species' favoured habitat. Birds were also reported from several tetrads south of Plymouth and around the Yealm and Erme as well as in the north-west of the county, where good numbers were recorded along the Devon and Cornwall border around Tamar

Lakes and into the Culm grassland. A TTV at one site recorded 20–50 singing males, while four sites held 11–20 birds and many others held between three and ten, suggesting loose colonies or at least birds congregating in suitable breeding habitat.

The numbers of tetrads with breeding evidence increased significantly from 151 in the 1977–85 survey to 193 during the current survey – an expansion consistent with the pattern of modest increases in western Britain reported in *Bird Atlas 2007–11*.

There would still appear to be a good range of suitable breeding habitats for Sedge Warbler across Devon and, barring any major crash in population due to catastrophic changes in the wintering or staging grounds, it should still be possible to encounter this secretive warbler and its creative song well into the foreseeable future.

*Text: Nik Ward / Photos: Neil Bygrave & (left) Dave Scott*
*Sedge Warbler sponsored by R Burridge*

Balmer *et al.* 2013: 544; Sitters 1988: 206; Tyler 2010: 526

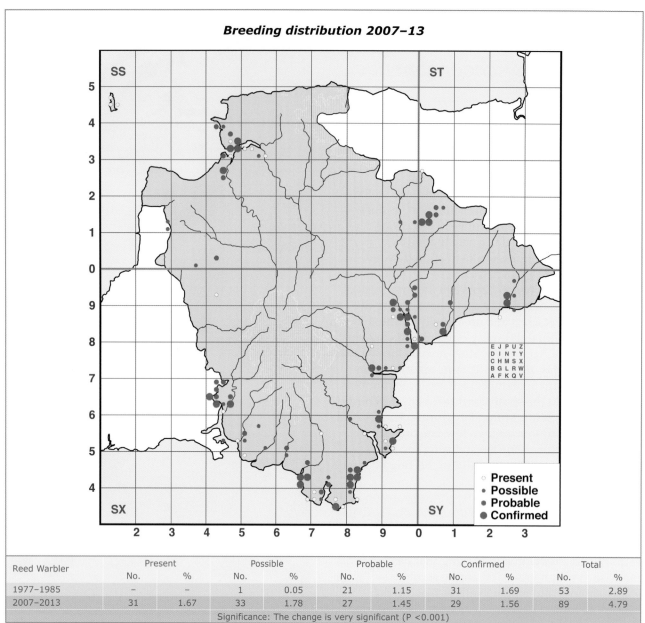

**Breeding distribution 2007–13**

| Reed Warbler | Present | | Possible | | Probable | | Confirmed | | Total | |
|---|---|---|---|---|---|---|---|---|---|---|
| | No. | % | No. | % | No. | % | No. | % | No. | % |
| 1977–1985 | – | – | 1 | 0.05 | 21 | 1.15 | 31 | 1.69 | 53 | 2.89 |
| 2007–2013 | 31 | 1.67 | 33 | 1.78 | 27 | 1.45 | 29 | 1.56 | 89 | 4.79 |
| Significance: The change is very significant (P <0.001) | | | | | | | | | | |

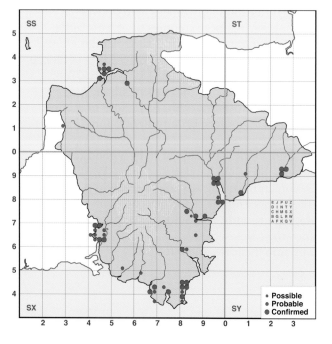

**Breeding distribution 1977–85**

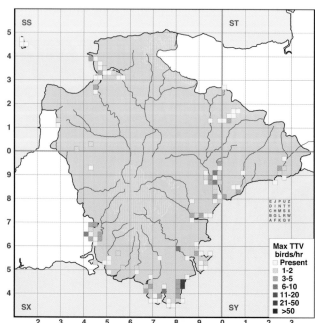

**Breeding-period abundance 2007–13**

# Reed Warbler

*Acrocephalus scirpaceus*

R EED WARBLERS return from their West African wintering quarters as early as the end of March and, despite finding little vegetation cover other than old stems in *Phragmites* reedbeds, can remain extremely elusive. They show high site fidelity, with birds returning from one year to the next to breed in the same patch of reeds (Vadász *et al.* 2008). The male usually stays quite low amongst the old reeds, delivering its slow monotonous chattering song in defence of its territory. As new growth develops through the spring the nest is camouflaged, so giving a measure of protection from predators. The nest is further protected by being built over water.

Comparison with the *Devon Tetrad Atlas 1977–85* shows that the overall distribution of Reed Warblers has remained fairly constant, as would be expected given that this species is a specialist found only where there are significant areas of *Phragmites*. However, there has been a significant rise in the number of occupied tetrads, although most of the increase is in 'possible' breeders and may also reflect records of birds on migration. It is not surprising that there are colonies around the upper end of the Tamar Estuary, around the Taw/Torridge, Exe and Teign Estuaries, at Slapton Ley and at South Milton Ley. Most of these have shown modest increases. Small gains have been seen around the South Hams, with probable breeding recorded on several of the estuaries there, but mostly around the Kingsbridge Estuary. In the Torbay area several small areas of suitable habitat have been developed, allowing breeding attempts to be made. One significant new breeding area has established along the Grand Western Canal in Mid Devon, where none was recorded by the 1977–85 survey. This part of the county is otherwise largely devoid of suitable habitat.

Slapton Ley holds the greatest abundance of Reed Warblers in the county, with some 20–50 pairs located around the Lower and Higher Leys (Whitehall 2006). However, habitat improvement around the western fringes of the Exe Estuary has allowed further expansion and in future this area may rival Slapton as Devon's main site.

Although any small reed-lined pond surrounded by rough wetland habitat may hold one or two pairs of Reed Warblers, it is unlikely the species will increase greatly in Devon unless new areas of reedbed are allowed to develop in low-lying wet valleys. Unlike its close cousin, the Sedge Warbler, Reed Warblers do not seem keen to colonize the higher altitudes of Dartmoor, preferring the low-lying floodplains. This reflects the fact that although rough wetland is commonly found on Dartmoor, it is too acidic for *Phragmites* reed (which prefers alkaline conditions and tolerates brackish water) on which Reed Warblers depend.

Although there are only a few suitable sites for the species in Devon, the Reed Warbler should be able to maintain its current population level into the future, provided the quality of the stands of *Phragmites* reed is maintained.

*Text: Nik Ward / Photo: Neil Bygrave*
*Reed Warbler sponsored in memory of F R (Ray) Smith*

Balmer *et al.* 2013: 546; Sitters 1988: 208; Tyler 2010: 530

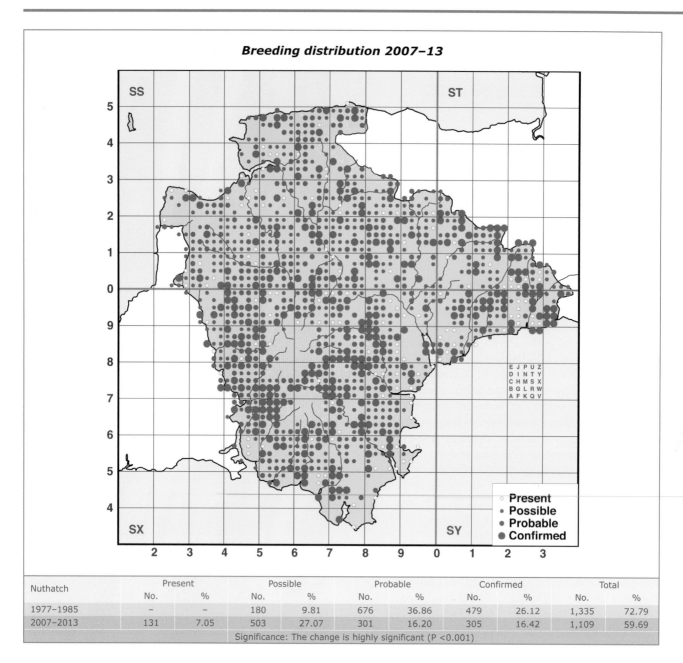

## Breeding distribution 2007–13

| Nuthatch | Present | | Possible | | Probable | | Confirmed | | Total | |
|---|---|---|---|---|---|---|---|---|---|---|
| | No. | % | No. | % | No. | % | No. | % | No. | % |
| 1977–1985 | – | – | 180 | 9.81 | 676 | 36.86 | 479 | 26.12 | 1,335 | 72.79 |
| 2007–2013 | 131 | 7.05 | 503 | 27.07 | 301 | 16.20 | 305 | 16.42 | 1,109 | 59.69 |
| Significance: The change is highly significant (P <0.001) | | | | | | | | | | |

## Breeding distribution 1977–85

## Breeding-period abundance 2007–13

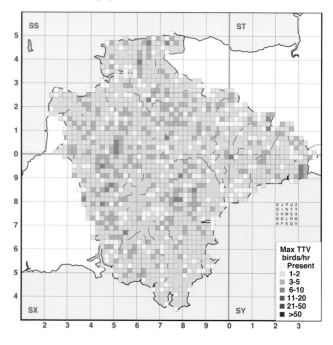

# Nuthatch
## *Sitta europaea*

THE NUTHATCH is a bird of habitats that contain mature broad-leaved trees, including urban and suburban parks and gardens, but is most numerous in more extensive broad-leaved woodland. Nuthatches have become regular visitors to garden feeders throughout the year and will use nestboxes for breeding. During the breeding period (March–September) the current survey found them in 67% of tetrads spread right across Devon, except for treeless areas of Dartmoor and Exmoor, and more extensive areas of agriculture.

Apparent losses in the number of occupied tetrads since the *Devon Tetrad Atlas 1977–85* may reflect under-reporting, as nationally the species has done well and expanded northwards in range during the same time period. Under-reporting in the breeding season is strongly suggested by a comparison of the breeding-period abundance map with the corresponding map for the winter period (October–February).

The pattern of tetrad occupancy across Devon is very similar between seasons, but winter abundance appears somewhat higher. Apparent declines in both occupancy and confirmed breeding since the 1977–85 survey have occurred throughout Devon but are more pronounced in North and East Devon, which is difficult to explain ecologically and so may be a result of differences in coverage. However, the decline could be a genuine consequence of the two prolonged severe winters (2010/11 and 2011/12) during the survey period. The survey period also saw high rainfall during several breeding seasons,

and in the post-fledging period, which may have had an adverse impact on populations. While the Breeding Bird Survey population trends for the UK as a whole show an increase since 1994, that for the South West region has shown a decline since 2010 (BTO BirdTrends 2014). Data from nests monitored by nestbox schemes indicate a low nest success rate during the survey period (PiedFly.net).

Nuthatches are resident in woodlands throughout the year and do not usually disperse far. This can be seen from the similarity between the breeding- and winter-period maps, and is also shown by ringing data (Wernham *et al.* 2002). The Nuthatch is benefiting from recent climatic trends and is predicted to become more abundant across Britain, especially in the south-west, as well as continuing to spread northwards (Renwick *et al.* 2012).

*Text: Malcolm Burgess / Photo: Barry Bowden*
*Nuthatch sponsored by Paul Bowen*

Balmer *et al.* 2013: 552; Sitters 1988: 244; Tyler 2010: 535

### Winter-period abundance 2007–13

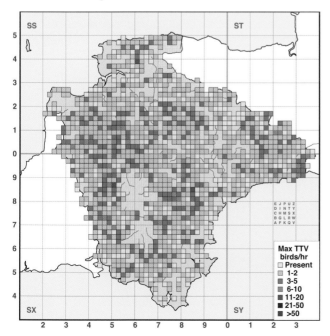

Max TTV birds/hr
- ☐ Present
- 1–2
- 3–5
- 6–10
- 11–20
- 21–50
- >50

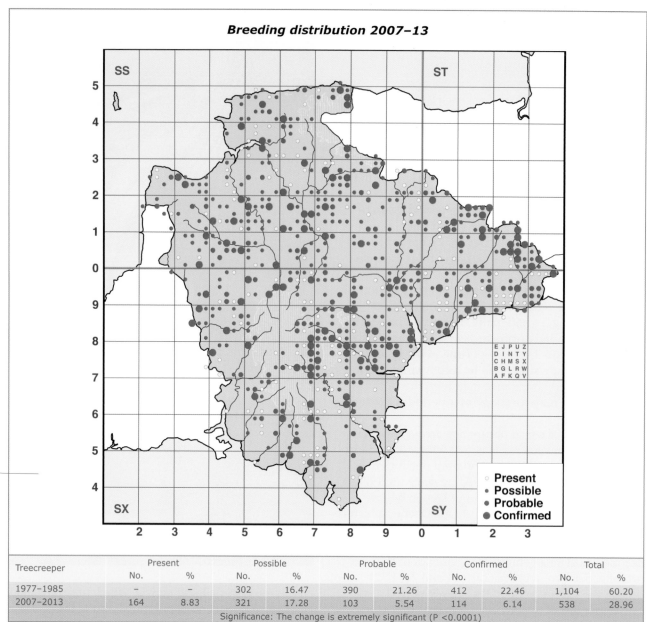

### Breeding distribution 2007–13

| Treecreeper | Present | | Possible | | Probable | | Confirmed | | Total | |
|---|---|---|---|---|---|---|---|---|---|---|
| | No. | % | No. | % | No. | % | No. | % | No. | % |
| 1977–1985 | – | – | 302 | 16.47 | 390 | 21.26 | 412 | 22.46 | 1,104 | 60.20 |
| 2007–2013 | 164 | 8.83 | 321 | 17.28 | 103 | 5.54 | 114 | 6.14 | 538 | 28.96 |
| | Significance: The change is extremely significant (P <0.0001) | | | | | | | | | |

### Breeding distribution 1977–85

### Breeding-period abundance 2007–13

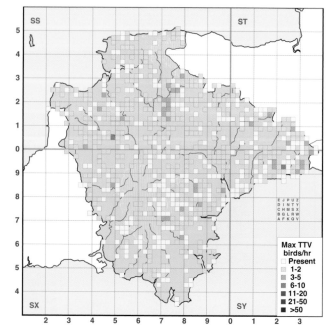

# Treecreeper
## *Certhia familiaris*

THE TREECREEPER is mainly a bird of broad-leaved woodland, although it is commonly found in rural or even suburban gardens containing mature trees. In this survey they were only found in 38% of tetrads during the breeding period (March–September) which strongly suggests that they are overlooked as a breeding bird, perhaps because of their high-pitched call, cryptic plumage and tendency to hide behind tree trunks and branches as they forage. The number of tetrads from which they were recorded is much lower than more easily observed woodland birds of the same habitats, such as Nuthatch, which again suggests under-reporting.

**Winter-period abundance 2007–13**

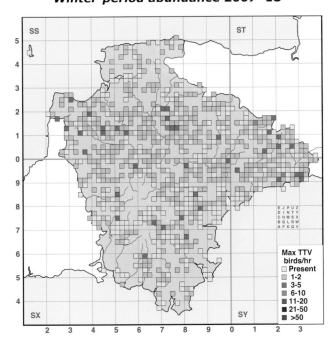

Max TTV birds/hr
- ☐ Present
- 1-2
- 3-5
- 6-10
- 11-20
- 21-50
- >50

In the *Devon Tetrad Atlas 1977–85*, Treecreepers were found across most of Devon except the treeless areas of Dartmoor and Exmoor and the less well-recorded parts of North and West Devon. The current survey still found them to be well distributed but much more thinly spread, with breeding evidence from 566 fewer tetrads than in 1977–85, a fall of 51%.

The winter-period map (October–February) fills some of the gaps in breeding distribution, given that Treecreepers are rather sedentary and breeding probably occurred in most of the tetrads where the species was found in winter. Nevertheless, a quite substantial decline since the *Devon Tetrad Atlas 1977–85* is still apparent, probably due to the exceptionally cold winters of 2009/10 and 2010/11 during the survey period. Treecreepers, being small and insectivorous, are well known to be seriously affected by such conditions, especially when prolonged cold periods occur in consecutive winters, as in this case. Conditions during the breeding seasons in this period were also unfavourable, especially in 2012 which was affected by high spring rainfall. Treecreepers regularly have two broods and so can recover quickly from such population crashes, although they are a fairly sedentary species and so do not rapidly recolonize if lost from areas. As woodland specialists they require well-wooded and well-connected landscapes if they are to recolonize quickly. Though Devon remains well-wooded, loss of connectivity due to a lack of hedging may be more of an issue than at the time of earlier atlases.

*Text: Malcolm Burgess / Photo: Barry Bowden*
*Treecreeper sponsored by Jon Valters*

Balmer *et al.* 2013: 554; Sitters 1988: 246; Tyler 2010: 536

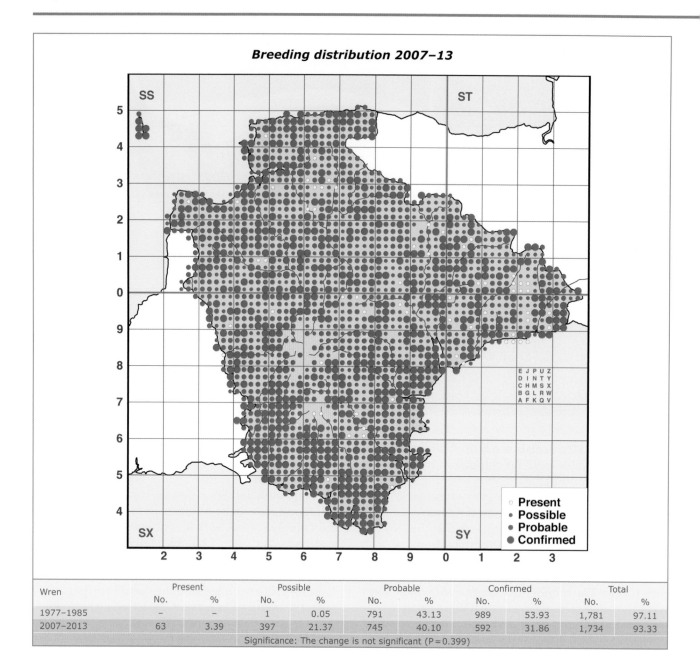

## Breeding distribution 2007–13

| Wren | Present | | Possible | | Probable | | Confirmed | | Total | |
|---|---|---|---|---|---|---|---|---|---|---|
| | No. | % | No. | % | No. | % | No. | % | No. | % |
| 1977–1985 | – | – | 1 | 0.05 | 791 | 43.13 | 989 | 53.93 | 1,781 | 97.11 |
| 2007–2013 | 63 | 3.39 | 397 | 21.37 | 745 | 40.10 | 592 | 31.86 | 1,734 | 93.33 |
| Significance: The change is not significant (P = 0.399) | | | | | | | | | | |

## Breeding distribution 1977–85

## Breeding-period abundance 2007–13

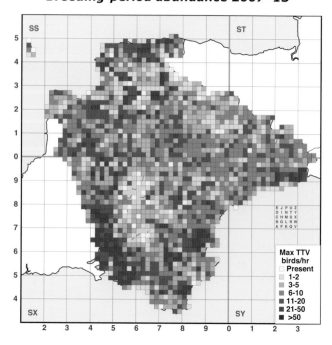

# Wren
*Troglodytes troglodytes*

THE DIMINUTIVE Wren is one of the most widely distributed and probably the most abundant breeding bird in the UK. It occurs in almost all habitats from sea level up to high moorland (*Bird Atlas 2007–11*).

During 2007–13, Wrens were found in 93% of tetrads compared to 97% in the *Devon Tetrad Atlas 1977–85*. Many of the tetrads showing the highest density of Wrens are near the coast, particularly in south-west Devon near Plymouth, around Torbay, on the East Devon coast and along the North Devon coast. Lower numbers were found in tetrads north of

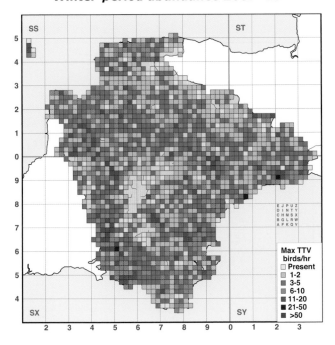

### Winter-period abundance 2007–13

Max TTV birds/hr
☐ Present
1-2
3-5
6-10
11-20
21-50
>50

Exeter and in much of north-east Devon along the border with Somerset and there were no records from the highest parts of Dartmoor. The winter distribution shows a very similar pattern, as would be expected for a largely sedentary species (Wernham *et al.* 2002).

The main factor affecting Wren population size is winter weather (Peach *et al.* 1995). Wrens are adversely affected in harsh conditions and the two hard winters of 2009/10 and 2010/11 are certain to have caused a decline in numbers, perhaps explaining the slight reduction in percentage of tetrads occupied. However, populations usually recover within a few years. In the late 1950s, the population in the Postbridge area was estimated to be around 250–500 pairs but, following the severe 1962/63 winter, only four singing males were found in 1963; numbers increased rapidly, however, and four years later, in 1967, the population was back to previous high levels (Dare & Hamilton 1968). Wrens indulge in communal roosting in cold winter weather to conserve heat and during 2007–13 the largest recorded roost was at Owley Farm, Glaze Valley, where 29 were counted entering a roost hole five metres up a gable-end wall on 25 December 2010 (*DBR*).

The Wren's sheer abundance and adaptability to a wide variety of habitats, combined with an ability to recover quickly after adverse winters, mean that significant changes in distribution in Devon are unlikely in the foreseeable future.

*Text: A W G John / Photo: Steve Hatch*
*Wren sponsored by Lizzie Little*

Balmer *et al.* 2013: 558; Sitters 1988: 178; Tyler 2010: 537

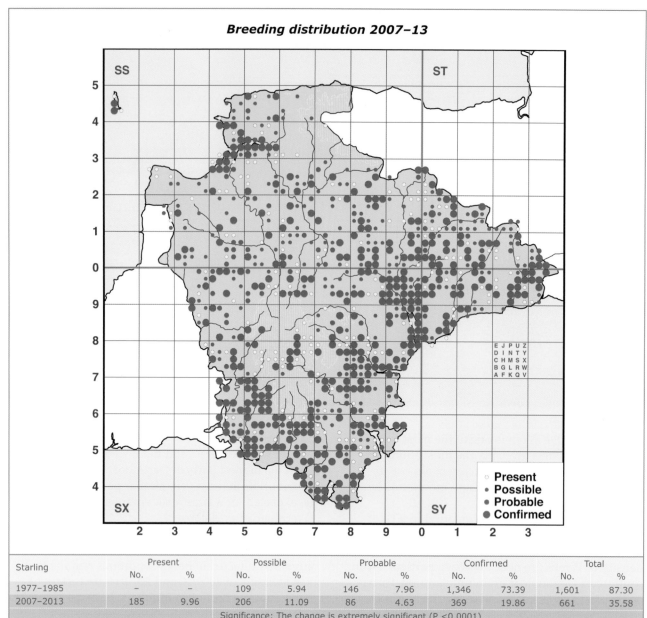

### Breeding distribution 2007–13

| Starling | Present | | Possible | | Probable | | Confirmed | | Total | |
|---|---|---|---|---|---|---|---|---|---|---|
| | No. | % | No. | % | No. | % | No. | % | No. | % |
| 1977–1985 | – | – | 109 | 5.94 | 146 | 7.96 | 1,346 | 73.39 | 1,601 | 87.30 |
| 2007–2013 | 185 | 9.96 | 206 | 11.09 | 86 | 4.63 | 369 | 19.86 | 661 | 35.58 |
| Significance: The change is extremely significant (P <0.0001) | | | | | | | | | | |

### Breeding distribution 1977–85

### Breeding-period abundance 2007–13

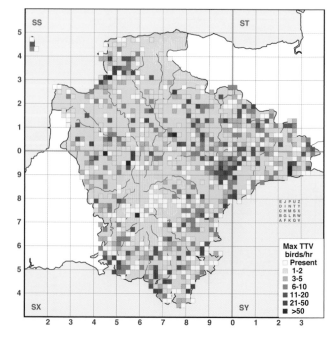

# Starling

## Sturnus vulgaris

**Red listed**

Widespread and familiar, partly because of their strong association with human-made habitats, ranging from agricultural land to city centres and gardens, Starlings are not always welcome visitors to garden feeders, cattle sheds or urban roosts sites, especially in large numbers. Except when breeding, Starlings typically occur in flocks, whether feeding or roosting. Post-breeding flocks start to form in June, and migrants from continental Europe augment numbers from October onwards. The large feeding flocks and often very large communal winter roosts mainly comprise continental migrants, which may remain into March (Wernham *et al.* 2002).

Current breeding in Devon appears to be mostly associated with human habitation and it seems unlikely that many pairs now breed in woodland, though they would be more easily overlooked in such habitats. Although breeding was confirmed in almost all 10-km squares in 2007–13, areas of absence over much of Dartmoor, around Exmoor and some coastal fringes become apparent at the tetrad level, and breeding was only recorded in 36% of tetrads across the county. Only one or two birds were recorded in most tetrads, although those with higher counts, including the eight with more than 50 individuals, are well scattered. However, at least some of these will represent post-breeding flocks and so it is unclear from the data how breeding density varies.

The current 46% occupancy (including 'presence only' in 10% of tetrads) is in stark contrast to that of

the *Devon Tetrad Atlas 1977–85* where breeding was recorded in 87% of tetrads. Thirty years ago, breeding Starlings were only really absent from Dartmoor, Haldon and some of the higher ground to the west and north of Okehampton, and there was a less obvious difference between north and south. The decrease of 47% in tetrad occupancy in Devon is paralleled by national trends. For example, there was a 50% decrease in numbers between 1995 and 2010 (Robinson *et al.* 2005) and a range contraction of 5% between the *Breeding Atlas 1968–72* and *Bird Atlas 2007–11*, mostly in the west, including South West England, where breeding densities are lower than in eastern England.

During the Atlas winter-period (October–February), Starlings were more evenly distributed and occurred in greater numbers, although, as with breeding birds, there were few records from the high ground of Dartmoor. In winter they are more likely to be recorded at garden feeders, and large feeding and roosting flocks are inevitably more conspicuous than the scattered breeding pairs of summer. They occurred in 86% of tetrads, almost twice the number now recorded during the breeding season (but coincidentally almost identical to the breeding occurrence in the *Devon Tetrad Atlas 1977–85*). Counts of more than 50 per tetrad were not infrequent in the south, but much more widespread in the north, probably a result of the very large and persistent winter roost at Okehampton Camp during the survey period. The high counts recorded may be of feeding flocks, pre-roost gatherings, birds flying to roost or migrants (given that the main autumn passage is within the Atlas winter period). Many roosts may not persist from year to year, and others, such as the one in the reedbeds at Slapton Ley, although known for over 200 years, may only be used in the autumn.

*Text: Peter Reay / Photo: Paul Sterry/NPL*
*Starling sponsored by Brent Birders – of South Brent Parish*

Balmer *et al.* 2013: 560; Sitters 1988: 260; Tyler 2010: 539

### Winter-period abundance 2007–13

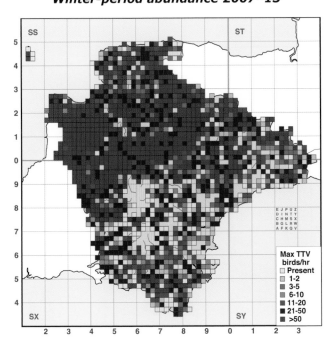

Max TTV
birds/hr
☐ Present
1-2
3-5
6-10
11-20
21-50
>50

## Breeding distribution 2007–13

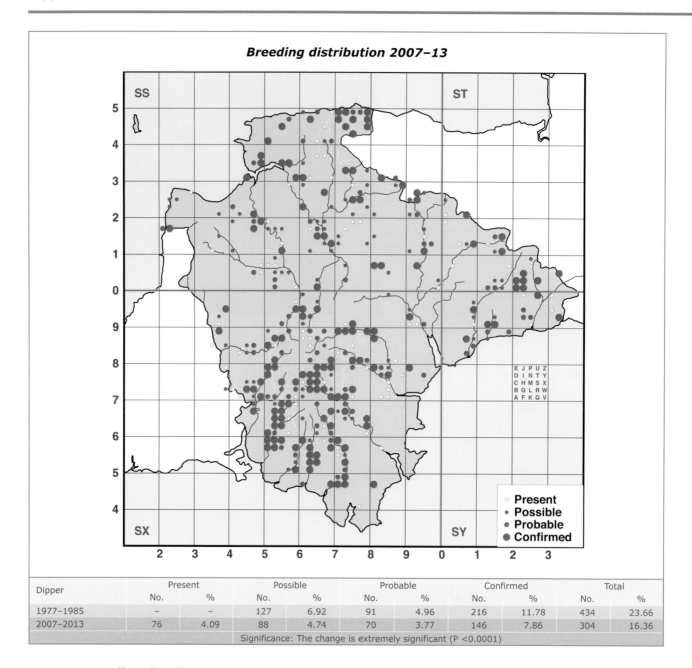

| Dipper | Present | | Possible | | Probable | | Confirmed | | Total | |
|---|---|---|---|---|---|---|---|---|---|---|
| | No. | % | No. | % | No. | % | No. | % | No. | % |
| 1977–1985 | – | – | 127 | 6.92 | 91 | 4.96 | 216 | 11.78 | 434 | 23.66 |
| 2007–2013 | 76 | 4.09 | 88 | 4.74 | 70 | 3.77 | 146 | 7.86 | 304 | 16.36 |
| Significance: The change is extremely significant (P <0.0001) | | | | | | | | | | |

## Breeding distribution 1977–85

## Breeding-period abundance 2007–13

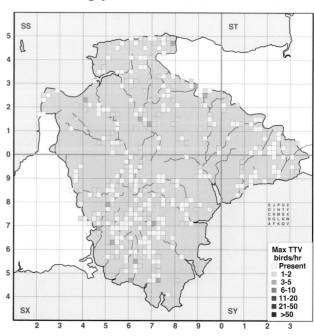

# Dipper
## Cinclus cinclus

Amber listed

THE DIPPER is a bird of fast-flowing streams and rivers, restricted to western Britain and common on many Devon rivers. The race occurring in Britain is *C. c. gularis*. There has been only one record of the continental Black-bellied Dipper (*C. c. cinclus*) in Devon, on 10 April 1983 at Avonwick.

There has been a marked reduction of around a third in the number of breeding registrations between the *Devon Tetrad Atlas 1977–85*, when it was recorded in 24% of tetrads, and 2007–13 when only 16% of tetrads held Dippers; this matches the long-term national trend of a 32% decline from 1970–2012 (SUKB 2012). The main reason for this decline is believed to be the acidification of rivers caused by conifer plantations (Tyler & Ormerod 1994) which results in fewer invertebrates and therefore lower breeding densities (longer territories) and lower productivity than on neutral (non-acidic) rivers.

Although Dippers still appear to be breeding plentifully on Dartmoor rivers such as the Okement, Tavy, Plym, Dart and Teign, numbers on some other rivers have suffered dramatic declines. When compared with the picture in 1977–85, many fewer Dippers were recorded in 2007–13 on the rivers Culm, Otter, Yeo and the upper River Exe; in North Devon there were fewer breeding records on the rivers Torridge and Bray, as well as on the western edge of Exmoor.

*Bird Atlas 2007–11* shows that the breeding density of Dippers in Devon is lower than that found in South Wales, northern England or Scotland.

### Winter-period abundance 2007–13

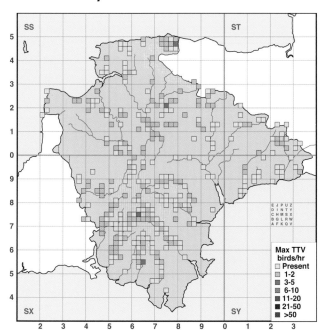

However, the number of young per breeding attempt in Britain has increased and Dippers are now breeding earlier, probably as a result of climate change (Crick & Sparks 1999).

After the breeding season there is some limited dispersal of young birds, generally within ten kilometres of their natal area. As a result, the winter-period range is much the same as that for the summer period. Having established a territory, Dippers remain on the same stretch of river year round. However, in winter they may roost communally in small numbers (occasionally up to ten or more) at suitable sites. Only in exceptionally cold winters, when smaller streams become frozen, are they forced to move downstream to seek open stretches of water.

As well as acidification of rivers, other factors affecting Dipper populations include runoff of agricultural chemicals into rivers, renovation of bridges making them unsuitable for nesting, predation by mink, and recreational disturbance. The warming climate, as well as causing earlier breeding, may well have unpredictable effects on Dippers and other river birds.

*Text: A W G John / Photo: Neil Bygrave*
*Dipper sponsored by Kevin & Donna Cox*

Balmer *et al.* 2013: 562; Sitters 1988: 176; Tyler 2010: 543

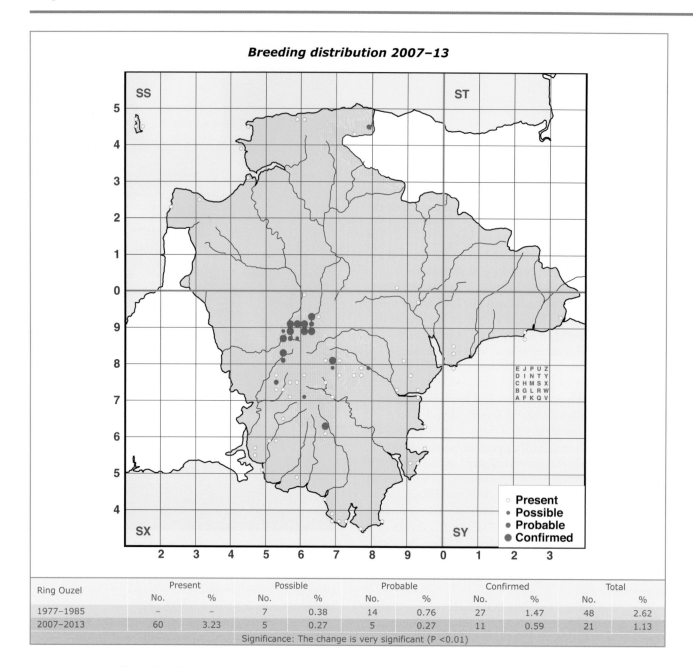

### Breeding distribution 2007–13

| Ring Ouzel | Present | | Possible | | Probable | | Confirmed | | Total | |
|---|---|---|---|---|---|---|---|---|---|---|
| | No. | % | No. | % | No. | % | No. | % | No. | % |
| 1977–1985 | – | – | 7 | 0.38 | 14 | 0.76 | 27 | 1.47 | 48 | 2.62 |
| 2007–2013 | 60 | 3.23 | 5 | 0.27 | 5 | 0.27 | 11 | 0.59 | 21 | 1.13 |
| Significance: The change is very significant (P <0.01) | | | | | | | | | | |

### Breeding distribution 1977–85

### Breeding-period abundance 2007–13

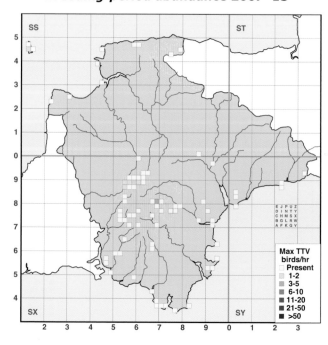

# Ring Ouzel
## *Turdus torquatus*
### Red listed

RING OUZELS, sometimes known as Mountain Blackbirds, are migrant breeders, wintering in the Atlas Mountains of Morocco and arriving back in Britain from late March (Wernham *et al.* 2002).

Ring Ouzels breed exclusively in upland landscapes, generally occupying steep slopes, often with crags or tors, and with a cover of shrubs such as heather or bilberry, although they also need grazed species-rich grassland close to nest sites to find invertebrate food for their young. Research has shown that juveniles switch to feed mainly on moorland berries from mid-July onwards (Sim *et al.* 2013) so a mix of habitats providing different food types as well as nest cover is essential throughout the summer.

In Devon, Dartmoor and Exmoor offer the only potential breeding locations. Other locations where presence is mapped correspond to passage birds on their way north in spring or south in the autumn.

Ring Ouzels were recorded in 81 tetrads (4%) during the current Atlas breeding period (March–September) and although this is very slightly higher than reported in the *Devon Tetrad Atlas 1977–85*, many of the 2007–2013 records related to passage birds. The number of tetrads containing confirmed breeding has dropped sharply, from 27 during the earlier Atlas to just 11 in the current survey, all of which were on Dartmoor, with just a single tetrad containing a probable breeding pair on Exmoor. The last known confirmed breeding on Exmoor was in 2002 (Ballance 2006).

The number of tetrads for which probable or possible breeding was recorded has also dropped. The *Devon Tetrad Atlas 1977–85* reported 14 and seven tetrads respectively, compared to just five in each category during the current survey. On Dartmoor there have been losses from the southern and central areas, leaving birds primarily concentrated in the north and with a shift towards the edges of the moor.

The decline in Devon reflects the situation across Britain, with *Bird Atlas 2007–11* reporting a 43% reduction in range in Britain since the *Breeding Atlas 1968–72*. The population decline is most probably being driven by a combination of loss of habitat quality, predation and disturbance, especially where the close mix of adequate nest cover and forage habitat is not available or is sub-optimal. Ring Ouzels are now highly vulnerable in Devon and their future here as one of our iconic upland breeding birds is far from certain.

*Text: Helen Booker / Photo: Steve Hatch*
*Ring Ouzel sponsored by the RSPB*

### Winter-period abundance 2007–13

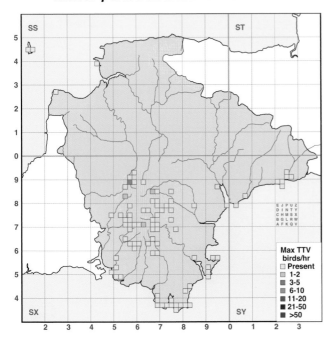

giving nature a home

Balmer *et al.* 2013: 564; Sitters 1988: 194; Tyler 2010: 547

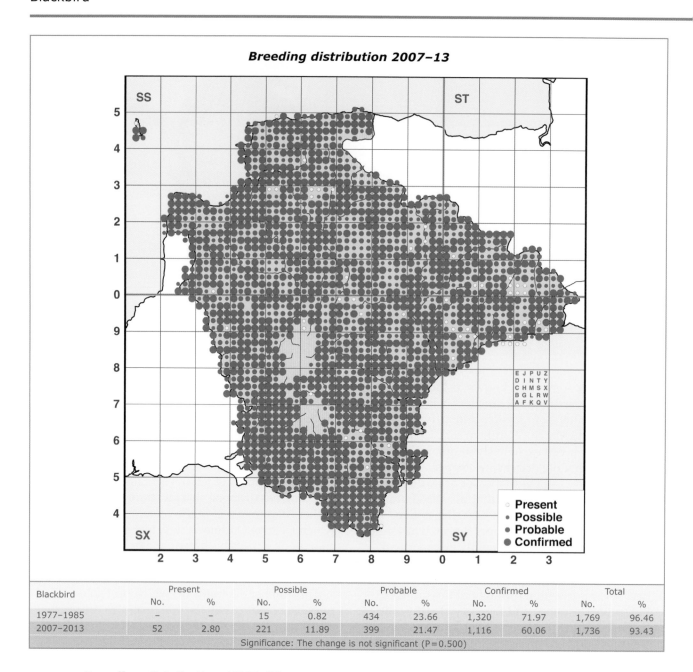

## Breeding distribution 2007–13

| Blackbird | Present | | Possible | | Probable | | Confirmed | | Total | |
|---|---|---|---|---|---|---|---|---|---|---|
| | No. | % | No. | % | No. | % | No. | % | No. | % |
| 1977–1985 | – | – | 15 | 0.82 | 434 | 23.66 | 1,320 | 71.97 | 1,769 | 96.46 |
| 2007–2013 | 52 | 2.80 | 221 | 11.89 | 399 | 21.47 | 1,116 | 60.06 | 1,736 | 93.43 |
| Significance: The change is not significant (P=0.500) | | | | | | | | | | |

## Breeding distribution 1977–85

## Breeding-period abundance 2007–13

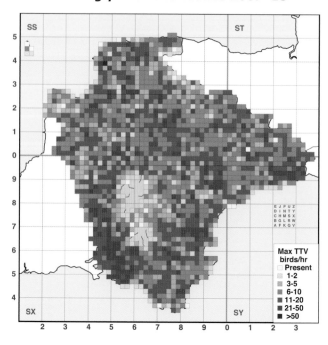

# Blackbird
## Turdus merula

THE BLACKBIRD is one of our most familiar and abundant species, occurring in almost every habitat where there is sufficient cover provided by trees and shrubs. Whilst breeding has been confirmed on Dartmoor and Devon Exmoor at altitudes of above 450 metres, densities are well below those in the lowlands, and several tetrads in these areas lack breeding-period records. Moorland-fringe areas of scrubby habitat associated with forestry plantations are particularly attractive to this ubiquitous species. On the high moors Blackbirds may compete with Ring Ouzels for suitable territories, with the later-breeding Ring Ouzel at a distinct disadvantage (Smaldon 2005). In the *Devon Tetrad Atlas 1977–85*, Blackbirds were recorded in 96% of tetrads and this pattern was largely repeated in the current survey, indicating a stable breeding population. It is highly likely that densities are rising in all areas of the UK except the extreme south-east of England (*Bird Atlas 2007–11*).

During the autumn, the resident population is augmented by large numbers of migrants from continental Europe, particularly from southern Scandinavia and the Low Countries and also from eastern England (Woods & Woods 2006), and many of these remain throughout the winter (Tyler 2010). At the same time, some birds that breed in southern Britain may move into north-west France. In 2010, 100 were recorded on Lundy on 13 October, while in 2012, arrivals included 108 at Soar on 22 October, 100 at Prawle on 23 October and 150 on Lundy on 25 October (*DBRs*). Spring passage is much less marked.

In winter, birds are found throughout the county except for the high moors, which appear largely vacated, and counts of over 50 are not uncommon in fields and orchards where there is an abundant food supply. The winter map suggests that the highest concentrations of birds are in the south-west of the county, with smaller populations in the north and east.

Blackbirds are omnivorous, feeding on a wide range of items, mainly invertebrates and various species of earthworms, but were recorded taking newts at Wembury and small frogs at Aveton Gifford in 2010 (*DBR*). Feeding activity is largely confined to the ground for much of the year, although large quantities of berries and fruit are taken in autumn.

### Winter-period abundance 2007–13

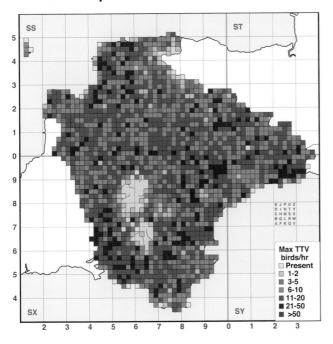

Max TTV birds/hr
- ☐ Present
- ☐ 1-2
- ☐ 3-5
- ■ 6-10
- ■ 11-20
- ■ 21-50
- ■ >50

*Text: Rob Macklin / Photo: Neil Bygrave*
*Blackbird sponsored by Robin & Anne Woods*

Balmer *et al.* 2013: 566; Sitters 1988: 196; Tyler 2010: 548

# Fieldfare

*Turdus pilaris*

**Red listed**

THE FIELDFARE is a widespread species, breeding sparsely in northern Britain and more abundantly in eastern France, Scandinavia, central and northern Europe and northern Asia, and wintering in Britain, Ireland and most of Europe, Asia Minor, the Middle East and west-central Asia. The European breeding population is in excess of 14 million pairs (BirdLife International 2015). From their northern breeding grounds up to one million Fieldfares migrate to Britain & Ireland in winter (*Bird Atlas 2007–11*). Although occasional birds are recorded in September, the main arrivals occur from mid-October to early November. Locally, Fieldfares are known as 'blue birds', presumably due to their blue-grey head and rump.

*Bird Atlas 2007–2011* showed a 4% increase in the national winter range since the *Winter Atlas 1981–84*. In Devon, the species was recorded in 73% of tetrads during the winter, compared to 92% of tetrads nationally. Most birds were found in the more clement areas, away from the coasts and high moors of Dartmoor and Exmoor.

Fieldfares move onto grassland once berry crops have been exhausted, often in company with other thrushes, particularly Redwings. Flocks of over 50 birds are not uncommon but numbers tend to increase markedly during cold weather. In 2010, several thousand moved west over Seaton between 6 & 9 January and again between 19 & 31 December.

During the breeding period, Fieldfares were noted in 7.7% of tetrads but, as with Redwings, northward migration to the breeding grounds occurs during March and April, with small numbers sometimes still passing through in May. There was no evidence of breeding in the county.

*Text: Rob Macklin / Photo: Adrian Davey*
*Fieldfare sponsored by Stella Beavan*

Balmer *et al.* 2013: 568; Sitters 1988: not treated; Tyler 2010: 550

### Winter-period abundance 2007–13

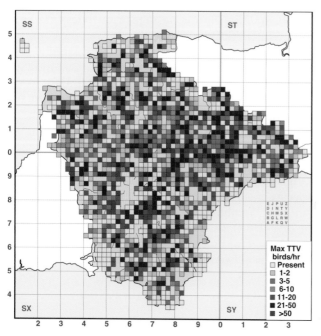

### Breeding-period abundance 2007–13

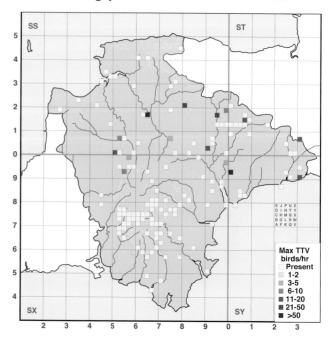

# Redwing
*Turdus iliacus*

**Red listed**

REDWINGS ARE familiar winter visitors to Devon, arriving from breeding grounds in northern Europe and Russia. They are readily identified from their flight calls as they pass overhead, sometimes in very large flocks and often at night. Although a few birds may arrive in Devon in September (exceptionally even earlier), the main autumn migration gets underway from mid-October and continues into November and December. The maximum autumn-passage count during the Atlas years was 4,600 flying north over Berry Head on 15 November 2012 (*DBR*).

Redwings were recorded in 83% of tetrads during the winter period (October–February), being widely distributed across the county. Winter density appears to be higher inland than on the coast or on the high moors of Dartmoor and Devon Exmoor, where the species seems to be largely absent.

Redwings generally switch to feeding on grassland once the autumn berry crop has been exhausted, and are frequently seen in the company of other thrushes, particularly Fieldfares. Flocks of up to 200 occur regularly and much larger numbers can be found during hard-weather movements, as was the case in early 2010 when 2,700 were at Dawlish Warren on 6 January and 2,200 at Thurlestone on 8 January (*DBR*).

Some Redwings continue to be seen from March to early May, involving a mix of lingering winter visitors and spring migrants; the latest spring record during the Atlas years was one on the Taw/Torridge Estuary on 18 May 2010 (*DBR*). The Atlas breeding-period map (March–September) reflects the presence of these birds, as well as a handful of early autumn migrants in the last week of September in three Atlas years – the earliest being on Dartmoor, 23 September 2012 (*DBR*). Altogether, there were records from almost 9% of tetrads.

*Text: Rob Macklin / Photo: Neil Bygrave*
*Redwing sponsored by Stella Beavan*

Balmer *et al.* 2013: 572; Sitters 1988: not treated; Tyler 2010: 555

### Winter-period abundance 2007–13

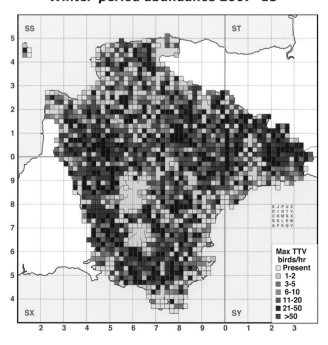

### Breeding-period abundance 2007–13

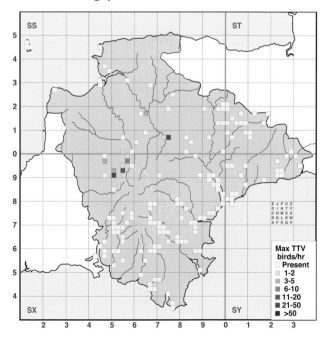

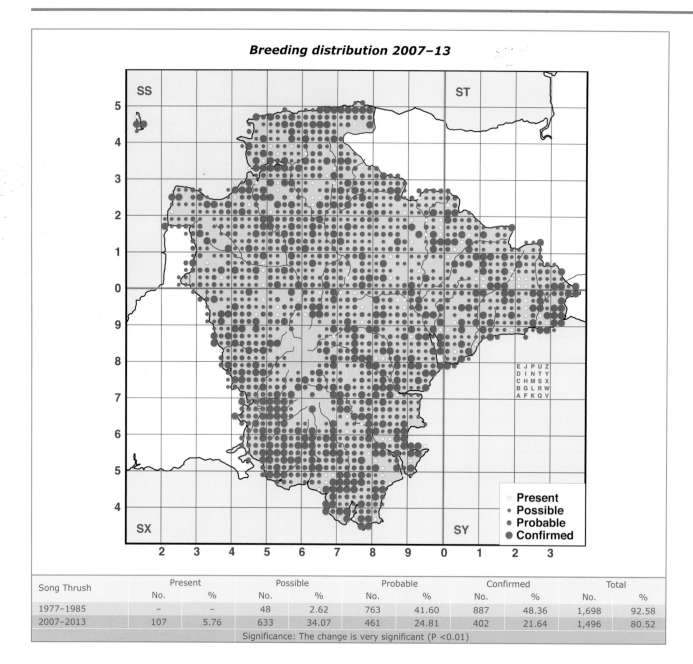

## Breeding distribution 2007–13

| Song Thrush | Present | | Possible | | Probable | | Confirmed | | Total | |
|---|---|---|---|---|---|---|---|---|---|---|
| | No. | % | No. | % | No. | % | No. | % | No. | % |
| 1977–1985 | – | – | 48 | 2.62 | 763 | 41.60 | 887 | 48.36 | 1,698 | 92.58 |
| 2007–2013 | 107 | 5.76 | 633 | 34.07 | 461 | 24.81 | 402 | 21.64 | 1,496 | 80.52 |
| Significance: The change is very significant (P <0.01) | | | | | | | | | | |

## Breeding distribution 1977–85

## Breeding-period abundance 2007–13

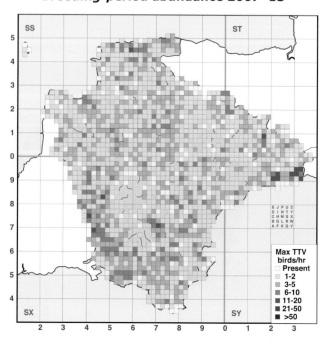

# Song Thrush
## Turdus philomelos

**Red listed**

Song Thrush is resident throughout the county and can readily be found where sufficient cover is provided by hedgerows, scrub, shrubby gardens, woods and gorse on moorland, although it is absent from the high treeless areas of Dartmoor and Exmoor. During fieldwork for the *Devon Tetrad Atlas 1977–85*, breeding evidence was found in approximately 93% of tetrads but this fell to about 81% for the present survey, with an even more significant decline in the number of tetrads for which breeding was confirmed, though the species remains widespread across the county.

During the period 1970–2010 there was a 54% decline in the UK population, although this masks a modest 13% increase between 1995 and 2010 (*Bird Atlas 2007–11*). Although Song Thrushes are doing rather better in Devon and other parts of western Britain – perhaps due to the relative abundance of grassland and higher rainfall – than in eastern and south-east England (*Bird Atlas 2007–11*), the reduction in frequency of confirmed breeding at tetrad level is a cause for concern.

Fewer juvenile Song Thrushes are surviving into their second year (BTO BirdTrends 2014) and although the causes are unclear, it may be that changes in farming practices are an important factor. Until the reasons are understood and addressed, the likelihood of numbers returning to their former levels is slim.

Although Song Thrushes are largely sedentary, in autumn small numbers of birds move out of the county to France and Iberia (Wernham *et al.* 2002), and some arrive. Most arrivals are recorded at coastal locations and usually involve small numbers (20–25), but there are occasional large influxes, such as 400 in the Start area on 23 October 2012 (*DBR*). In the same year, 150 were on Lundy on 25 October and four birds ringed there on 22 October were considered to be of the continental race *T. p. philomelos* (*DBR*). At other times during the winter period, Song Thrushes are to be found throughout the county and numbers can be exceptionally high during cold-weather movements. This was highlighted in 2010 by counts of 150 at Thurlestone on 7 January and 100 at Wembury on 9 January. Later in the year a severe cold spell brought 250 to the Thurlestone area on 23 December and 150 were at Wembury Beach on 19 December (*DBR*).

*Text: Rob Macklin / Photos: Dave Scott*
*Song Thrush sponsored by Roger Emslie-Henry*

Balmer *et al.* 2013: 570; Sitters 1988: 198; Tyler 2010: 552

### Winter-period abundance 2007–13

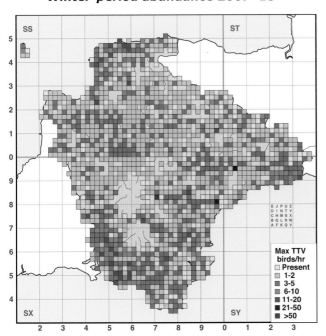

Max TTV birds/hr
- □ Present
- 1-2
- 3-5
- 6-10
- 11-20
- 21-50
- >50

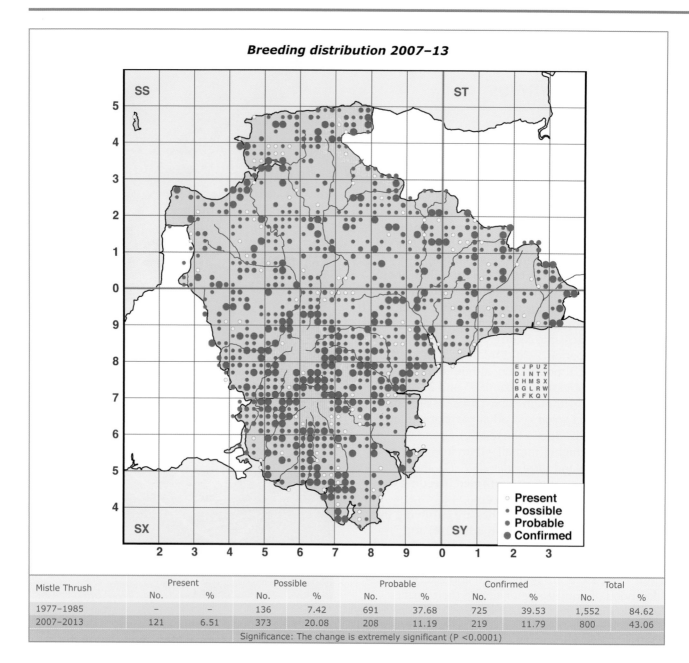

## Breeding distribution 2007–13

| Mistle Thrush | Present | | Possible | | Probable | | Confirmed | | Total | |
|---|---|---|---|---|---|---|---|---|---|---|
| | No. | % | No. | % | No. | % | No. | % | No. | % |
| 1977–1985 | – | – | 136 | 7.42 | 691 | 37.68 | 725 | 39.53 | 1,552 | 84.62 |
| 2007–2013 | 121 | 6.51 | 373 | 20.08 | 208 | 11.19 | 219 | 11.79 | 800 | 43.06 |
| Significance: The change is extremely significant (P <0.0001) | | | | | | | | | | |

**Legend:**
○ Present
● Possible
● Probable
● Confirmed

## Breeding distribution 1977–85

● Possible
● Probable
● Confirmed

## Breeding-period abundance 2007–13

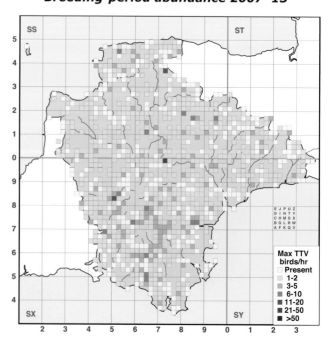

Max TTV
birds/hr
□ Present
1-2
3-5
6-10
11-20
21-50
>50

# Mistle Thrush
*Turdus viscivorus*

Red listed

MISTLE THRUSHES are familiar yet enigmatic birds. They are conspicuous while delivering their loud fluting song in short bursts from an exposed perch, foraging in the open or noisily defending their nests against predators. They occur right across the county and are thinly scattered in parks, gardens, woodland edges, open wooded country, conifer plantations and in suitable habitats on Dartmoor and Exmoor. Mistle Thrushes defend larger territories than other thrushes nesting in the same habitat (*BWP*), in which they feed mainly on invertebrates, fruit and berries. Individual birds will take up winter territories and defend heavily-laden berried trees from other thrushes.

This largely sedentary species (Wernham *et al.* 2002) has undergone a dramatic decline in Devon over the last 30 years. The *Devon Tetrad Atlas 1977–85* found evidence of breeding Mistle Thrushes in 84% of tetrads compared to just 48% during the current survey (plus presence only in a further 6.5%), an astonishing and worrying decline of 43% over a relatively short period of time.

The breeding-period map (March–September) shows a marked concentration of birds on Dartmoor and its surroundings, excluding the high moor. Other than this, the picture is very patchy, with large declines apparent across the county, particularly in the north and east. The decline reflects the national trend, the Breeding Bird Survey having shown a decline of 31% over the period 1995–2011 (Risely *et al.* 2013).

Post-breeding flocks numbering up to 30 or more are likely to be encountered from late summer into autumn, especially on the moors. Peak recent counts have included 84 at Burrator on 26 August 2006, 30 at Holne on 13 August 2011 and 34 at Clearbrook on 23 August (*DBRs*), but such large gatherings may now be increasingly unusual in the county.

The winter-period map (October–February) shows a concentration of birds towards the south of the county, with few to the north and east of Dartmoor. Numbers build up from October onwards, with migrants coming into the county from both the continent and elsewhere within the UK, and counts of 20 or more are not uncommon.

The underlying causes of the decline, which is linked to lower annual survival (BTO BirdTrends 2014), remain unclear but a reduction in food or habitat availability and an increase in predation are all possible contributory factors.

*Text: Rob Macklin / Photos: Dave Scott & (right) David Land*
*Mistle Thrush sponsored by Barbara Skinner*

Balmer *et al.* 2013: 574; Sitters 1988: 200; Tyler 2010: 557

### Winter-period abundance 2007–13

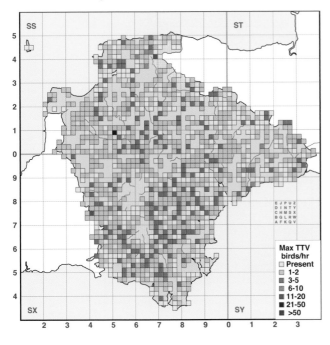

Max TTV birds/hr
- □ Present
- 1-2
- 3-5
- 6-10
- 11-20
- 21-50
- >50

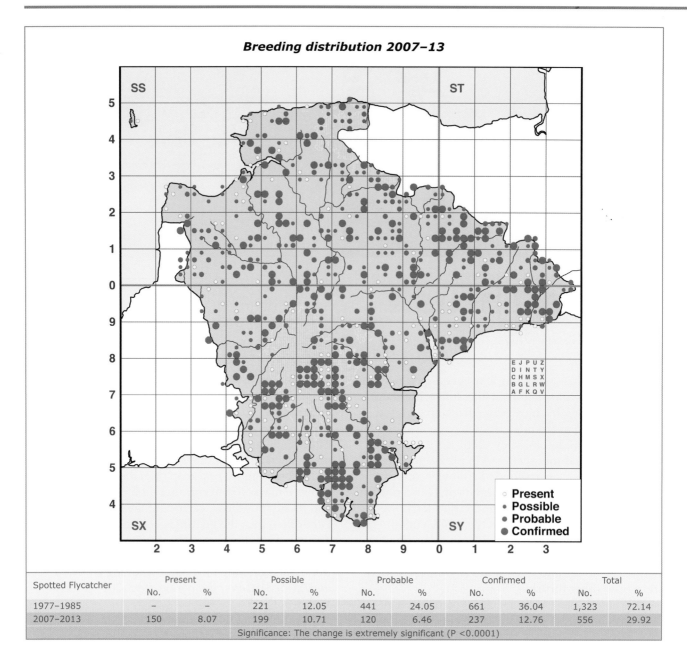

**Breeding distribution 2007–13**

| Spotted Flycatcher | Present | | Possible | | Probable | | Confirmed | | Total | |
|---|---|---|---|---|---|---|---|---|---|---|
| | No. | % | No. | % | No. | % | No. | % | No. | % |
| 1977–1985 | – | – | 221 | 12.05 | 441 | 24.05 | 661 | 36.04 | 1,323 | 72.14 |
| 2007–2013 | 150 | 8.07 | 199 | 10.71 | 120 | 6.46 | 237 | 12.76 | 556 | 29.92 |
| | Significance: The change is extremely significant (P <0.0001) | | | | | | | | | |

**Breeding distribution 1977–85**

**Breeding-period abundance 2007–13**

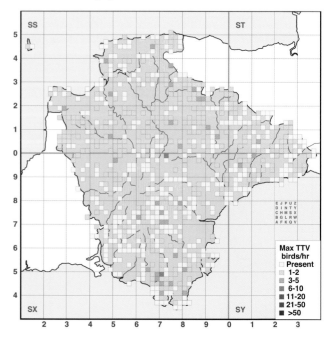

# Spotted Flycatcher
*Muscicapa striata*

**Red listed**

SPOTTED FLYCATCHERS are among the last trans-Saharan summer migrants to arrive back in the UK in spring, with nesting territories often not occupied until mid-May and some later still. They prefer glades and edges of mature but open broadleaf woodland, as well as large well-treed gardens. They often nest in holes in the walls of houses and outbuildings, especially where these are covered in ivy or other climbing plants, and take readily to open-fronted nestboxes.

The Atlas maps show that Spotted Flycatchers are widespread in Devon, with breeding confirmed in 237 tetrads. There are noticeable strongholds on Dartmoor and its western fringes, the South Hams and the Blackdown Hills, while elsewhere many of the occupied tetrads are along, or close to, river valleys. While the continued wide distribution is apparently encouraging, comparison between the maps for this Atlas and the *Devon Tetrad Atlas 1977–85* is sobering. The latter shows many 10-km squares – including almost the whole of northernmost Devon, arguably the former stronghold of the species in the county – with breeding confirmed for a majority of tetrads. Only one 10-km square (SX67), on Dartmoor, met this threshold during the current Atlas period.

The statistics for the two breeding Atlases shown in the table make for gloomy reading. The number of tetrads for which breeding was probable or confirmed fell by more than two-thirds between the two surveys. Even allowing for locally reduced coverage in some parts of the county, and for differences in methodology, the change is striking and part of a much wider, depressingly rapid decline affecting much of the UK and breeding populations elsewhere in Europe. Spotted Flycatcher is already on the 'red list' of birds of conservation concern,

reflecting a long-term European population decline of 42% for the period 1980–2012, though with little net change in the final ten years of that period (PECBMS 2014). The combined Breeding Birds Survey/Common Birds Census index for the UK shows a continuous and steep decline since records began in the late 1960s, with a loss of almost 90% of our Spotted Flycatchers between 1967 and 2011 (BTO BirdTrends 2014). BTO data also show a stable or slightly improving trend in fledging success since 1970, effectively ruling out poor breeding productivity as an explanation for the decline. Instead, it appears to be low first-year survival that is driving the decline, but the reasons underlying this are not yet understood (BTO BirdTrends 2014).

While autumn migration peaks in September, late-occurring migrants were recorded in every October during the Atlas period, the latest being a single bird at Slapton on 18 October 2012 (*DBR*).

Given that apparently suitable breeding habitat remains widespread in areas where 'Spot Flys' have been lost, those reasons seem likely to include factors affecting the migration routes and wintering grounds. As pointed out in *Bird Atlas 2007–11*, Spotted Flycatcher is one of several species (including Wood Warbler and Cuckoo) that winter in the humid tropical zone of West Africa and which are showing similar steep and rapid declines, suggesting a common cause. Recent research has been focusing on the potential impacts of climate and/or land-use change (e.g. Stevens 2007; Stevens *et al.* 2007).

*Text: Tim Davis & Tim Jones / Photo: Robin Khan*
*Spotted Flycatcher sponsored by Nick & Gill Townsend*

Balmer *et al.* 2013: 576; Sitters 1988: 228; Tyler 2010: 559

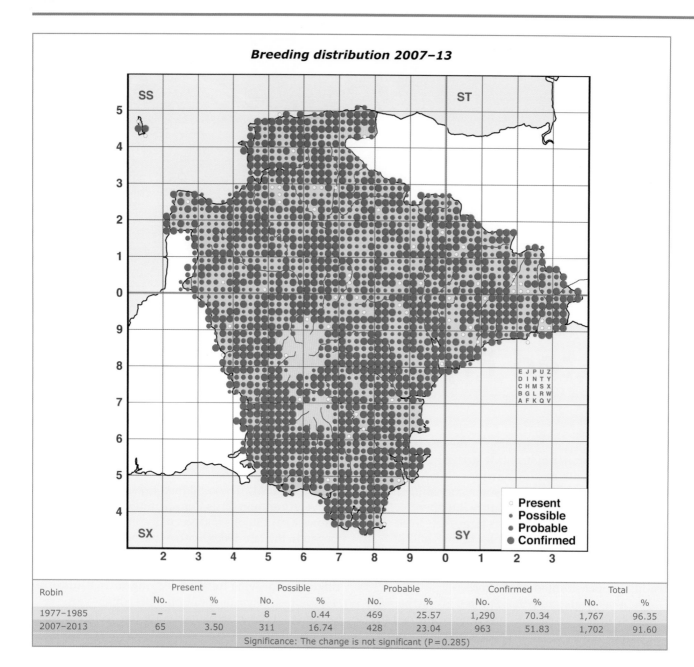

**Breeding distribution 2007–13**

| Robin | Present | | Possible | | Probable | | Confirmed | | Total | |
|---|---|---|---|---|---|---|---|---|---|---|
| | No. | % | No. | % | No. | % | No. | % | No. | % |
| 1977–1985 | – | – | 8 | 0.44 | 469 | 25.57 | 1,290 | 70.34 | 1,767 | 96.35 |
| 2007–2013 | 65 | 3.50 | 311 | 16.74 | 428 | 23.04 | 963 | 51.83 | 1,702 | 91.60 |
| Significance: The change is not significant (P = 0.285) | | | | | | | | | | |

**Breeding distribution 1977–85**

**Breeding-period abundance 2007–13**

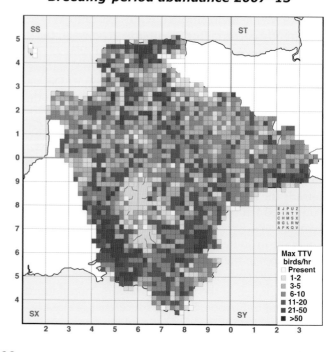

# Robin
*Erithacus rubecula*

Aᴅᴇʟɪɢʜᴛꜰᴜʟ and much-loved bird, happy to exploit any situation, especially those offered by humans, to get a meal, the Robin is one of our most widespread and abundant birds. The race *E. r. melophilos* is endemic to Britain and Ireland and is largely sedentary. In Devon it is widely distributed across most habitats except open moorland on Dartmoor and Exmoor. Pairs will nest as early as January in mild conditions but usually from March onwards.

### Winter-period abundance 2007–13

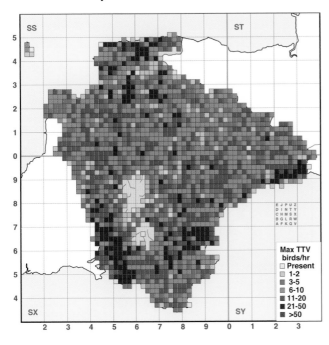

In the *Devon Tetrad Atlas 1977–85*, Robins were found in 96% of tetrads and this pattern was largely replicated during the breeding period of the current survey, with birds present in 95% of tetrads (91.6% with breeding evidence and 3.5% presence only). These statistics are in line with *Bird Atlas 2007–2011*, which found Robins breeding in 94% of all 10-km squares, with the areas of highest abundance including southern England. Robins breed in just about all habitats, including sites around human habitation, although breeding densities inevitably vary according to habitat suitability.

In autumn, numbers of Robins are swelled by continental immigrants of the race *E. r. rubecula* from September to November, peaking in October at coastal sites such as Berry Head, Prawle, Soar, Wembury, Stoke Point and Lundy. High autumn counts can also be made inland; for example, 74 were around Burrator Reservoir on 20 October 2010. Autumn coastal count peaks included 64 at Dawlish Warren on 24 October 2012, 65 on Lundy on 23 October 2012 and 83 at Prawle on 13 December 2009 (*DBRs*).

The winter abundance map is very similar to the breeding-period map, with Robins recorded right across the county with the exception of the higher parts of Dartmoor and Exmoor. Robins are less aggressively territorial in severe winters and hence more residents may be seen together on occasion.

*Text: Rob Macklin / Photo: Carole Bowden*
*Robin sponsored by Pamela Little*

Balmer *et al.* 2013: 578; Sitters 1988: 182; Tyler 2010: 561

# Nightingale
## *Luscinia megarhynchos*

**Red listed**

NIGHTINGALES ARE on the northern edge of their range in the UK and are now largely confined to the south-east of the country following a significant national range contraction between the *Breeding Atlas 1968–72* and *Bird Atlas 2007–11*.

During the current survey, Nightingales were recorded as 'present' in just ten tetrads (but eleven 10-km squares as a few records were submitted only at the 10-km level). There was no evidence of breeding and most if not all records probably related to passage migrants. The 10-km squares involved were two in the north of the county, one in the south-west and eight in the species' former Devon strongholds in the south and east (see map). Singing birds were recorded at Dawlish Warren on 23–24 April 2008, the Exeter area on 10 May 2009, Goodleigh on 23 May 2010, Exton on 15 April 2011, Exminster Marshes on 2 May 2012 and Christow on 2–20 May 2013 (*DBRs*). Other spring records related to non-singing birds, mainly at well-watched migration points. The only autumn record was at Berry Head on 1 September 2012.

The *Devon Tetrad Atlas 1977–85* found Nightingales in a total of 19 tetrads, comprising four with evidence of confirmed breeding, nine probable breeding and six possible breeding. The species last bred in the Chudleigh Knighton area in 1993 and in the Axmouth-Lyme Regis Undercliffs NNR in 1996 (Tyler 2010). The changes that have occurred in Devon reflect the major national decline of this iconic species, the reasons for which have recently been discussed by Holt *et al.* (2012). Possible factors include changes to the structure of British woodlands (e.g. from reduced management and increased deer grazing) and changes on the wintering grounds and along migration routes (BTO BirdTrends 2014).

Holt *et al.* (2012) stated: "It is a sobering fact that the Nightingale population of our country is declining steadily at a time when it should be gaining ground because of climate change. Something is seriously wrong."

*Text: Rob Macklin / Photo: Paul Sterry/NPL*
*Nightingale sponsored by Julia & George Harris*

Balmer *et al.* 2013: 580; Sitters 1988: 184; Tyler 2010: 564

### Breeding distribution 2007-13

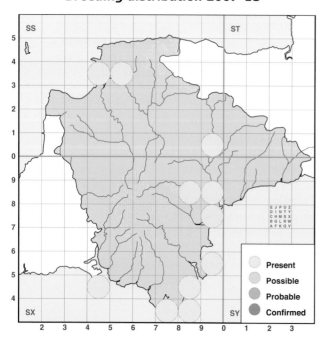

Present
Possible
Probable
Confirmed

### Breeding distribution 1977-85

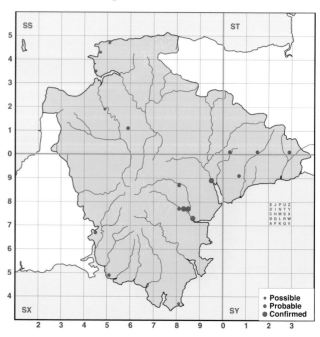

Possible
Probable
Confirmed

# Black Redstart
*Phoenicurus ochruros*

**Red listed**

BLACK REDSTART is mainly a passage and winter visitor to Devon, and only breeds regularly in south-east England, where it has a liking for industrial and man-made habitats.

During the current survey, Black Redstarts were recorded in 5% of tetrads in the breeding period (March–September), though the majority of records are likely to have involved spring migrants (see below).

In 2012, a pair nested in a large warehouse in the county, where two adults and three recently fledged juveniles were seen on 2 July. In the past, although breeding has been suspected, it was confirmed on only two other occasions: at Burlescombe in 1942 and Torquay in 1949. The *Devon Tetrad Atlas 1977–85* recorded only one instance of probable breeding.

Spring migration takes place from late February to early May, peaking during March, with occasional stragglers in June. High numbers occur in some springs as shown by a loose flock of 12 birds in a gulley at Start Point on 30 March 2013 (*DBR*).

Autumn migration peaks during October and November, with records coming mainly from coastal locations, including Lundy, where 12 were recorded on 26 October 2012 (*DBR*). During the Atlas winter period (October–February) Black Redstarts were found in 9% of tetrads, particularly on the north coast, the South Hams, along the coast to Exeter and along some river valleys. The winter abundance map in *Bird Atlas 2007–11* suggests that densities are highest in South West England, probably reflecting the usually milder conditions in our region.

*Text: Rob Macklin / Photo: Andrew Cunningham*
*Black Redstart sponsored by Lynne & Roger Doble*

Balmer *et al.* 2013: 584; Sitters 1988: 302; Tyler 2010: 567

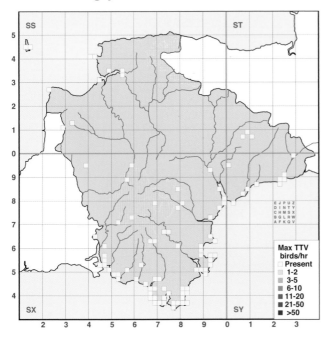

*Breeding-period abundance 2007-13*

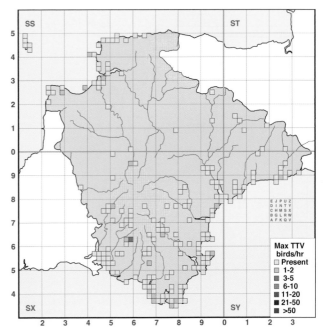

*Winter-period abundance 2007–13*

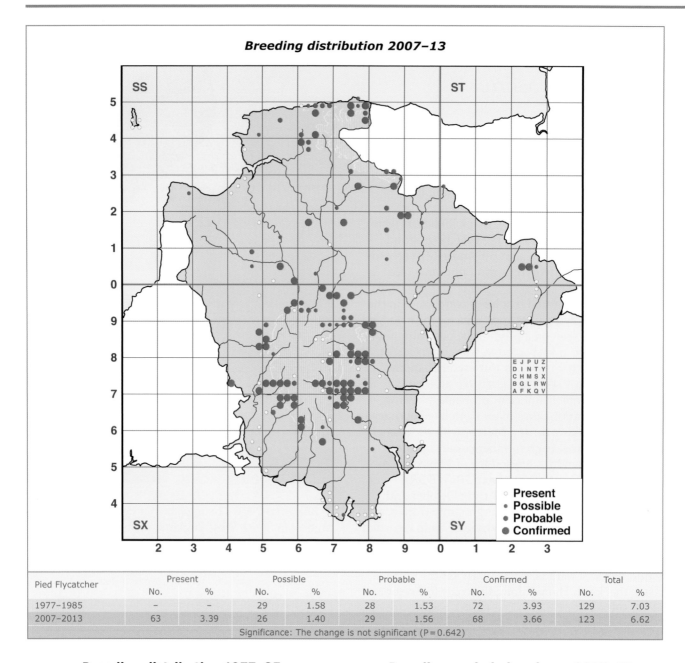

**Breeding distribution 2007–13**

| Pied Flycatcher | Present | | Possible | | Probable | | Confirmed | | Total | |
|---|---|---|---|---|---|---|---|---|---|---|
| | No. | % | No. | % | No. | % | No. | % | No. | % |
| 1977–1985 | – | – | 29 | 1.58 | 28 | 1.53 | 72 | 3.93 | 129 | 7.03 |
| 2007–2013 | 63 | 3.39 | 26 | 1.40 | 29 | 1.56 | 68 | 3.66 | 123 | 6.62 |
| Significance: The change is not significant (P = 0.642) | | | | | | | | | | |

**Breeding distribution 1977–85**

**Breeding-period abundance 2007–13**

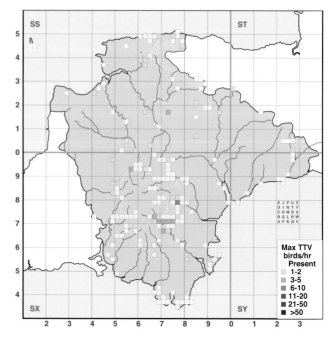

# Pied Flycatcher
## Ficedula hypoleuca

**Red listed**

IN BRITAIN, Pied Flycatchers are predominantly birds of upland deciduous woodlands, especially those dominated by oak, but they can also be found at lower densities in mixed woodlands (Lundberg & Alatalo 1992). Woods of more than one hectare in size are preferred, with higher densities occurring in larger woodlands and small woods occupied only in years when Pied Flycatchers are more abundant (Huhta 1998).

In Devon, populations are concentrated in the wooded periphery of Dartmoor and Exmoor, and in the more extensive oakwoods in between. Small populations are also found at low densities in a few parts of East Devon. The highest densities occur along the wooded Bovey, Holne and Teign river valleys on the southern side of Dartmoor. Although the number of occupied tetrads is very similar to that recorded in the *Devon Tetrad Atlas 1977–1985*, their distribution has changed, with more tetrads occupied on Dartmoor and fewer in North Devon.

Pied Flycatchers take readily to nestboxes and the gains on Dartmoor are largely due to the operation of nestbox schemes, improved reporting and near comprehensive coverage through a newly established monitoring network (www.PiedFly.net). Pied Flycatchers naturally nest in tree holes in woodlands with a more diverse structure than Devon's many formerly coppiced oak woodlands that are the focus of most nestbox schemes. The first such scheme began at Yarner Wood in 1955 and others followed in the 1970s and 1980s, initially concentrated around Dartmoor. The data obtained from these schemes have contributed to many scientific research projects. For example, tracking work using light-level data-loggers (geolocators) at Yarner Wood shows that males depart shortly after completing post-breeding moult in late July and travel across Spain and the western edge of the Sahara to wintering grounds centred on Guinea and Liberia, consistent with the location of the only recovery of a Devon-ringed bird.

Monitoring data show that population trends are the same across all Devon populations. Since a peak in 1990, numbers have declined and stabilized at a lower level. Nestbox availability has not changed significantly so these fluctuations probably reflect changes in climate/weather during the species' annual cycle, and/or habitat changes in West Africa. Pied Flycatchers are thought to be affected by the earlier onset of spring in their breeding areas, with increased mismatch between the timing of nesting and the peak availability of invertebrate food. However, monitoring data clearly show advancement in egg laying, with eggs currently laid about 12 days earlier than in the 1950s, and there is a trend for earlier spring arrival at Yarner Wood. Clutch size and long-term productivity have changed little, although productivity varies between years, with nest success lower in years where prolonged rainfall occurs during the nestling stage (Burgess 2014). At Yarner Wood the lowest productivity since 1955 was recorded during the current survey as a result of the wet spring of 2007.

During the Atlas period, the earliest arrival dates were all in the first two weeks of April, apart from 2011 when the first recorded bird appeared at Yarner on 27 March. Autumn passage gets under way in August and continues into October, the latest records in the Atlas years occurring on 23 October in both 2011, on Lundy, and 2012, at Prawle.

*Text: Malcolm Burgess / Photo: Carole Bowden*
*Pied Flycatcher sponsored by David H.W.Morgan,*
*Chittlehamholt, 1959–2004*

Balmer *et al.* 2013: 582; Sitters 1988: 230; Tyler 2010: 582

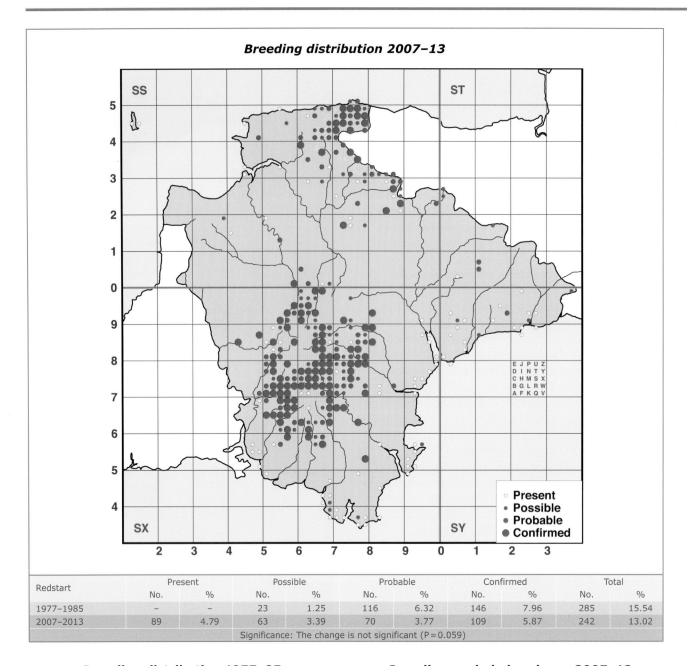

## Breeding distribution 2007–13

| Redstart | Present | | Possible | | Probable | | Confirmed | | Total | |
|---|---|---|---|---|---|---|---|---|---|---|
| | No. | % | No. | % | No. | % | No. | % | No. | % |
| 1977–1985 | – | – | 23 | 1.25 | 116 | 6.32 | 146 | 7.96 | 285 | 15.54 |
| 2007–2013 | 89 | 4.79 | 63 | 3.39 | 70 | 3.77 | 109 | 5.87 | 242 | 13.02 |
| Significance: The change is not significant (P=0.059) | | | | | | | | | | |

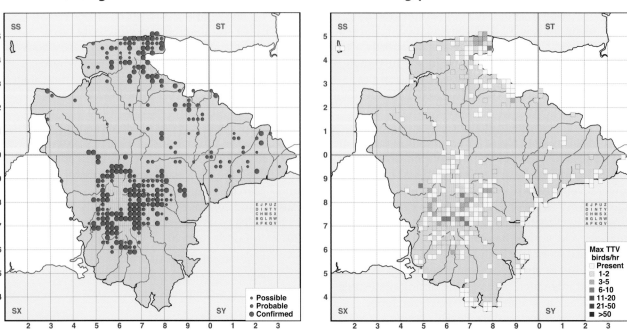

## Breeding distribution 1977–85

## Breeding-period abundance 2007–13

# Redstart
*Phoenicurus phoenicurus*

**Amber listed**

Together with Wood Warbler and Pied Flycatcher, the Redstart forms part of an iconic trio of summer migrants that draws birdwatchers back to the oakwoods of Dartmoor and Exmoor every spring. Yet Redstarts are not confined to mature woodland; they also breed in relatively open habitats, such as scrubby hedgebanks on the fringes of moorland. They may also nest in old buildings and take readily to nestboxes. The common factors are that there should be suitable holes for nesting, prominent song-posts and a diverse but relatively open vegetation structure with an abundance of invertebrate food (*BWP*). These requirements are typically met in more extensively managed landscapes, especially where nature conservation is an important consideration.

Although the UK conservation status of Redstarts is officially 'amber' at the time of writing, they appear to being doing rather better than quite a number of other trans-Saharan migrants – including both of the oakwood specialists mentioned above. BTO data from the Breeding Birds Survey and its predecessor schemes show that the national population index has recovered from a crash in the early 1970s (thought to be due to prolonged drought on the wintering grounds) and returned to, or even exceeded, the levels of the late 1960s. On the other hand, the species' range has contracted because of changes in farming practices and woodland management, although – as some apparently still suitable areas have never been reoccupied – this may not be the full story (*Bird Atlas 2007–11*).

This overall national picture is reflected in a comparison of the two Devon Atlases. The summary table shows that while the total number of tetrads showing evidence of possible, probable or confirmed breeding remained broadly similar between the two surveys, the number of tetrads with higher levels of proof (i.e. probable or confirmed breeding) fell by about a third, from 262 to 179. There are also indications of a range contraction in the county, with noticeable losses in East Devon and parts of North Devon, meaning that the species is increasingly confined to Dartmoor and Exmoor. That this is a continuation of a longer-term loss of Redstarts from much of Mid and East Devon is confirmed at the 10-km square level by a glance at the *Breeding Atlas 1968–72*, which shows a solid swathe of confirmed breeding dots for all except the far south and parts of the far north-west of Devon. Tyler (2010) reported that this was not always the case, however, citing rapid colonization and range expansion on Dartmoor in the 1950s.

*Bird Atlas 2007–11* shows that Dartmoor and Exmoor, along with the New Forest, are the most important remaining strongholds for Redstarts in southern England. With sensitive land management and continued habitat conservation measures, there seems good reason to be cautiously optimistic for the future; though that might ultimately be determined by climatic and land-use factors operating thousands of kilometres to the south.

Autumn migration is protracted, with records annual during October for all years of the Atlas (*DBRs*). Sixteen winter-period (October–February) records included one on Lundy on 26 October 2012 (*DBR*).

*Text: Tim Davis & Tim Jones / Photos: Steve Hatch*
*Redstart sponsored by Peter Ellicott*

Balmer *et al.* 2013: 586; Sitters 1988: 186; Tyler 2010: 569

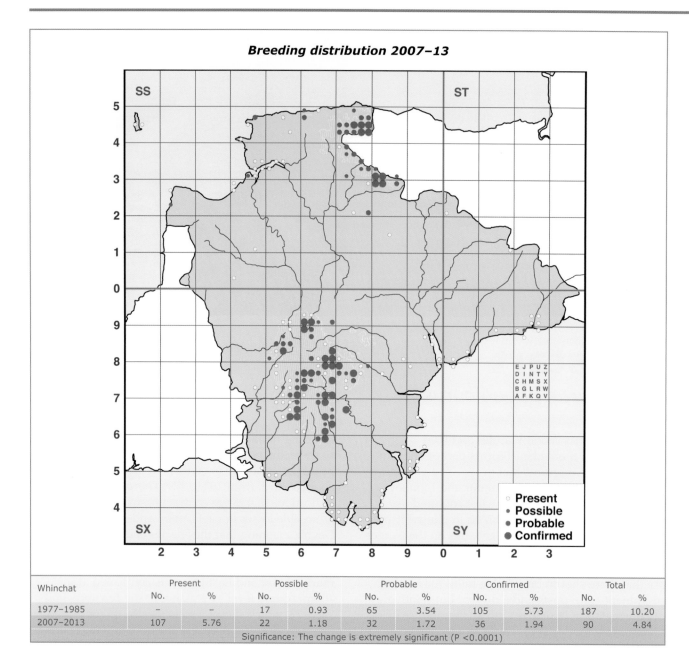

### Breeding distribution 2007–13

| Whinchat | Present | | Possible | | Probable | | Confirmed | | Total | |
|---|---|---|---|---|---|---|---|---|---|---|
| | No. | % | No. | % | No. | % | No. | % | No. | % |
| 1977–1985 | – | – | 17 | 0.93 | 65 | 3.54 | 105 | 5.73 | 187 | 10.20 |
| 2007–2013 | 107 | 5.76 | 22 | 1.18 | 32 | 1.72 | 36 | 1.94 | 90 | 4.84 |
| Significance: The change is extremely significant (P <0.0001) | | | | | | | | | | |

### Breeding distribution 1977–85

### Breeding-period abundance 2007–13

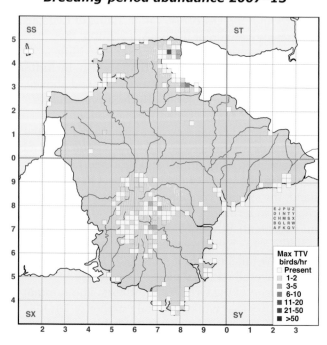

# Whinchat
## *Saxicola rubetra*

**Red listed**

WHINCHATS ARE trans-Saharan migrants, most arriving back on their UK breeding grounds in May and departing in late summer or early autumn, though the last passage migrants in Devon are typically recorded in November. They are very much birds of moorland and unimproved scrubby grassland with scattered prominent perches, such as afforded by hawthorn bushes or mature stands of bracken. These serve both as song-posts and lookouts from which to defend a territory, as well as perches for feeding, whether by sallying or dropping down onto the ground.

The Atlas breeding-period map is striking in that it shows Whinchats as being almost wholly confined to the higher ground of Dartmoor and Exmoor. Indeed, there was no instance of confirmed breeding away from these areas, both of which have extensive areas of suitable nesting habitat.

The summary table compares the main categories of breeding evidence from the *Devon Tetrad Atlas 1977–85* with those from the current Atlas. Although there were differences in coverage between the two Atlas periods, these statistics tell a clear story that makes depressing reading. The total number of tetrads for which breeding evidence was recorded fell by more than half between the two periods, while the number of tetrads in which breeding was confirmed declined by two-thirds.

A comparison of the various maps in the three national breeding Atlases and the two county tetrad

Atlases shows that the breeding range of Whinchat has contracted significantly in Devon. The *Breeding Atlas 1968–1972* shows confirmed breeding in the county for more than a dozen 10-km squares well away from the two National Parks, including Hartland and the East Devon heaths. By the time of the *Devon Tetrad Atlas 1977–85*, confirmed breeding outside the core zones was restricted to five 10-km squares, and this dwindled to zero in the most recent survey.

*Bird Atlas 2007–11* shows that – with the notable exception of Salisbury Plain, where extensive tracts of suitable habitat remain – Whinchats have become virtually extinct as a breeding species in southern England. While changes to farming practices have led to extensive losses of suitable habitat, it is likely that the population decline and range contraction are also driven by other factors, which may include climate change and/or other factors on the species' wintering grounds or along migration routes (BTO BirdTrends 2014). Whinchats winter mainly in the drier (Sudanian and Sahelian) savanna zones of Africa (Wernham *et al.* 2002) and may have been affected by both droughts and vegetation change induced by increasing human populations in these zones.

In spite of the losses described above, Devon remains a regionally important stronghold. It seems likely that large parts of Dartmoor and Devon Exmoor will remain 'Whinchat-friendly' for the foreseeable future, but whether this will be enough to maintain significant numbers of this upland jewel in the face of wider environmental change remains to be seen.

*Text: Tim Jones & Tim Davis / Photo: Steve Hatch*
*Whinchat sponsored by Rob Hubble & Stella Tracey*

Balmer *et al.* 2013: 588; Sitters 1988: 188; Tyler 2010: 571

## Winter-period abundance 2007–13

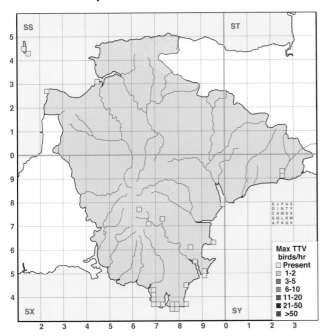

Max TTV birds/hr
- □ Present
- ■ 1-2
- ■ 3-5
- ■ 6-10
- ■ 11-20
- ■ 21-50
- ■ >50

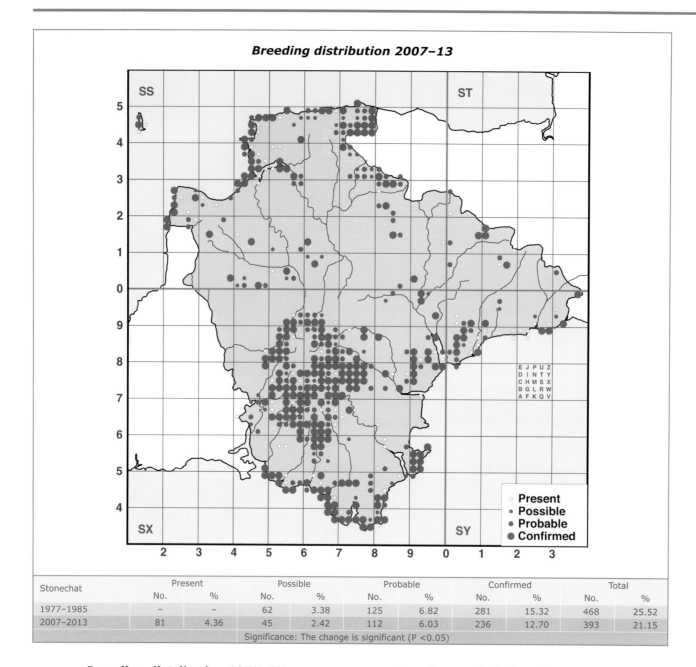

**Breeding distribution 2007–13**

| Stonechat | Present | | Possible | | Probable | | Confirmed | | Total | |
|---|---|---|---|---|---|---|---|---|---|---|
| | No. | % | No. | % | No. | % | No. | % | No. | % |
| 1977–1985 | – | – | 62 | 3.38 | 125 | 6.82 | 281 | 15.32 | 468 | 25.52 |
| 2007–2013 | 81 | 4.36 | 45 | 2.42 | 112 | 6.03 | 236 | 12.70 | 393 | 21.15 |
| Significance: The change is significant (P <0.05) | | | | | | | | | | |

**Breeding distribution 1977–85**

**Breeding-period abundance 2007–13**

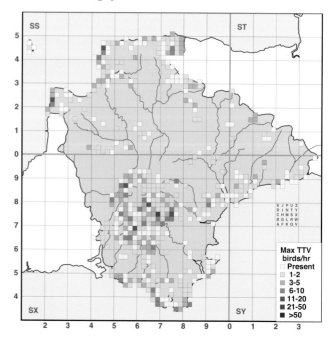

# Stonechat

*Saxicola rubicola*

STONECHATS ARE resident in Devon, primarily found on Dartmoor, Exmoor, the East Devon Commons and along both coasts, and their numbers in the county are enhanced by a significant autumn passage, a smaller spring passage and periodic influxes in winter.

Recent studies have shown the importance of Gorse to nesting Stonechats; this is an important component of up to 88% of territories. Western Gorse is particularly important on Dartmoor (Booker & Slader 2008).

During both the *Devon Tetrad Atlas 1977–85* and the breeding period (March to September) of the current survey, Stonechats were located in approximately 26% of tetrads, suggesting general overall stability. However, there were fewer tetrads with any breeding evidence in 2008–2013 and a noticeable shift in breeding distribution, with evidence of increased density on Dartmoor but some declines on Exmoor and the north coast hinterland. The south coast also showed a slight contraction in both range and number of confirmed breeding registrations. The breeding population can be much reduced after harsh winters – for example, breeding birds were absent from Lundy between 2010 and 2014 following the cold winters of 2009–2011 (*LFS Annual Reports*) – but can also recover remarkably quickly, with the breeding season stretching from mid-March to August and up to three broods in some years (*BWP*).

In early April 2012, a male showing the characteristics of *S. r. rubicola* (the subspecies from continental Europe) was holding territory, with a female in attendance, at Dawlish Warren.

In autumn and early winter some birds leave the high moors and relocate to coastal areas, although ringing data has shown that some of Devon's birds do migrate as far south as Spain (*DBRs*). The present survey also found Stonechats in 26% of tetrads during the winter months, with the highest concentrations on the coasts of North Devon and the South Hams. Substantial numbers were also found on the lower slopes of Dartmoor.

Autumn movements occur over a protracted period, with post-breeding dispersal merging into more definite migration stretching from summer into late autumn or early winter. However, numbers tend to peak from early September into October, as shown by counts of 43 at Prawle on 3 September 2011, 50 at Wembury on 7 September 2012 and 37 at Prawle on 10 October 2009 and 13 October 2010 (*DBRs*).

*Text: Rob Macklin*
*Photos: Gary Thoburn (top) & Tim White*
*Stonechat sponsored by Neil Trout*

Balmer *et al.* 2013: 590; Sitters 1988: 190; Tyler 2010: 574

## Winter-period abundance 2007–13

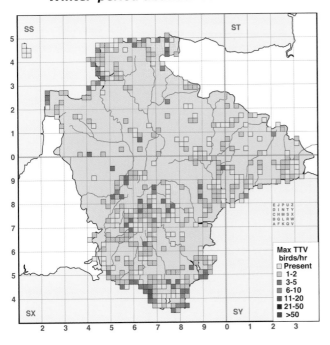

Max TTV birds/hr
- ☐ Present
- 1-2
- 3-5
- 6-10
- 11-20
- 21-50
- >50

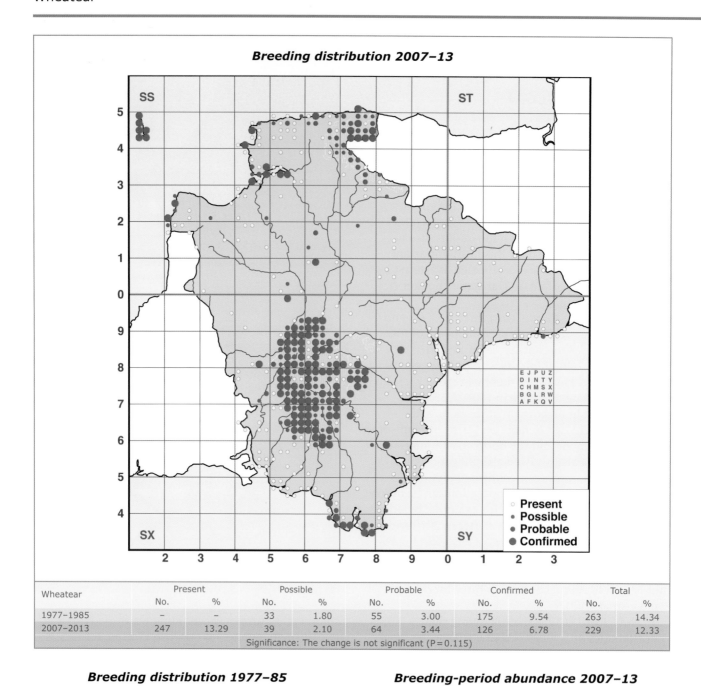

### Breeding distribution 2007–13

| Wheatear | Present | | Possible | | Probable | | Confirmed | | Total | |
|---|---|---|---|---|---|---|---|---|---|---|
| | No. | % | No. | % | No. | % | No. | % | No. | % |
| 1977–1985 | – | – | 33 | 1.80 | 55 | 3.00 | 175 | 9.54 | 263 | 14.34 |
| 2007–2013 | 247 | 13.29 | 39 | 2.10 | 64 | 3.44 | 126 | 6.78 | 229 | 12.33 |
| Significance: The change is not significant (P = 0.115) | | | | | | | | | | |

### Breeding distribution 1977–85

### Breeding-period abundance 2007–13

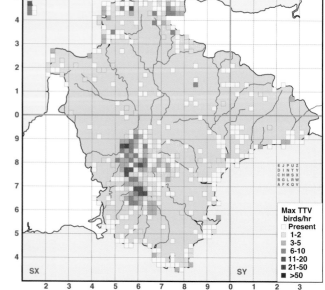

# Wheatear

## *Oenanthe oenanthe*

THE WHEATEAR is a summer visitor to the uplands and coasts of northern and western Britain, wintering in sub-Saharan Africa. In Devon the core breeding areas are Dartmoor, Exmoor and Lundy, with additional small pockets on the north coast of the mainland and along the coast of the South Hams.

The current survey showed Wheatears present in 25% of tetrads during the breeding period (March–September, thus embracing the whole of spring passage and peak autumn passage), with breeding evidence recorded in 12%. This suggests a small, but not significant, decrease since the *Devon Tetrad Atlas 1977–85*, when 14% of tetrads were occupied, and may reflect differing methodologies between the two Atlases. There were fewer instances of confirmed breeding for Dartmoor, Exmoor and the North Devon coast in 2008–2013, although the species remains widespread in these areas. Conversely, there were more occupied and confirmed breeding tetrads on the South Hams coast than in 1977–85.

In recent years the species has undergone a decline on Dartmoor through habitat change thought to be linked to a reduction in grazing (Booker & Slader 2008). Wheatears require areas of broken rock and stone walls for nesting, combined with areas of short sward for feeding, so past overstocking on Dartmoor led to a sharp increase in numbers (Smaldon 2005). With further reductions in livestock numbers on Dartmoor likely, a continued decline in numbers of breeding Wheatears seems inevitable, although this should not detract from the wider ecological benefits of lower grazing pressure.

### Winter-period abundance 2007–13

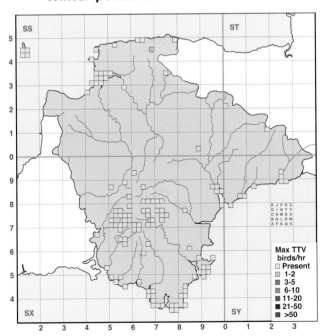

Birds on spring migration are eager to press north to breed and so are less likely to remain for any length of time at coastal staging sites, meaning that fewer large counts occur at this time. The first arrivals are in March – between 1st & 14th during the Atlas years (*DBRs*) – with peak counts typically averaging 20–50, although 200 were on Lundy on both 27 April 2010 and 20 April 2011, with 500 there on 1 May 2012 – the same date that 74 were at Soar (*DBRs*).

Autumn migration occurs from August to November, peaking in September, with three-figure counts regularly noted at coastal hotspots such as Lundy, Prawle and Soar. On 4 September 2011, over 500 birds were recorded between Start Point and Soar, while 400 were on Lundy on 1 October 2011 (*DBRs*).

Wheatears were recorded from a small number of tetrads during the winter period (October–February), though nearly all of these involved late-autumn migrants in October and November. The latest records during the Atlas years fell between 5 & 18 November, with the exception of one at Seaton Marshes on 15 December 2011, the latest ever for Devon (*DBRs*).

In addition to the nominate *O. o. oenanthe*, Greenland Wheatears *O. o. leucorrhoa* were recorded annually throughout the survey period, mainly at coastal migration hotspots, particularly Lundy.

*Text: Rob Macklin / Photos: John Clark (top) & Roy Churchill*
*Wheatear sponsored by Plymouth Branch of Devon Birds*

Balmer *et al.* 2013: 592; Sitters 1988: 192; Tyler 2010: 576

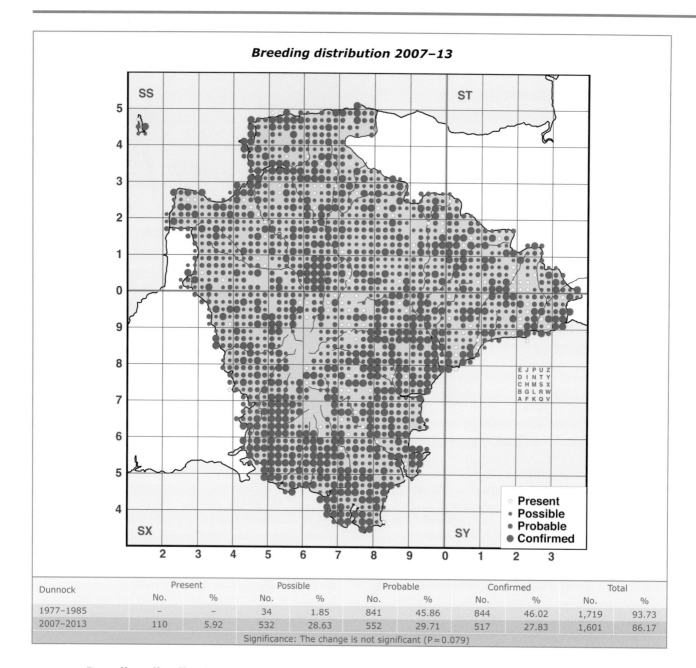

**Breeding distribution 2007–13**

| Dunnock | Present | | Possible | | Probable | | Confirmed | | Total | |
|---|---|---|---|---|---|---|---|---|---|---|
| | No. | % | No. | % | No. | % | No. | % | No. | % |
| 1977–1985 | – | – | 34 | 1.85 | 841 | 45.86 | 844 | 46.02 | 1,719 | 93.73 |
| 2007–2013 | 110 | 5.92 | 532 | 28.63 | 552 | 29.71 | 517 | 27.83 | 1,601 | 86.17 |
| Significance: The change is not significant (P = 0.079) | | | | | | | | | | |

**Breeding distribution 1977–85**

**Breeding-period abundance 2007–13**

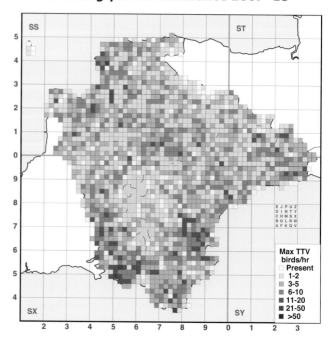

# Dunnock
## *Prunella modularis*

**Amber listed**

Dunnocks are found in hedgerows, gardens, open lowland woodland with a dense shrub layer, and heathland. They avoid the scrub-free high moorland of Dartmoor and Exmoor.

Comparison between the *Devon Tetrad Atlas 1977–85* and the current survey provides evidence of change in the breeding distribution of Dunnock in the county. Breeding across much of the lowland areas of Devon has diminished dramatically. The decline appears to have been less severe in more urban and suburban areas of South Devon. Some expansion into the fringes of the high moorland of Dartmoor is also evident. Probable and confirmed breeding records for Dunnock declined by 37% between the two surveys, though this may be due, at least in part, to differences in methodology and coverage. The combined totals for possible, probable and confirmed breeding records indicate a 6% decrease in the county since the mid-1980s, though this change is not statistically significant.

Nationally, data from the Common Birds Census and Breeding Bird Survey indicate that the UK Dunnock population fell by 27% between the mid-1970s and 2004, and as a consequence the Dunnock became a UK Biodiversity Action Plan Priority Species in 2007 (JNCC 2010). Baillie *et al.* (2014) report that clutch and brood sizes and number of fledglings per breeding attempt have fallen since the late 1990s. Fuller *et al.* (2005) suggest that lack of woodland management with consequent canopy

closure combined with increased browsing pressure from deer is likely to have reduced the suitability of this habitat for Dunnock. Agricultural intensification and consequent effects on food resources may also have been a factor that has influenced the albeit small and not significant decline in the Dunnock population of Devon. However, the underlying cause of the national and European decline remains uncertain (BTO BirdTrends 2014).

Agri-environmental schemes that support, for example, the presence of scrub and two- to three-year hedgerow cutting cycles in the farmed landscape will be important to reversing the decline in the Dunnock population in lowland Devon. Scrub encroachment on Dartmoor is also likely to benefit the species. The future of Dunnock in Devon is also likely to be strongly influenced by the extent to which the urban and suburban environment continues to provide food resources and suitable nesting habitat for this species.

*Text: Jerry Tallowin / Photo: Mike Langman*
*Dunnock sponsored by Stella Beavan*

Balmer *et al.* 2013: 594; Sitters 1988: 180; Tyler 2010: 585

### Winter-period abundance 2007–13

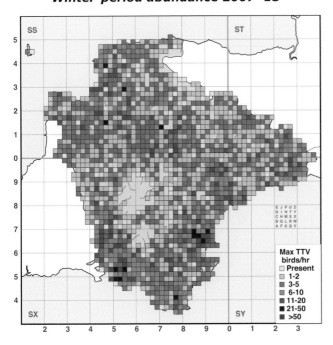

Max TTV birds/hr
☐ Present
☐ 1-2
☐ 3-5
☐ 6-10
☐ 11-20
☐ 21-50
■ >50

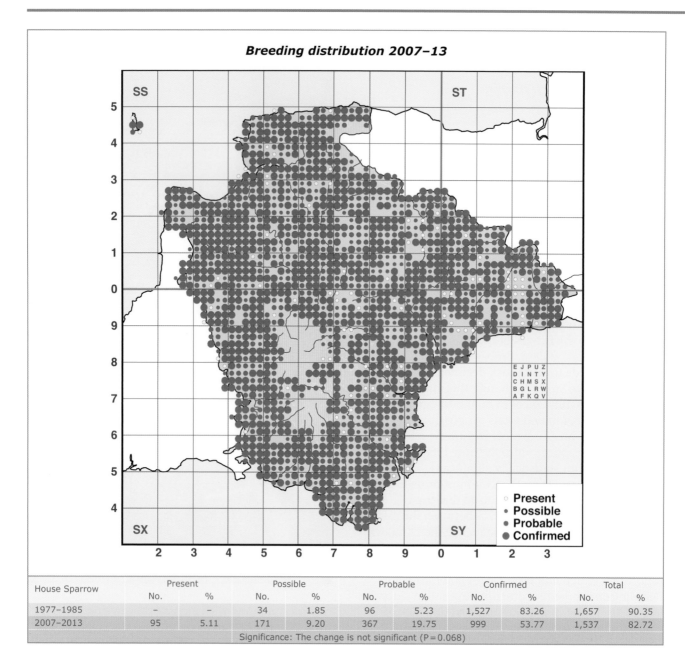

## Breeding distribution 2007–13

| House Sparrow | Present | | Possible | | Probable | | Confirmed | | Total | |
|---|---|---|---|---|---|---|---|---|---|---|
| | No. | % | No. | % | No. | % | No. | % | No. | % |
| 1977–1985 | – | – | 34 | 1.85 | 96 | 5.23 | 1,527 | 83.26 | 1,657 | 90.35 |
| 2007–2013 | 95 | 5.11 | 171 | 9.20 | 367 | 19.75 | 999 | 53.77 | 1,537 | 82.72 |
| Significance: The change is not significant (P=0.068) | | | | | | | | | | |

## Breeding distribution 1977–85

## Breeding-period abundance 2007–13

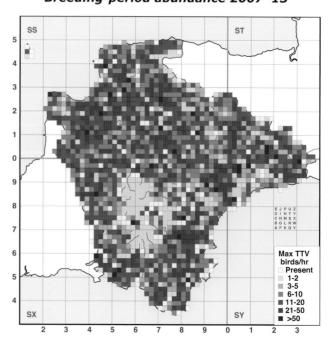

# House Sparrow

## *Passer domesticus*

**Red listed**

House Sparrows are widespread in both urban and rural environments. In Devon their range extends from coastal towns through the rural hinterland to the farms and towns on upland Dartmoor and Exmoor. Their characteristic chirping calls are a familiar sound around human dwellings and their presence can easily be detected, especially where colonies are located.

When breeding, House Sparrows require good feeding habitat nearby to provide a mixture of the invertebrates and seeds required by nestlings. After nesting, flocks venture out into the countryside to feed on cereal crops before and during harvesting. A study of House Sparrows in Kingsteignton in 2003 (Avon 2004) identified a link between nest sites and nearby hedgerows and particularly the presence of ivy, bramble and hawthorn. Garden feeding stations are important in supplementing natural food supplies and a survey of Devon Birds members reported that 88% of House Sparrow nest sites had bird feeders within 25 metres (Avon 2007).

D'Urban & Mathew (1892) described House Sparrows as extremely abundant in mainland Devon and as occasional visitors to Lundy. They bred intermittently on the island in the first half of the 20th century, but it was only in 1971 that the present-day population was established (Davis & Jones 2007), with breeding occurring annually since then. From 1991 onwards the population has been the subject of detailed scientific research led by the University of Sheffield (Davis & Jones 2007).

The current Atlas shows that the actual distribution of Devon's House Sparrow population has undergone little change. They were present in most tetrads, being absent only from the higher areas of Dartmoor and Exmoor. The *Devon Tetrad Atlas 1977–85* recorded breeding evidence in 90% of tetrads, while the corresponding figure for the present survey (not withstanding differing methodologies) was 87.5%.

Although the distribution of House Sparrows remains similar, there are signs of a decline in abundance. Breeding was confirmed in only 54% of tetrads compared with 83% in 1977–1985 (though if the number of possible and probable breeding records are included, the decline is not statistically significant). Nationally there has been a marked decline since the 1970s, though with regional and habitat variations (BTO BirdTrends 2014), and with some indications that House Sparrows are disappearing faster from towns and cities than from rural areas.

The House Sparrow population is likely to be affected by the switch to autumn sowing of cereals – which leads to reduced availability of winter stubbles for feeding and a reduction in invertebrates due to pesticide use – and a lack of suitable nest sites in modern houses, or older houses or barns which have been renovated.

The humble House Sparrow is often overlooked by birdwatchers, but the need for study and hard data is crucial if we are to monitor and understand their populations in the future and as land-use changes continue.

*Text: Jon Avon / Photo: Andrew Cunningham*
*House Sparrow sponsored by Paul Bowen*

Balmer *et al.* 2013: 596; Sitters 1988: 262; Tyler 2010: 587

### Winter-period abundance 2007–13

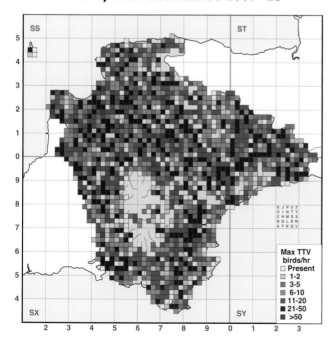

Max TTV birds/hr
☐ Present
■ 1-2
■ 3-5
■ 6-10
■ 11-20
■ 21-50
■ >50

# Tree Sparrow
## *Passer montanus*

**Red listed**

TREE SPARROWS appear always to have been scarce in Devon, at least in recorded ornithological history, and the periodic appearance and disappearance of small, scattered breeding colonies

### Breeding distribution 1977–85

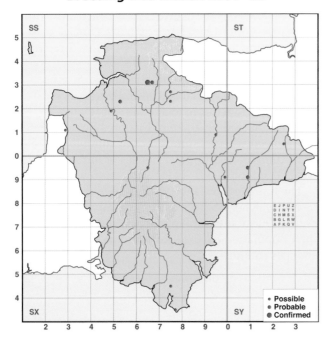

in the mid 20th century is summarized by Tyler (2010). Fieldwork for the *Devon Tetrad Atlas 1977–85* located Tree Sparrows in 16 tetrads, with confirmed breeding in only one, at West Buckland in North Devon, in 1978. There have been no known nesting attempts in the county since then (Tyler 2010, *DBRs*).

A marked contraction of the British wintering and, especially, breeding ranges occurred between the *Breeding Atlas 1968–72* and *Bird Atlas 2007–11*, particularly in southern England, with the core areas now far from the South West peninsula.

Given this context, it is unsurprising that in the current Atlas period Tree Sparrows were recorded in just five tetrads: one at a garden feeder in Lydford on 26 December 2010, one at a garden feeder near Cullompton on 10 August 2011, one present for about three weeks in a garden near Kingsbridge in November 2012, one at Coleton Fishacre on 12 May 2013 and one at Prawle on 17 May 2013 (*DBRs*). Given the isolated nature of these records and the fact that all but one were one-day occurrences, there is no suggestion that these were anything more than wandering individuals.

*Text: Tim Jones & Tim Davis / Photo: Paul Sterry/NPL*
*Tree Sparrow sponsored by Miss Angela McOran-Campbell*

Balmer *et al.* 2013: 598; Sitters 1988: 264; Tyler 2010: 589

# Waxwing
*Bombycilla garrulus*

DURING THE six winters covered by the Atlas there were two Waxwing 'irruptions' – in 2010/11 and again in 2012/13 – that saw much larger numbers than usual arrive in Britain from Fennoscandian and Russian breeding grounds, with numerous Devon sightings in both cases. Conversely, there was just one county record in each of the winters 2007/08 and 2008/09 (when a significant influx to Britain did not extend as far as Devon), and none at all for either 2009/10 or 2011/12. The map therefore reflects the pattern of occurrence during the two irruptions. In all, Waxwings were recorded from 77 tetrads in thirty-three 10-km squares, mainly in the south of the county.

Food sources noted during both irruptions included the berries of hawthorn, cotoneaster and, especially, rowan, as well as rose-hips, crab apples and flying insects (*DBRs* 2010–13). Given the species' propensity to feed on the berries of ornamental trees and shrubs, it is not surprising that the most prominent cluster of winter TTV records is in the Exeter area. Other smaller clusters include those centred on Barnstaple, Exmouth, Newton Abbot, Plymouth and Torbay, though there is also a wide scatter across more rural areas.

In both irruption winters, Waxwings first reached Devon in early November. In 2010/11 the maximum count at a single site was 36 in Plymouth on 22 December. Other sites holding at least ten birds included Bovey Tracey, Exmouth, Plympton and Stover Country Park; the last were three in Plymouth on 11 March. One seen in Dawlish at the beginning of January 2011 had been ringed in central Aberdeen on 19 October 2010, indicating onward southerly movement of birds arriving in Britain from the north-east (*DBR* 2011).

The 2012/13 irruption was even more spectacular, with several flocks of between 20 and 30 birds reported before the end of November, though numbers did not peak until much later in the winter, reaching a maximum of 51 at Chudleigh Knighton on 15 February. Other sites holding at least 40 birds included Bovey Tracey, Exeter, Exminster, Topsham and the A38 near Stover. The latest records were of 20 in Exeter on 10 April and one at Colyford on 26 April (*DBR* 2013).

*Text: Tim Jones & Tim Davis / Photo: Lee Collins*
*Waxwing sponsored by Martin Overy*

Balmer *et al.* 2013: 551; Sitters 1988: not treated; Tyler 2010: 533

## Winter-period abundance 2007–13

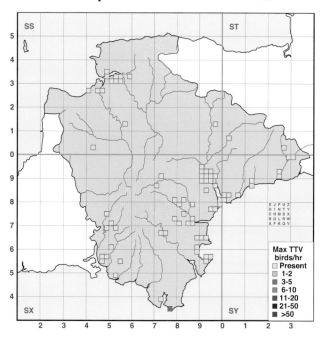

Max TTV birds/hr
☐ Present
▨ 1-2
▨ 3-5
■ 6-10
■ 11-20
■ 21-50
■ >50

# Yellow Wagtail

*Motacilla flava*

**Red listed**

YELLOW WAGTAILS are traditionally birds of wet grasslands, although in eastern England they also breed in arable crops (*Bird Atlas 2007–11*). They are summer visitors, migrating to and from wintering grounds in sub-Saharan Africa. Coastal pasture is the main habitat in Devon, particularly if grazing animals are present. The species' French name – Bergeronette printanière ('little shepherdess of spring') – nicely encapsulates this association with livestock. The British subspecies (*M. f. flavissima*) is by far the commonest in Devon; other races occur as scarce passage migrants or vagrants (see below).

Devon is very much on the western fringe of the UK breeding range (*Bird Atlas 2007–11*) and during the Atlas period only a single pair was confirmed to have bred, adjoining the Taw/Torridge Estuary, where they were successful in 2011 and 2012 (*DBRs*). Two possible breeding records from elsewhere may have referred to lingering passage migrants. The *Devon Tetrad Atlas 1977–85* confirmed breeding in two tetrads, both in the upper Exe Estuary, where breeding continued until 2003 but not since. Probable breeding was recorded at that time in the South Huish area, with possible breeding occurring in five other widely scattered tetrads. Tyler (2010) mentions a number of breeding records from the first half of the 20th century, mainly along the lower reaches of East Devon rivers, and it is always possible that this kind of sporadic breeding may occur in the future.

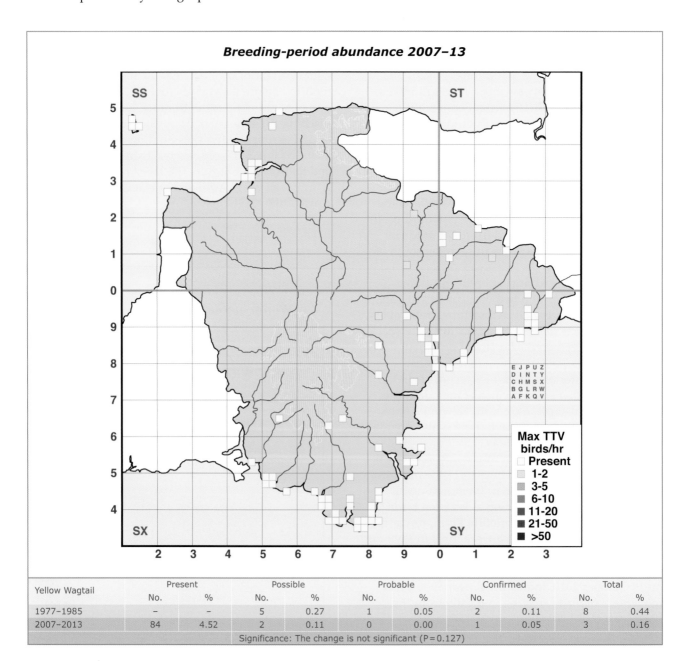

**Breeding-period abundance 2007–13**

Max TTV birds/hr
- □ Present
- 1-2
- 3-5
- 6-10
- ■ 11-20
- ■ 21-50
- ■ >50

| Yellow Wagtail | Present | | Possible | | Probable | | Confirmed | | Total | |
|---|---|---|---|---|---|---|---|---|---|---|
| | No. | % | No. | % | No. | % | No. | % | No. | % |
| 1977–1985 | – | – | 5 | 0.27 | 1 | 0.05 | 2 | 0.11 | 8 | 0.44 |
| 2007–2013 | 84 | 4.52 | 2 | 0.11 | 0 | 0.00 | 1 | 0.05 | 3 | 0.16 |
| Significance: The change is not significant (P = 0.127) | | | | | | | | | | |

Passage birds are frequent in both spring and autumn, mainly around south coast estuaries and headlands and the Taw/Torridge Estuary, though autumn movements are considerably more marked. Yellow Wagtails were recorded in 84 tetrads during the Atlas breeding period (March–September), which includes all of spring migration and peak autumn passage. The highest site count during the Atlas years was 75 at South Huish on 12 September 2011. That autumn saw a particularly strong passage through the county, with over 1,100 logged at 36 sites (*DBR*). The winter-period map (October–February) shows a scattering of late-autumn migrants, mainly at south coast sites and all but one in October, the latest of these at Berry Head on 30 October 2010 (*DBR*). The exception is a single bird caught and ringed in December 2010 at Colyford Water Treatment Works, and shown by DNA analysis to belong to one of the eastern subspecies (*DBR* 2013).

About ten Blue-headed Wagtails (*M. f. flava*), which breed in continental Europe, were recorded during the Atlas period, mainly in spring and mostly on the south coast. One or two birds with plumage intermediate between *M. f. flava* and *M. f. flavissima* (so-called 'Channel Wagtails') were seen on the Taw/Torridge Estuary in April 2012 (*DBR*).

Nationally, *Bird Atlas 2007–11* shows a considerable range contraction since earlier breeding atlases, as well as a decline in numbers. This is attributed to agricultural intensification (BTO BirdTrends 2014), particularly the conversion of grassland to arable, the change from hay-making to silage making, and the change to autumn-sown crops.

*Text: J M Lock / Photo: David Land*
*Yellow Wagtail sponsored by Olivia Rose Seaton*

Balmer *et al.* 2013: 600; Sitters 1988: 170; Tyler 2010: 590

### Breeding distribution 1977–85

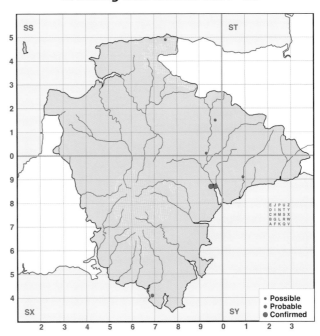

389

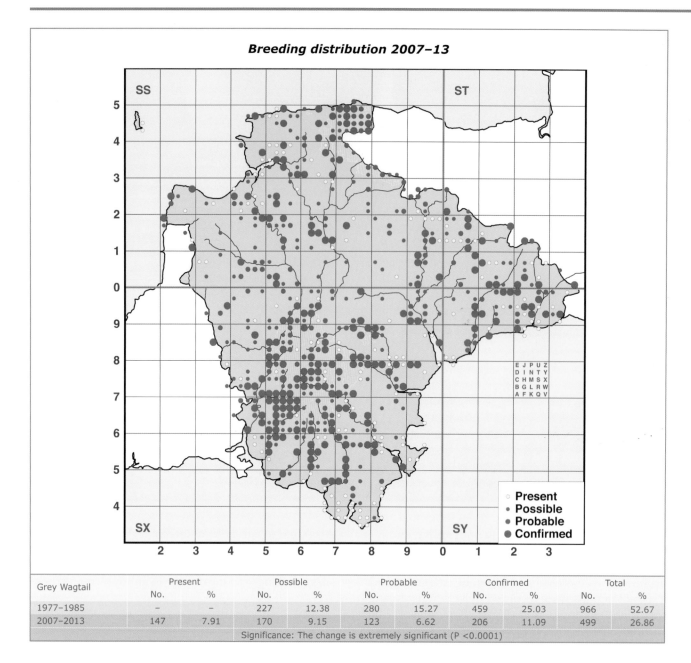

## Breeding distribution 2007–13

| Grey Wagtail | Present | | Possible | | Probable | | Confirmed | | Total | |
|---|---|---|---|---|---|---|---|---|---|---|
| | No. | % | No. | % | No. | % | No. | % | No. | % |
| 1977–1985 | – | – | 227 | 12.38 | 280 | 15.27 | 459 | 25.03 | 966 | 52.67 |
| 2007–2013 | 147 | 7.91 | 170 | 9.15 | 123 | 6.62 | 206 | 11.09 | 499 | 26.86 |
| | Significance: The change is extremely significant (P <0.0001) | | | | | | | | | |

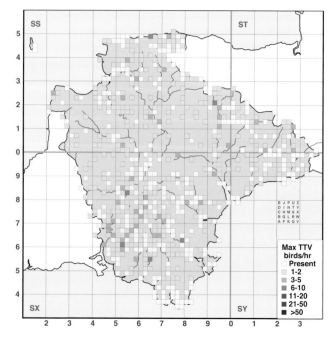

## Breeding distribution 1977–85

## Breeding-period abundance 2007–13

# Grey Wagtail
*Motacilla cinerea*

GREY WAGTAILS are waterside birds, associated particularly with fast-flowing upland streams, although they also occur along lowland rivers and even along quite small streams and ditches. They breed on steep banks and under rocks and bridges and often raise two or even three broods in a season. They are generally resident but in winter there is some dispersal from rivers to flooded grassland and pools, as well as to coasts, especially in hard weather. They are often associated with Dippers but are less strongly tied to fast-flowing rivers than that species, and are less sedentary.

During the Atlas period, there was breeding evidence (possible, probable or confirmed) in 499 tetrads (27%). Comparison with the *Devon Tetrad Atlas 1977–85* shows a 48% decrease in the number of tetrads from which records of at least possible breeding were made. This decline is concentrated away from the core upland areas of Dartmoor and Exmoor, and seems most marked along lowland rivers such as the Axe, Otter, Culm, Tamar, Taw and Torridge. Interestingly, the change does not show up at the 10-km square level, so that *Bird Atlas 2007–11* shows no decline in Devon. Rob Hubble, in his account in the *Devon Tetrad Atlas*, emphasizes the importance to this species of free-flowing unpolluted water, producing abundant insect life. It is possible that the decrease may be associated with a decline in water quality in rivers that flow through intensively farmed land. Here, increased siltation associated with maize cultivation and leakage of Ivermectin-type insecticides into the watercourses (Maclean 2010) may together be leading to a decline in the numbers of larger water insects such as caddisflies and mayflies, which form an important part of the diet of Grey Wagtails. It is worth noting that there has been no decline along the Avon, which flows almost entirely within a wooded valley without intensive cultivation. The decline may also be associated, at least in part, with the hard winters of 2009 and 2010 since Grey Wagtails are known to be susceptible to severe weather (*Bird Atlas 2007–11*).

The winter-period map (including TTV data for November to February) shows a general movement to lower altitudes and the coast, where, particularly in hard winters, food may be easier to find.

The *Devon Tetrad Atlas 1977–85* suggested, on the basis of counts along rivers, that one pair per kilometre was usual and that one or two pairs per occupied tetrad was a reasonable estimate. This would place the current population at between 500 and 1,000 pairs, as against the 1,000–2,000 estimated by the previous Atlas.

*Text: J M Lock / Photo: Mike Langman*
*Grey Wagtail sponsored by Kevin & Lin Johns*

### Winter-period abundance 2007–13

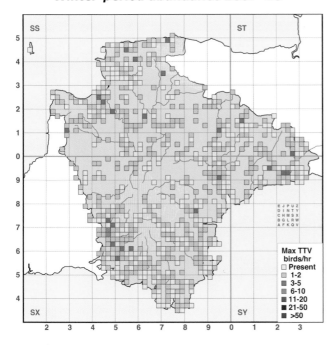

Max TTV birds/hr
- ☐ Present
- 1-2
- 3-5
- 6-10
- 11-20
- 21-50
- >50

Balmer *et al.* 2013: 602; Sitters 1988: 172; Tyler 2010: 596

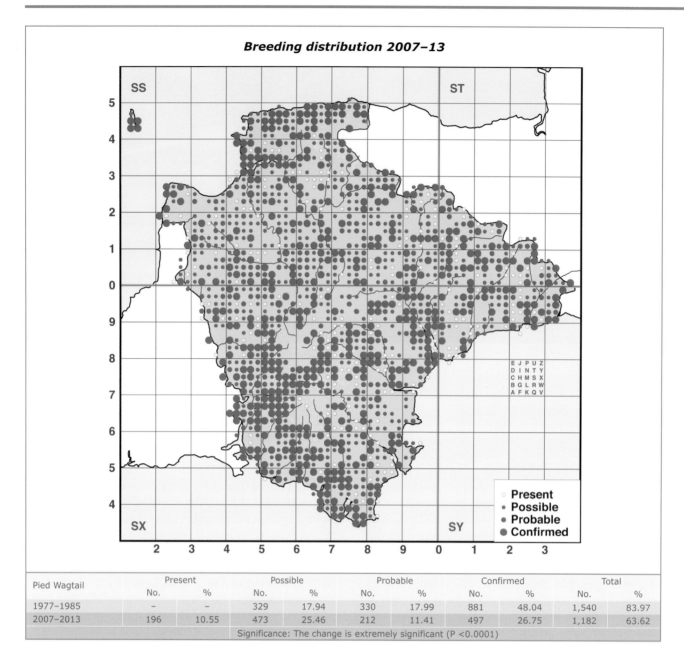

**Breeding distribution 2007–13**

| Pied Wagtail | Present | | Possible | | Probable | | Confirmed | | Total | |
|---|---|---|---|---|---|---|---|---|---|---|
| | No. | % | No. | % | No. | % | No. | % | No. | % |
| 1977–1985 | – | – | 329 | 17.94 | 330 | 17.99 | 881 | 48.04 | 1,540 | 83.97 |
| 2007–2013 | 196 | 10.55 | 473 | 25.46 | 212 | 11.41 | 497 | 26.75 | 1,182 | 63.62 |
| Significance: The change is extremely significant (P <0.0001) | | | | | | | | | | |

**Breeding distribution 1977–85**

**Breeding-period abundance 2007–13**

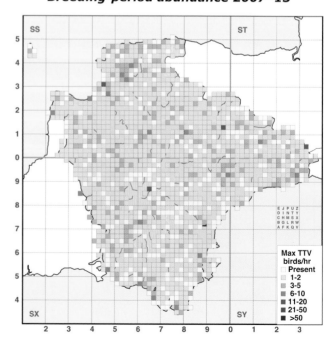

# Pied Wagtail

## Motacilla alba

Pied Wagtails, *M. a. yarrellii*, are ground-feeding and primarily insectivorous. They occur in habitats ranging from city centres to farmland, and from beaches to moorland streams, but are generally absent from woodland, heaths, wide open tracts of farmland and open moorland. They seem to be mostly associated with human habitation, or perhaps are more noticeable there. Ideal breeding habitats are nooks and crannies in buildings and walls, often near water. Scattered as individuals and small groups when feeding and breeding, they typically use communal roosts in autumn and winter, when numbers increase with the arrival of migrants from Scotland, northern England and perhaps continental Europe (Wernham *et al.* 2002). In winter these roosts are often in trees in city centres and supermarket and service station car parks, whereas on passage they are more likely to be in coastal reedbeds.

Breeding evidence was recorded in all 10-km squares, but in only 64% of tetrads, with absences from the parts of Dartmoor over 450 metres and smaller areas mostly in the north and east of the county where more unsuitable habitat such as woods and heaths prevails. Very few squares recorded more than five birds during TTVs, but those with between three and five were well distributed, even in areas where they were only sparsely recorded. Confirmed breeding was also well scattered but concentrated around major towns such as Plymouth, Exeter, Barnstaple and the Dartmoor corridor; this must be partly linked to the density of observers. Pied Wagtails were even more widespread in winter, with

79% of tetrads occupied. Although the broad pattern of gaps was similar to that found in the breeding season, the pattern probably reflects a greater usage of habitats such as farmland and coast in winter. The highest counts, including several of more than 20, were probably mostly related to winter roosts in Plymouth, Exeter and Barnstaple.

The *Devon Tetrad Atlas 1977–85* recorded breeding in 84% of tetrads, so there has been a significant decline of 23%, although the lower proportion of confirmed breeders in the current period may be due to differences in methodology and coverage. Nationally, Pied Wagtails are almost ubiquitous and show little change since the *Breeding Atlas 1968–72*, but numbers fluctuate, and the Breeding Bird Survey has shown an 11% decline from 1995 to 2010 (Risely *et al.* 2012). This has been in spite of a range expansion, mostly northwards in winter.

The continental and Icelandic-breeding race *M. a. alba*, 'White Wagtail', was recorded as present in 63 tetrads during the Atlas breeding period (March–September) and 20 during the winter period (October–February). Although there have been occasional breeding records and some of wintering in Devon, almost all of these records can be assumed to refer to passage migrants. The winter-period records are nearly all from the south coast, whereas those recorded in spring and early autumn include birds around the Taw/Torridge Estuary and on Lundy. Extensive studies at Slapton have shown that many of the birds passing through there are of Icelandic origin (Elphick 2009).

*Text: Peter Reay / Photos: Neil Bygrave (Pied Wagtail, top) & Paul Sterry/NPL (White Wagtail)*
*Pied Wagtail sponsored by Slapton Bird Observatory Ringing Group, Keith Grant & Dennis Elphick*

Balmer *et al.* 2013: 604; Sitters 1988: 174; Tyler 2010: 598

### Winter-period abundance 2007–13

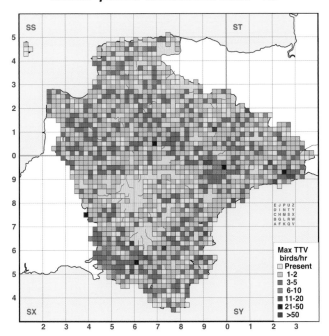

Max TTV birds/hr
- ☐ Present
- 1-2
- 3-5
- 6-10
- 11-20
- 21-50
- >50

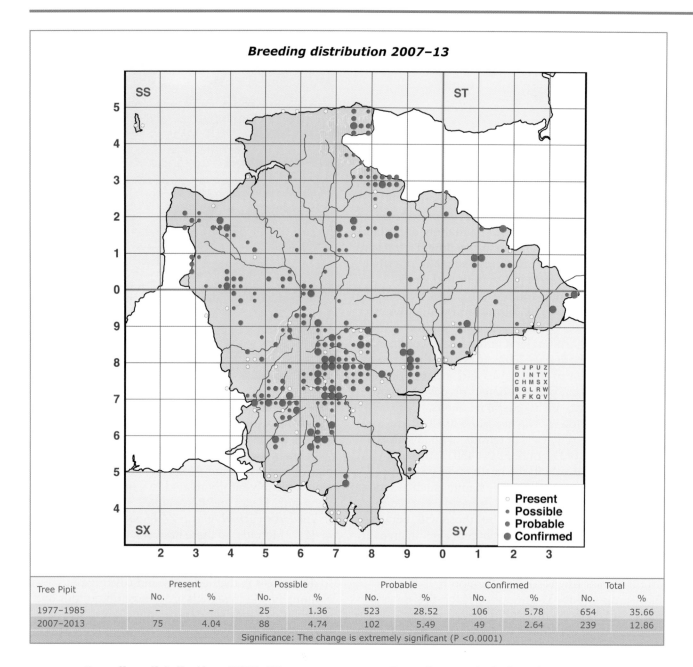

**Breeding distribution 2007–13**

| Tree Pipit | Present | | Possible | | Probable | | Confirmed | | Total | |
|---|---|---|---|---|---|---|---|---|---|---|
| | No. | % | No. | % | No. | % | No. | % | No. | % |
| 1977–1985 | – | – | 25 | 1.36 | 523 | 28.52 | 106 | 5.78 | 654 | 35.66 |
| 2007–2013 | 75 | 4.04 | 88 | 4.74 | 102 | 5.49 | 49 | 2.64 | 239 | 12.86 |
| Significance: The change is extremely significant (P <0.0001) | | | | | | | | | | |

**Breeding distribution 1977–85**

**Breeding-period abundance 2007–13**

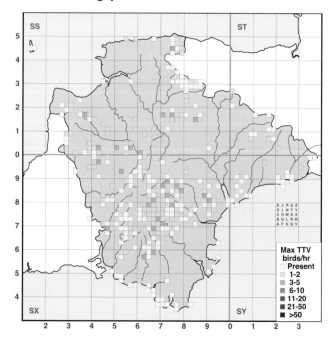

# Tree Pipit
## Anthus trivialis
Red listed

THE TREE Pipit is a bird mainly associated with conifer plantations, heathland and open deciduous woodland fringing upland areas. Within conifer plantations the highest breeding densities are found between two and five years after planting (Burton 2007) but the species also occurs at lower densities in newly harvested areas and in stands that are up to 11 years old.

The breeding-period maps (March–September) show that Tree Pipits are found right across Devon but most occupied areas are associated with moorland edges where there is abundant open woodland. They are absent from coastal and pastoral areas. There has been a significant decline since the *Devon Tetrad Atlas 1977–85*, with Tree Pipits found in 52% fewer tetrads during the current survey, while the number of tetrads for which breeding evidence was recorded fell by nearly two-thirds. These losses have occurred throughout Devon but are especially evident across North and West Devon. Dartmoor and Exmoor have retained Tree Pipits, while in East Devon distribution is now mainly limited to Haldon Forest and the Pebblebed Heaths. There have been small gains within Dartmoor, which probably reflects management of conifer plantations, with Tree Pipits benefiting in the short term from harvesting of mature conifer crops, and from felling

of larch plantations to control the spread of infection by the fungal pathogen *Phytophthora*. Suitable, if temporary, habitat is also created by the restoration of broadleaf woodland on felled conifer plantations.

The changes in Devon reflect the national picture, which shows that Tree Pipits have declined steeply since the mid-1980s (BTO BirdTrends 2014). Distribution and population trends are thought to reflect the changing availability of young woodland, especially plantation woodland (Burgess *et al.* 2015). The availability of this habitat is closely tied to past planting policy and Tree Pipits may have benefited from the large-scale planting that occurred in upland areas in the 1970s and 1980s, but as these plantations have matured they have become less suitable for the species. Tree Pipits may also be affected by factors operating outside the breeding season, along migration routes or at wintering ranges in Africa.

Late migrants accounted for records in six tetrads, all coastal except for a single bird on north-east Dartmoor, during the October–February Atlas period, the last dates all in the range 11–22 October (*DBRs*).

*Text: Malcolm Burgess / Photos: Dave Smallshire*
*Tree Pipit sponsored by Dave Cox*

Balmer *et al.* 2013: 606; Sitters 1988: 164; Tyler 2010: 605

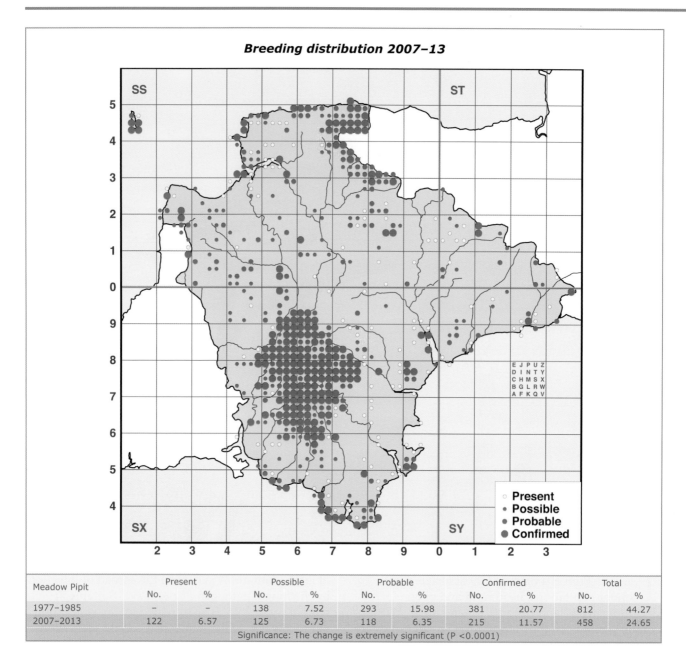

## Breeding distribution 2007–13

| Meadow Pipit | Present | | Possible | | Probable | | Confirmed | | Total | |
|---|---|---|---|---|---|---|---|---|---|---|
| | No. | % | No. | % | No. | % | No. | % | No. | % |
| 1977–1985 | – | – | 138 | 7.52 | 293 | 15.98 | 381 | 20.77 | 812 | 44.27 |
| 2007–2013 | 122 | 6.57 | 125 | 6.73 | 118 | 6.35 | 215 | 11.57 | 458 | 24.65 |
| | Significance: The change is extremely significant (P <0.0001) | | | | | | | | | |

## Breeding distribution 1977–85

## Breeding-period abundance 2007–13

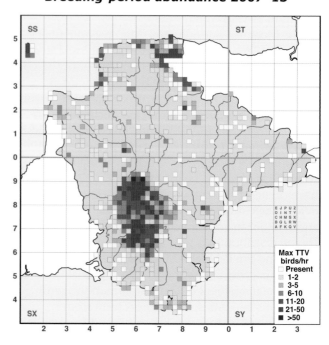

# Meadow Pipit
## *Anthus pratensis*

Amber listed

THE MEADOW Pipit breeds in rough grassland habitats, with marked concentrations on Dartmoor and Exmoor where it is the commonest breeding bird in many areas. Its beautiful parachute display flight is evocative of spring and summer in these wild places. An estimated 20,000–30,000 pairs are thought to nest on Dartmoor, making the National Park internationally important for this species (Smaldon 2005). Smaller numbers nest along the north and south coasts, favouring unimproved, traditionally managed grasslands such as those on Lundy. A wider range of habitats are used outside the breeding season, including arable farmland, while during prolonged cold spells some birds may occur in suburban gardens and around sewage works. Breeding territories are reoccupied from early March and nesting takes place between April and July, the species being typically double-brooded. Nests are difficult to find so it is likely that many probable and possible breeding records refer to actual breeding. Meadow Pipit is now the main host species for Cuckoos in Devon.

There has been a significant contraction in the Devon breeding range since the *Devon Tetrad Atlas 1977–85*, with 44% of tetrads yielding breeding evidence in the earlier survey, compared to only 25% in the current Atlas, with losses particularly evident in more lowland areas. The decline at county level reflects the 46% decline nationally shown in *Bird Atlas 2007–11* and is likely to be the result of

intensive farming, with a move towards silage production, maize and ryegrass monocultures at the expense of more extensively managed grassland.

Birds move off the high moors during the autumn and passage migrants arrive from further north. During the Atlas years the highest autumn passage counts were 1,000 at Beer Head on 17 September 2010, Lundy on 2 October 2011 and Prawle on 7 October 2012 (*DBRs*). There are few ringing recoveries of this species so it is difficult to assess whether flocks found scattered across the county in winter relate to migrants or local breeding birds, but they seem likely to be a mixture of the two. Substantial winter roosts occur on heathlands, such as on the southern edge of Dartmoor, to which birds return each evening from feeding areas in surrounding farmland where they favour field margins and weed-rich brassica crops, especially on organically farmed land. These roosts are often still present in late March when local birds are setting up territories, indicating that they contain at least a proportion of birds that breed further north. However, the highest winter count during the Atlas period was of 314 moving west over Dawlish Warren on 6 January 2010 during a prolonged spell of cold weather (*DBR*).

Looking ahead, the declining trend of recent decades looks likely to stabilize, with the breeding range increasingly confined to the moors and with a scattering of coastal grassland breeding sites where these are under conservation management.

*Text: John Walters / Photo: Neil Bygrave*
*Meadow Pipit sponsored by Hilary Thomas*

Balmer *et al.* 2013: 608; Sitters 1988: 166; Tyler 2010: 606

### Winter-period abundance 2007–13

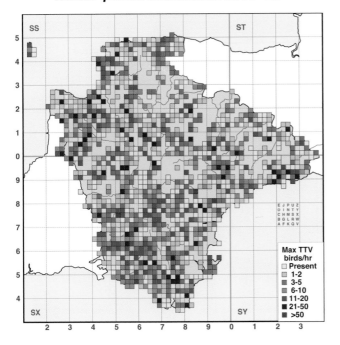

Max TTV birds/hr
- ☐ Present
- 1-2
- 3-5
- 6-10
- 11-20
- 21-50
- >50

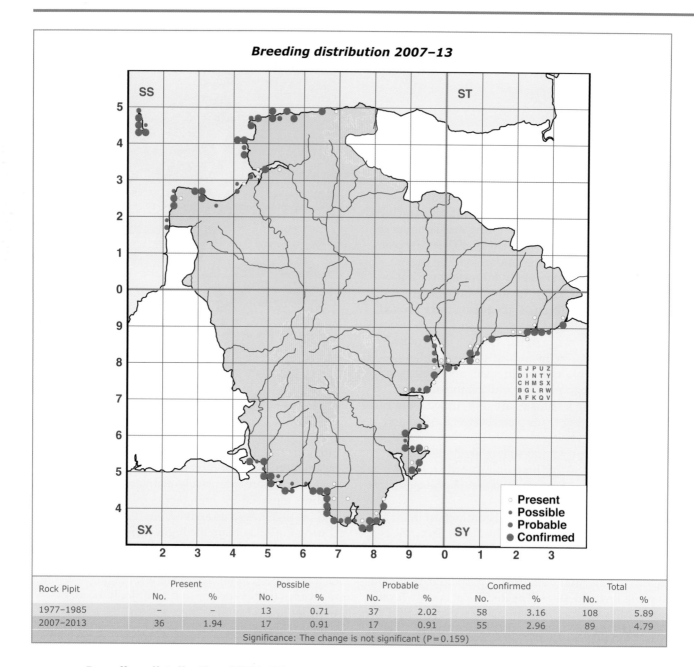

**Breeding distribution 2007–13**

| Rock Pipit | Present | | Possible | | Probable | | Confirmed | | Total | |
|---|---|---|---|---|---|---|---|---|---|---|
| | No. | % | No. | % | No. | % | No. | % | No. | % |
| 1977–1985 | – | – | 13 | 0.71 | 37 | 2.02 | 58 | 3.16 | 108 | 5.89 |
| 2007–2013 | 36 | 1.94 | 17 | 0.91 | 17 | 0.91 | 55 | 2.96 | 89 | 4.79 |
| Significance: The change is not significant (P=0.159) | | | | | | | | | | |

**Breeding distribution 1977–85**

**Breeding-period abundance 2007–13**

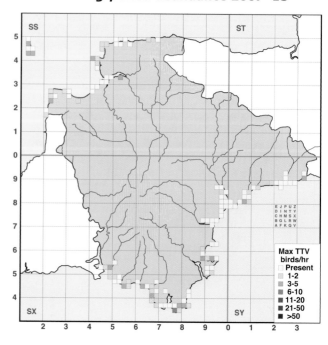

# Rock Pipit

## *Anthus petrosus*

IN THE introductory paragraph to the Rock Pipit account for the *Devon Tetrad Atlas 1977–85*, Charles Sawle described the species as "perhaps our most neglected bird" – an observation that still holds true more than a quarter of a century later. Its habitat frequently defies easy observation, particularly along the towering cliffs of much of the north coast, and with its cryptically drab plumage and discreet habits (except when song-flighting), this is a bird that is often 'out of sight, out of mind'. This is emphasized by the fact that no population trend data are available from the BTO as the species is not sufficiently covered by the Breeding Bird Survey.

The Atlas maps show, as would be expected, a broadly similar distribution in both breeding and winter periods, with Rock Pipits essentially restricted to the coasts. However, the slightly higher number of tetrads occupied in winter reflects a degree of dispersal and use of a broader range of habitat niches at this time of year, including a distinct increase in the use of estuarine sites.

During the Atlas breeding periods, Rock Pipits were recorded in 125 tetrads, with breeding confirmed in 55 of these. This compares to 108 tetrads for which possible, probable or confirmed breeding was recorded, including 58 instances of confirmed breeding, during the *Devon Tetrad Atlas 1977–85*, and suggests little overall change. This is probably to be expected, given that the species is not only largely sedentary (Wernham *et al.* 2002) but also the extent and quality of its nesting habitat in the county appears to have remained stable.

The most striking difference between the breeding maps for the two Devon Atlases is the apparent loss of confirmed breeding along the Exmoor coast. This is considered to be due to differences in coverage between the two surveys – the Exmoor coastline being particularly difficult of access – rather than to a population decline, and it is likely that nesting continues in most, if not all of these tetrads.

The Rock Pipits breeding in Devon (and therefore most wintering birds) belong to the nominate race *A. p. petrosus*. However, as detailed in the *Devon Tetrad Atlas* and by Langman *et al.* (2007), ringing and careful observation have proven that birds of the race *A. p. littoralis*, the Scandinavian Rock Pipit, occur in winter and on passage, though the races are only distinguishable in the field from late winter or early spring when Scandinavian birds acquire their distinctive breeding plumage. During the Atlas period, Scandinavian Rock Pipits occurred at Wembury from January to March 2011 and Colyford Common (Axe Estuary) annually, with up to 11 present there during the late winter of 2008/09 (*DBR*). It is likely that some winter records of Rock Pipits at other sites may include Scandinavian birds, or even Water Pipit *A. spinoletta*, which is only separable from Rock Pipit in winter when seen or heard well by experienced observers.

*Text: Tim Davis & Tim Jones / Photo: Paul Nunn*
*Rock Pipit sponsored by **DJEnvironmental***
*(Tim Davis & Tim Jones)*

Balmer *et al.* 2013: 610; Sitters 1988: 168; Tyler 2010: 609

### Winter-period abundance 2007–13

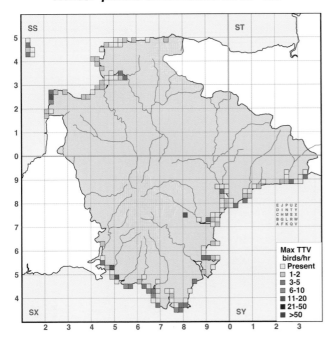

Max TTV birds/hr
- ☐ Present
- 1-2
- 3-5
- 6-10
- 11-20
- 21-50
- >50

# Water Pipit
## *Anthus spinoletta*

Amber listed

WATER PIPITS are scarce passage migrants and winter visitors, mainly to the upper parts of south coast estuaries, particularly the Axe and Exe, but also the Taw/Torridge Estuary on the north coast. Most records are of single birds, the highest count during the Atlas period being of 20 at Colyford Common (Axe Estuary) on 12 December 2008 (*DBR*). They frequent freshwater marshes and also saltmarsh grassland and beaches, such as at Prawle, where they feed along the tide line. There were records from 40 tetrads (just over 2%) during the Atlas winter period (October–February). Birds

sometimes linger into the early spring – there were records from 25 tetrads during the Atlas breeding period (March–September) – and moult into their striking breeding plumage before leaving. Though there is likely to be a degree of under-recording, the Devon winter population probably does not exceed 100 individuals but may be larger in spring as migrants pass through.

*Text: J M Lock / Photo: Paul Sterry/NPL*
*Water Pipit sponsored by Eric Wotton*

Balmer *et al.* 2013: 607; Sitters 1988: not treated; Tyler 2010: 612

**Breeding-period abundance 2007–13**

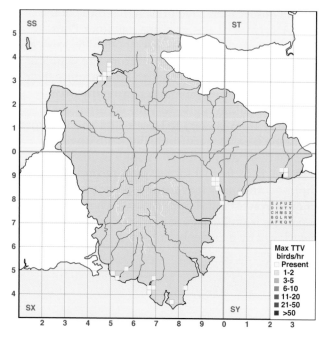

**Winter-period abundance 2007–13**

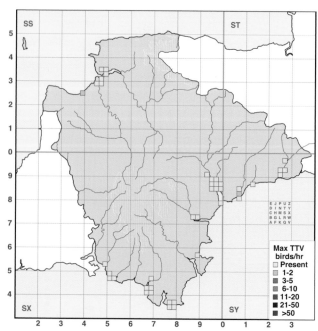

# Brambling
## *Fringilla montifringilla*

MIGRANTS TO Britain from northern European and Russian breeding grounds, Bramblings are mainly associated with beech woods in open country in early winter, but also with various other crops and, perhaps increasingly, garden feeders. In Devon they usually occur in small numbers among other finches, particularly Chaffinches, but occasionally in flocks of several hundred. They are scarce passage migrants at coastal watchpoints, especially in October/November, where their characteristic flight call reveals their presence overhead. In addition, some birds overwinter in the county between October and April, though numbers vary greatly from year to year, probably in response to food availability both here and on the continent. The maximum midwinter count during the Atlas years was 600 on the Exe Estuary in December 2010 (*DBR*).

The few breeding-period (March–September) records relate to late-departing and/or early-arriving wintering birds or passage migrants. Fairly large numbers can appear in April, such as the 130 recorded at Princetown in April 2011, the highest count in Devon that year (*DBR*). However, the latest spring passage date was 23 May 2009, while the earliest autumn arrival was 28 September 2008 (*DBRs*). During the winter period, there were records from all but five 10-km squares, all of these in the northern half of the county. This distribution may reflect observer bias, and certainly the only two counts of more than 50 individuals during a TTV were in the south, in the Exe area. It is difficult to draw firmer conclusions, bearing in mind the fluctuating numbers of this fickle visitor.

A Brambling ringed at Exmouth in March 2008 was recaptured in northern Norway in October of the same year (*DBR*).

*Text: Peter Reay / Photo: Neil Bygrave*
*Brambling sponsored by Mike & Jan Daniels*

Balmer *et al.* 2013: 614; Sitters 1988: not treated; Tyler 2010: 616

### Breeding-period abundance 2007–13

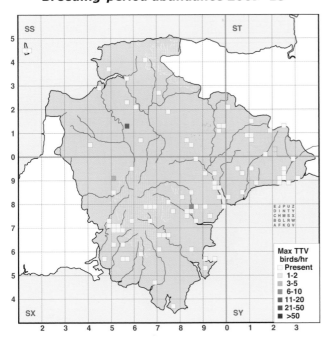

### Winter-period abundance 2007–13

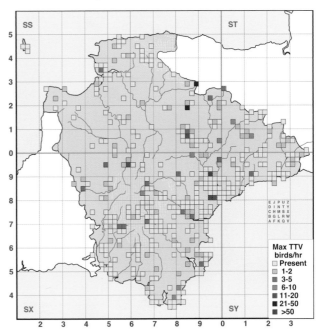

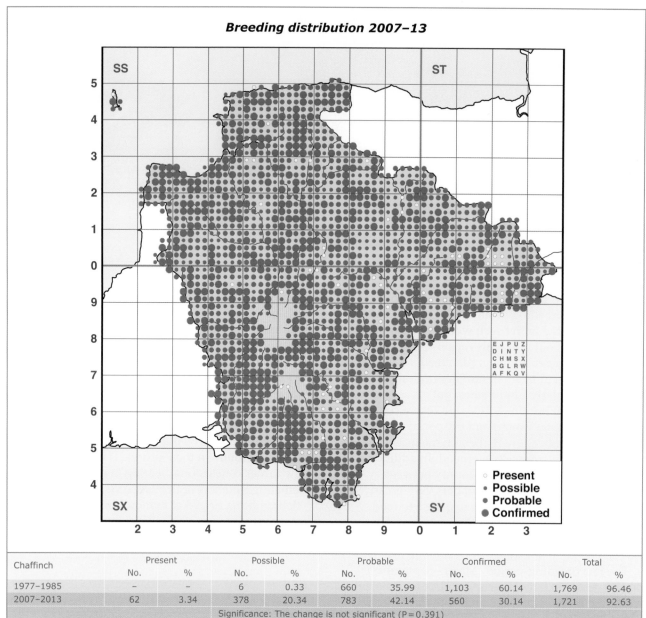

**Breeding distribution 2007–13**

| Chaffinch | Present | | Possible | | Probable | | Confirmed | | Total | |
|---|---|---|---|---|---|---|---|---|---|---|
| | No. | % | No. | % | No. | % | No. | % | No. | % |
| 1977–1985 | – | – | 6 | 0.33 | 660 | 35.99 | 1,103 | 60.14 | 1,769 | 96.46 |
| 2007–2013 | 62 | 3.34 | 378 | 20.34 | 783 | 42.14 | 560 | 30.14 | 1,721 | 92.63 |
| Significance: The change is not significant (P = 0.391) | | | | | | | | | | |

**Breeding distribution 1977–85**

**Breeding-period abundance 2007–13**

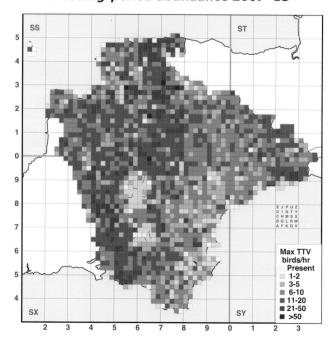

# Chaffinch
## *Fringilla coelebs*

V ERY VERSATILE in its habitat and feeding, the
Chaffinch is the most widespread and abundant
finch both nationally and in Devon. Its main
requirement seems to be simply the presence of trees
or bushes, so it occurs in forest and woodland,
scattered scrub, hedgerows, parks and gardens, rural
to urban. It often feeds on the ground, and winter
flocks may utilize human habitats ranging from
stubble fields to garden feeders, as well as more
natural bounty such as beech mast. Migrants from
the continent feature as components of both visible
migration at coastal watchpoints, and winter flocks.
Very large movements occur in some years,
especially in autumn; the highest count during the
Atlas years was 5,000 passing through Lundy on 25
October 2008 (*DBR*).

In view of the widespread occurrence of suitable
habitat in Devon, it is not surprising that Chaffinches
were found in nearly every tetrad in both the
breeding and winter periods. Only the treeless
uplands of Dartmoor appear to be avoided. In terms
of abundance, there were very few tetrads for which
fewer than three were counted during breeding-
period TTVs (April–July), but those with more than
ten were mostly in the western half or extreme east
of the county, and the few with more than 50 were
all in the north (perhaps reflecting the presence of
late-winter and/or spring passage flocks in April).
Abundance during the winter-period TTVs
(November–February) was more evenly spread,
including those tetrads returning counts of over 50
birds.

Breeding was recorded in 93% of Devon tetrads,
identical to the national figure (*Bird Atlas 2007–11*),
and not significantly different from the 96% in the
*Devon Tetrad Atlas 1977–85*. Although there were
more records of confirmed breeding during the
earlier survey, this is likely to reflect differences in
methodology and/or coverage rather than actual
change.

While most attention is directed towards species
whose numbers or distribution have changed
through time, it is surely equally interesting to find a
species which has been apparently unaffected by the
environmental changes thrust upon it. One can only
assume that its versatility in terms of habitat and diet
play a part in this, although the fact that abundance
was lower in the 1960s, probably due to organochlorine pesticides (Sitters 1988), shows that even
Chaffinches are not immune from human impact and
we should never be complacent.

*Text: Peter Reay / Photo: Andrew Cunningham*
*Chaffinch sponsored by Bob Heckford*

Balmer *et al.* 2013: 612; Sitters 1988: 266; Tyler 2010: 614

### Winter-period abundance 2007–13

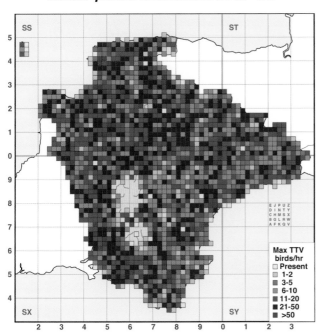

Max TTV
birds/hr
☐ Present
☐ 1-2
☐ 3-5
☐ 6-10
☐ 11-20
☐ 21-50
☐ >50

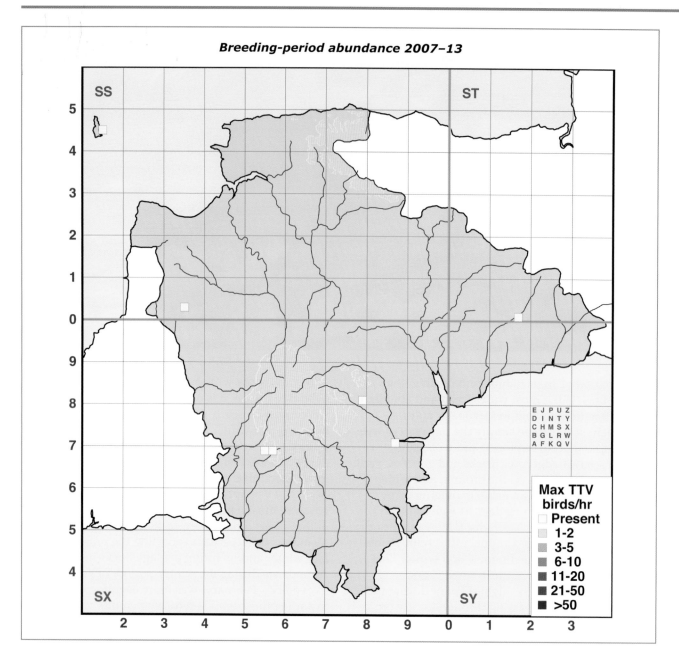

**Breeding-period abundance 2007–13**

Max TTV
birds/hr
☐ Present
  1-2
  3-5
  6-10
  11-20
  21-50
  >50

**Breeding distribution 1977–85**

• Possible
• Probable
• Confirmed

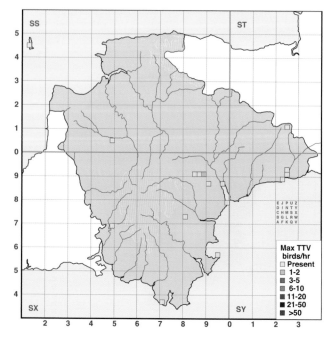

**Winter-period abundance 2007–13**

Max TTV
birds/hr
☐ Present
  1-2
  3-5
  6-10
  11-20
  21-50
  >50

# Hawfinch

*Coccothraustes coccothraustes*

**Red listed**

THE HAWFINCH is an uncommon winter visitor and passage migrant to Devon, but has bred sporadically in the past, the last recorded occurrence being in a mature oak at an unrevealed location in 2002.

It is a particularly shy species, frequenting open woodland and parkland where it is most often seen in the tops of tall trees but its wary nature makes detection difficult, the sharp flight call often being the only clue to its presence. It is therefore likely to be under-recorded. During the Atlas period Hawfinches were recorded annually (with the exception of 2007) in very small numbers (mainly single birds, with a maximum flock size of eight west of Exeter in November 2010), but with little in the way of regularity of occurrence (*DBRs*). In some years it was found during the first-winter period and not again that year, but in other years it was not recorded before autumn. Most occurrences were in the southern half of Devon, east of Dartmoor. There were no records of possible, probable or confirmed breeding.

There is some evidence of a decline in East Devon since the *Devon Tetrad Atlas 1977–85*, with records from eight tetrads in the region at that time, compared with just one during the current survey, but overall numbers are so low that it is difficult to draw any definite conclusion.

Occasional influxes have occurred in the past, such as in 2001, when Devon was the third-ranking county in England for the species. During the Atlas period there were scattered records of passage migrants in both spring and autumn, including the registrations shown for Lundy and south-coast headlands.

*Text: Roger Doble / Photo: David Land*
*Hawfinch sponsored by Richard Behenna*

Balmer *et al.* 2013: 636; Sitters 1988: 276; Tyler 2010: 640

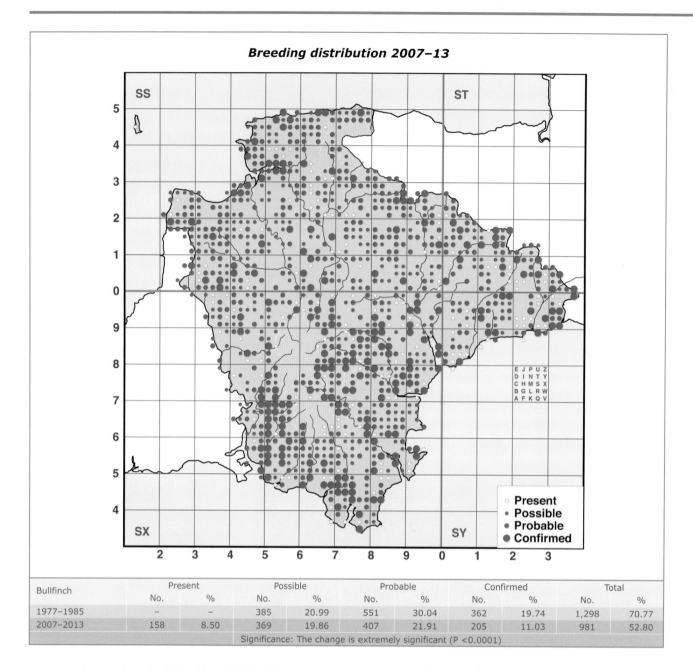

## Breeding distribution 2007–13

| Bullfinch | Present No. | % | Possible No. | % | Probable No. | % | Confirmed No. | % | Total No. | % |
|---|---|---|---|---|---|---|---|---|---|---|
| 1977–1985 | – | – | 385 | 20.99 | 551 | 30.04 | 362 | 19.74 | 1,298 | 70.77 |
| 2007–2013 | 158 | 8.50 | 369 | 19.86 | 407 | 21.91 | 205 | 11.03 | 981 | 52.80 |
| Significance: The change is extremely significant (P <0.0001) | | | | | | | | | | |

## Breeding distribution 1977–85

## Breeding-period abundance 2007–13

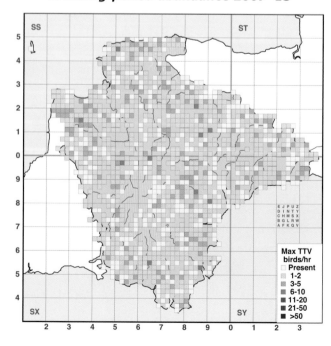

# Bullfinch
*Pyrrhula pyrrhula*

Amber listed

BULLFINCHES ARE distributed across most of Europe, breeding from parts of Spain and Turkey, north to well within the Arctic Circle (*BWP*). In Britain and Ireland, *Bird Atlas 2007–11* recorded breeding evidence in 83% of 10-km squares.

This is a species frequently seen in pairs, which are thought to remain together for several years. They are remarkably inconspicuous during the nesting season, during which they seemingly disappear only to return suddenly in late summer as a family party, or during the winter months as a pair again. This secretive behaviour makes confirmation of breeding a particular challenge.

Bullfinches inhabit a wide range of habitats, including farmland, mixed and broadleaf woodland, and rural and suburban gardens but are almost absent in areas of exposed open country with few trees, such as the more exposed parts of Devon's coastline or high Dartmoor and Exmoor. Adult Bullfinches are almost exclusively plant-eaters, their diet consisting mainly of buds, berries and seeds, but invertebrates are important in the diet of nestlings (Limbrunner *et al.* 2001). They are relatively sedentary birds in Britain and Ireland.

Nationally, there was a rapid decline in the late 1970s and early 1980s, and in spite of evidence of an upturn after 2000, numbers were 39% lower in 2011 than they were in 1967 (*Bird Atlas 2007–11*). Comparison between the *Devon Tetrad Atlas 1977–85* and the current survey shows that while the range of Bullfinch in the county has remained much the same, there was an 18% reduction in the number of tetrads for which breeding evidence was recorded.

The number of occupied tetrads appears to have declined in particular in south-eastern parts of the county, from East Devon to Plymouth, as well as in North Devon around Barnstaple. It is interesting that the apparent decline appears to have been especially marked around urban areas, since the account in the *Devon Tetrad Atlas 1977–85* made the point that centres of human population coincided with particularly high densities of Bullfinches. It is possible that levels of urbanization have increased to a point at which urban areas are no longer suitable for such high densities. However, national analyses of Bullfinch decline and subsequent recovery have failed to find any clear reasons (*Bird Atlas 2007–11*).

*Text: Naomi Barker / Photos: Barry Bowden*
*Bullfinch sponsored by Rob Hubble & Stella Tracey*

Balmer *et al.* 2013: 634; Sitters 1988: 282; Tyler 2010: 638

### Winter-period abundance 2007–13

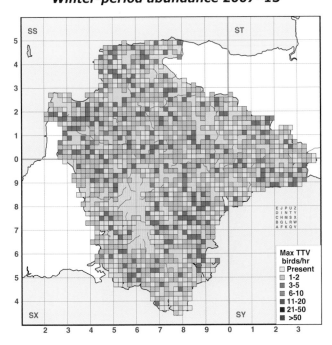

Max TTV birds/hr
- ☐ Present
- 1-2
- 3-5
- 6-10
- 11-20
- 21-50
- >50

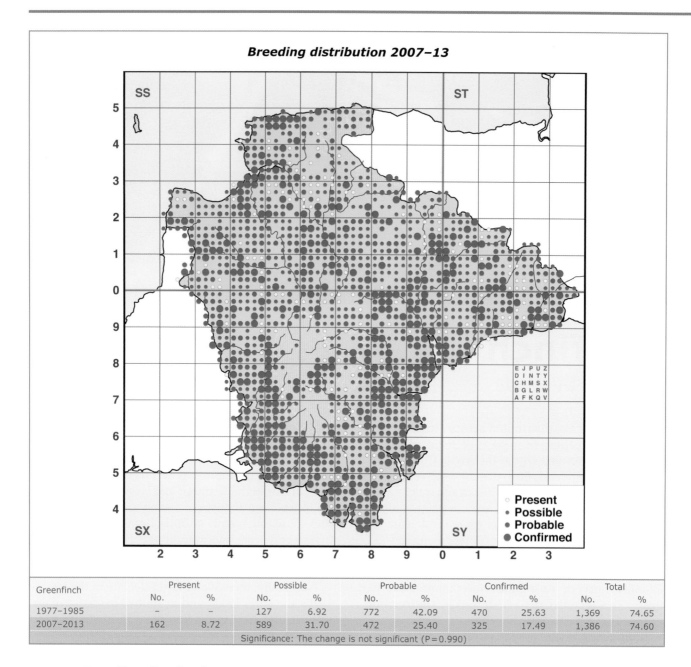

## Breeding distribution 2007–13

Present ○
Possible ●
Probable ●
Confirmed ●

| Greenfinch | Present | | Possible | | Probable | | Confirmed | | Total | |
|---|---|---|---|---|---|---|---|---|---|---|
| | No. | % | No. | % | No. | % | No. | % | No. | % |
| 1977–1985 | – | – | 127 | 6.92 | 772 | 42.09 | 470 | 25.63 | 1,369 | 74.65 |
| 2007–2013 | 162 | 8.72 | 589 | 31.70 | 472 | 25.40 | 325 | 17.49 | 1,386 | 74.60 |
| Significance: The change is not significant (P = 0.990) | | | | | | | | | | |

## Breeding distribution 1977–85

Possible ●
Probable ●
Confirmed ●

## Breeding-period abundance 2007–13

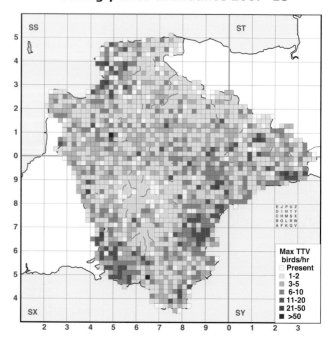

Max TTV
birds/hr
☐ Present
1-2
3-5
6-10
11-20
21-50
>50

# Greenfinch

*Chloris chloris*

GREENFINCHES ARE found in woods, hedges, orchards, farmland, parks and gardens. The breeding-period map shows absences from the open moorland of Dartmoor and Exmoor and from the wet heaths of the Culm Measures in north-west Devon and the Blackdown Hills in the east of the county. High densities tend to be associated with suburban areas, where mature gardens provide good nesting cover and where food resources are supplemented by bird-table feeding. In contrast, much of the intensively farmed areas of the county support low breeding densities of Greenfinches, or none at all, particularly where the landscape is dominated by permanent grassland.

Between the *Devon Tetrad Atlas 1977–1985* and the current survey there has been a reduction in the number of tetrads showing probable or confirmed breeding, from approximately 68% to about 43%, but the number of 'possible breeding' tetrads more than quadrupled. The total number of tetrads for which any category of breeding evidence was recorded suggests that there was no significant change in breeding range between Atlases, but that it was more difficult to prove breeding in 2007–13 than in 1977–85. This could be due to methodological or coverage differences, but may also reflect a fall in Greenfinch numbers.

The reduction in the number of tetrads with confirmed or probable breeding accords with national trends in the population of this species in recent years (BTO BirdTrends 2014). In South West England, Greenfinch numbers were estimated to have declined by 30% since 1994 (Risely *et al.* 2013). Trichomonosis, a disease caused by the protozoan parasite *Trichomonas gallinae*, has almost certainly had a major impact on the population in the UK, including Devon, since it was first recognized in 2005 (Robinson *et al.* 2010).

Agricultural land management practices are also likely to have had a significant influence on numbers in parts of Devon. Greenfinches feed on grain and weed seeds during the winter months. Wilson *et al.* (1996) found that stubble fields were strongly preferred to the virtual exclusion of other field types. Therefore autumn sowing of crops such as wheat and oilseed rape that involve high levels of herbicide weed control provide little if any winter seed resources. Permanent grassland and in particular tightly grazed grass fields that contain little if any plant seed heads in winter have no food value. Autumn flailing of hedges and hedge banks is also likely to remove much of the seed resource that would otherwise have been available to this and other finch species.

Apart from a trend towards earlier nesting and egg laying there is no evidence to date that climate change is influencing the Greenfinch population in Devon.

The future of the Greenfinch in Devon is likely to be strongly influenced by the extent to which urban and suburban areas continue to provide nesting habitat and supplementary feeding opportunities. The continuation of agri-environmental schemes that support the provision of winter stubbles in the farmed landscape will also be critical in maintaining Greenfinch populations in the wider countryside.

*Text: Jerry Tallowin / Photo: Barry Bowden*
*Greenfinch sponsored by Patrick Green*

Balmer *et al.* 2013: 616; Sitters 1988: 270; Tyler 2010: 620

## Winter-period abundance 2007–13

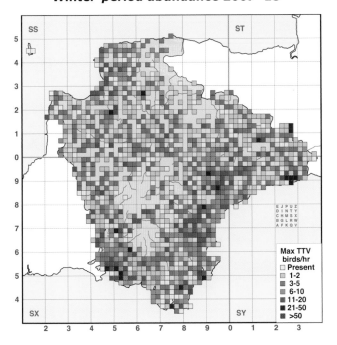

Max TTV birds/hr
□ Present
□ 1-2
■ 3-5
■ 6-10
■ 11-20
■ 21-50
■ >50

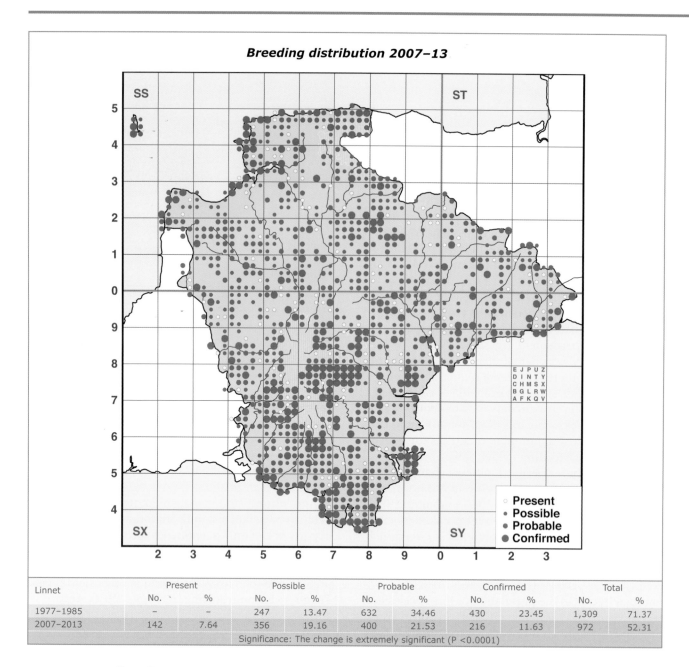

### Breeding distribution 2007–13

| Linnet | Present | | Possible | | Probable | | Confirmed | | Total | |
|---|---|---|---|---|---|---|---|---|---|---|
| | No. | % | No. | % | No. | % | No. | % | No. | % |
| 1977–1985 | – | – | 247 | 13.47 | 632 | 34.46 | 430 | 23.45 | 1,309 | 71.37 |
| 2007–2013 | 142 | 7.64 | 356 | 19.16 | 400 | 21.53 | 216 | 11.63 | 972 | 52.31 |
| Significance: The change is extremely significant (P <0.0001) | | | | | | | | | | |

### Breeding distribution 1977–85

### Breeding-period abundance 2007–13

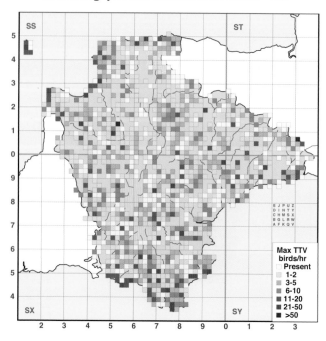

# Linnet
## *Linaria cannabina*
Red listed

THIS ATTRACTIVE finch is a familiar bird in Devon where in spring and early summer it can often be found singing from prominent vegetation. It particularly favours heathland and moorland with sufficient gorse or bramble cover, and areas of coastal scrub. However, the Linnet is also at home in smaller numbers in agricultural areas, especially where rough pasture and mature hedgerows occur, and can be found throughout the Devon countryside.

Whilst the species remains widespread in Devon, in comparison with the *Devon Tetrad Atlas 1977–85* the population is now more thinly distributed, with a 25% decline in the number of tetrads from which

breeding evidence (possible, probable, confirmed) was obtained. The 1977–85 survey found that there had been a significant decline in numbers during the 1970s, attributed to the intensification of agriculture, resulting in a reduction of winter stubbles and thus a depleted food supply. The figures indicate that this trend continues in Devon, reflecting widespread losses nationally (*Bird Atlas 2007–11*).

In winter the species largely withdraws from the core breeding areas, being found mainly on mudflats, saltmarshes and adjoining farmland, though a significant proportion of Linnets breeding in Britain and Ireland migrate to France and Spain for the winter (Wernham *et al.* 2002), with notable passage through Devon in both spring and autumn (*DBR*s). Linnets were recorded in all but three 10-km squares during the Atlas winter period, wintering flocks particularly favouring the Exe and Taw/Torridge Estuaries and their hinterlands. The maximum recorded flock size varied between 200 and 550 in most winters, but 1,500 were near the Exe Estuary in early February 2012 and a hard-weather movement brought an exceptional 2,171 to the Exe in January 2010 (*DBR*s).

The continued intensification of farming practices is liable to result in further losses of both breeding and wintering Linnets in the wider agricultural landscape, but the main breeding areas appear secure. The National Parks of Dartmoor and Exmoor, along with many important coastal areas, are managed more extensively and enjoy a high level of protection.

*Text: Roger Doble / Photo: Steve Hatch*
*Linnet sponsored by Hilary Thomas*

Balmer *et al.* 2013: 622; Sitters 1988: 276; Tyler 2010: 626

### Winter-period abundance 2007–13

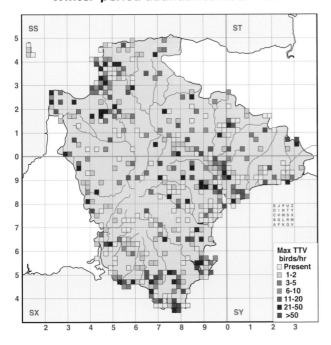

Max TTV
birds/hr
☐ Present
■ 1-2
■ 3-5
■ 6-10
■ 11-20
■ 21-50
■ >50

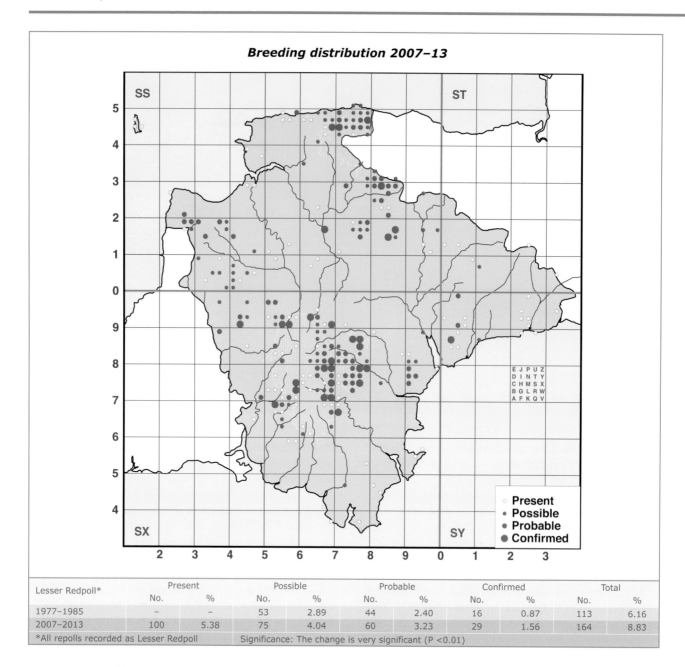

**Breeding distribution 2007–13**

| Lesser Redpoll* | Present | | Possible | | Probable | | Confirmed | | Total | |
|---|---|---|---|---|---|---|---|---|---|---|
| | No. | % | No. | % | No. | % | No. | % | No. | % |
| 1977–1985 | – | – | 53 | 2.89 | 44 | 2.40 | 16 | 0.87 | 113 | 6.16 |
| 2007–2013 | 100 | 5.38 | 75 | 4.04 | 60 | 3.23 | 29 | 1.56 | 164 | 8.83 |
| *All repolls recorded as Lesser Redpoll | | | Significance: The change is very significant (P <0.01) | | | | | | | |

**Breeding distribution 1977–85**

**Breeding-period abundance 2007–13**

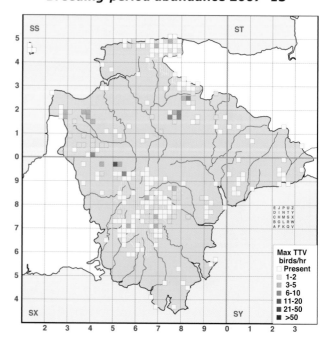

# Lesser Redpoll
## *Acanthis cabaret*

**Red listed**

Lesser Redpoll was split from Common Redpoll *A. flammea* in 2001 by the BOU (Knox *et al.* 2001), though not without some controversy (Stoddart 2013); elsewhere in Europe they are generally treated as one species. Favoured nesting habitat includes young, scrubby birch and conifer woodland, so during the breeding season the species is most often encountered on the fringes of Dartmoor, on the East Devon Pebblebed Heaths, the plantations of Haldon and the plantations and marginal farmland of the Culm Measures in north-west Devon. Although their display flight is noisy and energetic, Redpolls can be rather retiring and breeding can be difficult to prove, so confirmed breeding is perhaps under-recorded.

Breeding was first recorded in Devon in 1954 and by the time of the *Devon Tetrad Atlas 1977–85* occurred sparsely wherever there was suitable habitat. There has been a subtle increase in both the number and distribution of breeding records across the county since then, with increases around the upland fringes more than compensating for losses on the Culm Measures and the Pebblebed Heaths. Nationally, the species has increased in recent years after a very large decline, the cause of which is not well understood but may have been driven by both reduced survival and lower productivity (BTO BirdTrends 2014). As conifer plantations mature they become less attractive to Lesser Redpolls; this has been implicated in recent declines and may help explain the reductions in south-east and north-west Devon.

In winter, Lesser Redpolls are found widely across the county, often in small numbers, together with Siskins, feeding in birch and alder along streams and rivers. The use of garden feeding stations appears to be increasing. Birds are highly mobile and may be easily overlooked unless the distinctive flight-call is heard, so the mapped records may underestimate total numbers. A dedicated ringing effort, supported by tape-luring, at Vogwell, eastern Dartmoor, resulted in a total of 235 birds being ringed during 2011 (*DBR*). The largest flocks recorded during the Atlas years were 50+ at Squabmoor in January 2008 and 50 at Woodbury in October 2011 (*DBRs*). The maps include records submitted as 'Common/Lesser Redpoll', the two species being very difficult to separate in the field without good views. Winter numbers may be boosted by birds from elsewhere in the UK (for example, recent ringing movements between Devon and both Yorkshire and Hampshire) and perhaps from continental Europe; one recent recovery involved a Devon-ringed bird in France. Visible migration is recorded at coastal watchpoints in both spring and autumn.

*Text: Jeremy Barker / Photo: Paul Sterry/NPL*
*Lesser Redpoll sponsored in memory of Jan Daniels*

Balmer *et al.* 2013: 626; Sitters 1988: 266*; Tyler 2010: 630

### Winter-period abundance 2007–13

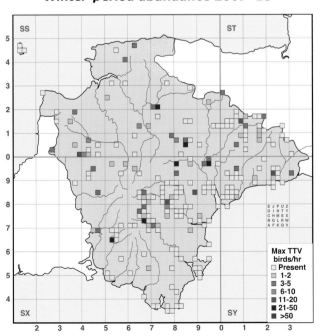

Max TTV
birds/hr
□ Present
1-2
3-5
6-10
11-20
21-50
>50

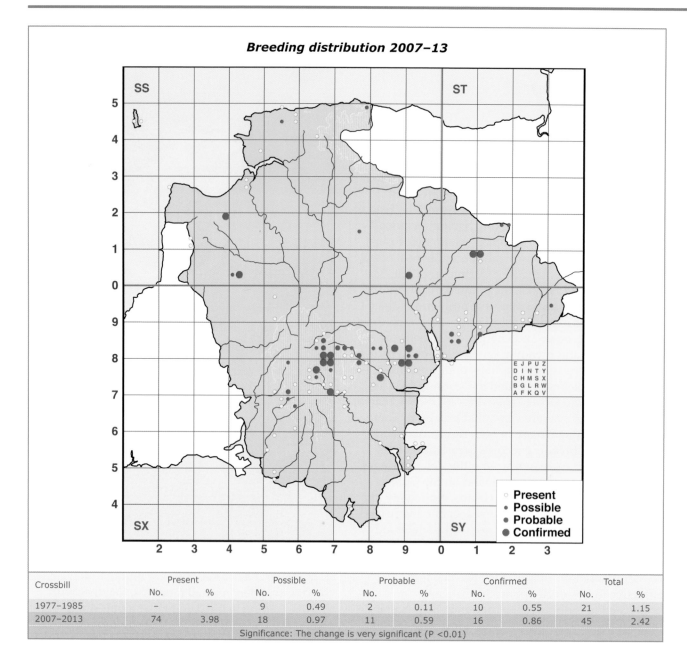

**Breeding distribution 2007–13**

| Crossbill | Present | | Possible | | Probable | | Confirmed | | Total | |
|---|---|---|---|---|---|---|---|---|---|---|
| | No. | % | No. | % | No. | % | No. | % | No. | % |
| 1977–1985 | – | – | 9 | 0.49 | 2 | 0.11 | 10 | 0.55 | 21 | 1.15 |
| 2007–2013 | 74 | 3.98 | 18 | 0.97 | 11 | 0.59 | 16 | 0.86 | 45 | 2.42 |
| Significance: The change is very significant (P <0.01) | | | | | | | | | | |

**Breeding distribution 1977–85**

**Breeding-period abundance 2007–13**

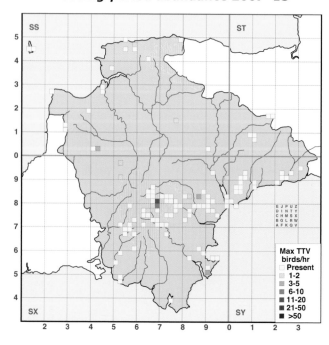

# Crossbill
*Loxia curvirostra*

THE CROSSBILL is a highly specialized species with a bill adapted specifically for extracting seed from pinecones. Its main habitat is therefore coniferous forests, where it feeds with great dexterity, sometimes taking seed *in situ* and at other times snipping off the whole cone, carrying it to a perch and steadying it with one foot before extracting its prize. Crossbills also eat buds and fruit from deciduous trees, as well as insects, especially caterpillars. Usually seen high in trees or in flight, they need a good water supply for drinking because of the very dry nature of their staple diet. Good views can sometimes be obtained as birds come down to drink from pools or puddles on forestry tracks.

In summer, the core area for the species is across Dartmoor to Haldon and into the coniferous plantations of East Devon. Breeding is very much related to food supply and can take place at any time between December and June, with a peak between February and April (Tyler 2010). Breeding was proved during the Atlas surveys in the Dartmoor and Haldon regions, together with more isolated pockets across more northern parts of Devon.

During the winter period, significant flocks and family parties were found across the breeding areas, but there were also scattered records throughout the county, including several from coastal areas. As a specialist feeder, the species will wander extensively if the cone crop fails in a given area, and the resident population is sometimes boosted by irruptions from Europe for that reason. Thus, birds are sometimes encountered away from the usual habitat.

### Winter-period abundance 2007–13

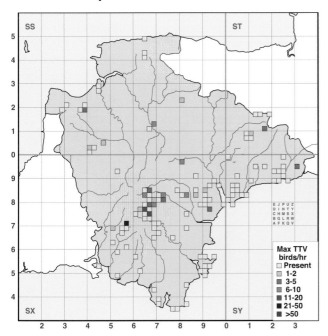

The maps certainly show the species has increased in the county since the *Devon Tetrad Atlas 1977–85*, both in range and density. Breeding evidence was found in 45 tetrads during the current survey compared with 21 tetrads during fieldwork in 1977–85. Given the tendency for periodic irruptions to boost populations temporarily, there are inevitably ups and downs, but there appears to be a trend towards Crossbills becoming increasingly widespread in the county.

Nevertheless, the future of the species in Devon is very much linked to the management of conifer plantations to ensure continued availability of suitable cone-bearing trees of fruiting age across wide areas. Clear felling and replanting with broadleaved woodland or reversion to heathland will be detrimental to Crossbills.

*Text: Roger Doble / Photo: John Deakins*

Balmer *et al.* 2013: 630; Sitters 1988: 280; Tyler 2010: 634

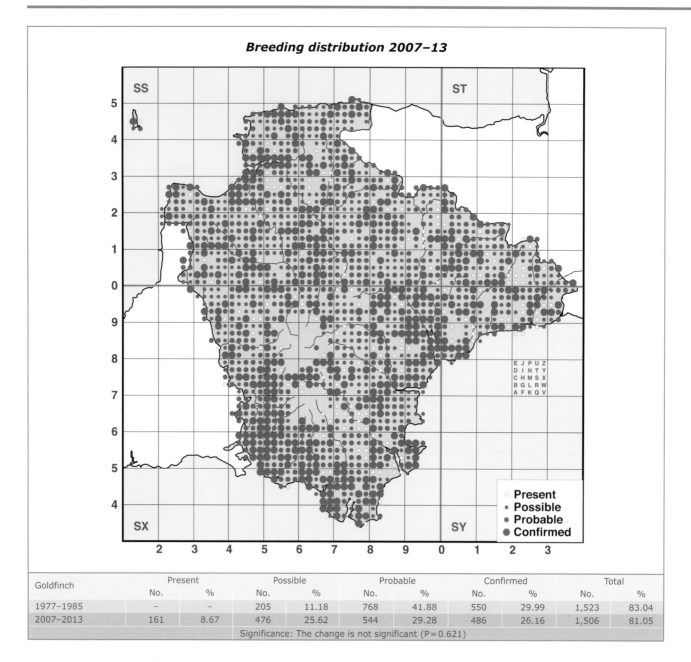

**Breeding distribution 2007–13**

| Goldfinch | Present | | Possible | | Probable | | Confirmed | | Total | |
|---|---|---|---|---|---|---|---|---|---|---|
| | No. | % | No. | % | No. | % | No. | % | No. | % |
| 1977–1985 | – | – | 205 | 11.18 | 768 | 41.88 | 550 | 29.99 | 1,523 | 83.04 |
| 2007–2013 | 161 | 8.67 | 476 | 25.62 | 544 | 29.28 | 486 | 26.16 | 1,506 | 81.05 |
| Significance: The change is not significant (P = 0.621) | | | | | | | | | | |

**Breeding distribution 1977–85**

**Breeding-period abundance 2007–13**

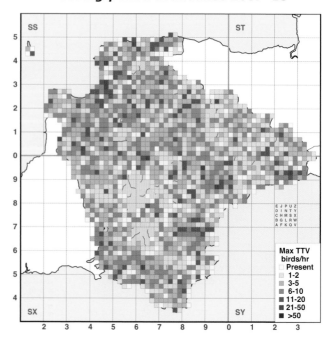

# Goldfinch
## *Carduelis carduelis*

GOLDFINCHES ARE found in a wide variety of habitats in Devon, including arable and pasture farmland, orchards, parkland and gardens, scrub, reedbeds, coastal saltmarsh and dune systems. They show a strong preference for lowland habitats, with the apparent exception of the county's wet and dry heathlands. Both the breeding-period and winter-period maps particularly illustrate that the species avoids the high moorland and bogs of Dartmoor and Exmoor. Goldfinches are also less frequently found in conifer woodlands.

The species' distribution, particularly during the non-breeding period, is almost certainly influenced by the occurrence of its favoured food – the seeds of the plant family Asteraceae such as groundsels, ragworts, dandelions and thistles. The provision of niger seed at garden feeding stations has also probably influenced the local distribution and density in the county. In contrast to adult Goldfinches, nestlings have an almost exclusively invertebrate diet. The present survey indicates that much of the intensively farmed areas of Devon now support only low breeding densities, probably as a result of restricted food availability (see below).

There is little evidence of a significant change in the breeding distribution of Goldfinches in Devon between the *Devon Tetrad Atlas 1977–85* and the present survey. There was, however, a notable reduction in the number of tetrads for which probable or confirmed breeding was recorded, perhaps due in part to methodological differences between the two Atlases. Nationally, data from the

Common Bird Census and Breeding Bird Survey indicate that despite sizeable inter-decadal population fluctuations since the 1960s, the UK's Goldfinch population has not shown a long-term reduction (BTO BirdTrends 2014). The fluctuations can be explained almost entirely by variability in annual survival rates (Baillie *et al.* 2014), most likely arising from agricultural intensification and consequent reductions in the availability of weed seed. However, garden feeding may have partly offset dwindling food resources in the intensively farmed landscape and may help explain the lack of any contraction in the the species' breeding range in Devon.

Goldfinches appear to be more abundant in the winter, with concentrations in the Exe Valley, south-east Devon, the north, and the Torbay hinterland; this may be due to large numbers of young joining the flocks, or it may reflect the arrival of birds from continental Europe. Goldfinches feed on seeds during the winter months and show a strong preference for stubble fields (Wilson *et al.* 1996), with rough grasslands that contain seeding thistles also used. Autumn-sown crops, such as wheat and oilseed rape, provide little if any winter seed resources, and neither do intensively managed grasslands.

The continuation of agri-environmental schemes that support unimproved grassland, rough pasture and winter stubbles containing arable weed seed will be critical to maintaining Goldfinch populations in Devon. Apart from a trend towards earlier nesting and egg laying there has been no other evidence to date that climate change is likely to influence their numbers in the county.

*Text: Jerry Tallowin / Photo: Steve Hatch*
*Goldfinch sponsored by Jackie Newman*

Balmer *et al.* 2013: 618; Sitters 1988: 272; Tyler 2010: 621

### Winter-period abundance 2007–13

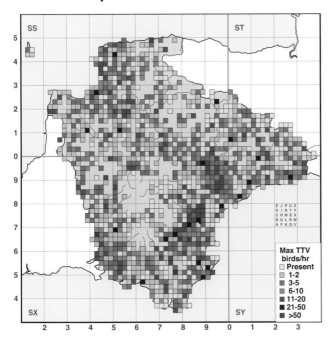

Max TTV birds/hr
- □ Present
- 1-2
- 3-5
- 6-10
- 11-20
- 21-50
- >50

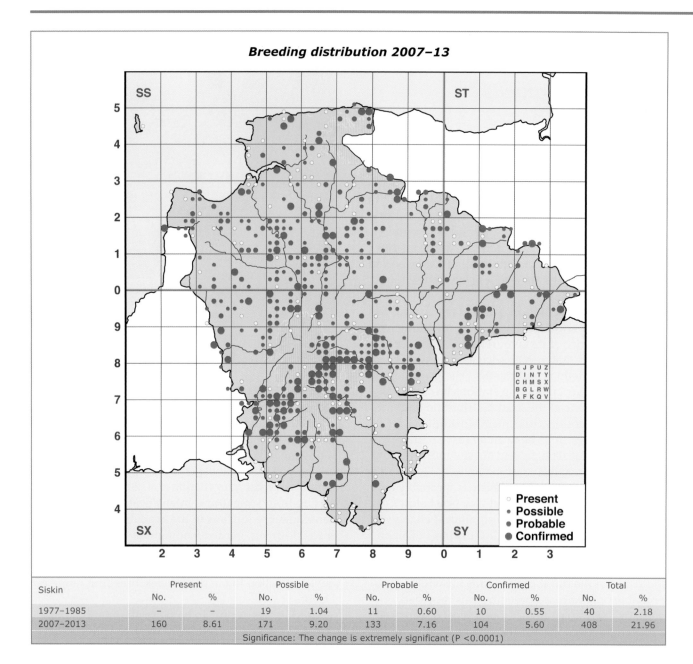

## Breeding distribution 2007–13

| Siskin | Present | | Possible | | Probable | | Confirmed | | Total | |
|---|---|---|---|---|---|---|---|---|---|---|
| | No. | % | No. | % | No. | % | No. | % | No. | % |
| 1977–1985 | – | – | 19 | 1.04 | 11 | 0.60 | 10 | 0.55 | 40 | 2.18 |
| 2007–2013 | 160 | 8.61 | 171 | 9.20 | 133 | 7.16 | 104 | 5.60 | 408 | 21.96 |
| Significance: The change is extremely significant (P <0.0001) | | | | | | | | | | |

### Breeding distribution 1977–85

### Breeding-period abundance 2007–13

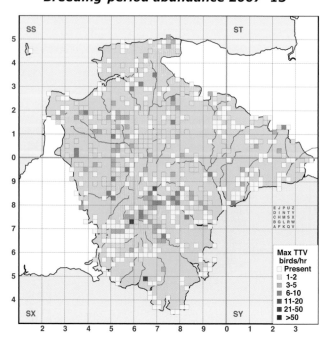

# Siskin
*Spinus spinus*

UNTIL THE middle of the 20th century, Siskins were breeding birds of the Scottish conifer forests and only winter visitors to England, along with birds from northern Europe. Expansion of conifer plantations, especially of Sitka spruce, enabled Siskins to gradually colonize most of northern Britain, Wales and South West England as a breeding bird. Dartmoor was their Devon stronghold by the time of the *Devon Tetrad Atlas 1977–85* survey, with outlying populations in the upper Plym and Haldon areas. At that time only about 2% of the Devon tetrads had breeding records, but expansion continued and the present survey shows that 22% of tetrads now have breeding Siskins – an astonishing tenfold increase in 30 years.

Siskins are early nesters and fledged young can be seen by mid-April. They usually have two broods, but may have three, and newly fledged young can be seen as late as September. Young Siskins can disperse rapidly, so their presence does not necessarily indicate breeding nearby.

The breeding-season (April–July) TTVs show that tetrads with Siskins had mostly between three and ten Siskins per hour, with only three tetrads with more, two of which were on Dartmoor. The winter (November–February) TTVs show that 35.6% of tetrads had records of Siskins, with many having 20 or more birds per hour. The winter population is increased not only by the young of the year but by many birds from continental Europe passing through in September, October and November. There is a strong passage of birds returning north in February and March, with birds ringed in Devon being recovered in Scotland and northern Europe, and vice versa (see figure). There was a major autumn influx in October 2007 (just outside the Atlas period), but the highest passage count during the survey was of 829 flying west at Prawle on 8 October 2011 (*DBR*). The largest winter flocks were 200 along the upper River Coly on 1 February 2009 and at Lydford Forest on 12 February 2010 (*DBRs*).

Siskins are now a frequent sight on garden feeders across Devon, both in summer and in winter, and it is this change in feeding behaviour, together with the planting and maturing of conifer plantations, that is thought to be responsible for their remarkable range expansion. As a typically northern species, it might have been expected that the Siskin's range would be retreating northward as the climate warms, but it has done the opposite. It seems that, in this species at least, environmental and behavioural changes can counteract the effects of a warming climate.

*Text: Mike Hounsome / Photo: Adrian Davey*
*Siskin sponsored by Mike Hounsome*

Balmer *et al.* 2013: 620; Sitters 1988: 274; Tyler 2010: 623

### Winter-period abundance 2007–13

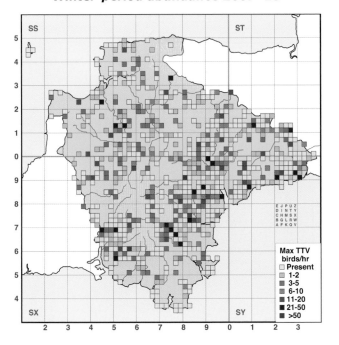

Max TTV birds/hr
- □ Present
- 1-2
- 3-5
- 6-10
- 11-20
- 21-50
- >50

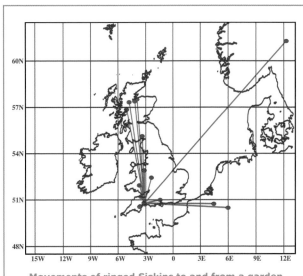

Movements of ringed Siskins to and from a garden in East Devon. Source: M Hounsome, personal data.

# Serin

## Serinus serinus

ASSOCIATED WITH gardens, parks and other wooded areas on mainland Europe where it is a common breeder, the Serin is now a very rare passage migrant in Devon, typically along the south coast in spring, but there are also historic breeding records for the county. The *Devon Tetrad Atlas 1977–85* recorded confirmed breeding at three sites, probable breeding at two and possible breeding at five more. However, the anticipated colonization of southern counties did not materialize and the number of records has actually declined considerably since the 1990s. During the current Atlas period, Serins were recorded as present at just three sites in the breeding season, Colaton Raleigh on 7 May 2010, Prawle on 10 May 2011 and Berry Head between 25 and 27 May 2012; and at three in winter, at Haven Cliff on 6 November 2007, Orcombe Point on 21 October 2012 and Soar on the same day (*DBRs*). There was no evidence of breeding.

*Text: Peter Reay / Photo: Paul Nunn*

Balmer *et al.* 2013: 629; Sitters 1988: 268; Tyler 2010: 618

# Lapland Bunting

## Calcarius lapponicus

Amber listed

PRIMARILY OCCURRING as a scarce autumn-passage migrant and very scarce winter visitor, in Devon the Lapland Bunting is a bird of estuaries, saltmarshes and coastal headlands. It was first recorded in the county, on Lundy, as recently as 1942, whilst the first mainland record was not until 1961. The species is now recorded annually in small numbers in Devon.

The winter-period map (October–February) demonstrates the Lapland Bunting's affinity for coastal sites, but somewhat disguises the fact that during the Atlas years more than half of the county's Lapland Bunting records came from Lundy, maintaining the trend of preceding decades.

Nationally, there was an expansion in range (as measured by the number of occupied 10-km squares) of 151% between the *Winter Atlas 1981–84* and *Bird Atlas 2007–11*, though this was largely attributable to an exceptional influx in autumn 2010. This phenomenon was reflected in Devon, with passage through Lundy extending from 29 August to 15 November, including a maximum count of 33 on 7 October, while records from 19 mainland sites involved up to 35 birds in total – far and away the best year during the Atlas period (*DBR* 2010).

*Text: Roger Doble*

Balmer *et al.* 2013: 640; Sitters 1988: not treated; Tyler 2010: 643

### Breeding distribution 1977–85

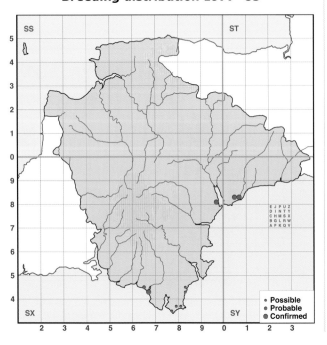

### Winter-period abundance 2007–13

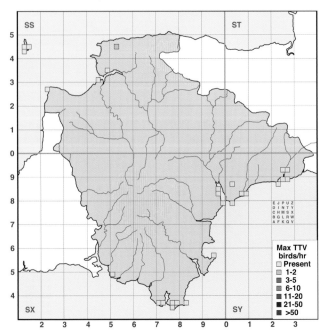

# Snow Bunting
## *Plectrophenax nivalis*
**Amber listed**

SNOW BUNTINGS are uncommon winter visitors and passage migrants in Devon. Though breeding mainly at Arctic and sub-Arctic latitudes, a small population nests on the high tops of the Cairngorms and the north-west Highlands. In winter there is a southbound emigration from northern Europe to wintering grounds on upland moors or coastal areas with shingle beaches and saltmarshes, especially those with stubble fields in the near vicinity.

Occurrences in Devon are almost entirely confined to these habitat types, with the main concentrations being on Lundy, the coast of the North Devon mainland, and Dartmoor.

Whilst not conspicuous in their winter plumage, birds are generally quite approachable as they feed on the ground, so that – with care – close and prolonged views are possible.

Most records involve ones or twos, though small flocks are occasionally encountered. Six were reported from Northam Burrows in October 2010, whilst an exceptional 20 were on Lundy in October 2011 (*DBRs*). Typically, around 20 individuals are recorded in any year, though there are infrequent influxes in excess of 40 (Tyler 2010).

Nationally, there has been a 34% increase in the number of occupied 10-km squares since the *Winter Atlas 1981–84*, with gains most apparent in the uplands of northern Britain (*Bird Atlas 2007–11*). Although numbers in Devon remain very small,

there was also an increase in the number of occupied 10-km squares between the *Winter Atlas 1981–84* and the current survey.

*Text: Roger Doble / Photo: Barry Bowden*
*Snow Bunting sponsored by Garry Hillard*

Balmer *et al.* 2013: 638; Sitters 1988: not treated; Tyler 2010: 641

### *Winter-period abundance 2007–13*

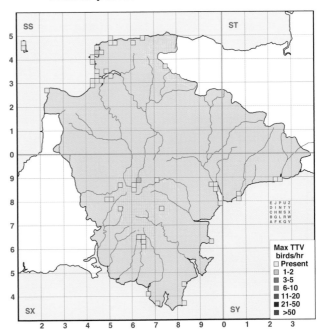

Max TTV birds/hr
- □ Present
- 1-2
- 3-5
- 6-10
- 11-20
- 21-50
- >50

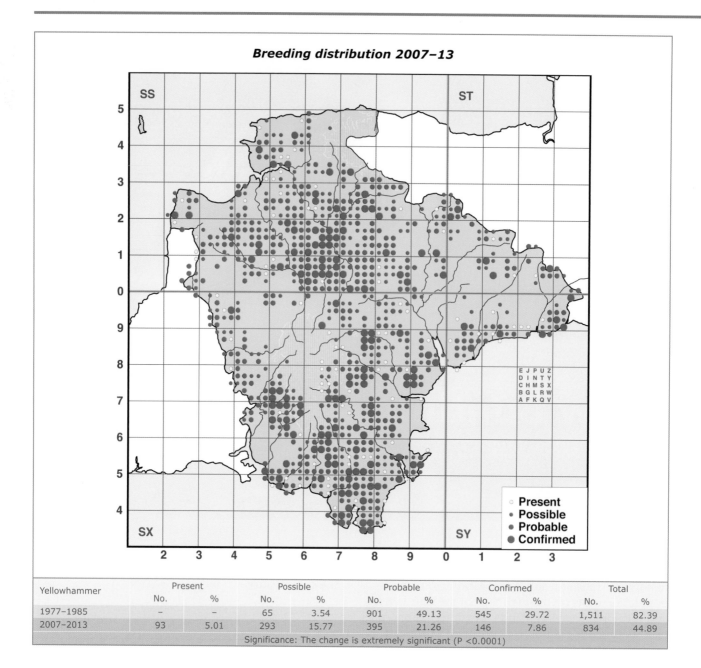

### Breeding distribution 2007–13

| Yellowhammer | Present | | Possible | | Probable | | Confirmed | | Total | |
|---|---|---|---|---|---|---|---|---|---|---|
| | No. | % | No. | % | No. | % | No. | % | No. | % |
| 1977–1985 | – | – | 65 | 3.54 | 901 | 49.13 | 545 | 29.72 | 1,511 | 82.39 |
| 2007–2013 | 93 | 5.01 | 293 | 15.77 | 395 | 21.26 | 146 | 7.86 | 834 | 44.89 |
| Significance: The change is extremely significant (P <0.0001) | | | | | | | | | | |

### Breeding distribution 1977–85

### Breeding-period abundance 2007–13

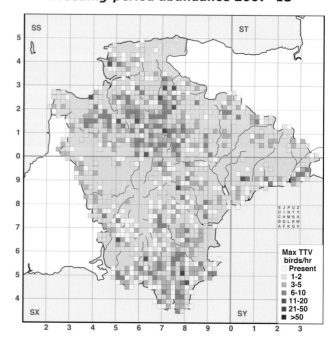

# Yellowhammer
## *Emberiza citrinella*

**Red listed**

THE SIGHT and sound of a male Yellowhammer singing in farmland or on a gorse-covered common brings gladness to the heart, no doubt explaining the local Devon name of 'gladdie'.

Formerly a common hedgerow bird of farmland in the 19th century, and described by Moore (1969) as "abundant", Yellowhammers have suffered a severe decline in their Devon distribution, with evidence of breeding falling from 82% of tetrads in the *Devon Tetrad Atlas 1977–85* to 45% during the current survey. The worrying 55% national decline between 1970 and 2012 (*State of UK Birds 2014*) is probably due to intensification of agriculture, including crop spraying, loss of hedgerows and the decline of mixed farming systems.

Yellowhammers are closely associated with cereal farming and both insect larvae and cereal grains are important in the diet of nestlings. Although Yellowhammers were recorded in the breeding season from all except one 10-km square, the tetrad map shows that they are now absent or very scarce in the more coastal parts of North Devon, in the area north and north-west of Dartmoor, and east of the Exe. Breeding density is highest in the South Hams and in an area of northern Devon bounded by South Molton, North Tawton and Bradworthy towards the Cornish border.

A detailed survey of farmland birds in 227 tetrads in South Devon in both 2003 and 2009 revealed a 15% decline in the number of Yellowhammer

territories (from 1,584 to 1,347) between the two years, and a reduction in the number of occupied tetrads from 179 to 167 (Stanbury *et al.* 2010). Several studies on Dartmoor have also shown declines. During the 1950s and 1960s, a population of 50–100 pairs was present in the Postbridge area, largely in young conifer plantations (Dare & Hamilton 1968). However, by the early 1990s, when the trees had grown up, only nine singing males were present. An area of Roborough Down, surveyed for Dartford Warblers in 2009, held 18 or 19 Yellowhammer territories, compared to around 30 in 2000 (Smaldon 2010). In a well-watched Sampford Spiney garden, a Garden Bird Survey from 1991 to 2010 found that Yellowhammers changed in status from being regular spring visitors, with weekly maxima of nine or ten in 1991 and 1993, to rare visitors – only six singles were seen between 1995 and 2010 (Smalley & John 2010).

The contraction of the Yellowhammer's range in Devon is also reflected in the winter-period map because this species is largely sedentary. There has been a decline in winter survival due to reductions in winter seed availability, and it is possible that the loss could be reversed by increasing winter stubbles or by supplementary feeding (*Bird Atlas 2007–11*).

*Text: A W G John / Photo: Neil Bygrave*
*Yellowhammer sponsored by Michael & Diane Stamp*

Balmer *et al.* 2013: 642; Sitters 1988: 286; Tyler 2010: 646

### Winter-period abundance 2007–13

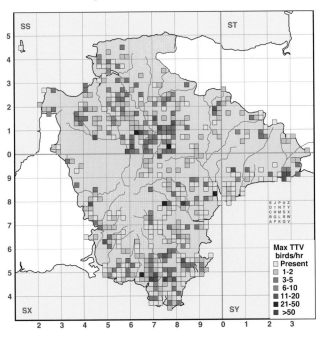

Max TTV birds/hr
☐ Present
☐ 1-2
▨ 3-5
▨ 6-10
■ 11-20
■ 21-50
■ >50

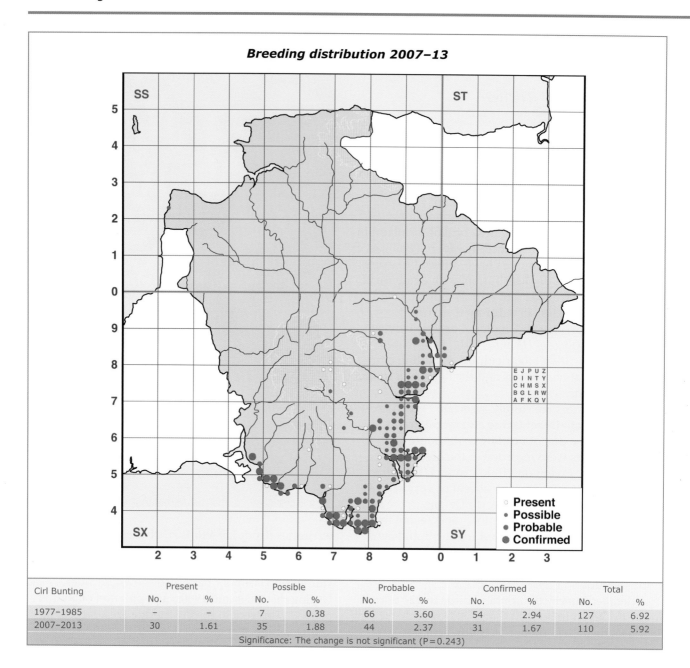

## Breeding distribution 2007–13

| Cirl Bunting | Present | | Possible | | Probable | | Confirmed | | Total | |
|---|---|---|---|---|---|---|---|---|---|---|
| | No. | % | No. | % | No. | % | No. | % | No. | % |
| 1977–1985 | – | – | 7 | 0.38 | 66 | 3.60 | 54 | 2.94 | 127 | 6.92 |
| 2007–2013 | 30 | 1.61 | 35 | 1.88 | 44 | 2.37 | 31 | 1.67 | 110 | 5.92 |
| Significance: The change is not significant (P = 0.243) | | | | | | | | | | |

## Breeding distribution 1977–85

## Breeding-period abundance 2007–13

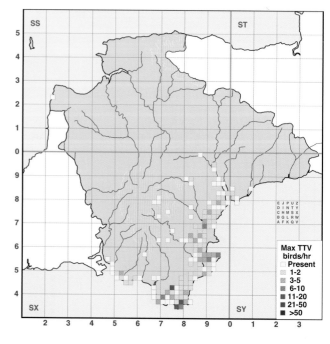

# Cirl Bunting

## *Emberiza cirlus*

**Red listed**

CIRL BUNTING is a resident of mixed farmland, requiring both grassland and arable habitats combined with hedges or areas of scrub. It frequents an often undulating landscape of small fields and favours south-facing slopes enclosed by Devon hedges. The presence of spring-sown barley with winter stubbles is usually the key habitat factor determining presence and success of the species. Formerly distributed across much of southern and central England (Aplin 1892), the Cirl Bunting population underwent a catastrophic collapse in the mid-1960s. By the end of fieldwork for the *Devon Tetrad Atlas 1977–85*, Devon was the species' final UK stronghold, marking a retreat to the county where Cirl Bunting was first recorded in England in 1800 (Montagu 1833).

Devon remains the national stronghold for breeding Cirl Buntings, though a small population has recently been re-established in south Cornwall. Their current distribution is centred on coastal farmland between Plymouth and Exeter, with some inland records from Dartmoor and the Teign valley. Cirl Buntings are largely sedentary, typically not moving further than two kilometres between breeding and wintering areas (Evans 1996). However, they have recently recolonized East Devon, and since the Atlas period have also been reported in North Devon in April 2014 (pers. comm.).

The species' range has contracted since the *Devon Tetrad Atlas 1977–85*, with the loss of most

populations to the north and east of Exeter. It was during the 1977–85 fieldwork period that the last pairs disappeared from the north of the county, with none found in 1982 (Brown & Grice 2005). Numbers reached their lowest ebb in 1989 when only 114 pairs were recorded in 50 tetrads in South Devon (Evans 1992). Although there has been an overall range contraction, consolidation and expansion of the population in South Devon means that the number of occupied tetrads actually increased slightly between the two Devon Atlases, taking into account the 30 tetrads in which the species was 'present' in 2007–13 but without evidence of breeding.

Since the early 1990s, a species recovery project run by the RSPB has worked with farmers to provide vital habitat for Cirl Buntings, resulting in population growth to over 860 pairs in 2009 (Stanbury *et al.* 2010). If this trend continues, there should be in the region of 1,000 pairs by 2015. While the future for Cirl Buntings is far from secure, as the species continues to rely on sympathetic management and is also vulnerable to the effects of severe winter weather, it is perhaps not too much to hope that Devon's Cirl Buntings can pioneer the recolonization of southern England.

*Text: Cath Jeffs / Photo: Steve Hatch*
*Cirl Bunting sponsored by Nigel Hewitt*

Balmer *et al.* 2013: 644; Sitters 1988: 288; Tyler 2010: 648

### Winter-period abundance 2007–13

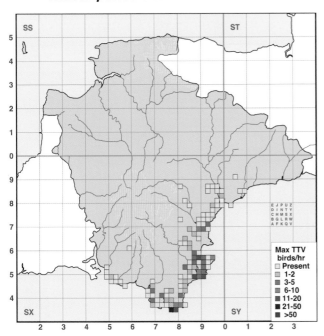

Max TTV birds/hr
- ☐ Present
- 1-2
- 3-5
- 6-10
- 11-20
- 21-50
- >50

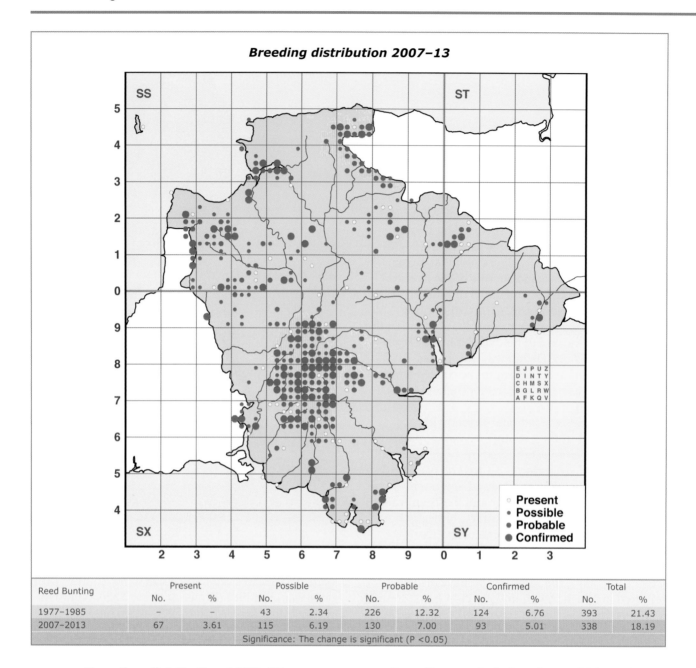

## Breeding distribution 2007–13

| Reed Bunting | Present | | Possible | | Probable | | Confirmed | | Total | |
|---|---|---|---|---|---|---|---|---|---|---|
| | No. | % | No. | % | No. | % | No. | % | No. | % |
| 1977–1985 | – | – | 43 | 2.34 | 226 | 12.32 | 124 | 6.76 | 393 | 21.43 |
| 2007–2013 | 67 | 3.61 | 115 | 6.19 | 130 | 7.00 | 93 | 5.01 | 338 | 18.19 |
| | Significance: The change is significant (P <0.05) | | | | | | | | | |

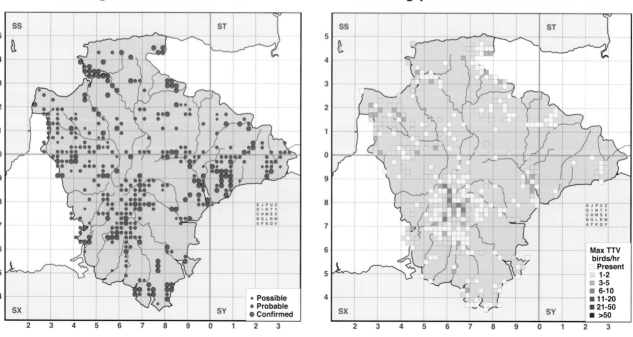

## Breeding distribution 1977–85

## Breeding-period abundance 2007–13

# Reed Bunting
## *Emberiza schoeniclus*

REED BUNTINGS occupy a wide variety of wetland habitats during the breeding season, including freshwater and brackish marshes and swamps, reedbeds, fen-meadows and peat bogs. The species has recently expanded its breeding range to drier habitats such as young conifer plantations and oilseed rape crops (Cramp *et al.* 1994). The mires of Dartmoor, Exmoor, the Culm region of the north-west of the county and the wetlands associated with the estuaries of our major rivers are the most important breeding areas for Reed Buntings in Devon, with intensively farmed areas supporting few, if any, due to the scarcity of suitable nesting habitat and food. Favoured wintering areas appear to be relatively restricted: just 13 tetrads yielded TTV counts of more than six birds, compared to nearly 100 such tetrads during the breeding period. In winter, Reed Buntings tend to move to drier habitats such as stubble fields, ungrazed/unmown field margins and overgrown ditches. However, intensive agricultural practices have severely reduced the availability of these important winter habitats. Some birds now come to garden feeders.

The breeding distribution shows a major shift between the *Devon Tetrad Atlas 1977–85* and the present survey. The species has colonized Dartmoor and Exmoor, where the main concentrations now occur, but moved away from lowland regions of the county. East Devon in particular shows a dramatic reduction, and even the Culm region, a former breeding stronghold for the species, shows extensive losses. Overall, there has been a 36% reduction in the number of tetrads for which confirmed or probable breeding was recorded (though this figure falls to 14% if possible breeding is also included in the calculation). Data from BTO monitoring surveys show that the Reed Bunting population remained relatively stable nationally between 1966 and 2012 (BTO BirdTrends 2014). However, this apparent numerical stability masks important demographic and ecological changes, which include the colonization of drier habitats and in particular the use of oilseed rape for breeding. Oilseed rape appears to have become crucial in reducing the dependency of Reed Buntings on wetlands (Gruar *et al.* 2006).

Small numbers of migrants were recorded annually at coastal watchpoints during the Atlas years, while the largest winter flock reported was 60 at Woodbury on 9 January 2011 (*DBR*). This came shortly after a period of severe cold at the end of 2010.

The continuation of agri-environmental schemes and nature conservation initiatives that support the maintenance and creation of wetlands – such as Culm grasslands, riparian buffer zones with tall vegetation, and winter stubbles – will be critical to maintaining the lowland-breeding population in Devon. However, the long-term future of the Reed Bunting's current core range, much of which is under some form of conservation management, looks most likely to be influenced by the effects of climate change on the wetlands of Dartmoor and Exmoor.

*Text: Jerry Tallowin / Photo: Mike Langman*
*Reed Bunting sponsored by R Burridge*

Balmer *et al.* 2013: 646; Sitters 1988: 290; Tyler 2010: 655

### Winter-period abundance 2007–13

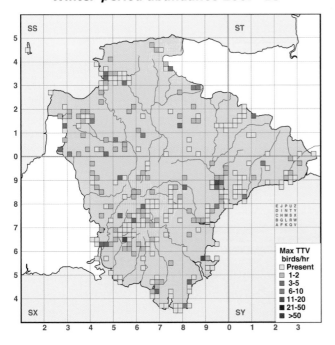

Max TTV birds/hr
□ Present
▫ 1-2
▪ 3-5
■ 6-10
■ 11-20
■ 21-50
■ >50

# Other species recorded

## British List Category A, B and C species

### Pink-footed Goose
*Anser brachyrhyncus*                                    Amber listed

Though an abundant wintering species in parts of northern and eastern Britain, 'Pink-feet' are very rare visitors to Devon. Overall there were records of one to three individuals from 19 tetrads in nine 10-km squares, covering sites around the Avon, Exe and Taw/Torridge Estuaries, the River Dart, Rackerhayes Lake, the South Huish area and Lundy. These occurred in all months from September to May and perhaps included some feral or escaped individuals as well as genuinely wild birds.

*Text: Tim Jones & Tim Davis*

### White-fronted Goose
*Anser albifrons*

European White-fronted Goose  *A. a. albifrons*          Red listed
Greenland White-fronted Goose  *A. a. flavirostris*       Red listed

'Whitefronts' are rare in Devon and were recorded in just 15 tetrads in nine 10-km squares, mainly around the Axe and Exe Estuaries. Almost all records for which birds were identified to sub-species level involved the nominate race, which breeds in the Russian Arctic. The only confirmed records for the Greenland-breeding race *A. a. flavirostris* were of a single bird on the Exe Estuary in November 2011, and four at South Huish Marsh in November 2012. The largest flock – of *A. a. albifrons* – was of 19 in flight off the Teign Estuary in November 2008.

*Text: Tim Jones & Tim Davis / Photo: (Greenland White-fronted Goose) David Land*

### Barnacle Goose
*Branta leucopsis*                                       Amber listed

Most Barnacle Geese seen in Devon are considered to be from escaped or feral stock, though strong circumstantial evidence indicates that wild birds occur from time to time and there is at least one ringing recovery that proves this (Tyler 2010). During the breeding period, 'Barnies' were recorded in 14 tetrads, including six in the Exe catchment and estuary, three around the nearby Teign and Otter Estuaries, four in the far south-west of the county, and one in North Devon, but there was no reported evidence of nesting. Winter records were both more numerous and more widespread, involving 25 tetrads in thirteen 10-km squares. A flock of five, thought likely to be wild birds, spent a week on the Exe Estuary in late February and early March 2012 (*DBR*). *Bird Atlas 2007–11* found that the range of the naturalized British population had expanded by 88% since the *Breeding Atlas 1988–91*.

*Text: Tim Jones & Tim Davis*

## Red-breasted Goose
### Branta ruficollis

This strikingly beautiful Siberian-breeding goose is a rare vagrant to Devon, though only one of 13 records prior to the Atlas period was regarded as being of wild origin (Tyler 2010). An adult, first seen at East Budleigh in late October 2009 and which relocated to the Exe Estuary from early December and remained into 2010, was considered by the BBRC as a probable escape. What was presumed to be the same bird returned to the Exe Estuary in October 2010 and was joined by a second adult (also considered an escape) in December, both staying into 2011. Finally, a first-winter bird, regarded by the BBRC as being of wild origin, was on the Exe Estuary from November 2011 to March 2012 (DBRs).

*Text: Tim Jones & Tim Davis*

## Ruddy Shelduck
### Tadorna ferruginea

While genuinely wild vagrants of this African and Eurasian species are considered to have occurred historically in the UK, there are no accepted records of wild birds in Devon, with all documented occurrences in the county thought to relate to feral birds originating from captive stock (Tyler 2010). During the Atlas period there were records in just two areas (though covering three tetrads in the winter period and two in the breeding period). Those in the Torbay region were thought to relate to free-flying birds that escaped from Paignton Zoo in 2003 (DBR 2012). Of three original escapees, two were still present in 2008, but only one remained from 2009 onwards. The only records from elsewhere were two at Kenwith Castle, north Devon, in late December 2008.

*Text: Tim Jones & Tim Davis*

## American Wigeon
### Anas americana

This species is the North American counterpart to our Eurasian Wigeon and is a rare visitor to Devon and the rest of the UK. During the Atlas period, single drakes were seen on the Taw/Torridge Estuary (October/November 2007) and on the Exe Estuary in April 2011 and again from October 2011 to March 2012 (DBRs).

*Text: Tim Jones & Tim Davis / Photo: David Land*

## Green-winged Teal
### Anas carolinensis

This American counterpart of the Eurasian Teal *Anas crecca* is a regular transatlantic vagrant to the UK. Two birds, both adult males, were recorded during the Atlas period, in December 2012 and January 2013, at Portworthy Mica Dam and the Axe Estuary respectively (DBRs).

*Text: J M Lock*

## Ring-necked Duck
### Aythya collaris

During the Atlas period there were six records of this transatlantic vagrant from North America, though possibly involving only four individuals. A drake was seen at Tamar Lakes on 12 February 2010 and what may have been the same bird was then on Roadford Reservoir from 2 March to 2 April. In 2012 a female was at Slapton from 22 October and stayed until 6 April 2013 and a first-winter drake was present at the same site between 13 February and 13 April 2013. A female that frequented Hennock between 2 February and 12 March 2013 may have been the bird seen at Stover on 18 February (DBRs).

*Text: Stella Beavan*

## King Eider
### *Somateria spectabilis*

A first-winter male of this Arctic-breeding vagrant to Britain was found near the mouth of the Taw/Torridge Estuary in February 2008 where it remained until early May. It reappeared in smarter second-winter plumage on 12 October of the same year and was last seen on 8 November. This was the first and, to date, only record for Devon (*DBR*, Bastin 2009).

*Text: J M Lock*

## Surf Scoter
### *Melanitta perspicillata*

One or two individuals of this North American species wintered along the south coast, usually off Dawlish Warren but also east to Seaton Bay, between 2007 and early 2012. In particular, a first-winter female first seen off Dawlish Warren on 2 November 2007 was widely assumed to have wintered in the same area in each of the following four winters and was last seen on 18 February 2012. Other records included a first-winter male at Broadsands, Torbay, 12 December 2007; a second-summer male off Dawlish Warren, 20 June–30 August 2008; and a female off the north coast at Downend, near Croyde, 28–30 October 2012 (*DBRs*).

*Text: J M Lock*

## Smew
### *Mergellus albellus*              Amber listed

Smew are uncommon winter visitors to Devon, with the key sites being the Exe Estuary, Slapton Ley and the Taw/Torridge Estuary, as well as some inland waters, particularly Roadford Reservoir. The species was not recorded in the first three winters of the Atlas period, and indeed had not been recorded since 2003 (Tyler 2010). However, during the winters 2009/10 to 2012/13 Smew were found in 21 tetrads. Most records were of redheads and generally referred to ones and twos but an exceptional five birds were present at Beesands Ley in February 2012, the highest number seen at one site in the county since 1991 (Tyler 2010).

*Text: Ray Jones / Photo: David Land*

## Lady Amherst's Pheasant
### *Chrysolophus amherstiae*

In its native Burma and south-west China, Lady Amherst's Pheasant prefers dense dark forests with thick undergrowth. It was introduced to Britain in 1828 and established a feral population in Bedfordshire which has subsequently gone into possible terminal decline (Tyler 2010). First recorded in Devon in 2002, this species was recorded in four tetrads during the Atlas years: in 2009, 2011 and 2013, all sightings being of single males (*DBRs*).

*Text: Ray Jones*

## Golden Pheasant
### *Chrysolophus pictus*

Introduced into Norfolk and Suffolk in the 1870s, Golden Pheasant is native to the dark dense forests of western China. In Devon it was first noted at Lynton in 1942 and during the current Atlas period was recorded from four different tetrads. The origin of these birds is uncertain as there is no evidence that there is a wild breeding population in the county.

*Text: Ray Jones*

## Fea's /Zino's Petrel
### Pterodroma feae /P. madeira

These very similar species, from a genus known as 'Gadfly Petrels' (Darlaston 2010) breed on the Cape Verde Islands and the Desertas Islands off Madeira (Fea's Petrel) and on mainland Madeira (Zino's Petrel) but roam widely outside the breeding season. They are virtually indistinguishable in the field and though only Fea's Petrel has been admitted to the British List, most individuals are recorded as Fea's /Zino's. In 2009, two were seen from the south coast: one at Prawle Point in August and the other off Budleigh Salterton in October (*DBRs*).

*Text: J M Lock*

## Macaronesian Shearwater
### Puffinus baroli

A vagrant species, with the first Devon record being a calling adult on Lundy above the road up from the Landing Bay during 2010 and 2011 (Townend 2012). A calling individual was also caught and ringed on Skomer (Pembrokeshire) in 1981 and returned in 1982 (James 1986). The decline of the North Atlantic breeding population means that such occurrences may be even rarer in the future. During the Atlas period there was one further accepted record: a single bird passing off Berry Head on 6 June 2012 (*DBR*). Four days after the end of the Atlas period a single bird was recorded off Start Point on 4 August 2013 (*DBR*).

*Text: Mike Langman*

## Night-heron
### Nycticorax nycticorax

This small, stocky, mainly nocturnal heron occurs in Devon as a vagrant from continental Europe. Singletons are occasionally found at freshwater wetlands, usually near the south coast, and mainly in March/April. In March 2012, a group of four (three adults and a first-summer bird) was found at Woolacombe, on the north coast, later dispersing to other sites (*DBR* 2012).

*Text: Robert Hurrell*

## Purple Heron
### Ardea purpurea

Purple Herons are vagrants to Devon, with most birds occurring between April and June in reedbeds and marshlands. This species bred for the first time in the UK in 2010 in Kent and although there were five summer records for Devon during the Atlas period (a juvenile in August 2010, two separate adults in April 2011 and two separate adults in April/May 2012), all of these were considered to be passage migrants and there was no suggestion of breeding (*DBRs*).

*Text: Robert Hurrell / Photo: David Land*

## Black Stork
### Ciconia nigra

This vagrant from breeding grounds in parts of France and Spain, and more widely across central and eastern Europe, was recorded three times during the Atlas period. One was in the Tavy/Tamar Estuary area in April 2010, and another, believed to be the same individual, was on Dartmoor in May that year. In addition, one flew over North Molton in May 2013 (*DBRs*).

*Text: J M Lock*

## White Stork
### *Ciconia ciconia*

White Storks are very scarce in Devon and there was only a single record of a presumed genuine vagrant during the Atlas period, when one was seen in late September 2010 near Prawle Point. A bird seen on the Axe Estuary and in the north of the county in April/May 2011 carried a leg-ring that proved it had escaped from captivity in northern England (*DBRs*).

*Text: J M Lock*

## Black Kite
### *Milvus migrans*

Black Kite was added to the Devon list as recently as 1981 and has since become a rare passage migrant to Devon. The nearest breeding populations are throughout much of France and elsewhere in continental Europe where there has been a moderate increase (p<0.05) since 1982 (BirdLife International 2015). During the Atlas period records came from nine tetrads, reflecting an apparent increase in the frequency of 'overshooting' birds, including one staying from 23 July to 15 August 2011 (*DBR*).

*Text: Mark Darlaston*

## Short-toed Eagle
### *Circaetus gallicus*

One of these snake-eating raptors that breed in southern and eastern Europe flew over Dawlish Warren on 16 October 2011 (Collins 2012). It was moving west and was also seen at Exmouth and Lyme Regis shortly afterwards. This was the first Devon record and only the second for Britain. It was thought to have been the same individual as one on Jersey a few days previously.

*Text: J M Lock*

## Montagu's Harrier
### *Circus pygargus*                                    Amber listed

Although this species is the Society's emblem, and is named after George Montagu, a pioneer in Devon ornithology, it last bred in the county in 1976 and is now a rare passage migrant and the UK's rarest breeding raptor (Musgrove *et al.* 2013). During the March–September Atlas period the species was recorded in 11 tetrads in nine 10-km squares, with a generally south to south-east distribution in the county, and mostly in April or May.

*Text: Mark Darlaston*

## Rough-legged Buzzard
### *Buteo lagopus*

Rough-legged Buzzard is an occasional vagrant to Devon from continental Europe. A first-year bird was present on Lundy between 9 November and 7 December 2008 (*DBR*).

*Text: Mark Darlaston*

## Spotted Crake
### *Porzana porzana*                                    Amber listed

This inconspicuous, skulking crake is a scarce passage migrant in Devon but is undoubtedly much overlooked. One (a juvenile) was on the Taw/Torridge Estuary in August/September 2009, one was found dead at Ugborough in August 2010 and one was on the Axe Estuary in September/October 2012. In addition, the remains of a Spotted Crake were found at a Peregrine eyrie in Exeter in October 2011, the crake presumably having been caught while migrating over the city at night (*DBRs*).

*Text: J M Lock*

## Little Crake
*Porzana parva*

At home in natural reedbeds bordering eutrophic lakes and ponds of eastern Europe, Little Crake is an accidental visitor to Devon that can occur at any time of year. The only Devon record during the current Atlas period was an adult male at Exminster Marshes from 9–23 April 2008 (*DBR*). This was the first record for mainland Devon since a bird on the Otter Estuary in 1939; the last Lundy record was in 1983.

*Text: Ray Jones*

## Purple Gallinule
*Porphyrio martinicus*

A juvenile of this American species was found freshly dead in a garden near Mary Tavy in January 2011 (Harris 2012). This was the first record for Devon and the third for the UK. Individuals from the northern part of the range are migratory and this bird must have been blown off course by autumn storms.

*Text: J M Lock*

## Great Bustard
*Otis tarda*

A Great Bustard reintroduction project (**www.greatbustard.org**) began on Salisbury Plain (Wiltshire) in 2004 and the first chicks were raised in 2009. Wandering wing-tagged individuals from this initiative were seen in the South Hams in November and December 2011 and near Exmouth in May 2012 (*DBRs*).

*Text: J M Lock*

## Stone-curlew
*Burhinus oedicnemus*     Amber listed

The Stone-curlew is a rare summer visitor to the UK with a localized breeding distribution well to the east of Devon. Conservation action since the 1980s has resulted in a 124% increase since 1995 and in 2010 the UK population was estimated at some 375 pairs (*Bird Atlas 2007–11*). Occurrences in Devon are rare; records during the Atlas period, all on or near the south coast, came in 2007, 2008, 2012 (3) and 2013 (2 or 3; *DBRs*). The sighting in 2007 of a bird colour-ringed as a pullus in Norfolk suggests that some of the records are of British-bred birds. There was an unsuccessful breeding attempt in 2001 (Rylands 2007).

*Text: John Waldon*

## Black-winged Stilt
*Himantopus himantopus*

Black-winged Stilt is a vagrant in Devon, typically 'overshooting' in spring from southern European breeding grounds. With possibly as many as seven individuals, 2012 was an exceptional year when at least three were recorded from the Exe Estuary and two from the Taw/Torridge Estuary in April and May (*DBR*). There were no records in any other Atlas years.

*Text: J M Lock / Photo: Rob Jutsum*

## American Golden Plover
### Pluvialis dominica

This transatlantic vagrant, which breeds in arctic North America and winters in South America, was recorded three times during the Atlas period. One was seen on the Exe Estuary in May 2008, with another there in October/November 2010, and a third was on the Taw/Torridge Estuary in June 2011 (*DBRs*).

*Text: J M Lock*

## Kentish Plover
### Charadrius alexandrinus

Kentish Plovers occur only as rare passage migrants in Devon. There are four Atlas records: females on Dawlish Warren on 13–14 May 2009 and 23–26 April 2010, and a female on the Axe Estuary on 3 May 2012. In addition a juvenile was recorded at Dawlish Warren on 9 August 2009 (*DBRs*). It is surprising that Kentish Plovers are so infrequently recorded in Devon as there is a thriving population of 350–400 pairs just 150 km away on the other side of the English Channel on the coast of Normandy (Debout 2009).

*Text: Humphrey Sitters / Photo: (left) Lee Collins*

## Temminck's Stint
### Calidris temminckii

With only 25 records for the county, Temminck's Stint is a rare passage migrant to Devon marshes. The only records during the Atlas period were of one on Exminster Marshes on 18 May 2008, one at Thurlestone Marsh on 30 August 2010 and a juvenile at Black Hole Marsh on 17 November 2011 (*DBRs*).

*Text: Humphrey Sitters*

## White-rumped Sandpiper
### Calidris fuscicollis

A single individual of this small wader, which breeds in the Canadian Arctic and winters in South America, was seen during the Atlas period on the Axe Estuary on 7–8 November 2011 (*DBR*). This was the ninth record for Devon.

*Text: J M Lock*

## Buff-breasted Sandpiper
### Calidris subruficollis

Six of these Nearctic vagrants were recorded for short periods in two Atlas autumns (2010 & 2011). Arriving between 2 September and 2 October, they frequented short grassland habitats close to coastal cliffs at Soar, East Prawle, Higher Brownstone and Lundy, and adjoining the Taw/Torridge and Exe Estuaries (*DBRs*).

*Text: Peter Dare / Photo: (right) Lee Collins*

# Pectoral Sandpiper
*Calidris melanotos*

This transatlantic vagrant was recorded in six consecutive years (2008–2013) during the Atlas period. One on Exminster Marshes on 29 May 2012 was the only spring record. The Axe Estuary provided four autumn records and Lundy three; the rest came mainly from the south coast but there was also one on the Taw/Torrdge Estuary in 2012. Three were together on the Exe Estuary in September 2012. A late autumn juvenile was at Thurlestone Marsh on 6 November 2011. On the last two days of the Atlas period, 30 & 31 July 2013, one was at Black Hole Marsh, staying until 1 August (*DBRs*).

*Text: Humphrey Sitters*

# Semipalmated Sandpiper
*Calidris pusilla*

This small wader, which breeds in the Canadian Arctic and Alaska, migrating to winter around the Caribbean and the coasts of northern South America, is a fairly regular transatlantic vagrant to Britain. During the Atlas period there were three records of juveniles in late summer or early autumn: at Dawlish Warren in August/September 2008 and August 2010, and on the Axe Estuary and Seaton Beach in September/October 2011 (*DBRs*). These were the sixth to eighth records for the county.

*Text: J M Lock / Photo: (left) Steve Waite*

# Wilson's Phalarope
*Phalaropus tricolor*

One of these vagrants from North American breeding grounds, which prefer marshes and wet meadows to open water, was at Bowling Green Marsh and Exminster Marsh (Exe Estuary) on 2–7 September 2009 (*DBR*).

*Text: Stella Beavan*

# Red-necked Phalarope
*Phalaropus lobatus*                                                          **Red listed**

This phalarope, which breeds throughout the Arctic, as well as in the Hebrides and Shetland, is much rarer in Devon than the Grey Phalarope. There was only one record during the Atlas period, from Velator, Taw/Torridge Estuary, in November 2007. The bird was eventually killed by a Carrion Crow (*DBR*).

*Text: J M Lock*

# Grey Phalarope
*Phalaropus fulicarius*

Small numbers of between one and twenty individuals were seen each autumn of the Atlas period, between August and November but mainly in September, along both coastlines. A few birds were seen in January, in 2007, 2009 and 2012. Sightings in the south came from Wembury, Thurlestone, South Huish, Avon Estuary, Slapton, Berry Head, Dawlish Warren and Exmouth; and in the north at Hartland Point, the Taw/Torridge Estuary and Lundy. Some sought shelter in bays and inlets and a few came inland onto freshwaters at South Milton Ley and Tamar Lakes, and one even strayed onto a Dartmoor reservoir at Venford. A bird was at Roadford Reservoir in October 2009, and one spent two weeks there in October–November 2013. (*DBRs*).

*Text: Peter Dare / Photo: (right) Rob Jutsum*

## Spotted Sandpiper
### *Actitis macularius*

During the Atlas period, single birds of this Nearctic vagrant were recorded three times during the autumn months of September to November, on the upper reaches of the Exe (twice) and Plym Estuaries. One individual stayed over the winter at each site.

*Text: Peter Dare / Photo: (left) David Land*

## Solitary Sandpiper
### *Tringa solitaria*

The Solitary Sandpiper is a transatlantic vagrant to Britain. The single Devon record – the first for the county – during the Atlas period was of a bird that frequented Black Hole Marsh, 10–15 October 2010 (*DBR*, Waite 2011).

*Text: J M Lock*

## Lesser Yellowlegs
### *Tringa flavipes*

This attractive Nearctic wader breeds in Alaska and the Canadian Arctic and winters in the Caribbean and South America, occurring in Britain as a fairly regular transatlantic vagrant. There was just one record during the Atlas period: an individual overwintered on the Plym Estuary in 2012–2013 (*DBRs*).

*Text: J M Lock / Photo: (right) David Land*

## Marsh Sandpiper
### *Tringa stagnatilis*

Marsh Sandpipers breed in northern Eurasia (mainly Russia) and have a vast winter range stretching from the Mediterranean to Australia. Though fairly regular vagrants to Britain, they have only been recorded three times in Devon. The third record occurred during the Atlas period: a juvenile on the Exe Estuary in August 2008 (*DBR*).

*Text: J M Lock*

## Long-billed Dowitcher
### *Limnodromus scolopaceus*

There were two autumn records of this Nearctic vagrant, at freshwater marshes beside the estuaries of the Axe in November 2010, and Exe from 24 October 2007. The latter bird overwintered and was last seen on 29 March 2008 (*DBRs*).

*Text: Peter Dare*

## Gull-billed Tern
### Gelochelidon nilotica

This vagrant marsh tern from continental European breeding grounds was recorded twice during the Atlas period: one flew over Topsham in May 2009 and two were on the Exe Estuary on 28 June 2010, with one of these (or perhaps a third bird) present on the Exe from 1–10 July (*DBRs*).

*Text: J M Lock*

## Whiskered Tern
### Chlidonias hybrida

This scarce passage migrant from southern European breeding grounds occurs only rarely in Devon. Most records are in spring, especially the month of May. The only occurrence during the current Atlas period was no exception, with one at Lower Tamar Lake on 8 May 2008 (*DBR*).

*Text: Stella Beavan*

## White-winged Black Tern
### Chlidonias leucopterus

This species, a vagrant from eastern Europe, was recorded once during Atlas surveys: an adult moulting out of summer plumage was at Slapton on 8 August 2008.

*Text: J M Lock*

## Sabine's Gull
### Xema sabini

A highlight of a good autumn seawatch, Sabine's Gull is a scarce, yet regular, passage species along the Devon coast. Pelagic when not breeding, these gulls mostly remain offshore, with the few seen from land usually following onshore gales. With records within the Atlas period from 2008 to 2012, almost all were typical of the county and came from the south coast, with the only north coast record being two birds seen off Hartland Point on 11 September 2008 (*DBR*). Records from the south coast were from well-watched points between Thurlestone and Seaton. Most frequently seen between September and October, birds were also recorded in August 2008 and December 2011 (*DBRs*).

*Text: Jeremy Barker / Photo: (left) Lee Collins*

## Bonaparte's Gull
### Chroicocephalus philadelphia

The North American counterpart of the Black-headed Gull is a rare visitor to Devon, with all records to date from the south coast of the county. During the Atlas period a first-winter bird was seen at Bowling Green Marsh on 20 & 21 May 2008. A second-year individual was on the Otter from 13–29 April 2011 and also seen at Dawlish from 18 April–19 July, and one in adult plumage was in the same locality on 29 August. In 2012 an adult/near adult was at Dawlish Warren from 21 October until 18 November and at Teignmouth from 8–15 December. In 2013 an adult was present at Bowling Green Marsh from 2–18 May (*DBRs*). Some of these records may relate to the same returning bird.

*Text: Jeremy Barker / Photo: (right) Gary Thoburn*

## Laughing Gull
### Larus atricilla

Laughing Gull is a very rare visitor to the county from North America, with just a handful of records since the first in 1984 (Tyler 2010). During the Atlas period a single second-winter bird was at Countess Wear (Exe Estuary) on 15 December 2007 (*DBR*). It was thought to be the same bird that ranged widely around the Exe Estuary, including a brief visit to the Axe Estuary, in the months prior to the start of the Atlas period. This bird was typical both in locality and timing, as all Devon records have been coastal and during either late autumn or in winter (Tyler 2010).

*Text: Jeremy Barker / Photo: (left) Paul Nunn*

## Ring-billed Gull
### Larus delawarensis

Since the heady days of the mid-1990s, when up to 17 new birds occurred in a single year, Ring-billed Gulls seem to have become genuine rarities again in Devon, with none being recorded since 2008. There was just one record – on the Exe Estuary in April 2008 – during the Atlas breeding period, and three during the winter period – on the Axe between 20 & 23 January and 10 March 2008, and at Slapton Ley on 3 February 2008 (*DBRs*). Given that Ring-billed Gulls continue to increase in number on the eastern seaboard of North America (Environment Canada 2014; Sauer *et al.* 2014) and in Ireland and the west of mainland UK (*Bird Atlas 2007–11*), the lack of more recent records in Devon is somewhat perplexing.

*Text: Jeremy Barker / Photo (right) Mike Langman*

## Caspian Gull
### Larus cachinnans                                                    Amber listed

This is a species with a complex taxonomic history and was previously considered conspecific with both Herring Gull and Yellow-legged Gull. Caspian Gulls are very rare in Devon and were first recorded in 2006. Identification is not straightforward and the species may easily be overlooked amongst gatherings of other large gulls. The dozen or so records during the Atlas years all came from the Axe, Exe and Otter Estuaries – areas with concentrations of large gulls, especially in late summer when immature birds are wandering, that are regularly scrutinized by dedicated and expert gull-watchers.

*Text: Jeremy Barker*

## American Herring Gull
### Larus smithsonianus

The second Devon record of this North American counterpart to our own Herring Gull occurred in 2009 when a first-winter bird was on the Otter Estuary, 13–20 February, and at Budleigh Salterton, 6–16 March (*DBR*).

*Text: Stella Beavan*

## Alpine Swift
### *Apus melba*

This vagrant from continental European breeding grounds was recorded in seven tetrads during the Atlas period, usually singly in any year. One was recorded on Colyford Common on 24 August 2009; in 2010, a remarkable five birds were recorded between March and July at Yelverton, Exminster, Musbury, Plymouth and Berry Head; and in 2012 one was noted on Lundy on 5 April (*DBRs*).

*Text: Stella Beavan*

## Blue-cheeked Bee-eater
### *Merops persicus*

A lone individual of this spectacular vagrant from northern Africa and the Middle East was photographed at Braunton Burrows on 30 June 2009 (*DBR*). This was only the second Devon record (the previous occurrence having been in 1987) and the tenth for Britain.

*Text: J M Lock*

## Bee-eater
### *Merops apiaster*

The Bee-eater is a stunningly colourful species and an occasional visitor to Devon, seen mostly during the spring as birds overshoot their southern European and north-west African breeding grounds. During the period of this Atlas they were recorded in June 2010 (up to eight birds in total), April 2011 (one) and May 2012 (one) in seven very scattered tetrads in both North and South Devon, including Lundy (*DBRs*).

*Text: Helen Booker*

## Roller
### *Coracias garrulus*

One of these magnificent vagrants from southern and eastern European breeding grounds flew over Teignmouth on 1 May 2012 (*DBR*). Accepted by the BBRC, this was only the thirteenth record for Devon.

*Text: Stella Beavan*

## Red-footed Falcon
### *Falco vespertinus*

There were two records of this vagrant from continental Europe during the Atlas period: a first-summer male at Prawle on 29 May 2008 and a female at Exminster and Powderham Marshes (Exe Estuary), 11–13 June 2010 (*DBRs*).

*Text: Mark Darlaston*

## Gyr Falcon
### *Falco rusticolus*

A very rare winter/passage vagrant to Devon from Arctic breeding grounds. During the Atlas period a white phase bird was at Saunton Sands on 18 March 2010 (*DBR*), the eleventh accepted record for the county.

*Text: Mark Darlaston / Photo: Rob Jutsum*

## Ring-necked Parakeet
### Psittacula krameri

The stronghold for Ring-necked Parakeet remains Greater London, but *Bird Atlas 2007–11* shows that breeding occurred in Weymouth in neighbouring Dorset. Wandering individuals occasionally reach Devon, particularly in winter, and it is possible that they may be breeding in one or more large towns/cities by the time of the next Atlas. During the current Atlas period at least one was recorded in Exeter in 2008, two individuals in Plympton and over the Otter Estuary in 2010 and an unusually high six widely separated birds in 2012 (*DBRs*).

*Text: Stella Beavan*

## Red-eyed Vireo
### Vireo olivaceus

This striking warbler-like bird breeds in the USA and Canada and winters in South America, north of the Amazon basin. It is one of the more regular transatlantic passerine vagrants to Britain and Ireland, and one at Wembury Point in October 2008 constituted the 11th Devon record (*DBR*).

*Text: J M Lock*

## Woodchat Shrike
### Lanius senator

This very scarce 'spring overshoot' visitor from southern European breeding grounds was noted in every spring of the Atlas period, with single adults appearing at or near coastal sites, mainly in April or May. Of the 13 sightings, eight were from the south coast, to the west of Start Point, and five were in the north including three on Lundy, the earliest being 18 April 2013 at South Efford Marsh, Aveton Gifford, and the latest 27 June 2009 on Lundy (*DBRs*).

*Text: Peter Dare*

## Hooded Crow
### Corvus cornix

Hooded Crows are rare passage migrants in Devon and there were only two accepted records during the current Atlas period. A bird seen near Great Torrington on 15 May 2012 may have been the same individual seen on Lundy on 17 May, where it remained until 28 May (*DBR*).

*Text: Stella Beavan*

## Penduline Tit
### Remiz pendulinus

Penduline Tits are found in thickets and scrub, usually near water, and are very occasional winter visitors to Devon. During the Atlas period a single male was recorded in five tetrads in two clusters: around Paignton between 14 January and 1 April 2009 after first appearing at Slapton Ley on 7 January (*DBR*). It has long been predicted that this species will colonize Britain from continental Europe (Sharrock 1976), and if this happens, occurrences are likely to become more regular in Devon.

*Text: Malcolm Burgess / Photo: Tim White*

## Short-toed Lark
### Calandrella brachydactyla

Short-toed Larks are rare vagrants to Devon from continental European or North African breeding grounds. During the Atlas period they were recorded from four tetrads, one at Budleigh Salterton (October 2011), one at Dawlish Warren (May 2013) and up to four on Lundy (May 2008 and May & September 2012) from where come more than half of all Devon records (Tyler 2010). Most records for the county are either from May–June or September–October. Birds are usually found in short dry grassland or in stubble fields, sometimes in company with other lark species.

*Text: J M Lock*

## Red-rumped Swallow
### Cecropis daurica

This species is a nationally scarce migrant occurring mainly as a spring overshoot from southern European breeding grounds. There were records in three years during the Atlas period: 2009 (two), 2011 and 2012 (four), mostly in May or early June, though two of the 2012 records were in October. All were near the south coast with the exception of one on Lundy in 2012 (*DBRs*).

*Text: J M Lock*

## Pallas's Warbler
### Phylloscopus proregulus

In spite of its regularity in eastern Britain, Pallas's Warbler remains a vagrant in Devon. During the survey period, birds occurred in autumn in only two years, 2010 and 2011, when ones and twos totalling about ten individuals occurred between 13 October and 5 November at a handful of migration hotspots on the south coast (Berry Head, Start Point, Prawle, East Soar). The only other record concerned a wintering bird at Kenwith LNR, North Devon, in January 2009 (*DBRs*).

*Text: Tim Jones*

## Radde's Warbler
### Phylloscopus schwarzi

This medium-sized brownish leaf-warbler breeds from southern Siberia east to the Korean peninsula and winters in south-east Asia. Vagrants occur in Britain annually, though mainly along the east coast. During the Atlas period one was seen at Prawle in October 2008, constituting the seventh Devon record (*DBR*).

*Text: J M Lock*

## Dusky Warbler
### Phylloscopus fuscatus

This vagrant warbler, which breeds in central Asia and winters in northern India and south-east Asia, was recorded once during the Atlas period, when one was at Orcombe Point in late October 2011 (*DBR*).

*Text: J M Lock / Photo: Paul Nunn*

## Western Bonelli's Warbler
### *Phylloscopus bonelli*

Western and Eastern (*P. orientalis*) Bonelli's Warblers were recognized as separate species on the British List in 1997. Western Bonelli's Warbler breeds in south-west Europe and north-west Africa and is a fairly regular vagrant to Britain. One trapped and ringed on Lundy on 4 September 2010 was the only occurrence during the Atlas period, but the third for Devon (*DBR*).

*Text: Mike Tyler*

## Barred Warbler
### *Sylvia nisoria*

Barred Warblers are rare passage migrants in Devon, recorded mainly between August and November. They are seen in most years, most frequently on Lundy or along the south coast. During the Atlas period single birds were recorded in October/November 2008 at Berry Head, October 2011 at Dawlish Warren and in September 2012 at both Prawle and East Soar (*DBRs*).

*Text: Mike Tyler*

## Subalpine Warbler
### *Sylvia cantillans*

This typically 'spring overshoot' species is a very scarce passage migrant from southern European breeding grounds. It is very much a Lundy speciality and, true to form, all the records during the Atlas period came from there. All were in spring: a second-year female (9 June 2010), an adult male (24 April 2011) and two second-year males trapped and ringed on 30 May 2012, one remaining until 2 June (*DBRs*). The BOU split Moltoni's Subalpine Warbler *S. subalpina* from Subalpine Warbler with effect from 2015 and further splits are possible. However, during the Atlas period only one species was included in the British List and this is the approach followed here.

*Text: J M Lock / Photo: Paul Sterry/NPL*

## Savi's Warbler
### *Locustella luscinioides*　　　　Red listed

Savi's Warbler is a vagrant in Devon. During the current Atlas period, singing males were recorded at three sites in the south of the county: Slapton Ley (24–30 April 2011), the Exe Estuary at Topsham (11–23 June 2012) and Mansands (30 May 2013). These were the 19th to 21st records for the county. The *Devon Tetrad Atlas 1977–85* reported records from five tetrads, and on six occasions singing continued for over a week, thus inferring 'probable breeding', although there was no confirmation.

*Text: Mike Tyler*

## Icterine Warbler
### *Hippolais icterina*

Icterine Warblers breed in northern, central and eastern Europe and winter in sub-Saharan Africa. There have been a few breeding records in Britain, all in Scotland (*Bird Atlas 2007–11*) but they are primarily scarce passage migrants, especially along the east coast. Singles were on Lundy in September 2008 and at Prawle in August 2009 (*DBRs*).

*Text: J M Lock*

## Melodious Warbler
### *Hippolais polygotta*

Melodious Warbler is a rare passage migrant in Devon, occurring mainly in late summer and autumn, with August and September the peak months. During the Atlas period there were records of single birds (several of which were trapped and ringed) in five years: at Pig's Nose Valley, Prawle in September 2009 and August 2011, Lundy in September 2010 and September 2012 (two records), Slapton Higher Ley in August 2011, Start Point in August 2012 and Velator (Taw/Torridge Estuary) in July 2013 (*DBRs*).

*Text: Mike Tyler*

# Aquatic Warbler
## *Acrocephalus paludicola*                    **Red listed**

Aquatic Warbler is a very rare autumn passage migrant in Devon from central and eastern European breeding grounds, but is recorded in August/September most years. During the Atlas period, eight were recorded, all on the south coast, with half being individuals trapped and ringed at South Milton Ley. A maximum of two birds were recorded in any Atlas year (2009, 2010 & 2011; *DBRs*).

*Text: Mike Tyler / Photo (top) Paul Sterry/NPL*
*Aquatic Warbler sponsored by South Milton Ley*

# Paddyfield Warbler
## *Acrocephalus agricola*

This vagrant *Acrocephalus* warbler breeds from the Black Sea eastwards to Kazakhstan and winters in Iran and the Indian subcontinent. A single bird, the first for Devon, was caught and ringed on Lundy in October 2008 (*DBR*, Smith 2009).

*Text: J M Lock*

# Great Reed Warbler
## *Acrocephalus arundinaceus*

This larger version of the Reed Warbler migrates from sub-Saharan Africa, where it spends the winter, to breed throughout continental Europe and north-west Africa. In Devon it is a very rare vagrant, with 11 records up to 2010 when the only bird recorded during the Atlas period was on 26 September 2010, a juvenile unexpectedly trapped and ringed in the Higher Ley at Slapton.

*Text: Nik Ward*

# Rose-coloured Starling
## *Pastor roseus*

Between one and five of these wanderers from south-east European breeding grounds were recorded in each year of this survey. A total of 13 birds were seen in widely dispersed but mainly coastal locations in both the south and north of the county, including Lundy. Adult birds were recorded mainly in June but once in July, while juvenile birds were recorded mainly in September but once in October. A further juvenile overwintered at Exminster in 2012/13 and was present from 12 December to 23 April (*DBRs*).

*Text: Stella Beavan / Photo: (bottom) David Land*

# Black-throated Thrush
## *Turdus atrogularis*

Black-throated Thrush breeds in central Asia east of the Ural Mountains and winters further south, to northern India. A first-winter male was seen at Scorriton Down, southern Dartmoor, in October 2009. This was the first record for Devon (*DBR*, Walters 2010).

*Text: J M Lock*

## American Robin
### *Turdus migratorius*

The American Robin breeds across North America and south into Mexico, wintering in the southern United States, Central America, Cuba and the Bahamas. One was recorded during the Atlas period: a first-winter bird at Exminster Marshes on 11–16 November 2010 (*DBR*).

*Text: Rob Macklin / Photo (bottom) David Land*

## Bluethroat
### *Luscinia svecica*

Two races of Bluethroat have been recorded in Devon: the nominate Red-spotted Bluethroat *L. s. svecica* which breeds from Scandinavia through northern Siberia to western Alaska, wintering in the Mediterranean, Africa and the Indian subcontinent; and the White-spotted Bluethroat *L. s. cyanecula* which breeds in southern and central Europe through to the Carpathians and winters in the Mediterranean and the Sahel region of Africa. Both are very rare passage migrants in the county. During the Atlas years there were only four records: a first-year bird on Lundy from 28 September to 1 October 2008, a female on Lundy on 9 May 2010, and, in 2013, males of the white-spotted race at Prawle on 30 March and at Start Point on 6 April (*DBRs*).

*Text: Rob Macklin / Photo: (right) Paul Sterry/NPL*
*Bluethroat sponsored in memory of F R (Ray) Smith*

## Red-flanked Bluetail
### *Tarsiger cyanurus*

Red-flanked Bluetail breeds eastwards from Finland and Estonia across Siberia, and in a separate belt from the Himalayas to west China. The number and frequency of British records has increased markedly in recent years as its range has expanded westwards (Mikkola & Rajasärkkä 2014). This species occurred once during the Atlas period, a first-year bird on Lundy on 18 October 2010, constituting the third record for Devon (*DBR*).

*Text: Rob Macklin*

## Red-breasted Flycatcher
### *Ficedula parva*

Red-breasted Flycatchers are scarce passage migrants recorded in most years in Devon, most frequently during the Atlas period on Lundy (November 2007, September 2009 and October 2012), but also on the south coast of the mainland at East Soar in September 2008 and October 2010 and at Berry Head in October 2012 (*DBRs*).

*Text: Rob Macklin*

## Siberian Stonechat
*Saxicola maurus*

Siberian Stonechat was formerly treated as a subspecies of Stonechat but since 2011 has been recognized by the BOU as a distinct species. It breeds from eastern Finland across much of Russia to Mongolia, and winters from north-east Africa to south-east Asia. A female or first-winter male at Middle Soar for several days in late October 2012 was the third accepted record for Devon (*DBR*). The previous occurrences were in September–October 2001 (Tyler 2010).

*Text: J M Lock*

## Desert Wheatear
*Oenanthe deserti*

This wheatear breeds from North Africa eastwards through Arabia to Mongolia, and winters further south. It is a vagrant to Britain and an elegant first-winter male that spent four days at Mansands in November 2011 attracted much attention (*DBR*). This was the only Devon record during the Atlas period.

*Text: J M Lock*

## Pied Wheatear
*Oenanthe pleschanka*

There are only two Devon records of this accidental visitor, the most recent being a first-winter male, at Skern, Taw/Torridge Estuary, from 16 to 19 November 2007 (*DBR*).

*Text: Rob Macklin / Photo: Roy Churchill*

## Richard's Pipit
*Anthus richardi*

Individuals of this primarily late-autumn vagrant to Devon from north Eurasian breeding grounds were recorded in five consecutive years (2008–2012) during the Atlas period, mainly from open grassy areas on the south coast and Lundy: 2008, two to four individuals on Lundy on four dates in October; 2009, one on Lundy, 23 October; 2010, one on Lundy, 4 October; 2011, singles at Beer Cemetery Fields, 19 October and Dawlish Warren, 6 November; and 2012, one on Lundy, 30 April, with presumably the same bird 5 & 8 May, one on the Otter Estuary, 8–12 October, one at Soar, 13 October, and possibly the same bird at Bolberry, 21 October (*DBR*s).

*Text: J M Lock*

## Tawny Pipit
*Anthus campestris*

Tawny Pipits breed in southern Europe and North Africa and winter south of the Sahara desert, in the Sahel. They are scarce passage migrants in Britain, occurring in both spring and autumn. The only Devon record during the Atlas period was of a single bird on Lundy on 17 September 2008 (*DBR*).

*Text: J M Lock*

## Olive-backed Pipit
### *Anthus hodgsoni*

There were two accepted records, the fourth and fifth for Devon, of this vagrant from north Eurasian breeding grounds during the Atlas period, both on Lundy, on 23–24 October 2009 and 7 October 2012 (*DBRs*). Three of the five county records have come from Lundy; the others from the south coast.

*Text: J M Lock*

## Red-throated Pipit
### *Anthus cervinus*

This vagrant from north Eurasian breeding grounds was recorded three times during the Atlas period, twice on the south coast at Orcombe Point, 23 October 2009 and 9 October 2012, and once on Lundy, 22 October 2008, whence the majority of the 16 accepted Devon records have come (*DBRs*).

*Text: J M Lock*

## Common Rosefinch
### *Erythrina erythrina*

Though reported almost annually on Lundy in recent decades, including in all years of the current survey, Common Rosefinches are extremely rare in mainland Devon, the only Atlas record being of a first-summer male in song at Princetown on 23 May 2012. Female and immature birds are, however, unobtrusive and easily overlooked. On Lundy there were two spring records, both of singing males (on 9–10 June 2008 and 28 & 31 May 2013), while autumn records involved up to 14 individuals, mostly first-winter birds (*DBRs*).

*Text: Roger Doble*

## Trumpeter Finch
### *Bucanetes githagineus*

Trumpeter Finches breed from the Canary Islands eastwards across North Africa and the Middle East, though a few also breed in southern Spain. One bird, the first of this species for Devon, was on Lundy from 13–25 May 2011 and attracted large numbers of visiting admirers. What was probably the same bird was seen on the nearby mainland at Morte Point just a few days later, on 2 June (*DBR*; Jones 2012).

*Text: J M Lock / Photo: Shaun Barnes*

## Twite
### *Linaria flavirostris*                                            **Red listed**

A breeding bird of the Scottish Highlands & Islands and the Pennines of northern England, the Twite's winter distribution is mainly coastal, with most occurring in northern and eastern Britain (*Bird Atlas 2007–11*). It is a very rare passage migrant and winter visitor in Devon, the only record during the Atlas period being one at Skern (Taw/Torridge Estuary) in December 2007 (*DBR*).

*Text: Roger Doble*

# Common Redpoll
## *Acanthis flammea*

A very rare, though possibly overlooked, visitor to Devon. Separation of Common and Lesser Redpoll is difficult so it is possible that birds recorded as 'Common/Lesser Redpoll' could include *A. flammea*. Common Redpolls breed from northern Eurasia to Greenland and winter in small numbers through much of the UK (*Bird Atlas 2007–11*), though predominantly in the north and east. They are most likely to be found associating with Lesser Redpolls. Ironically, single birds were trapped and ringed a few days before the Atlas period (a first-winter female on Lundy on 26 October 2007) and shortly after fieldwork finished (on Dartmoor on 17 November 2013) – the sixth and seventh county records (*DBRs*).

*Text: Jeremy Barker*

# Ortolan Bunting
## *Emberiza hortulana*

Ortolan Buntings are vagrants to Devon. Most records during the survey period came from Lundy where they occurred annually in autumn (between 16 September and 3 October) from 2008 to 2012, inclusive, but not in 2007 or 2013. All these were single birds, with the exception of 2012 when two birds were probably involved. The only mainland sighting was at Beer Head on 22 August 2009 (*DBRs*).

*Text: Roger Doble / Photo: (right) Tom Bedford*

# Little Bunting
## *Emberiza pusilla*

An unobtrusive and possibly overlooked species, Little Bunting is a vagrant to Devon where it is less than annual, occurring mainly in late autumn. Of the 24 accepted records since 1937, 14 have been from Lundy. During the Atlas years the species was only noted in 2012: two caught and ringed at South Milton Ley – one on 19 March and a second bird on 28th, with one lingering until 16 April – and one on Lundy on 24 October (*DBR*).

*Text: Roger Doble / Photo (left) David Land*

# Corn Bunting
## *Emberiza calandra*                                   **Red listed**

Never regarded as common in Devon, the *Devon Tetrad Atlas 1977–85* had records of Corn Bunting from just six tetrads, with only one confirmed breeding record, at West Prawle in the South Hams in 1984, which remains the last-known instance of breeding in the county (Tyler 2010). They are now effectively vagrants in Devon with the only records during the current survey involving single birds at Orcombe, Exmouth in November 2007 and November 2010, on Lundy in May 2009, at Hartland Point (two birds) in March 2009, and at Beer Head in September/October 2010 (*DBRs*).

*Text: Roger Doble*

# Category D and E species

## Helmeted Guineafowl
### Numida meleagris

Helmeted Guineafowl is native to sub-Saharan Africa. Domestic birds, often kept because of their loud alarm calls, stray widely into open fields close to farms, and feral breeding has been recorded elsewhere in Britain. Birds, occasionally over ten individuals, were recorded in 19 widely scattered tetrads in the Atlas years of 2008, 2009, 2011 and 2012 (*DBRs*).

*Text: Ray Jones*

## Northern Bobwhite
### Colinus virginianus

This small quail, native to the eastern and central United States, was recorded once during the Atlas period, in 2009, at Sampford Spiney (*DBR*). It is unknown whether it was an escape or a deliberate introduction.

*Text: J M Lock*

## Californian Quail
### Callipepla californica

This decorative quail, a native of the western United States and Mexico, was seen on four occasions in various parts of the county during the survey period (*DBRs* 2011, 2012). These records surely refer to aviary escapes.

*Text: J M Lock*

## Indian Peafowl
### Pavo cristatus

Peacocks and peahens are widely kept in the gardens of large houses in spite of their destructive foraging and loud, harsh calls. Many are full-winged and regularly stray. There were records from 25 widely distributed tetrads during the Atlas years (breeding and winter periods combined), including four with evidence of probable breeding. Of these, two were in south-east Devon and two in the north-west of the county.

*Text: J M Lock*

## Reeves's Pheasant
### Syrmaticus reevesii

Reeves's Pheasant is native to the evergreen forests of central and eastern China. When introduced in England in 1894 and earlier in Scotland, it showed a preference for farmland close to wooded areas. It was recorded in Devon in nine widely dispersed tetrads during the Atlas years (*DBRs*).

*Text: Ray Jones*

## Swan Goose
### Anser cygnoides

This species breeds in north-eastern Asia and winters in China. It is the ancestor of the tame 'Chinese Goose' and it is not always clear whether published reports of Swan Goose actually refer to the domesticated form. However, birds of one or other taxon were reported from the Teign and Exe Estuaries in most years of the survey period (*DBRs*). A further complication is reported hybridization with Greylag Goose *A. anser* (e.g. *DBR* 2013).

*Text: J M Lock*

# Bar-headed Goose
## *Anser indicus*

As its scientific name suggests, this striking goose is native to Asia, where it migrates across the high Himalayas between breeding grounds in the continental interior and wintering sites located mainly in northern India. *Bird Atlas 2007–11* states that Bar-headed Geese – all of which in Britain and Ireland have originated from captive collections – have the capacity to become locally common. This species was not mapped for the *Devon Tetrad Atlas 1977–85*, but Tyler (2010) notes its almost annual occurrence during the period 1989–2008. For the present Atlas there were records for 20 tetrads, covering eight 10-km squares, with most occurrences on and around the Exe Estuary and the South Hams estuaries.

*Text: Tim Jones & Tim Davis*

# Snow Goose
## *Anser caerulescens*

Records of Snow Geese are likely to be escapes from captivity (*Bird Atlas 2007–11*) and they readily hybridize with other geese. One was recorded at Kitley Pond (near the Avon Estuary) on 15 November 2008 and two white forms were at Exminster Marshes (Exe Estuary) on 10 January 2010. Hybrid birds were at New Bridge, Bishops Tawton (lower River Taw) in April 2009, and two at Exminster Marshes in May that year were likely to have been the same birds there in January 2010 (*DBRs*).

*Text: Stella Beavan*

# Muscovy Duck
## *Cairina moschata*

Larger than our native Mallard, the Muscovy Duck is a native of Mexico, Central and South America, where it inhabits swamps, lakes, streams and nearby farmland. It was brought to Britain by early explorers in the 16th century and domesticated and is now common on many urban lakes and in farmyard populations. Hybridization between Muscovy and other domesticated ducks, as well as with the native Mallard, is commonplace in many farmyards. Muscovy Ducks are widespread in Devon, most notably in the south of the county, where some breeding may have taken place away from farmyard sites.

*Text: Ray Jones*

# Ringed Teal
## *Callonetta leucophrys*

A single bird of this South American dabbling duck species was at Clennon Valley in April 2008 – undoubtedly a stray from a waterfowl collection (*DBR*).

*Text: J M Lock*

# Wood Duck
## *Aix sponsa*

This extremely decorative North American duck appeared in five of the Atlas years, usually on south coast estuaries but also inland. It is widely kept in waterfowl collections and a few do breed in the wild in England. An unringed fully winged female or immature bird was offshore in Dawlish Bay on 25 November 2007 and males were seen on the River Dart in June 2008 and Blatchford Lake in July of the same year. A male was at Yarner Wood in April and May 2012 and another at Hackney Marshes and the Teign Estuary during March 2013 (*DBRs*). During the Atlas period there was one 'possible' breeding record of three birds, male and female, in the Woodtown area, south-west of Bideford in April 2010.

*Text: J M Lock*

## Crested Duck
### *Lophonetta specularioides*

One of these natives of temperate South America appeared briefly on the Exe Estuary in April 2011 (*DBR*) – undoubtedly a stray from a waterfowl collection.

*Text: J M Lock*

## Falcated Duck
### *Anas falcata*

This species – which breeds in north-east Asia (mainly in south-east Siberia) and winters from northern India eastward to Japan – is widely kept in wildfowl collections in Europe. During the Atlas period a single adult drake was seen on the Exe Estuary from January to May 2008, having first occurred at the same site as a first-winter bird from November 2006 to January 2007. The status of this species in Devon prior to the Atlas period was reviewed by Knott (2007).

*Text: Tim Jones & Tim Davis*

## Chiloë Wigeon
### *Anas sibilatrix*

All UK occurrences of this native of South America are attributable to escapes from wildfowl collections. During the Atlas period single males (perhaps just one well-travelled bird) were noted on the Exe and Otter Estuaries and at Slapton and Mansands Leys (*DBRs*). There were regular reports from the winter period 2007/08 until November 2010, but none during the latter years of Atlas fieldwork.

*Text: Tim Jones & Tim Davis*

## Laysan Duck
### *Anas laysanensis*

One of these small ducks, confined naturally to Laysan Island in the Pacific Ocean, was at Braunton in May 2012 – undoubtedly a stray from a waterfowl collection (*DBR*).

*Text: J M Lock*

## Turkey Vulture
### *Cathartes aura*

Turkey Vultures are native to North and South America. A bird named 'Jackson' escaped from a collection in Northampton and spent some time in Devon in July/August 2010 before being recaptured (*DBR*).

*Text: J M Lock*

## Lanner Falcon hybrid
### *Falco biarmicus* hybrid

Hybrids between various falcons, including in their ancestry Peregrine *F. peregrinus*, Lanner *F. biarmicus*, Saker *F. cherrug* and occasionally Gyr/Greenland Falcon *F. rusticolus*, are bred and kept by falconers and sometimes escape. A presumed Lanner hybrid was seen at Dawlish Warren in September 2012 (*DBR*).

*Text: J M Lock*

## Saker Falcon
### *Falco cherrug*

One of these large falcons, native to eastern Europe and the Middle East, was seen at Exminster Marshes in November 2010 (*DBR*). It was assumed to be an escaped falconer's bird.

*Text: J M Lock*

# Harris's Hawk
## *Parabuteo unicinctus*

One of these much-kept falconer's birds native to the Americas was recorded near Abbotsham in December 2008 (*DBR*). A mixed pairing of male Harris's Hawk and female Common Buzzard *Buteo buteo* bred in central Plymouth 2010–2013, producing hybrid 'Hazzard' young (pictured) in at least three years (Hopper 2014).

*Text: Mark Darlaston / Photo: Steve Hopper*

# Laughing Dove
## *Spilopelia senegalensis*

One of these Turtle Dove-sized doves, native to Africa, the Middle East and southern Asia, caused some excitement when it fed and sang in Seaton gardens in June 2013 (*DBR*). Never before recorded in the county, where had it escaped from?

*Text: J M Lock*

# Cockatiel
## *Nymphicus hollandicus*

This small long-tailed Australian parrot is often kept as a cagebird and was seen in the wild in four of the survey years: 2008, 2009, 2012 & 2013 (*DBR*s). In 2008 several must have escaped simultaneously as flocks of six were twice seen in and around Exeter.

*Text: J M Lock*

# Budgerigar
## *Melopsittacus undulatus*

This small, long-tailed parrot, nomadic in its native Australia, is very widely kept as a cagebird and escapes inevitably occur. Birds were seen in the wild in Devon in 2008 and 2010 (*DBR*s).

*Text: J M Lock*

# Grey Parrot
## *Psittacus erithacus*

Famed for its intelligence and ability to mimic human speech and other sounds, this parrot is widely kept as a cagebird. As it is a species of the humid tropics of Africa, it is perhaps not surprising that the one bird seen in the wild during the survey period, at Wrangaton in 2012, was "thin and weak" (*DBR*).

*Text: J M Lock*

# Rosy-faced Lovebird
## *Agapornis roseicollis*

A tiny largely green parrot, Rosy-faced Lovebird is native to the arid regions of Namibia but is also kept as a cagebird. Two were in a garden in Exeter in December 2010, and one in South Brent in December 2011 (*DBR*s). It seems unlikely that they would have survived for long in the wild.

*Text: J M Lock*

## Northern Red-shouldered Macaw
### Diopsittaca nobilis

The remains of one of these South American parrots were found on the tideline near Ilfracombe in May 2009 (*DBR*). Presumably an escaped cagebird, its origins are impossible to determine.

*Text: J M Lock*

## Eurasian Eagle-Owl
### Bubo bubo

Birds of this Eurasian species were recorded in 2011 and 2013 in North and East Devon respectively (*DBRs*). A few Eagle Owls breed in the wild in Britain and although the adults are sedentary the juveniles disperse widely. It is, however, most likely that the Devon records refer to locally escaped or deliberately released birds.

*Text: J M Lock*

## Greater Blue-eared Starling
### Lamprotornis chalybaeus

One of these glossy dark-blue starlings, native to the drier savannah regions of Africa, was seen in a garden at Fremington in July 2010 (*DBR*). It was doubtless an escaped cagebird.

*Text: J M Lock*

## Southern Red Bishop
### Euplectes orix

Several species of bishop, variously coloured in black, brown, red and yellow, inhabit the grasslands of Africa where they are also crop pests. A Southern Red Bishop, presumably an escaped cagebird, was in a remote garden in the Hartland area in late 2007 and early 2008 (*DBR* 2007) and a female bishop, thought most likely to have been this species, was at Dawlish Warren in August 2010 (*DBR*).

*Text: J M Lock*

## Atlantic Canary
### Serinus canaria

A 'wild-plumaged' individual of this much-kept cagebird was at Dawlish Warren in October 2008 (*DBR*). Its original home is the Canary Islands off western Africa, where it occurs commonly on all four islands.

*Text: J M Lock*

## House Finch
### Carpodacus mexicanus

A bird of this species, native to Mexico and spreading northwards in the western United States following introduction there, was at Prawle between June and October 2010 (*DBR*). It was presumed to be an escaped cagebird.

*Text: J M Lock*

# Bibliography & References

Photo: (Dipper) John Clark

**Adams, T. 2006.** Exe Estuary Black-tailed Godwits – sightings of ringed birds. *Devon Bird Report* 77: 56–57.

**Allen, D.J. 2004.** *Heathland in East Devon and the Blackdown Hills.* English Nature.

**Animal Health and Veterinary Laboratories Agency (AHVLA). 2014.** UK Ruddy Duck Eradication Programme Project Bulletin, April 2014. Three-page bulletin available as a PDF download at: http://www.nonnativespecies.org/download Document.cfm?id=1121, accessed 27 July 2014.

**Anon. 2010**. Structure of the agricultural industry and the UK at June. https://www.gov.uk/government/ statistical-data-sets/structure-of-the-agricultural- industry-in-england-and-the-uk-at-june, accessed 3 June 2015.

**Anon. 2013.** The British Survey of Fertiliser Practice – Fertiliser use on Farm Crops for Crop Year 2012. www.gov.uk/government/uploads/system/uploads/ attachment_data/file/192605/fertiliseruse-report2012- 25apr13.pdf, accessed 3 August 2015.

**Aplin, O.V. 1892.** On the distribution of the Cirl Bunting in Great Britain. *The Zoologist* (series 3) 16: 121–128 & 174–181.

**Appleton, G. 2012.** Swifts start to share their secrets. *BTO News* 299: 16–17.

**Arcos, J. M. 2011.** Â¿Cuantas pardelas baleares hay? Discrepancias entre los censos en colonias y en el mar. In: X. Valeiras, G. Muoz, A. Bermejo, J.M. Arcos & A.M. Paterson (eds), *Actas del 6 Congreso del GIAM y el Taller internacional sobre la Ecologãa de Paios y Pardelas en el sur de Europa*, pp. 117–121. Boletín del Grupo Ibérico de Aves Marinas.

**Austin, G.E. 2002.** Determining Greylag and Canada Goose habitat associations during their breeding season. *BTO Research Report No. 286*. BTO, Thetford.

**Austin, G.E., Calbrade, N.A., Mellan, H.J., Musgrove, A.J., Hearn, R.D., Stroud, D.A., Wotton, S.R. & Holt, C.A. 2014.** *Waterbirds in the UK 2012/13: The Wetland Bird Survey.* BTO, RSPB & JNCC, in association with WWT. BTO, Thetford.

**Austin, G.E., Read, W.J., Calbrade, N.A., Mellan, H.J., Musgrove, A.J., Skellorn, W., Hearn, R.D., Stroud, D.A., Wotton, S.R. & Holt, C.A. 2014.** *Waterbirds in the UK 2011/12: The Wetland Bird Survey.* BTO, RSPB & JNCC, in association with WWT. BTO, Thetford.

**Avon, J. 2004.** A study of House Sparrows in Kingsteignton, South Devon. *Devon Bird Report* 76: 259–261.

**Avon, J.D. 2005.** Operation Wader – Project Officer's Report. 124 pp. Duchy of Cornwall/Dartmoor National Park Authority.

**Avon, J.D. 2007a.** DBWPS members' survey of House Sparrow nest sites 2005. *Devon Birds* 60(1): 35–39.

**Avon, J. 2007b.** Breeding waders on Dartmoor 2006. *Devon Birds* 60(2): 35–36.

**Baillie, S.R., Marchant, J.H., Leech, D.I., Massimino, D., Sullivan, M.J.P., Eglington, S.M., Barimore, C., Dadam, D., Downie, I.S., Harris, S.J., Kew, A.J., Newson, S.E., Noble, D.G., Risely, K. & Robinson, R.A. 2014.** BirdTrends 2014: trends in numbers, breeding success and survival for UK breeding birds. *BTO Research Report 662.* BTO, Thetford. http://www. bto.org/birdtrends, accessed 12 February 2014–18 October 2015.

**Balk, L., Hägerroth, P-Å., Åkerman, G., Hanson, M., Tjärnlund, U., Hansson, T., Hallgrimsson, G.T., Zebuhr, Y., Broman, D., Morner, T. & Sundberg, H. 2009.** Wild birds of declining European species are dying from a thiamine deficiency syndrome. *Proceedings of the National Academy of the Sciences of the United States of America* 106: 12001–12006.

**Ballance, D.K. 2006.** *A History of the Birds of Somerset.* Isabelline Books, Falmouth.

**Ballance, D.K., Grimmond, R., Moss, S., Thomas, J. & Tigwell, E. 2014.** *Somerset Atlas of breeding and wintering birds 2007–2012.* Somerset Ornithological Society, Combe St Nicholas.

**Balmer, D.E., Gillings, S., Caffrey, B.J., Swann, R.L., Downie, I.S. & Fuller, R.J. 2013.** *Bird Atlas 2007–11: The breeding and wintering birds of Britain and Ireland.* BTO Books, Thetford.

**Banks, A.N., Burton, N.H.K., Calladine, J.R. & Austin, G.E. 2009.** Indexing winter gull numbers in Great Britain using data from the 1953 to 2004 Winter Gull Roost Surveys. *Bird Study* 56: 103–119.

**Banks, A.N., Crick, H.Q.P., Coombes, R., Benn, S., Ratcliffe, D.A. & Humphreys, E.M. 2010.** The breeding status of Peregrine Falcons *Falco peregrinus* in the UK and Isle of Man in 2002. *Bird Study* 57: 421–436.

**Barker, S., Burrough, A., Cordrey, L., Merry, K. & Wedge, C. 2011.** Conserving the wildlife of traditional orchards. *British Wildlife* 23: 8–16.

**Bastin, N-J. 2009.** King Eider on the Taw/Torridge Estuary – twice! *Devon Birds* 62(3) (*Devon Bird Report* 81): 207–208.

**Berthold, P. & Terrill, S.B. 1988.** Migratory behaviour and population growth of Blackcaps wintering in Britain and Ireland: some hypotheses. *Ringing and Migration* 9: 153–159.

**Bird Atlas 2007–11.** See Balmer *et al.* 2013.

**BirdFacts 2005.** See Robinson, R.A. 2005.

**BirdLife International. 2014.** IUCN Red List of Birds. http://www.birdlife.org/europe-and-central-asia/ european-red-list-birds-0, accessed on 28 April 2014.

**BirdLife International. 2014.** Species factsheets. http://www.birdlife.org/datazone/species, accessed on various dates.

**Birds of the Western Palearctic.** See:

*Vol. I Ostrich to Ducks.* Cramp *et al.* 1977.

*Vol. II Hawks to Bustards.* Cramp *et al.* 1980.

*Vol. III Waders to Gulls.* Cramp *et al.* 1983.

*Vol. IV Terns to Woodpeckers.* Cramp *et al.* 1985.

*Vol. V Tyrant Flycatchers to Thrushes.* Cramp *et al.* 1988.

*Vol. VI Warblers.* Cramp *et al.* 1992.

*Vol. VII Flycatchers to Shrikes.* Cramp *et al.* 1993.

*Vol. VIII Crows to Finches.* Cramp *et al.* 1994.

*Vol. IX Buntings and New World Warblers.* Cramp *et al.* 1994.

**BirdTrends 2014.** See Baillie *et al.* 2014.

**Boldreghini, P., Meininger, P.L. & Santolini, R. 1992.** Preliminary results of ringing Mediterranean Gulls (*Larus melanocephalus*) in the Netherlands, Belgium and Italy. *Avocetta* 16: 73–74.

**Booker, H. & Price, D. 2014a.** Breeding seabirds 'take off' on Lundy – results of the 2013 Breeding Seabird Survey. *Devon Birds* 67(2): 29–31.

**Booker, H. & Price, D. 2014b.** Manx Shearwater recovery on Lundy: population and distribution change from 2001 to 2013. *Journal of the Lundy Field Society* 4: 105–116.

**Booker, H. & Slader, P. 2008.** The status and distribution of three Dartmoor birds, following a major survey in 2006. *Devon Birds* 61(1): 24–29.

**British Ornithologists' Union. 2013.** The British List: A Checklist of Birds of Britain (8th edition). *Ibis* 155: 635–676.

**Broughton, R.K. 2009.** Separation of Willow and Marsh Tit in Britain: a review. *British Birds* 102: 604–616.

**Broughton, R.K., Hill, R.A., Bellamy, P.E. & Hinsley, S.A. 2010.** Dispersal, ranging and settling behaviour of Marsh tits *Poecile palustris* in a fragmented landscape in lowland England. *Bird Study* 57: 458–472.

**Broughton, R.K. & Hinsley, S.A. 2015.** The ecology and conservation of the Marsh Tit in Britain. *British Birds* 108: 12–29.

**Brown, A. & Grice, P. 2005.** *Birds in England.* T. & A.D. Poyser, London.

**BTO, 2012.** Tracking Lesser Black-backed Gulls. *http://www.bto.org/science/migration/tracking-studies/tracking-lesser-black-backed-gulls,* accessed 1 June 2014.

**Burfield, I. & Van Bommel, F. 2004.** *Birds in Europe.* BirdLife International, Cambridge.

**Burgess, M.D. 2014.** Restoring abandoned coppice for birds: few effects of conservation management on occupancy, fecundity and productivity of hole nesting birds. *Forest Ecology and Management* 330: 205–217.

**Burgess, M.D., Bellamy, P., Gillings, S., Noble, D., Grice, P.V. & Conway, G. 2015.** The impact of changing habitat availability on population trends of woodland birds associated with early successional plantation woodland. *Bird Study* 62: 39–55.

**Burton, N.H.K. 2007.** Influences of restock age and habitat patchiness on Tree Pipits *Anthus trivialis* breeding in Breckland pine plantations. *Ibis* 149, Supplement s2: 193–204.

**Cannon, A. 2000.** *The Garden BirdWatch Handbook.* Second edition. BTO, Thetford.

**Charman, E.C., Smith, K.W., Dillon, I.A., Dodd, S., Gruar, D.J., Cristinacce, A., Grice, P.V. & Gregory, R.D. 2012.** Drivers of low breeding success in the Lesser Spotted Woodpecker *Dendrocopos minor* in England: testing hypotheses for the decline. *Bird Study* 59: 255–265.

**Charman, E.C., Smith, K.W., Gruar, D.J., Dodd, S. & Grice, P.V. 2010.** Characteristics of woods used recently and historically by Lesser Spotted Woodpeckers *Dendrocopos minor* in England. *Ibis* 152: 543–555.

**Cholewa, M. & Wesołowski, T. 2011.** Nestling food of European hole-nesting passerines: do we know enough to test the adaptive hypotheses on breeding seasons? *Acta Ornithologica* 46: 105–116.

**Collins, L. 2012.** New to Devon: Short-toed Eagle *Circaetus gallicus* at Dawlish Warren. *Devon Birds* 65(3) (*Devon Bird Report* 84): 191–192.

**Collins, L. 2014.** My 2013 ring-reading challenge at Dawlish Warren. *Devon Birds* 67(1): 21–30.

**Conway, G.J., Burton, N.H.K., Handschuh, M., & Austin, G.E. In prep.** Changes in breeding populations of Ringed Plover *Charadrius hiaticula* and Little Ringed Plover *C. dubius* in the United Kingdom.

**Conway, G., Wotton, S., Henderson, I., Eaton, M., Drewitt, A. & Spencer, J. 2009.** The status of breeding Woodlarks *Lullula arborea* in Britain in 2006. *Bird Study* 56: 310–325.

**Coulson, J.C. 2011.** A long-term study of the population dynamics of Common Eiders *Somateria mollissima*: why do several parameters fluctuate markedly? *Bird Study* 57: 1–18.

**Cramp, S., Brooks, D.J., Dunn, E., Gillmor, R., Hall-Craggs, J., Hollom, P.A.D., Nicholson, E.M., Ogilvie, M.A., Roselaar, C.S., Sellar, P.J., Simmons, K.E.L., Snow, D.W., Vincent, D., Voous, K.H., Wallace, D.I.M & Wilson, M.G. (eds). 1992.** *Handbook of the Birds of Europe, the Middle East, and North Africa: The Birds of the Western Palearctic, Vol. VI: Warblers.* Oxford University Press, Oxford.

**Cramp, S., Brooks, D.J., Dunn, E., Gillmor, R., Hall-Craggs, J., Hollom, P.A.D., Nicholson, E.M., Ogilvie, M.A., Roselaar, C.S., Sellar, P.J., Simmons, K.E.L., Voous, K.H., Wallace, D.I.M & Wilson, M.G. (eds). 1988.** *Handbook of the Birds of Europe, the Middle East, and North Africa: The Birds of the Western Palearctic, Vol. V: Tyrant Flycatchers to Thrushes.* Oxford University Press, Oxford.

**Cramp, S., Brooks, D.J., Dunn, E., Gillmor, R., Hollom, P.A.D., Hudson, R., Nicholson, E.M., Ogilvie, M.A., Olney, P.J.S., Roselaar, C.S., Simmons, K.E.L., Voous, K.H., Wallace, D.I.M., Wattel, J. & Wilson, M.G. (eds). 1985.** *Handbook of the Birds of Europe, the Middle East, and North Africa: The Birds of the Western Palearctic, Vol. IV: Terns to Woodpeckers.* Oxford University Press, Oxford.

Cramp, S., Perrins, C.M., Brooks, D.J., Dunn, E., Gillmor, R., Hall-Craggs, J., Hillcoat, B., Hollom, P.A.D., Nicholson, E.M., Roselaar, C.S., Seale, W.T.C., Sellar, P.J., Simmons, K.E.L., Snow, D.W., Vincent, D., Voous, K.H., Wallace, D.I.M & Wilson, M.G. (eds). 1993. *Handbook of the Birds of Europe, the Middle East, and North Africa: The Birds of the Western Palearctic, Vol. VII: Warblers.* Oxford University Press, Oxford.

Cramp, S., Perrins, C.M., Brooks, D.J., Dunn, E., Gillmor, R., Hall-Craggs, J., Hillcoat, B., Hollom, P.A.D., Nicholson, E.M., Roselaar, C.S., Seale, W.T.C., Sellar, P.J., Simmons, K.E.L., Snow, D.W., Vincent, D., Voous, K.H., Wallace, D.I.M & Wilson, M.G. (eds). 1994a. *Handbook of the Birds of Europe, the Middle East, and North Africa: The Birds of the Western Palearctic, Vol. VIII: Crows to Finches.* Oxford University Press, Oxford.

Cramp, S., Perrins, C.M., Brooks, D.J., Dunn, E., Gillmor, R., Hall-Craggs, J., Hillcoat, B., Hollom, P.A.D., Nicholson, E.M., Roselaar, C.S., Seale, W.T.C., Sellar, P.J., Simmons, K.E.L., Snow, D.W., Vincent, D., Voous, K.H., Wallace, D.I.M & Wilson, M.G. (eds). 1994b. *Handbook of the Birds of Europe, the Middle East, and North Africa: The Birds of the Western Palearctic, Vol. IX: Buntings and New World Warblers.* Oxford University Press, Oxford.

Cramp, S., Simmons, K.E.L., Brooks, D.J., Collar, N.J., Dunn, E., Gillmor, R., Hollom, P.A.D., Hudson, R., Nicholson, E.M., Ogilvie, M.A., Olney, P.J.S., Roselaar, C.S., Voous, K.H., Wallace, D.I.M., Wattel, J. & Wilson, M.G. (eds). 1983. *Handbook of the Birds of Europe, the Middle East, and North Africa: The Birds of the Western Palearctic, Vol. III: Waders to Gulls.* Oxford University Press, Oxford.

Cramp, S., Simmons, K.E.L., Ferguson-Lees, I.J., Gillmor, R., Hollom, P.A.D., Hudson, R., Nicholson, E.M., Ogilvie, M.A., Olney, P.J.S., Voous, K.H. & Wattel, J. (eds). 1977. *Handbook of the Birds of Europe, the Middle East, and North Africa: The Birds of the Western Palearctic, Vol. I: Ostrich to Ducks.* Oxford University Press, Oxford.

Cramp, S., Simmons, K.E.L., Gillmor, R., Hollom, P.A.D., Hudson, R., Nicholson, E.M., Ogilvie, M.A., Olney, P.J.S., Roselaar, C.S., Voous, K.H., Wallace, D.I.M. & Wattel, J. (eds). 1980. *Handbook of the birds of Europe, the Middle East, and North Africa: the birds of the Western Palearctic, Vol. II: Hawks to Bustards.* Oxford University Press, Oxford.

Crick, H.Q.P. & Sparks, T.H. 1999. Climate change related to egg-laying trends. *Nature* 399: 423–424.

Dare, P.J. 1970. The movements of Oystercatchers *Haematopus ostralegus L.* visiting or breeding in the British Isles. *Fishery Investigations, Series 2.* 25(9): 1–137.

Dare, P.J. 1999. Large movements and ground assemblies of Buzzards in Devon. *Devon Birds* 52(2): 3–9.

Dare, P.J. 2015. *The Life of Buzzards.* Whittles Publishing, Dunbeath.

Dare, P.J. & Hamilton, L.I. 1968. Birds of the Postbridge area, Dartmoor, 1956-1967. *Devon Birds* 21: 22–31, 64–79.

Darlaston, M. 2009. Red Kites – updates and comments. *Devon Birds* 62(1): 23–25.

Darlaston, M. 2010. 'Gadfly' encounters off British and Irish headlands – personal 'views' of one of the most enigmatic seabirds. *Devon Birds* 63(2): 3–16.

Darlaston, M. 2012. How many Balearics? *Devon Birds* 65(3) (*Devon Bird Report* 84): 50.

Darlaston, M. 2014. Six (or seven) shearwater heaven! *Devon Birds* 67(2): 35–37.

Darlaston, M. & Johnson, P. 2003. Survey of Peregrines in Devon – 2002. *Devon Bird Report* 75: 224–227.

Davis, T. 2011. The further travels of Spoonbill FJ9. *Devon Birds* 64(2): 35–37.

Davis, T.J. & Jones, T.A. 2007. *The Birds of Lundy.* DBWPS and LFS, Berrynarbor.

Davis, T. & Jones, T. 2010. Another colour-ringed Spoonbill and its travels. *Devon Birds* 63(2): 34–35.

Davis, T. & Jones, T. 2013. Birds on Lundy 2012. *Annual Report of the Lundy Field Society* 62: 19–61.

Davis, T. & Jones, T. 2014. Birds on Lundy 2013. *Annual Report of the Lundy Field Society* 63: 21–55.

Debout, G. 2009. Gravelot à collier interromput *Charadrius alexandrinus* en Basse-Normandie. *Alauda* 77: 1–19.

Delany, S., Scott, D., Dodman, T. & Stroud, D. 2009. *An Atlas of Wader Populations in Africa and Western Eurasia.* Wetlands International, Wageningen, The Netherlands.

Denerley, C. 2013. *The impact of land use change on a brood parasite system: Cuckoos, their hosts and prey.* PhD Thesis, University of Aberdeen.

Devon Hedges. www.devonhedges.org/DevonHedges.pdf, accessed 14 March 2015.

Dixon, C, 1899. *Bird-Life in a Southern County.* Walter Scott Ltd., London.

Dixon, N. & Drewitt, E.J.A. 2012. A 15-year study of the diet of urban-nesting Peregrines. *Devon Birds* 65(1): 19–30.

D'Urban, W.S.M. & Mathew, M.A. 1892. *The Birds of Devon.* R.H. Porter, London.

Dymond, J.N. 1980. *The Birds of Lundy.* Devon Bird Watching & Preservation Society, Exeter.

Eaton, M.A., Aebischer, N.J., Brown, A.F., Hearn, R.D., Lock, L., Musgrove, A.J., Noble, D.G., Stroud, D.A. & Gregory, R.D. 2015. Birds of Conservation Concern 4: the population status of birds in the United Kingdom, Channel Islands and Isle of Man. *British Birds* 108: 708–746.

Eaton, M.A., Balmer, D.E., Bright, J., Cuthbert, R., Grice, P.V., Hall, C., Hayhow, D.B., Hearn, R.D., Holt, C.A., Knipe, A., Mavor, R., Noble, D.G., Oppel, S., Risely, K., Stroud, D.A. & Wotton, S. 2013. *The state of the UK's birds 2013.* RSPB, BTO, WWT, NRW, JNCC, NE, NIEA & SNH, Sandy, Bedfordshire.

Eaton, M.A., Cuthbert, R., Dunn, E., Grice, P.V., Hall, C., Hayhow, D.B., Hearn, R.D., Holt, C.A., Knipe, A., Marchant, J.H., Mavor, R., Moran, N.J., Mukhida, F., Musgrove, A.J., Noble, D.G., Oppel, S., Risely, K., Stroud, D.A., Toms, M & Wotton, S. 2012. *The state of the UK's birds 2012*. RSPB, BTO, WWT, CCW, NE, NIEA, SNH and JNCC. Sandy, Bedfordshire.

Ellicott, P. 2012. Where do Swallows go in winter? The migration strategies of *Hirundo rustica* as shown by ringing in Devon. *Devon Birds* 65(2): 10–14.

Ellicott, P.W. 1975. The Sand Martin in Devon. *Devon Birds* 28: 3–16.

Elphick, D. 2009. Movements of Slapton Ley NNR Alba Wagtails *Motacilla alba* and the national and Icelandic context of White Wagtails *M. a. alba*. *Devon Birds* 62(1): 28–35.

Elphick, D. 2011. Addditional Slapton Ley NNR Swallow (*Hirundo rustica*) data, 2002–2010. *Devon Birds* 64(2): 3–10.

Ens, B.J., Briggs, K.B., Safriel, U.N. & Smit, C.J. 1996. Life history decisions during the breeding season. In: J.D. Goss-Custard (ed.), *The Oystercatcher: from individuals to populations,* p. 192, Oxford University Press, Oxford.

Environment Canada. 2014. North American Breeding Bird Survey – Canadian Trends Website, Data-version 2012. http://www.ec.gc.ca/ron-bbs/P001/A001/?lang=e, accessed 25 April 2014.

Evans, A.D. 1992. The numbers and distribution of Cirl Buntings *Emberiza cirlus* breeding in Britain in 1989. *Bird Study* 39:17–22.

Evans, A.D. 1996. The importance of mixed farming for seed-eating birds in the UK. In: D. Pain & M.W. Pienkowski (eds), *Farming and Birds in Europe: the Common Agricultural Policy and its implications for bird conservation,* pp. 331–357. Academic Press, London.

Exmoor Mires Project: http://www.exmoormires.org.uk/index.cfm?articleid=8699, accessed 30 January 2015.

Fray, R., Pennington, M., Riddington, R., Meek, E., Higson, P., Forsyth, A., Leitch, A., Scott, M., Marr, T., Rheinallt, T. ap & Olofson, S. 2012. An unprecedented influx of Iceland Gulls in the northeastern Atlantic in January/February 2012. *British Birds* 105: 263–272.

Fuller, R.J., Noble, D.G., Smith, K.W. & Vanhinsbergh, D. 2005. Recent declines in populations of woodland birds in Britain: a review of possible causes. *British Birds* 98: 116–143.

Geary, S. 1993. Communally roosting Magpies in Plymouth in the 1992/93 winter. *Devon Birds* 46: 32–37.

Geary, S. 2000. Dartmoor Moorland Breeding Bird Survey 2000, incorporating a survey of Rhôs Pasture. Dartmoor National Park Authority.

Geary, S. 2001. Breeding density of Magpie and Carrion Crow in central Plymouth 1994–95. *Devon Birds* 54(3): 10–19.

Geary, S. 2002. Communally roosting Magpies in Plymouth 1992–98. *Devon Birds* 55(2): 13–19.

Gibbons, D.W., Reid, J.B. & Chapman, R.A. 1993. *The New Atlas of Breeding Birds in Britain and Ireland: 1988–1991.* Poyser, London.

Gillings, S. & Fuller, R.J. 2009. How many Eurasian Golden Plovers *Pluvialis apricaria* and Northern Lapwings *Vanellus vanellus* winter in Great Britain? Results from a large-scale survey in 2006/07. *Wader Study Group Bulletin* 116: 21–28.

Grahame, N., Riddaway, R., Eadie, A., Hall, B & McCallum, E. 2009. Exceptional hailstorm hits Ottery St Mary on 30 October 2008. *Weather* 64: 255–263. http://onlinelibrary.wiley.com/doi/10.1002/wea.458, accessed 23 September 2015.

Great Bustard Group. http://greatbustard.org, accessed 16 July 2015.

Gruar, D., Barritt, D. & Peach, W.J. 2006. Summer utilization of Oilseed Rape by Reed Buntings *Emberiza schoeniclus* and other farmland birds. *Bird Study* 53: 47–54.

Hagemeijer, W.J.M. & Blair, M.J. (eds). 1997. *The EBCC Atlas of European Breeding Birds: their distribution and abundance.* T. & A.D. Poyser, London.

Harris, J. 2012. New to Devon: American Purple Gallinule *Porphyrio martinica* on Dartmoor. *Devon Birds* 65(3) (*Devon Bird Report* 84): 189–190.

Harris, M.P. & Wanless, S. 1997. Breeding success, diet and brood neglect in the Kittiwake (*Rissa tridactyla*) over an 11-year period. *ICES Journal of Marine Science* 54: 615–623.

Harris, S.J., Risely, K., Massimino, D., Newson, S.E., Eaton, M.A., Musgrove, A.J., Noble, D.G., Procter, D. & Baillie, S.R. 2014. *The Breeding Bird Survey 2013. BTO Research Report 658.* British Trust for Ornithology, Thetford.

Harrop, A.H.J., Collinson, J.M., Dudley, S.P., Kehoe, C. & The British Ornithologists' Union Records Committee (BOURC). 2013. The British List: a Checklist of birds of Britain (8th edition). *Ibis* 155: 635–676.

Hayhow, D.B., Conway, G., Eaton, M.A., Grice P.V., Hall, C., Holt C.A., Kuepfer, A., Noble, D.G., Oppel, S., Risely, K., Stringer, C., Stroud, D.A., Wilkinson, N., & Wotton, S. 2014. *The state of the UK's birds 2014.* RSPB, BTO, WWT, JNCC, NE, NIEA, NRW & SNH, Sandy, Bedfordshire.

Hayman, R.W. 1981. Rooks nesting on Pylons. *Devon Birds* 34: 20–21.

Hinsley, S. A., Bellamy, P. E., Newton, I. & Sparks, T. H. 1995. Habitat and landscape factors influencing the presence of individual breeding bird species in woodland fragments. *Journal of Avian Biology* 26: 94–104.

Holt, C.A., Austin, G.E., Calbrade, N.A., Mellan, H.J., Hearn, R.D., Stroud, D.A. Wotton, S.R. & Musgrove, A.J. 2012. *Waterbirds in the UK 2010/11: The Wetland Bird Survey.* BTO, RSPB & JNCC, in association with WWT. BTO, Thetford.

Holt, C.A., Hewson, C.M. & Fuller, R.J. 2012. The Nightingale in Britain: status, ecology and conservation needs. *British Birds* 105: 172–187.

Hoodless, A.N. & Powell, A. 2010. Origins of wintering Woodcock: initial findings. *Game & Wildlife Conservation Trust Review of 2009*: 18–19. GWCT, Fordingbridge.

Hopper, S. 2014. Plymouth "Hazzard" or not? *Devon Birds* 67(1): 8–11.

Huhta, E.S.A., Jokimakp, J. & Rahko, P. 1998. Distribution and reproductive success of the Pied Flycatcher *Ficedula hypoleuca* in relation to forest patch size and vegetation characteristics; the effect of scale. *Ibis* 140: 214–222.

Hurrell, L.H. & Hurrell, R.H. 2014. Little Egret (*Egretta garzetta*) roosting and breeding activity on Drake's Island, 2012. *Devon Birds* 67(1): 34–35.

Hutchinson, C.D. 1986. Greenshank. In: P. Lack, *The Atlas of Wintering Birds in Britain and Ireland*, pp. 220–221. Poyser, Calton.

Ivimey-Cook, R.B. 1984. *Atlas of the Devon Flora. Flowering Pants and Ferns*. The Devonshire Association for the Advancement of Science, Literature and Art, Exeter.

James, P.C. 1986. Little Shearwaters in Britain and Ireland. *British Birds* 79: 28–33.

Jarvis, D. 2008. Variations in territory size and habitat preference of Wrens. *Devon Birds* 61(2): 32–34.

Jarvis, D.J. 2004. Pylon nesting Rooks in north east Devon. *Devon Birds* 57(2): 23–24.

Jarvis, D.J. 2009. Multiple breeding by Collared Doves. *Devon Birds* 62(1): 36–37.

Jenks, D. 1998. Wintering Blackcaps in a Torquay garden. *Devon Birds* 51: 3–9.

Jenks, D.G. 2004. *A History of Devonshire Ornithology*. Isabelline Books, Falmouth.

JNCC. 2010. UK BAP priority bird species. http://jncc.defra.gov.uk/page-5163, accessed 13 March 2014.

John, A.W.G. & Roskell, J. 1985. Jay movements in autumn 1983. *British Birds* 78: 611–637.

Jones, T. (compiler). 2012. New to Devon: Trumpeter Finch *Bucanetes githagineus* on Lundy. *Devon Birds* 65(3) (*Devon Bird Report* 84): 195.

Jones, T. & Davis, T. 2009. A review of Spoonbills in Devon with special reference to the Taw & Torridge Estuary. *Devon Birds* 62(2): 19–30.

Knijff, P. de., Spek, V. van der. & Fischer, J. 2012. Genetic identity of grey chiffchaffs trapped in the Netherlands in autumns of 2009–11. *Dutch Birding* 34: 386–392.

Knott, M. 2007. A Falcated Duck *Anas falcata* in Devon. *Devon Birds* 60(2): 37–38.

Knox, A.G., Helbig, A.J., Parkin, D.T. & Sangster, G. 2001. The taxonomic status of Lesser Redpoll. *British Birds* 94: 260–267.

Lack, P. 1986. *The Atlas of Wintering Birds in Britain and Ireland*. T. & A.D. Poyser, Calton.

Lack, P.C. 1989. Overall and regional trends in warbler populations of British farmland over 25 years. *Annales Zoologici Fennici* 26: 219–225.

Langman, M. 2005. Continents apart. *Devon Birds* 58(1): 14–20.

Langman, M., Jewels, A. & Reay, P. 2007. A Review of Devon subspecies. *Devon Birds* 60(2): 16–29.

Last, J. & Burgess, M. 2015. Nestboxes and fieldcraft for monitoring Willow Tits. *British Birds* 108: 30–36.

Lehikoinen, A., Jaatinen, K., Vahatalo, A.V., Clausen, P., Crowe, O., Deceuninck, B., Hearn, R., Holt, C.A., Hornman, M., Keller, V., Nilsson, L., Langendoen, T., Tomankova, I., Wahl, J. & Fox, A.D. 2013. Rapid climate driven shifts in wintering distributions of three common waterbird species. *Global Change Biology* 19: 2071–2081.

Lehikoinen, A., Kilpi, M. & Ost, M. 2006. Winter climate affects subsequent breeding success of eiders. *Global Change Biology* 12: 1355–1365.

Lewis, A.J.G., Amar, A., Charman, E.C. & Stewart, F.R.P. 2009. The decline of the Willow Tit in Britain. *British Birds* 102: 386–393.

Limbrunner, A., Bezzel, E., Richarz, K. & Singer, D. 2001. *Enzyklopädie der Brutvögel Europas, Band 2.* Kosmos.

Lockwood, W.B. 1981. Etymological observations on brambling, bunting, fieldfare, godwit, wren. In: Y.L. Arbeitman & A.R. Bomhard (eds), *Bono Homini Donum: Essays in Historical Linguistics, in Memory of J. Alexander Kerns*, pp. 189–201. John Benjamins Publishing Company, Amsterdam. doi: 10.1075/cilt.16

Loyd, L.R.W. 1929. *The Birds of South-East Devon.* London, H.F. & G.Witherby.

Ludescher, F.-B. 1973. Sumpfmeise (*Parus p. palustris* L.) und Weidenmeise (*P. montanus salicarius* Br.) als sympatrische Zwillingsarten. *Journal für Ornithologie* 114: 3–56.

Lundberg, A. & Alatalo, R. V. 1992. *The Pied Flycatcher.* T. & A.D. Poyser, London.

Maclean, I.M.D., Austin, G.E., Rehfisch, M.M., Blew, J., Crowe, O., Delany, S., Devos, K., Deceuninck, B., Gunther, K., Laursen, K., van Roomen, M. & Wahl, J. 2008. Climate change causes rapid changes in the distribution and site abundance of birds in winter. *Global Change Biology* 14: 2489–2500.

Maclean, N. (ed.). 2010. *Silent Summer. The State of Wildlife in Britain and Ireland.* Cambridge University Press, Cambridge.

Mallord, J.W., Charman, E.C. & Cristinacce, A. 2012. Habitat associations of Wood Warblers *Phylloscopus sibilatrix* breeding in Welsh oakwoods. *Bird Study* 59: 403–415.

Marchant, J.H., Hudson, R., Carter, S.P. & Whittington, P. 1990. *Population trends in British breeding birds.* BTO, Tring.

Mead, C. 2000. *The State of the Nation's Birds.* Whittet, Stowmarket.

**Meteorological Office. 2014.** *UK climate.* http://www.metoffice.gov.uk/climate, accessed 2 October 2015.

**Mikkola, H. & Rajasärkkä, A. 2014.** The Red-flanked Bluetail in Europe: range expansion and population trends. *British Birds* 107: 561–566.

**Montagu, G. 1833.** *Ornithological Dictionary of British Birds* (new edition). Orr & Smith, London.

**Moore, R. 1969.** *The Birds of Devon.* David & Charles, Newton Abbot.

**Mudge, G.P., Crooke, C.H., Booth, R.G. & Smith, S.E.A. 1979.** An ecological study of the breeding bird populations and vegetation communities on open moorland areas of Dartmoor in 1979. RSPB & DNPA, Exeter.

**Mudge, G.P., Davies, M., Crooke, C.H., Booth, R.G. & Smith, S.E.A. 1981.** Breeding bird populations of the open moorland of Dartmoor in 1979. *Devon Birds* 34: 28–46.

**Musgrove, A.J., Aebischer, N.J., Eaton, M.A., Hearn, R.D., Newson, S.E., Noble, D.G., Parsons, M., Risely, K. & Stroud, D.A. 2013.** Population estimates of birds in Great Britain and the United Kingdom. *British Birds* 106: 64–100.

**Musgrove, A.J., Austin, G.E., Hearn, R.D., Holt, C.A., Stroud, D. A. & Wotton, S. R. 2011.** Overwinter population estimates of British waterbirds. *British Birds* 104: 364–397.

**Natural England. 2014.** National Character Area profiles: data for local decision making. https://www.gov.uk/government/publications/national-character-area-profiles-data-for-local-decision-making.

**Newton, S.F. 2004.** Roseate Tern. In: P.I. Mitchell, S.F. Newton, N. Ratcliffe & T.E. Dunn, *Seabird Populations of Britain and Ireland: results of the Seabird 2000 Census (1998–2002),* pp. 302–314. T. & A.D. Poyser, London.

**Ockendon, N., Hewson, C.H., Johnston, A. & Atkinson, P.W. 2012.** Declines in British-breeding populations of Afro-Palaearctic migrant birds are linked to bioclimatic wintering zone in Africa, possibly via constraints on arrival time advancement. *Bird Study* 59: 111–125.

**Ouwehand, J., Ahola, M.P., Ausems, A.N.M.A., Bridge, E.S., Burgess, M., Hahn, S., Hewson, C.M., Klaassen, R.H.G., Laaksonen, T., Lampe, H.M., Velmala, W. & Both, C. 2015.** Light-level geolocators reveal migratory connectivity in European populations of pied flycatchers *Ficedula hypoleuca. Journal of Avian Biology* 46: doi: 10.1111/jav.00721

**PACEC. 2006.** *The Economic and Environmental Impact of Sporting Shooting.* Public and Corporate Economic Consultants, Cambridge.

**Parrinder, E.D. 1989.** Little Ringed Plovers *Charadrius dubius* in Britain in 1984. *Bird Study* 36: 147–153.

**Peach, W., Baillie, S. & Underhill, L. 1991.** Survival of British Sedge Warblers *Acrocephalus schoenobaenus* in relation to west African rainfall. *Ibis* 133: 300–305.

**Peach, W., Du Feu, C. & McMeeking, J. 1995.** Site tenacity and survival rates of Wrens *Troglodytes troglodytes* and Treecreepers *Certhia familiaris* in a Nottinghamshire wood. *Ibis* 137: 497–507.

**Pearce-Higgins, J.W., Dennis, P., Whittingham, M.J. & Yalden, D.W. 2010.** Impacts of climate on prey abundance account for fluctuations in a population of a northern wader at the southern edge of its range. *Global Change Biology* 16: 12–23.

**PECBMS (Pan-European Common Bird Monitoring Scheme). 2014.** Trends in common birds in Europe, 2014 update. http://www.ebcc.info/index.php?ID=557, accessed 16 March 2015.

**Perring, F.H. & Walters, S.M. (eds). 1962.** *Atlas of the British Flora.* Thomas Nelson & Sons Ltd, London.

**Perrins, C.M. 1965.** Population fluctuations and clutch-size in the Great Tit, *Parus major* L. *Journal of Animal Ecology* 34: 601–647.

**Perry, R. 1940.** *Lundy, Isle of Puffins.* Drummond, London.

**PiedFly.Net.** http://www.piedfly.net, accessed 31 December 2014.

**Porter, R., Brown, A. & Lock, L. 2010.** *English Seabird Monitoring Project, South West England 2006–2009.* Unpublished report, RSPB Exeter & NE Peterborough.

**Potts, G.R. 2012.** *Partridges.* HarperCollins, London.

**Price, D. 1977.** Canada Goose, Mute Swan and Shelduck in Devon, 1976. *Devon Birds* 30: 21–27.

**Price, D. 1993.** Breeding season survey of Shelduck in Devon in 1992. *Devon Birds* 46(2): 37–39.

**Price, D.J. 2010.** Ups and downs on the Exe Estuary – Bar-tailed and Black-tailed Godwits. *Devon Birds* 63(1): 8–14.

**Price, D. & Booker, H. 2002.** Manx Shearwaters on Lundy. *Report of the Lundy Field Society* 51: 95–103.

**Price, D. & Booker, H. 2014.** Breeding seabirds 'take off' on Lundy – results of the 2013 Breeding Seabird Survey. *Devon Birds* 67(2): 29–31.

**Pulman, G.P.R. 1875.** *The Book of the Axe.* Longman, Green, Reader & Dyer, London.

**Rackham, O. 2006.** *Woodlands.* HarperCollins, London.

**Ratcliffe, D.A. 1993.** *The Peregrine Falcon.* T. & A.D. Poyser, London.

**Reay, P. & Kent, P. 2011.** Tamar Avocets – how many now? *Devon Birds* 64(1): 15–22.

**Renwick, A.R., Massimino, D., Newson, S.E., Chamberlain, D.E., Pearce-Higgins, J.W. & Johnston, A. 2012.** Modelling changes in species' abundance in response to projected climate change. *Diversity and Distributions* 18: 121–132.

**Risely, K., Massimino, D., Johnston, A., Newson, S.E., Eaton, M.A., Musgrove, A.J., Noble, D.G., Procter, D. & Baillie, S.R. 2012.** *The Breeding Bird Survey 2011.* BTO Research Report 624. British Trust for Ornithology, Thetford.

**Risely, K., Massimino, D., Newson, S.E., Eaton, M.A., Musgrove, A.J., Noble, D.G., Procter, D. & Baillie, S.R. 2013** *The Breeding Bird Survey 2012.* BTO Research Report 645. British Trust for Ornithology, Thetford.

**Robins, M. & Jutsum, R. 1987.** Dartmoor Environmental Baseline – 1986 Breeding Bird Survey, RSPB, Exeter.

**Robinson, R.A. 2005.** *BirdFacts: profiles of birds occurring in Britain and Ireland (BTO Research Report 407).* BTO, Thetford. http://www.bto.org/birdfacts, accessed between 24 April 2014 and 04 May 2015.

**Robinson, R.A., Lawson, B., Toms, M.P., Peck, K.M., Kirkwood, J.K., Chantrey, J., Clatworthy, I.R., Evans, A.D., Hughes, L.A., Hutchinson, O.C., John, S.K., Pennycott, T.W., Perkins, M.W., Rowley, P.S., Simpson, V.R., Tyler, K.M. & Cunningham, A.A. 2010.** Emerging infectious disease leads to rapid population declines of common British birds. *PLoS One* 5:e12215. doi:10.1371/journal.pone.0012215.

**Robinson, R.A., Siriwardena, G.M. & Crick, H.Q.P. 2005.** Status and population trends of Starling *Sturnus vulgaris* in Great Britain. *Bird Study* 52: 252–260.

**Rock, P. 2005.** Urban gulls: problems and solutions. *British Birds* 98: 338–355.

**Rogers, D. 2008.** The Heronries Census in Devon: 1928–2007. *Devon Birds* 61(1): 10–15.

**Ross-Smith, V., Robinson, R.A., Banks, A.N., Frayling, T.D., Gibson, C.G. & Clarke, J.A. 2014.** The Lesser Black-backed Gull in England: how to solve a conservation conundrum. *Seabird* 27: 41–61.

**Rowell, H.E. & Spray, C.J. 2004.** The Mute Swan *Cygnus olor* (Britain and Ireland populations) in Britain and Northern Ireland 1960/61–2000/01. *Waterbird Review Series.* The Wildfowl & Wetlands Trust/Joint Nature Conservation Committee, Slimbridge.

**RSPB. 1997.** *Seabirds of Southern Waters.* RSPB & English Nature, Exeter.

**RSPB. 2009.** Ruddy ducks and white-headed ducks. http://www.rspb.org.uk/forprofessionals/policy/species/nonnative/ruddyducks.aspx, accessed 11 July 2014.

**Rylands, K. 2005.** Woodlark in Devon, 2002–2004. Unpublished RSPB Report.

**Rylands, K. 2007.** Stone Curlew breeding in Devon. *Devon Birds* 60(1): 33–34.

**Sangster, G., Collinson, J.M., Crochet, P-A., Knox, A.G., Parkin, D.T., Svensson, L. & Votier, S. C. 2011.** Taxonomic recommendations for British Birds: seventh report. *Ibis* 153: 883–892.

**Sangster, G., Collinson, J.M., Helbig, A.J., Knox, A.G. & Parkin, D.T. 2005.** Taxonomic recommendations for British Birds: third report. *Ibis* 147: 821–826.

**Sauer, J. R., Hines, J. E., Fallon, J. E., Pardieck, D.J., Ziolkowski, Jr. & Link, W. A. 2014.** The North American Breeding Bird Survey, Results and Analysis 1966–2012. Version 02.19.2014, USGS Patuxent Wildlife Research Center, Laurel, MD.

**Saunders, N. & Wheatley, S. 2012.** Atlantic Puffin (*Fratercula arctica*) population, distribution and productivity on Lundy in 2009 & 2010. *Journal of the Lundy Field Society* 3: 111–124.

**Scuffil, N.P. 2005.** The use of vocal individuality as a monitoring tool for a population of Cetti's Warblers *Cettia cetti.* Unpublished MSc Thesis.

**Sharrock, J.T.R. 1976.** *The Atlas of Breeding Birds in Britain and Ireland.* T. & A.D. Poyser, Calton, Staffordshire.

**Sherman, G. In prep.** Ecology of Common Guillemots on Lundy: 1. Provisioning rates vs parental attendance 2012–2015. Unpublished manuscript.

**Sim, I.M.W., Ludwig, S.C., Grant, M.C., Loughrey, J.L., Rebecca, G.W. & Redpath, S. 2013.** Seasonal variation in foraging conditions for Ring Ouzels *Turdus torquatus* in upland habitats and their effects on juvenile habitat selection. *Ibis* 155: 42–54.

**Sitters, H.P. 1988.** *Tetrad Atlas of the Breeding Birds of Devon.* DBWPS, Yelverton.

**Sitters, H.P. & Tomkovich, P.S. 2010.** Arctic Biodiversity Trends 2010 – Selected Indicators of Change. CAFF International Secretariat, Akureyri, Iceland. www.arcticbiodiversity.is.

**Smaldon, R. 2005.** *The Birds of Dartmoor.* Isabelline Books, Falmouth.

**Smaldon, R. 2010.** Dartford Warbler survey of Roborough Down, April/June 2009. *Dartmoor Bird Report 2009*: 121–123.

**Smaldon, R. 2013.** Goosander roost counts 2012. *Dartmoor Bird Report* 2012: 100–102.

**Smalley, J. & John, T. 2010.** Dartmoor Garden Bird Survey confirms Yellowhammer decline. *Dartmoor Bird Report 2009*: 116.

**Smith, J.C. 2009.** New to Devon: Paddyfield Warbler on Lundy. *Devon Birds* 62(3) (*Devon Bird Report* 81): 206–207.

**Smith, K.W. 1997.** Nest site selection of the great spotted woodpecker *Dendrocopos major* in two oak woods in southern England and its implications for woodland management. *Biological Conservation* 80: 283–288.

**Smith, K.W. & Smith, L. 2013.** The effect of supplementary feeding in early spring on the breeding performance of the Great Spotted Woodpecker *Dendrocopos major. Bird Study* 60: 169–175.

**Snow, D.W. & Perrins, C.M. 1998.** *The Birds of the Western Palearctic,* Concise Edition. Two volumes. Oxford University Press, Oxford.

**Somerset Ornithological Society. 2004.** *Somerset Birds 2003,* pp 39–40. Somerset Ornithological Society.

**Stace, C. 2010.** *New Flora of the British Isles,* Third Edition. Cambridge University Press, Cambridge

**Stanbury, A., Davies, M., Grice, P., Gregory, R. & Wotton, S. 2010.** The status of the Cirl Bunting in the UK in 2009. *British Birds* 103: 702–711.

**Stanbury, A., Davies, M. & Wotton, S. 2010.** Trends in some farmland birds in South Devon, 2003–2009. *Devon Birds* 63(2): 17–22.

**State of the UKs Birds. See:**

2012. Eaton *et al.* 2012.

2013. Eaton *et al.* (2013).

2014. Hayhow *et al.* 2014.

**Stevens, D. 2007.** The Spotted Flycatcher Enquiry – 50 years on. *Devon Birds* 60(2): 30–34.

Stevens, D., Barber, L. & Bone, R. 2007. The RSPB/Natural England Spotted Flycatcher Project in South Devon: 2006. *Devon Birds* 60(2): 13–15.

Stoddart, A. 2013. Redpolls: a review of their taxonomy, identification and British status. *British Birds* 106: 708–736.

Summers, R.W., Underhill, L.G., Nicoll, M., Strann, K-B. & Nilsen, S.Ø. 2004. Timing and duration of moult in three populations of Purple Sandpipers *Calidris maritima* with different moult/migration patterns. *Ibis* 146: 394–403.

Tabb, T. 2004. Secrets of the Egret. *Devon Birds* 57(2): 25–26.

Taylor, A.M. 1986. Manx Shearwaters on Lundy: ringing information and other observations. *Report of the Lundy Field Society* 36: 23–24.

Taylor, T. 2004. Birds on Lundy, 2003. *Report of the Lundy Field Society* 53: 20–43.

Taylor, T. 2007. Birds on Lundy, 2005. *Report of the Lundy Field Society* 55: 21–48.

Toms, M. 2014. *Owls*. HarperCollins, London.

Townend, C. 2012. New to Devon: Macaronesian Shearwater *Puffinus baroli* on Lundy. *Devon Birds* 65(3) (*Devon Bird Report* 84): 193–194.

Townsend, D.J., Dugan, P.J. & Pienkowski, M.W. 1984. The unsociable plover – use of intertidal areas by Grey Plovers. In: P.R. Evans, J.D. Goss-Custard & W.G. Hale (eds), *Coastal waders and wildfowl in winter*, pp. 140–159. Cambridge University Press, Cambridge.

Tucker, V. 2007. South Huish Water Meadows – the first decade of a reserve created from scratch. *Devon Birds* 60(1): 21–25.

Turner, J. 2009. Ringed Plovers breeding in Devon. *Devon Birds* 62(1): 37–39.

Turton, W. & Kingston, J.F. 1830. *The Natural History of the District of Teignmouth, Dawlish and Torquay.* Croydon.

Tyler, M. 2010. *The Birds of Devon*. DBWPS, Exeter.

Tyler, S.J. & Ormerod, S.J. 1994. *The Dippers*. T. & A.D. Poyser, London.

Vadász, C., Német, Á., Karcza, Z., Lóránt, M., Biró, C. & Csörgő, T. 2008. Study on breeding site fidelity of *Acrocephalus* warblers in central Hungary. *Acta Zoologica Academiae Scientiarum Hungaricae* 54 (Supplement 1): 167–175.

Waite, S. 2011. Solitary Sandpiper *Tringa solitaria* at Black Hole Marsh, Axe Estuary – new to Devon. *Devon Birds* 64(3) (*Devon Bird Report* 83): 178.

Walmesley White, W. 1931. *Bird Life in Devon*. London, Jonathan Cape.

Walters, J. 2010. Black-throated Thrush *Turdus atrogularis* on Scoriton Down, Dartmoor – new to Devon. *Devon Birds* 63(3) (*Devon Bird Report* 82): 207–209.

Waterhouse, G. 2014. The Wetland Bird Survey on the Kingsbridge and Salcombe Estuary, 1974 to 2013. Part 1 – Introduction, history and general overview. *Devon Birds* 67(2): 3–16.

Watson, M., Aebischer, N.J., Potts, G.R., & Edwald, J.A. 2007. The relative effects of raptor predation and shooting on overwinter mortality of Grey Partridges in the United Kingdom. *Journal of Applied Ecology* 44: 972–982.

Wernham, C.V., Toms, M.P., Marchant, J.H., Clark, J.A., Siriwardena, G.M. & Baillie, S.R. (eds). 2002. *The Migration Atlas: movements of the birds of Britain and Ireland*. T. & A.D. Poyser, London.

Wetlands International. 2006. *Waterbird Population Estimates – Fourth edition*. Wetlands International, Wageningen.

White, S. & Kehoe, C. 2014. Report on scarce migrants in Britain in 2008–10. *British Birds* 107: 142–176.

Whitehall, B. 2003. Little Egret – first reported Devon breeding record. *Devon Bird Report* 75: 228.

Whitehall, B. 2003. Slapton Ley – Part 4 – Monitoring at Slapton. *Devon Birds* 56(2): 11–25.

Whitehall, B. 2006. The distribution of Reed and Sedge Warblers at Slapton Ley in 2004 and 2005. *Devon Birds* 59(1): 24–34.

Whitehall, B. 2008. Observations on a summering pair of Marsh Harriers at Slapton in 2006. Was this a breeding attempt? *Devon Birds* 61(2): 14–16.

Whitehall, B. 2009. Variation in breeding numbers of Great Crested Grebe at Slapton Ley. *Devon Birds* 62(3) (*Devon Bird Report* 81): 46.

Wilson, J.D., Taylor, R. & Muirhead, L.B. 1996. Field use by farmland birds in winter: an analysis of field type preferences using resampling methods. *Bird Study* 43: 320–332.

Wiseman, E.J. 2012. Honey-buzzards in southern England. *British Birds* 105: 23–28.

Woods, R. & Woods, A. 2006. The Norfolk Blackbird that winters in Devon. *Devon Bird Report* 77: 94–95.

Wotton, S., Conway, G., Eaton, M., Henderson, I. & Grice. P. 2009. The status of the Dartford Warbler in the UK and the Channel Islands in 2006. *British Birds* 102: 230–246.

Wotton, S., Gibbons, D.W., Dilger, M. & Grice, P.V. 1998. Cetti's Warblers in the United Kingdom and the Channel Islands in 1996. *British Birds* 91: 77–89.

# Appendix 1

# Observers

The following have all contributed to the database of 1,124,856 records on which this work is based. Without their input, which in some cases was immense, this work would not have been possible; we are hugely grateful to them all. Some volunteers have, very sadly, not lived to see the published Atlas but we hope that, in some small way, acknowledging their involvement will be a fitting tribute.

*Photo: (Ring Ouzel) Chris Townend*

Mr Peter Abbott
Mr Philip Abbott
Mrs Marion Adams
Mr Nick Adams
Mr Trevor Adams
Mr David Agombar
Mr Mike Alexander
Mr P Aley
Mr John Allan
Mr Richard Allan
Mr Adrian Allen
Mr Colin Allen
Mr Jamie Allen
Miss Jenepher Allen
M Allen
Mr Terry Allen
Mr Laurence Allnatt
Mr Mark Allott
Mrs P Allwright
Ms S Alsbury
Mrs Dawn Anderson
Mrs Susan Anderson
B J Andrew
Mrs Diane Andrews
Mr Paul Anness
Mr Stephen Anstey
Mr Philip Apps
Mr Mike Archer
Mr John Arnfield
Mrs Esther Arnold
Mr Nigel Arnold
Mr Richard Arnold
Miss Kate Ashbrook
Mr Nicholas Ashman
Miss Mandy Atherton
Mr Anthony Atkinson
Mr Chris Attewell
B P Austin
Mr Michael Austin
Ms Penny Avant
Dr M I Avery
Mr Jon Avon
Mr Steven Ayers
Mr Peter Ayley

Miss H Ayshford
Mr David Back
Mr David Bagott
Ms Catherine Bailey
Ms Diane Bailey
Miss Juliet Bailey
Dr Louise Bailey
Willa Bailey
Rev Chris Baillie
Dr S R Baillie
Mr D Bainbridge
Mrs Ann Bairstow
Mr M H Baker
Miss Sarah Baker
Mr Kevin Balding
Mrs Angela Baldock
Mr N Baldock
Mr Tim Baldwin
Mr John Ball
Mrs Kay Ball
Mr David Ballance
Mrs Judy Ballard
Ms Dawn Elizabeth Balmer
Peter Banks
Mr Tim Banks
Mrs A M Barker
Mr Jeremy Barker
Mrs Naomi Barker
Mr S R J Barker
Mrs Joyce Barkla
Mr P Barlow
Mr Roy Barlow
Mr John Barnes
Mrs Prunella Barnes
P R Barnes
Miss Rose Louise Barnes
Mrs Liz Barnett
Ms Valerie Barns
Mr John Barr
Ms Jacqueline Barrett
Mr R W Barrow
Mr Nigel Bastin
Mr S M Bates
Mr Christopher Batey

Mr G S Batho
Mr John Bathurst
Miss Jennifer Karen Batten
Dr Nick Bayly
Mrs J Beal
L Beard
Mr Archibald Beattie
J W Beatty
Stella Beavan
Mr Michael Beer
Dr Richard Beer
Mrs Stephanie Beer
Mr Stewart Beer
Mr Trevor Beer
Mr Mason Bell
Mr Michael Bell
Mr I J Bennallick
Mr Jim Bennett
Mr Peter Gordon Bennett
Mrs Maureen Bennett
Mrs Val Bentley
D Best
Lt Col N W Beswick
Mr Andrew Bevan
Mr Martin Bevan
Mr Robert Billingsley
Mr Alastair Binham
G Birchall
Mr Steven Bird
Mr John Birkett
Ms Liz Biron
Ms Alex Birtles
Ms Lesley Bizley
Mr Gavin Black
Mr Mark Blacksell
Mr William Blumsom
Mr Chris Bollen
Mr Rod Bone
Mr W J G Boot
Mr Robin Borwick
Mr Simon Boswell
Mrs Coral Botteley
Mr J E Bottom
Mr Robert Boulton

Miss Alison Bourne
Dr Myles Bowen
Mr Ronald Bowers
Mr D Boyce
Mr Matthew Boyer
Mr Arthur Boyt
Mr David Brabban
Mr James Bracher
Mr John Bradbeer
S M Bradley
Mr Hugh Bradshaw
Mr Paul Brady
Miss Geraldine Braes
D M Braund
J & K Braven
Mr Andrew Bray
Mr Mark Breaks
Mrs M A Breakspear
Mr John Breeds
Mr R H Brennan
Ms Clare Brewster
Mr N Briden
Mr Adrian Bridge
Mr R G Broadie
Mrs Rebecca Brokenshire
Mr A H Brooking
Mr Michael Brooking
Dr Colin Brooks
Mr John Broomhead
Mr Biggs Brown
Mr Graham Brown
R M Brown
Mrs Stephanie Brown
Prof D M Bryant
D Bryant
B Bryne
Mrs R Bubb
Mr L W Buchanan
Mr Martin Buckland
Mrs Janine Buckle
Mr Maurice Dexter Budden
J D Bude
Mr A J Bull
S Bullen

Dr Malcolm Burgess
Mrs N Burgum
Mr Tim Burkinshaw
Miss Molly Burnley
A N M Burns
Mr P J Burston
Mr R G Burston
Mr Alan Burton
G Butcher
Mr Pete Butcher
Mr Roger Butcher
Mr Brian Butler
Mr Paul Butler
Mr John Butter
Mr Tony Butters
Mr Ivan Buxton
Mr John Byrne

Mr Chris Caldwell
Mr David Callahan
Mr Andrew Camp
Mr Donald Campbell
Mr Geoff Campbell
Mrs Irene Cann
Mr Steven Carey
Mrs V Carnell
Mr Ben Carpenter
Mrs Evelyn Carpenter
Mrs Anne Carrington-
    Cotton
Mr Brian Carter
Mr Derek Carter
Dr N Carter
Mr Paul Carter
Mr Tony Carter
Mr Barry Catlin
D Cawthraw
Mr David Chadwick
Mr A P Chamberlin
Mr David Chambers
Mr Philip Chambers
Miss Nina Chan
Mr Nicholas Chandler
Mr Chris Chapman
Miss Janet Chapman
P Chapman
Mr R A Chapman
Mr S E Chapman
Mr Christopher Charlton
Miss Mabel Cheung
J Chilton
Mr Dave Chown
Dr Roger Christopher
Mr David Churchill
Mr Kieran Claiden-Yardley
M Claire
Mr David Clark
Mr Frank Charles Clark
Miss Stephanie Clark
T Clark
D Clarke
Miss Felicity Clarke
Mr R M Clarke
Mr D Clegg
Mr John Clements

Mr Maurice Clements
Ms Heather Coats
T D Codlin
C Cole
Mrs Felicity Cole
Ms M Coleman-Cooke
A Coles
Mr Mark Collier
Miss Christine Collinge
S Collins
Mr M Collis
Mr M Comber
Mr Peter Combridge
Ms Audrey Compton
J Connors
Dr Greg Conway
Mr Henry Cook
Miss Lisa Cook
Mr Robert Cooke
Mr Cooper
Dr Alison Cooper
Mr Andrew Cooper
Mr Dale Cooper
Mr Edward Cooper
Mr Geoffrey Cooper
Mr Jamie Cooper
Miss Melanie Cooper
Mr Philip Cooper
Mr Christopher Coppock
Mr David Cornish
Mr Christopher Corrigan
Mr Nigel Cottle
Mrs Claire Cotton
D Cotton
Miss Naomi Coulson
F Court
C Courtney
Mr Mark Coventry
Mr Peter Cowlard
Mr Dave Cox
Mr Kevin Cox
L Cox
R Cox
Dr Helen Crabtree
Mr Brian Cracknell
S J Craft
Mrs Georgina Craig
Mrs Ann Crawford
Mr Richard Crawford
Mr Dave Crawshaw
Mr Peter Crispin
Mr Robert Crispin
Mr Robert Crompton
Mr Neil Croton
Mr Patrick Crowley
Mr Andrew Cudmore
Ms Jane Cumming
Mr Andrew Cunningham
Mr David Curtis
R J Curtis
Dr Abraham Cutajar
Mr Brian Cuttell
Mr Mark Cutts
Mr Kenneth Cypher

Mr Chris Dale
E J Daniels
Mrs Janet Daniels
Jan & Mike Daniels
Mr Mike Dannatt
Mr Mark Darlaston
Mr Laurie Daunt
Mr Allan David
Mr Keith Davies
Mrs Mary Davies
Mr Sidney Davies
Mr Steven Davies
Tony Davies
Mr Terence John Davis
Mr Tim Davis
Mr William Deakins
Mr Rod Dean
G Deare
Mr Chris Dee
Mrs Mandy Dee
Mrs Ann Deem
A Demora
Mr Bob Dennison
Mr Stephen Dewey
Mr James Diamond
Lt Col R C Dickey
Mr Tom Dingwall
Ms Clare Diprose
J R Dixon
Mr Roger Doble
Mr Brian Dodd
Mr Anthony Dorman
Mr Paul Douch
B Doughty
Dr Robert Doughty
Mr Chris Doust
Mr John Downes
Miss Katie Downes
Mr Hud Downham
Mr M J D'Oyly
Mr Ed Drewitt
Mrs Jane Elizabeth Druett
Ms Nicola Duckworth
Mrs Pamela Dudley
Mr John Duffy
Mr Barry Dunn
Dr Robert Dunn

Mr T G Easterbrook
Gary & Anna Easton
Mr Malcolm Easton
Mr Seumus Eaves
Mr Kenneth Ebsworthy
Dr Martin Eccles
Mr Alun Edwards
Mr Andrew Edwards
Mrs C Edwards
Mr Eirwen Edwards
Mr Stephen Gary Edwards
Mr H R Egelstaff
Mr Martin Elcoate
Mr Steve Elcoate
Mr Steve Elford
Mr Andrew Ellard
Mr Greg Elliott-Moustache

Mr Brian Ellis
D L Ellis
Mr Ian Ellis
Mrs Jan Ellis
Ms Susan Ellis
Mr Tor Elm
Mrs Marion Elmes
Mr Dennis Elphick
Mr Robert Emery
S England
Mrs Erica Evans
Ms Jennifer Evans
Mr Lyn Evans
Mrs Mair Evans
Mr Michael Evans
Mr Ah Eveleigh
Mr James Evry

R Facey
Mr James Fairclough
Mr Jonathan Fairhurst
Mr Malcolm Fairley
D P Farncombe
Dr Andre Farrar
Mr Charles Farrell
Mr Matthew Farrier
N Fawcett
Mr Alastair Feather
Dr Jill Fell
Mr Kenneth Fenner
Mr Jonathan Fenton
Mr Robin Fenton
Mr Terry Fenton
Ms Maria Fernandes
Mr David Charles Fieldsend
Mr Ian Fisher
Mrs Janice Fisher
Mr Stephen Fitt
Mr Alastair Flannagan
Mr K Fleming
Mrs Gillian Flinn
Mr Paul Floyd
Mr Phil Flynn
Alan Ford
Mr Bob Ford
Ms Jane Ford
Mrs Jennifer Ford
Mr Sam Forest
Mrs Jill Forshaw
Dr Thomas Forster
Miss Claire Foster
Mr Neill Foster
Mr Nevil Fowler
Mr M Fox
Mr R J Fox
D Frazer
Mrs Deborah Frazer
Mrs S D Frearson
Mrs Sarah Freeman
P J Freestone
Miss Alissa Fremeaux
Ms F Freshney
Mr D J Fricker
Mr Christopher Furley
J Gale

Ms Sarah Gallifent
Howard Gannaway
Mrs Jacqueline Mary
  Gardner
Mr Ian Gasper
Mr Richard Gatehouse
Dr Rodney Alan Gayer
Mr David Gayton
Mr Robert Gaze
Mr Chris Gent
M George
Mrs Lesley Gerber
Mr K. F German
Miss Linda Gerrard
Dr David Gibbons
B D Gibbs
Mrs Judi Gibbs
Mr Trevor Gibson-Poole
Mr Derek Gilby
Mrs Annabel Gilding
Mr Robert Gill
Reverend T W Gladwin
Mr Dave Glaves
Mrs Elizabeth Glazier
Mr Ron Gleadle
J Glen
Mrs Gill Glover
Mr Phillip Goble
T Goddard
Mr Nicholas Godden
Mr Robert Godden
Mr Edward Godsiffe
F GoldsmIth
Mrs Sue Goldthorpe
Mr Clive Alexander Good
Mr Peter Goodfellow
Mrs Diana Gorringe
Mr Mike Goss
Miss S J Gough
Mr Alan Gracie
Mrs Maren Gracie
Mr Stuart Graham
Mr Tim Graham
Mr Keith Grant
Mr Kevin Grant
M G Grant
Mr Peter Grant
Mr Mark Grantham
Mr Ian Gray
Mr Stuart Green
Mr Martin Greene
Mr Colin Greenfield
Mr Steve Greenhalgh
D Greenhill
Mr Ron Greenwood
S Greeves
Mrs Gillian Margaret
  Gregory
Mr Paul Gregory
Mrs Marian Griffiths
Mr Robin Griffiths
Mr Simon Griffiths
Mr R Grimmond
Mr Andrew Grinter
Mrs R D Gross

Mr Anthony Gutteridge
Mr R D Gynn

Mr Peter Crispin Hack
Mr David Haines
Ms Rosamund Hall
Mr Timothy Hall
Mr R M Halliwell
Mrs Jane Halsey
Mr Roger Halsey
Mr Richard Keith Halstead
Mr R G Hamar
Mr Mark David
  Hammonds
Mr Michael Hamzij
S F Hancock
Mr Peter Hancocks
Mrs Carol Hanley
Mr Andrew Hanlon
Miss Deborah Hanlon
Miss Claire Hansell
Mr Alan James Hardie
Mrs Julia Harding
Mr Roger Hardy
T Hare
S Hares
Mr Christopher Harper
Mr Anthony Harris
Professor Duncan Harris
Mrs E M Harris
Mr George Harris
Mr Joe Harris
Mrs Julia Harris
K S Harris
Mr Roger Harris
Mr Andrew Harrison
Mrs M Harrison
Mr Rob Harrison
R Hart
Dr Ian Hartley
Mr Eddie Harwood
Dr Vicky Hassell
Dr Jeremy Hatch
Mr S R Hatch
Mrs Julie Hatchett
Mrs Wendy Hatton
Mr Rupert Hawley
Mr Mark Haworth-Booth
Mr Bret Hawthorne
Mr John Hawtree
Mr Richard Haydon
Dr Bill Haynes
Mrs Margaret Hayter
Mr R L Haythornthwaite
Mr Ian Hayward
Mr P J Hazelwood
Mrs Nichola Heading
Mrs Maggie Heal
Mr G W Hearnden
Mrs Helen Heathman
Mr Paul Heatley
Mr Steve Hedditch
Mr Brian Hedley
T Hedworthy
Mr David Helliar

Mr Nigel Hewitt
Mr P J Hewitt
Mr Roger Hewitt
Mr Richard Hibbert
Mr R Hicks
Mr Rupert Higgins
Mr John High
Mr Joe Higman
Miss Hill
C Hill
Mr I Hill
Mr Roy Hilliard
Mrs Rachel Hilton
Mr Matt Hines
Mrs Caroline Hirst
Mr Mike Hitch
M P Hobson
Mr Tim Hodge
Mr Paul Hodges
Ms Julie Hogg
Mrs Angela Holdsworth
Mrs C Holdsworth
Mr Jeremy William Holgate
Mr Richard Hollis
Mr Darryl Keith Holloway
Mr Timothy N Holloway
A Holmes
Mr Jeffrey David Holmes
Miss Susan Holoran
Mrs Jenny Holter
Mr Tony Holwill
P Holyday
T Honoir
Mr B Hook
Miss Denise Hooper
Peter Hopkin
Mr Christopher Horsfield
Mrs Christine Horsley
Dr Michael Hounsome
Dr Tim Hounsome
Mr Lance Housley
Dr Ian Howard
Prof Peter Howard
Miss Denise Howe
Mrs Karin Howes
Mr Alan Hubbard
Mrs Sandra Hubbard
Mr R J Hubble
Mr James Hudson
Mr Richard Hudson
Mr P Huggett
Mrs Ann Hughes
Julian Hughes
Mr Nick Hull
J C Humphreys
Mr David Humphreyson
Mrs Sally Elizabeth Hunt
Mr Ian Hunt
Mr Dennis Hursthouse
R Husbands
Dr Nevil Hutchinson
Mrs Sheena Hutchinson
Mr A Hutchison

M Iddon

Mr Marc Illa
Ms Sally Irwin
Mr Laurie Ison
Mrs Alison Isserlis
Mr Peter Izzard

Mrs Jane Jackson
Mr Jake Jacobs
Mr Robert Jacobs
Mrs Louise Jaggard
Mr Jonah James
Mr Kenneth Jarratt
Mr Danny Jarvis
Mr Kevin Mark Jarvis
Vendela Jarvis
E S S Jay
Mrs M Jeeves
Mr Joshua Jenkins Shaw
Ms Sara Jennett
Mr Trevor Jennings
Mr Paul Jepson
Mr David Jeremy
Mr Anthony John
Mr Kevin Johns
Mr Ceri Jones
Mr Chris Jones
Mrs Christine Jones
Ms Elizabeth Jones
Mr Glenn William Jones
Mrs Louise Jones
N Jones
P Jones
Mr Ray Jones
Mr R A Jones
R I Jones
Mr Sam Jones
Mr Tim Jones
Mr Derek Jopson
Mr Charles Joynson
Mr Derek Julian
Mr Robert Jutsum

W Kani
Dr Angela Kannan
W Keatley
Gerard Keele
Miss Wendy Kellett
Mr Roy Kelly
Mrs Sarah Kelman
Mr Harvey Kendall
Mr David Kennett
Mr Peter Kent
Mrs Sarah Kent
Mrs Lynne Kett
Mr Christopher Khan
Mr Robin Khan
Mrs Elisabeth Kincaid
Dr David King
Mrs Rhiannon King
Mrs Ann Kingston
Mr Melvyn Kirby
Mr G R Kirk
Mr C E F Kitchin
K Kite
Mr David Knight

Mr Rex Knight
Ryan Knight
J Knightbridge
Mr David Knowles
Mr Dudley Knowles

Miss Penny Ladd
Mr I W Lakin
Mr David Lamacraft
Mr John Lamb
Mr Nicholas Langdon
Mr Mike Langman
Mr Andy Lansdell
Mr P D Latham
Mr David Lathbury
Mrs Annette Laurie
Ms Jan Laursen
Mrs Rozel Lawlor
Mr M R Lawn
Mr John Laws
Dr Vincent Lea
Miss Helen Leach
Mr Simon Leach
Ms Anna Leatherdale
Mr David Lee
Mr Jonathon Lees
J Legg
Mr James William Leonard
Mr Colin Lever
M J Lewandowski
Mr Barrie Lewis
Ms Carole Lewis
Rev David Lewis
Mr Gareth Lewis
Mrs Vanessa Lewis
R J Lillicrap
Ms Christine Lindsay
A M Linington
D List
Ms Suzanne Litherland
Dr Cris Little
L M Little
Mr Roger Little
Mr Arthur Livett
Mr Alan Livsey
Mr John Lloyd
Mr M G Lobb
Dr J M Lock
Mr David Lockyer
Mr Paul Lott
Mr Ian Loudon
Mr Raymond Lovett
Mrs Anne Lowe
Mr Sam Luttman
Mr Howard Lyne
Mrs Suzanne Lyus

Mr Ben Macdonald
Mr R N Macklin
Mrs Angela Macpherson
Mrs Mary Madden
Mr Charles Madge
Miss Abigail Madgett
Dr Paul Madgett
Mrs Ro Madgett

Mr Christopher Mandry
I Manfield
Mrs Jacqui Mansell
Mr John Marchant
Mr Robert Marchant
Dr Jenny Maresh
Mr Philip Marlow
Mr Nick Marriner
Mrs Eileen Marsh
Mrs H Marshall
Mr Joshua Marshall
J Marshall
Mr Matthew Marshall
Mr John Martin
Mr Jonathan Martin
Mr Jon Martin
Mr Simon Charles Martin
Mr Cyril Matthews
Mrs Sylvie Matthews
Mr Andrew Maundrell
C Maxwell
Mrs Jan Maxwell
Mr Steve May
Mr Patrick Mayer
Mr Darren Maynard
S Mayne
Miss Maxine McAdams
Dr John McCaig
Ms Marian McCain
Mr Frank McCarthy
Ms Sarah McCourt
Mr Ian McCulloch
Mrs Christine McDonald
Mr Peter McDonald
Mr Stuart Mcfarlane
Miss Debbie McGahey
Dr Alistair McGowan
Mr Neal Terence Mckenna
P A F McKenzie-Lloyd
Mr Ian Mclean
Mr Ivor Mclean
Mr Jon McLeod
Ms Pam McLeod
Mrs Sara McMahon
Mr Derek McNulty
Mr Bill McOwan
Mr Neville Meek
Mr Richard Menari
S Menzie
Mrs Val Mercer
Mr Simon Metcalfe
Dr Richard Mark Meyer
Ms Gillian Middleton
Mr Alistair Hugh Miller
Mrs Carole Miller
Mr David Miller
Mr H J Miller
R Miller
Mr Bernie Millington
Mr Barrie Mills
Miss Jenny Mills
Mrs Jill Mills
Mr John Milner
M Milton
Rev Carl Mitchell

Mr David Mitchell
Mr Michael Mitchell
Mr Paul Mitchell
Mr Gary Mock
Mr David Montier
Mr Ian Moore
Mr Nick Moran
Mr Geoffrey Morgan
Mr Kenneth Jon Morgan
Mr Steve Morgan
Mr Colin Morris
Ray Morris
Mr John Morrison
Mr K Mortimore
Dr M E Moser
Mrs Jane Moss
Mr Robert Moss
A Mowbray
Mr G F Moysey
Ms Maureen Muckersie
Ms Stephanie Muddell
R C Mudge
Mrs Sally Mulford
Ms C M Mulholland
Mrs Debby Mullier
Dr Roderick Muncey
Mr Barry Mung
Dr D A Murdoch
Mrs Susan Murphy
Dr Andy Musgrove
Mr Roger Musgrove
Mr Steve Mynard

R H J Nash
Mr Steve Neal
C Neale
Mr Aidan Patrick Neary
Miss Kaitlin Neeson
Mrs Judith Nevard
Dr S P Newman
Mr Gerald Nicholas
Mr Jim Nicholson
D J Nickeas
L I Nickell
Mr Joshua Nightingale
Mr Brian Nixon
Mrs Jane Noakes
Ms Bernadette Noble
Mr Cameron Norsworthy
Mr Stephen North

Mr Pádraig Ó Meachair
Mr Darren Oakley-Martin
Mrs Jill O'Brien
Mr J B O'Connell-Davidson
Mr J O'Hanlon
Mr Brian O'Leary
Mr J C C Oliver
Mr S J Oliver
Mr Stuart Olliver
Mr Kevin O'neill
L Orchard
Mr Cliff Orman
P Orman
Mr Patrick Orme

Mr Rupert Ormerod
Dr Richard Orton
Mr Eric Osbaldeston
Mr Alan Osborne
Mrs Doreen Overy
Mr Martin Overy

Mr Ray Packham
Mr N G Page
Mrs Judith Palmer
Mr Ian Park
Mrs Melanie Parker
Mr S J Parker
Mr David Parkinson
C Parr
Dr Charles Parry
Mr Michael Passman
Mr John Patterson
Mr David Paull
Mrs Anita Payne
Mr Bob Payne
Mr David Payne
Geoff Pearce
Mr Kelvin Pearce
I Pearson
Mr Robin Pearson
Mr Roger Peart
R Peck
Mr Peter Penning
Mr R F Penticost
Mr Geoff Penton
Miss Sarah Perring
Mr Anthony Perry
Sonia Peter
Mr Jeremy Peters
J Pett
Ms Jan Phillips
Dr Margaret Phillips
Mrs Margaret Phillips
Mr Roy Phillips
Mr Lawrence Pierce
Miss Josette Pinkney
Mr Michael Pittaway
Dr Roger Poland
Mr Steve Polkinghorne
Mr Martin Polley
L Polson
Mr N D Pomiankowski
Mrs Wendy Pope
Mr Geoffrey Pople
Mrs Jill Portsmouth
Mr Kevin Postones
Mr Nicholas Potter
Mrs Lynne Poulson
Mr David Powell
Mr Tony Powell
Nick Pratt
Mr David Price
John Prince
C E Pritchard
Mr David Pritchard
V Prouse
Mr Frank Prowse
Mr Colin Puddy
M Pugh

Mr John Pullen
Mrs Maxine Putnam
Mr Robert Henry
  Alexander Putnam
Dr Graham Pyatt

Miss Laura Anne Quaye
Mr C B Quinn
Mr Bill Quinton

Mr Douglas Radford
Dr Andre Raine
J Ralley
Mr Ian Ralphs
Mr D J Ramsden
Mr John Randall
Mrs Marie Randall
Miss Nicky Ranger
Dr Graham Rankin
Mr Tom Raven
B Rawlings
Dr Neil Rawlings
Mrs Judith Read
Mr Robert Ready
Mr Peter Reay
Mr Colin Reed
Mr Gerald Rendle
Mrs Pamela Reynolds
Mr Tom Reynolds
Mr Alex Rhodes
B Rhodes
R Rhodes
Mr Anthony Richardson
Mr Peter Richardson
Mr Ollie Richings
Mr M J Ridley
Mrs Joyce Riley
Ms Kate Risely
Mr John Rivoire
Mr John Rix
Dr Barrie Roberts
Mrs Diana Roberts
Mrs Helen Roberts
Ms Jenny Roberts
Mr Julian Roberts
Mrs Tracy Roberts
Miss J J Robertson
Mr Peter Robinson
Mrs Jodie Robson
Ms Tania Roe
D Rogers
Miss Shelagh Rogers
Mr M P Roser
Mr A S Rosney
A Ross
Mr Chris Ross
Ms Mary Ross
Mr Jim Rosser
Mr Nick Rossiter
Mrs Anne Rowe
Dr George Rowing
Mrs June Roy
Mr Doug Rudge
Ms Lorna Rusbridge
Mr Jonathan Ruscoe

Mr Jim Rushforth
M Rushton
Dr Colin Ryall
Mr J Ryall
Ms Margaret Ryan
Miss Clare Ryland
Mr Kevin Rylands

M J Saffery
Mr Sammy Sahonta
Mr William Salmon
Mr Alan Salter
Mr Michael Salter
I Sampson
M L H Sampson
Mr P Sandell
Ms Denise Sanders
Mr Perry Sanders
Mrs Dianne Sandland
Mrs E L Saunders
Mrs Margaret Ann Sawers
A D Scott
D A Scott
Mr Roger John Seabrook
Mrs Heather Searle
Mr Darrell Sefton
Mr Paul Selby
Mr Paul Seligman
Dr R M Sellers
Mr David Seward
Mr David Sexton
Miss Michele Julia
  Seymour
Mr Brian Sharkey
Mrs Jill Sharland
Mr Julian Sharman
Mr Alasdair Shaw
Mr C N Shepherdson
Mr Mel Shepherd-Wells
Mrs P R Shepley
A Sheppard
Mr Christopher Ian
  Godfrey Sherman
Mr Grant Karl Sherman
Mrs Linda Sherwood
Miss Amanda Sheward
Mr John Francis Short
Mr Robin Shrubsole
Mr Stephen Shutt
T Simon
Mr Jonathan Simons
D Simpkin
Mr David Thomas Simpson
Mr Brian Sims
Mrs Karen Sims
Mr Julian Sinclair
Mr Peter Sketch
Miss Estelle Skinner
Mr Jack Skuse
Mr Roger Smaldon
Mrs June P Smalley
Mr Dave Smallshire
Mrs Sally Smart
Mr David Smith
Mrs Janet Smith

Mr Marcus Smith
Mr Michael Smith
Mr P A Smith
Mrs Pam Smith
Mr Peter Smith
Miss Rebecca Smith
Mr Tim Smith
Mr Wilfred L Smith
D Smith
Mrs Angela Snape-Batten
Mr Malcolm Snelgrove
Mr Matt Southam
Mr Patrick Sparkes
R Spencer
Mr C P Sperring
Mrs Julia Springett
Mr Christopher Derek
  Stacey
Mr P B Stanbrook
Mr Frank Stanford
L Staves
Mr Ray Steele
Mrs Anne Stevens
Mr P G Stevens
Mr P J Stevens
Mrs D J Stevenson
Mr Thomas Stevenson
Mr Bob Stockhausen
D R Stoddard
Mr Chris Stone
Miss Emma Stone
Mr G W Stone
Mrs Anne Stormont
Mr Ashley Stow
Mr Peter Strangeman
Mr Alan Straw
Dr David Stroud
M Summers
S Sutcliffe
Mr M P Sutherland
Mr Luke Sutton
Mr Paul Sutton
Mr J L Swallow
Mr Robert Swift
Mrs S Sykes

Mr Bruce Taggart
Mr R E Tallack
Mr Jeremy Tallowin
Mrs Celia Tanner
Mrs Jackie Tayler
Mr A Taylor
Mr Andrew Taylor
Miss Kelly Taylor
Mr Philip Taylor
Mr Robin Taylor
Mr Simon Taylor
Mr Richard Teague
Mr Simon Teale
Mr Ray Teesdale
Mrs Lesley Thatcher
Mr B Theaker
Mr R M Thewlis
Mr Andrew Thomas
Mrs Barbara Thomas

Mrs Debbie Thomas
Mr Ernie Thomas
G F Thomas
Mr Julian Thomas
J M Thomas
Mr Nigel Thomas
Dr Elizabeth Thompson
Mrs Joan Thompson
P J Thompson
Ms G A Thornton
Mr Christopher John
  Thorpe-Dixon
Mrs Val Tidball
Ms Eve Tigwell
Mr Malcolm Tinnelly
Mrs Anne Tippett
Mr James Tirrell
Mr A B Tomczynski
Mr W V Tomkins
Mr David Tomlinson
Mr Simon Tonge
Mr Chris Townend
Anita Townsend
Mr Philip Townsend
Mr Paul Toynton
Ms S Tracey
Mr Paul Treen
Mr Charles Trollope
Mr Henry Trollope
N Troup
Mr Neil Trout
Mr Robin Trundle
Mr K Tucker
Mr Simon Tucker
Mr Vic Tucker
Mr Christopher Tudge
Mr Luke Turner
Mr Malcolm Turner
Mrs Ruth Turner
Mr Matthew Twiggs
Mr Gordon Twinberrow
Dr John Twyford
Mrs Annette Twyman
Mr David Tyler
Mr M W Tyler
Dr S J Tyler
Mr Adrian Tysoe

Mr Geoff Upton

Mrs Maddie van de
  Wetering
Mr Martin Vaughan
Mr Glenn Vernall
Ms Toni Vernelli
A Viceda
D Viles
Miss Donna Vince
Mr Trevor Vincett
Mr Graham Vine
R Virden
Mrs Caroline Helen
  Vodden

Dr R K Waite

Mr Steve Waite
Mr Richard Wakeford
Mr John Waldon
Mr Christopher Walford
Dr Colin Walker
Mr Graham Walker
Mr David Wall
Mrs Laura Walsh
N R Walter
Mr David Walters
Mr J M Walters
R S Warbrick
Mr Kevin Waterfall
Mr Gordon Waterhouse
Mr Alex Waterson
Mr Graham Watson
Mr Michael Watson
Mr Nigel Watson
Dr D Wawman
Mr Richard Weaving
Mr Daniel Webb
Mr P Webb
T Webb
Mr W J Webber
Mr D J Wedd
C M Weedon
Mr Peter Weeks
Mr John Wells
Mr Tom Wells

Mr Gary Welsby
Mr Mark West
Mrs Liz Westwood
Mrs Anne Wheatcroft
Mr Stephen Wheatley
Mrs Fiona Whitby
Mr David White
Mr D R White
Mr W J White
Mr Barrie Whitehall
Mr Tony Whitehead
Mr Adam Whitehouse
Mr A Whitfield
Mrs Janet Whitfield
Ms Janice Whittington
Mr John Wicks
Mr Michael Wilcock
P Wilde
Dr A Wilkie
Mr Ian Wilkins
Mr David Wilkinson
Mr Jonathan Willans
Mrs Ann Willcocks
Mr Alan Williams
Mr Andy Williams
Mr Francis Williams
Mr Gareth Williams
Miss Helen Williams
Mr M J Williams

Mr Robert Williams
Mrs Rose Williams
Mr Tim Williams
Mr Tom Williams
Mr C S Williamson
Mrs Judy Willis
Mr Nigel Willits
Mr M J Willmott
Mrs Gill Wilson
Dr Helen Wilson
Mr Ian Wilson
Mr Tony Wilson
I J Wilton
Mr Richard Wiltshire
Miss Kim Winstone
Mrs Barbara Winter
Mr Patrick Wise
Mr B R Withers
Mrs Audrey Wolstenholme
Mrs Janice Wood
Mr John Wood
Mr Nicholas Wood
Christopher Woodham
Mrs Heather Woodland
Mrs Jen Woodland
Mr John Woodland
Mr A E L Woods
Mr Tim Worfolk
Mrs Jean Worthington

Mr Neil Wragg
Mr Paul Wren
Mr Barry Wright
K M H Wright
Mr Michael Wright
Mr Rodney Wright
Mr David Wulff
Mr M J Wyatt
Ms Freda Wyn
Mr Anthony Wynn

In addition to those specifically named above, members of the following groups submitted records through their parent bodies:

Barn Owl Trust
BirdTrack
BTO via their numerous surveys and schemes
Dartmoor Study Group
Devon Birds
Lundy Field Society
Game & Wildlife Conservation Trust
RSPB

**Black-headed Gull – widespread in winter in Devon but a scarce breeding bird.**

*Photo: Charlie Fleming*

# Appendix 2

# Gazetteer

Where large areas are identified a two-figure reference is given which includes at least part of the named feature. Only very specific places are given a six-figure reference.     *Photo: (Snow Bunting) Steve Hatch*

| | | | |
|---|---|---|---|
| Arlington Court Estate | SS6040 | Burgh Island | SX6443 |
| Arlington | SS6140 | Burlescombe | ST0716 |
| Appledore | SS4630 | Burrator Reservoir | SX5567 |
| Ashburton | SX7569 | Bursdon Moor, Hartland | SS2620 |
| Aveton Gifford Bridge | SX6947 | | |
| Avon Dam | SX6765 | Caddow Combe | SS7550 |
| Avonwick | SX7158 | Challacombe N Devon | SS6940 |
| Axe Estuary | SY2590 | Challacombe Dartmoor | SX6979 |
| Axmouth | SY2591 | Charleton Bay, Kingsbridge | SX7441 |
| Aylesbeare Common | SY0590 | Chettiscombe | SS9614 |
| | | Chittlehampton | SS6325 |
| Babbacombe | SX9265 | Christow | SX8384 |
| Baggy Point | SS4140 | Chudleigh | SX8679 |
| Bantham | SX6643 | Chudleigh Knighton | SX8377 |
| Barnstaple | SS5533 | Claw Moor Plantation | SS4002 |
| Beer Cemetery Fields | SY2288 | Clearbrook, Yelverton | SX5265 |
| Beer Cliffs | SY2288 | Clennon Valley/Ponds | SX8859 |
| Beer Head | SY2288 | Clovelly | SS3124 |
| Beesands | SX8141 | Colyford Common/Marshes/LNR | SY2592 |
| Beesands Ley | SX8141 | Colaton Raleigh | SY0787 |
| Bellever Plantation | SX6477 | Coleton Fishacre | SX9050 |
| Bere Alston | SX4466 | Colyton | SY2493 |
| Berry Head NNR | SX9456 | Combe Martin | SS5846 |
| Bideford | SS4526 | Countess Wear | SX9489 |
| Bideford Bay | SS4231 | Crediton | SS8300 |
| Bishop's Tawton | SS5630 | Crow Point | SS4631 |
| Blackdown Hills | ST11 | Croyde | SS4439 |
| Blackhill Quarry Pool | SY0285 | Cullompton | ST0107 |
| Black Hole Marsh, River Axe | SY2591 | | |
| Black Tor Beare | SX5689 | Dart Estuary | SX8756 |
| Blatchford Lake, Cornwood | SX6159 | Dartmoor | SX68 |
| Bolberry | SX6939 | Dawlish | SX9676 |
| Bolberry Down | SX6838 | Dawlish Warren | SX9879 |
| Bolt Head | SX7236 | Decoy Country Park/Lake | SX8670 |
| Bolt Tail | SX6639 | Downend, Croyde | SS4338 |
| Bovey Tracey | SX8178 | Drake's Island | SX4652 |
| Bowling Green Marsh | SX9787 | | |
| Bradworthy | SS3214 | East Devon Commons | SY08 |
| Branscombe | SY1988 | East Lyn Valley | SS7348 |
| Braunton Burrows | SS43 | East Soar | SX7237 |
| Braunton Marsh | SS4734 | Eggesford Forest | SS6910 |
| Brendon Common | SS7644 | Elwill Bay | SS6449 |
| Brixham | SX9355 | Exe Estuary | SX9884 |
| Broadmoor Farm, Cudlipptown | SX5278 | Exeter | SX9293 |
| Buckfastleigh | SX7366 | Exeter Canal | SX9587 |
| Budleigh Salterton | SY0781 | Exminster (Deepway Lane) | SX9487 |
| Bull Point | SS4646 | Exminster Marshes | SX98 |

| | | | |
|---|---|---|---|
| Exmoor | SS64 | Mamhead (Obelisk) | SX9280 |
| Exmouth | SY0081 | Mansands Ley | SX9253 |
| Exton | SX9886 | Mary Tavy | SX5079 |
| | | Matford | SX9389 |
| Fernworthy Plantation | SX6584 | Meeth | SS5308 |
| Fernworthy Reservoir | SX6684 | Meeth LNR/Quarry | SS5308 |
| Fire Beacon Hill | SX8653 | Meldon Reservoir | SX5691 |
| Foreland Point | SS7551 | Mortehoe | SS4645 |
| | | Morte Bay | SS4341 |
| Glaze Valley, South Brent | SX6759 | Morte Point | SS4445 |
| Glenthorne, Somerset | SS7949 | Moretonhampstead | SX7586 |
| Goodleigh, Barnstaple | SS5934 | Morwenstow, Cornwall | SS2015 |
| Grand Western Canal | ST01 | Musbury | SY2794 |
| Great Hangman | SS6048 | Mutter's Moor | SY1088 |
| Great Torrington | SS4919 | | |
| | | New Bridge, Bishops Tawton | SS5728 |
| Hackney Marshes | SX8772 | Newton Abbot | SX8671 |
| Haldon Forest | SX8884 | North Molton Ridge | SS7732 |
| Haldon Ridge | SX8884 | North Tawton | SS6601 |
| Halwill Junction | SX4499 | Northam Burrows | SS4430 |
| Hangman Point | SS5848 | Northam Pebble Ridge | SS4330 |
| Hardisworthy | SS2220 | | |
| Hartland | SS2624 | Obelisk, Mamhead | SX9280 |
| Hartland Forest | SS2819 | Okehampton | SX5895 |
| Hartland Point | SS2227 | Okehampton Camp | SX5892 |
| Hatherleigh | SS5404 | Orcombe Point | SY0279 |
| Haven Cliff | SY2689 | Ore Stone/Thatcher Rock | SX9562 |
| Heddon Valley | SS6548 | Otter Estuary | SY0782 |
| Hembury Fort/Woods | SX7368 | Otter Valley | ST2005 |
| Hennock Reservoirs | SX8083 | Ottery St Mary | SY0995 |
| Holdstone Hill/Down | SS6147 | Owley Farm, Glaze Valley | SX6759 |
| Holne | SX7170 | | |
| Hooe, Plymouth | SX5052 | Paignton Zoo | SX8759 |
| Hope Cove | SX6739 | Pebblebed Heaths (East Devon) | SY08 |
| Hope's Nose | SX9463 | Peppercombe, Buck's Mills | SS3824 |
| Huntsham Lake | ST0020 | Petrockstowe | SS5109 |
| Huxham | SX9497 | Pig's Nose Valley | SX7636 |
| | | Piles Copse | SX6462 |
| Instow Marsh | SS4732 | Plym Estuary | SX4953 |
| | | Plymouth Breakwater | SX4750 |
| Jenny's Cove, Lundy | SS130457 | Plymouth (City Centre) | SX4754 |
| | | Plymouth Sound | SX4752 |
| Kennick Reservoir | SX8084 | Plympton | SX5256 |
| Kenwith Castle, Abbotsham | SS4327 | Portlemouth | SX7538 |
| Kingsbridge | SX7344 | Portworthy | SX5560 |
| Kingsbridge Estuary | SX7441 | Postbridge | SX6478 |
| Kingsteignton | SX8673 | Powderham Park | SX9683 |
| Kitley Pond | SX5551 | Prawle Point | SX7735 |
| | | Princetown | SX5873 |
| Labrador Bay | SX9370 | Puffin Gully, Lundy | SS134481 |
| Lannacombe | SX8037 | Puslinch, Yealmpton | SX5650 |
| Lee Bay | SS4746 | | |
| Lee Moor | SX5661 | Rackerhayes Ponds, Kingsteignton SX8672 | |
| Little Hangman | SS5848 | Radford Lake | SX5052 |
| Lobb | SS4738 | River Avon (water meadows) | SX7047 |
| Lopwell Dam | SX4765 | River Axe, nr Seaton Marsh | SY2590 |
| Lower Tamar Lake | SS2911 | River Barle | SS9223 |
| Lundy | SS14 | River Bovey, North Bovey | SX7483 |
| Lydford | SX5285 | River Bray | SS6935 |
| Lydford Forest | SX4983 | River Coly | SY2394 |
| Lyme Bay | SY38 | River Creedy | SS8402 |
| Lyme Regis, Dorset | SY3492 | River Culm | ST0612 |
| Lyme Regis Undercliff NNR | SY3090 | River Dart Country Park | SX7370 |
| Lynton | SS7249 | River Erme | SX6249 |
| | | River Exe, nr Topsham | SX9786 |

| | | | |
|---|---|---|---|
| River Gara | SX8148 | Tamar Bridge (Plymouth) | SX4358 |
| River Lyn | SS7448 | Tamar/Tavy Estuary | SX4461 |
| River Meavy | SX5268 | Tamar Lakes | SS2911 |
| River Okement, Okehampton | SX5895 | Tamar Estuary | SX4363 |
| River Otter, nr Otterton | SY0885 | Tamerton Foliot | SX4661 |
| River Plym | SX5155 | Tavistock | SX4874 |
| River Tamar | SX4363 | Tavistock Woodlands | SX4273 |
| River Tavy | SX4562 | Taw/Torridge Estuary | SS4631 |
| River Taw | SS4732 | Teign Estuary | SX9272 |
| River Teign | SX7889 | Teignmouth | SX9473 |
| River Torridge | SS4629 | Thurlestone Bay | SX6641 |
| River Yeo, nr Lapford | SS7307 | Thurlestone Marsh | SX6742 |
| Roadford Reservoir | SX4291 | Tiverton | SS9512 |
| Roborough | SX5062 | Topsham | SX9688 |
| Roborough Down | SX5165 | Torbay | SX9060 |
| | | Torcross | SX8242 |
| St Philip's Stone, Lundy | SS129463 | Torquay | SX9364 |
| Salcombe | SX7338 | Totnes | SX8060 |
| Salcombe Estuary | SX7439 | Trenchford Reservoir | SX8082 |
| Sampford Spiney | SX5372 | Trendlebere Down | SX7779 |
| Saunton Sands | SS43 | Trentishoe | SS6348 |
| Seaton | SY2590 | Trentishoe Down | SS6347 |
| Seaton Seafront | SY2489 | Trinity Hill | SY3095 |
| Seven Rock Point | SY3290 | Two Bridges | SX6074 |
| Sharkham Point | SX9354 | | |
| Sherpa Marsh | SS4835 | Upottery Airfield, Smeatharpe | ST1810 |
| Sherrycombe | SS6048 | Upper Tamar Lake | SS2812 |
| Sherwood Green, Gt. Torrington | SS5520 | | |
| Sidmouth | SY1287 | Valley of Rocks | SS7049 |
| Skern | SS4531 | Velator | SS4835 |
| Slapton Ley | SX8243 | Venford Reservoir | SX6871 |
| Slapton Sands | SX8344 | Venn Ottery | SY0791 |
| Smallhanger Waste | SX5859 | Vogwell | SX7281 |
| Soar | SX7037 | | |
| Sousson's Down | SX6779 | Wembury | SX5148 |
| South Brent | SX6960 | Wembury Bay | SX5147 |
| South Hams Leys | SX8243 | West Buckland | SS6531 |
| South Huish Marsh | SX6841 | West Prawle | SX7637 |
| South Milton (village) | SX6942 | Westward Ho! | SS4329 |
| South Milton Ley | SX6842 | Wimbleball Lake, Somerset | SS9730 |
| South Molton | SS7125 | Wistlandpound Reservoir | SS6441 |
| Squabmoor | SY0484 | Wistman's Wood | SX6177 |
| Start Bay | SX84 | Witheridge | SS8014 |
| Start Point | SX8337 | Woodbury | SY0386 |
| Sticklepath, Okehampton | SX6494 | Woodtown | SS4123 |
| Stock Canon | SX9398 | Woody Bay | SS6749 |
| Stockland | ST2404 | Wrafton Pond | SS4835 |
| Stockland Turbaries | ST20 | Wringapeak | SS6749 |
| Stoke Gabriel | SX8457 | | |
| Stoke Point | SX5645 | Yarner Wood | SX7778 |
| Stover Country Park | SX8375 | Yealm Estuary | SX5347 |
| Straight Point | SY0379 | Yelverton | SX5267 |
| Swincombe Reservoir, N. Devon | SS6942 | | |

# Appendix 3

# Scientific names of plants and animals other than birds

The nomenclature of the flora follows that given in Stace (2010).

*Photo: (Wren) Steve Hatch*

## PLANTS

| | | | |
|---|---|---|---|
| alder | *Alnus* spp. | Horned Pondweed | *Zannichellia palustris* |
| Alder | *Alnus glutinosa* | Italian Rye-grass | *Lolium multiflorum* |
| Beech | *Fagus sylvatica* | larch | *Larix* spp. |
| Bell Heather | *Erica cinerea* | Ling (Heather) | *Calluna vulgaris* |
| Bents | *Agrostis* spp. | lousewort | *Pedicularis* spp. |
| Bilberry | *Vaccinium myrtillus* | Marram | *Ammophila arenaria* |
| birch | *Betula* spp. | Mat Grass | *Nardus stricta* |
| Blackthorn | *Prunus spinosa* | moss | not identified to generic |
| Bracken | *Pteridium aquilinum* | | or specific level |
| Bramble | *Rubus fruticosus* agg. | Niger | *Guizotia abyssinica* |
| Bulrush | *Typha latifolia* | oak | *Quercus* spp. |
| Canadian Waterweed | *Elodea candensis* | Pedunculate Oak | *Quercus robur* |
| Cock's-foot | *Dactylis glomerata* | Sessile Oak | *Quercus petraea* |
| Common Cottongrass | *Eriophorum angustifolium* | Perrenial Rye-grass | *Lolium perenne* |
| Common Nettle | *Urtica dioica* | Pondweed | *Potamogeton* spp. |
| Common Reed | *Phragmites australis* | Purple Moor-grass | *Molinia caerulea* |
| Corsican Pine | *Pinus nigra* | Ragwort | *Senecio jacobaea* |
| cotoneaster | *Cotoneaster* spp. | Reedmace | see Bulrush |
| crab apple | *Malus* spp. | Rowan | *Sorbus aucuparia* |
| Cross-leaved Heath | *Erica tetralix* | Scots Pine | *Pinus sylvestris* |
| dandelion | *Taraxacum* spp. | Sheep's Fescue | *Festuca ovina* |
| Deergrass | *Trichophorum germanicum* | Sitka Spruce | *Picea sitchensis* |
| Douglas Fir | *Pseudotsuga taxifolia* | Sphagnum moss | *Sphagnum* spp. |
| elder | *Sambucus* spp. | thistle | not identified to generic |
| Eelgrass eelgrass | *Zostera* spp. | | or specific level |
| elm | *Ulmus* spp | Tormentil | *Potentilla erecta* |
| False Oat-grass | *Arrhenatherum elatius* | Water-crowfoot | *Ranunculus* spp. |
| fescue | *Festuca* spp. | Water-milfoil | *Myriophyllum* spp. |
| gorse | *Ulex* spp. | Western Hemlock-spruce | *Tsuga heterophylla* |
| Gorse | *U. europaeus* | Western Red-cedar | *Thuja plicata* |
| Western Gorse | *U. galli* | Whortleberry (Bilberry) | *Vaccinium myrtillus* |
| Great Wood-rush | *Luzula sylvatica* | willow | *Salix* spp. |
| Greater Tussock-sedge | *Carex paniculata* | Yew | *Taxus baccata* |
| Groundsel | *Senecio vulgaris* | | |
| Hawthorn | *Crataegus monogyna* | | |
| Hazel | *Corylus avellana* | | |
| Heath Bedstraw | *Galium saxatile* | | |
| Heather (Ling) | *Calluna vulgaris* | | |
| Hogweed | *Heracleum sphondylium* | | |
| Holly | *Ilex aquifolium* | | |

**Bell Heather and Western Gorse at Fire Beacon Hill, East Devon.**

*Photo: East Devon AONB*

## ANIMALS

| | | | |
|---|---|---|---|
| Anchovy | *Engraulis encrasicolus* | 'Messenger' pigeons | *Columba livia domestica* |
| Bass | *Dicentrarchus labrax* | mullet | *Mugil* spp. |
| Brill | *Scophthalmus rhombus* | newt | *Lissotriton* spp. |
| Brown Trout | *Salmo trutta* | Pilchard | *Sardina pilchardus* |
| caddisfly | *Trichoptera* spp. | Plaice | *Pleuronectes platessa* |
| Cod | *Gadus morrhua* | Polychaete worms | *Polychaeta* spp. |
| Common Frog | *Rana temporaria* | rat | *Rattus* spp. |
| cranefly | Tipulidae | Black Rat | *Rattus rattus* |
| Dab | *Limanda limanda* | Brown/Common Rat | *Rattus norvegicus* |
| Dace | *Leuciscus leuciscus* | Red Fox | *Vulpes vulpes* |
| Dormouse | *Muscardinus avellanarius* | sand eels | *Ammodytes* spp. |
| Eel | *Anguilla anguilla* | Salmon | *Salmo salar* |
| European Sprat | *Sprattus sprattus* | Stoat | *Mustela ermine* |
| Flounder | *Platichthys flesus* | Turbot | *Scophthalmus maximus* |
| Herring | *Clupea harengus* | Whiting | *Merlangius merlangus* |
| Mackerel | *Scomber scombrus* | Wild boar | *Sus scrofa* |
| mayfly | *Ephemeroptera* spp. | | |

# Appendix 4

## Altitudinal distribution of tetrads and species

### ALTITUDINAL DISTRIBUTION OF TETRADS

A map of altitudes in Devon is shown in Figure A. Dartmoor and Exmoor are prominent while most of the coastal areas are low-lying. Apart from the moors and the coasts, most of the county lies between 100 and 200 metres above sea level.

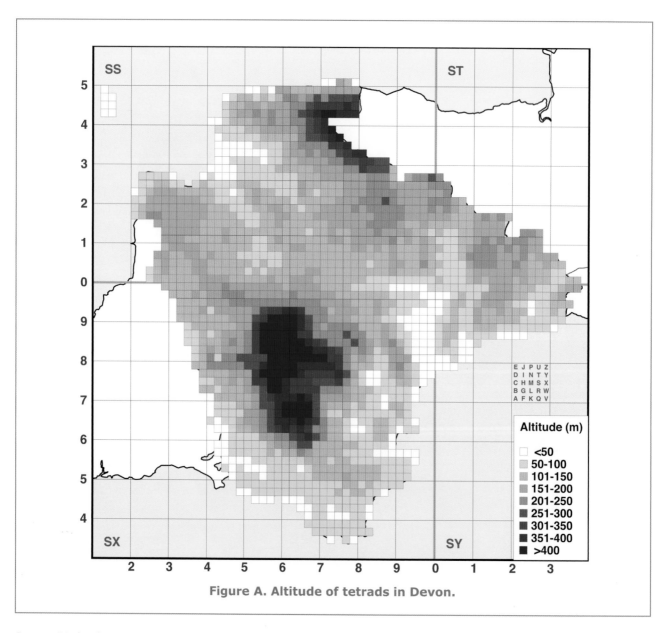

**Figure A. Altitude of tetrads in Devon.**

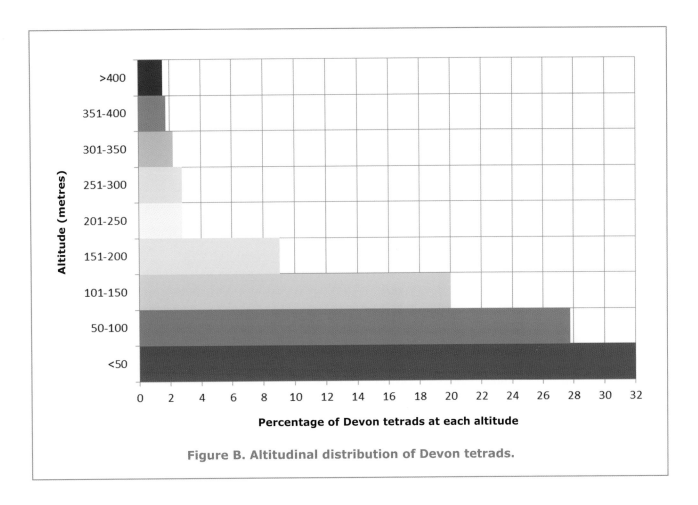

Figure B. Altitudinal distribution of Devon tetrads.

Another way to view the distribution of altitudes in Devon is to display the percentage of all the tetrads that occur at various altitudes (Figure B). It is clear that most of Devon is below 200 metres, with only 11% (mainly Dartmoor and Exmoor) being above 200 metres. These upland areas have an avifauna distinct from most of the rest of Devon.

## ALTITUDINAL DISTRIBUTION OF SPECIES IN THE BREEDING PERIOD

The altitudinal distribution of Devon tetrads is graphically represented in Figure C, overleaf. If a breeding species has no altitudinal preference it will show a similar pattern to this, but deviation from this pattern would demonstrate a preference.

It should be borne in mind that it is unlikely that birds show any preference for altitude *per se*, but rather that they choose breeding sites by their environmental qualities, especially the vegetation type and structure which are themselves dependent on conditions found at particular altitudes. It is also possible that an apparent preference is forced upon birds by human activity ousting them from their preferred habitat, leaving them only in suboptimal areas. Skylarks, for example, prefer grassland or crops at low to middle altitudes and naturally occur at low densities in upland areas (see chart on page 487), but their preferred habitats have been made unsuitable by human activity so that they now appear to prefer higher altitudes.

So, for example, the Carrion Crow (see chart on page 476) shows no altitudinal preference as its pattern is not significantly different from the distribution of tetrads. This means that Carrion Crows occur in the same proportions as the tetrads, i.e. they have no preference. The Red Grouse occurs only above 300 metres, Lesser Whitethroats are coastal and lowland birds, while Curlews are birds of the middle altitudes, etc. Most of the common species appear to have little altitudinal preference or prefer middle altitudes, while coastal species are obviously confined to the lower ones.

The charts on pages 475–490 show the altitudinal distribution of species based upon the number of records at each altitude.

*Text: Mike Hounsome*
*Photo: (Golden Plover) Steve Hatch*

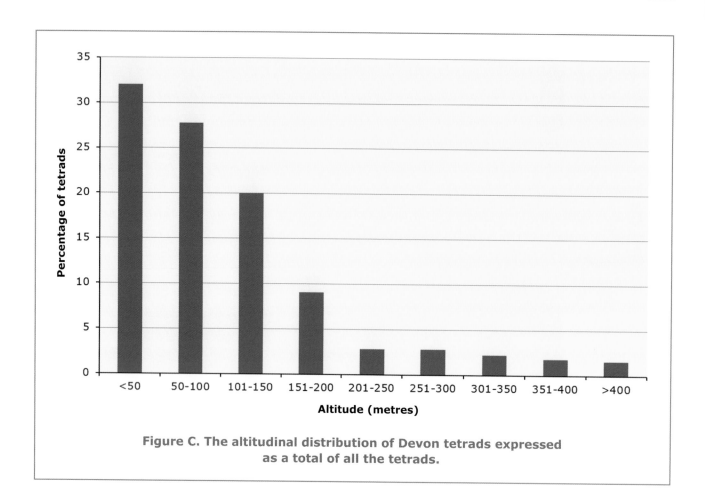

Figure C. The altitudinal distribution of Devon tetrads expressed as a total of all the tetrads.

## Table A. Species which show a significant altitudinal preference in the breeding period (significant * <0.05, very significant ** <0.01, highly significant *** <0.001, extremely significant **** <0.0001).

| | | | |
|---|---|---|---|
| Barn Owl **** | Golden Plover * | Mallard *** | Shag **** |
| Blackbird *** | Goldfinch **** | Mandarin ** | Shelduck **** |
| Blackcap **** | Grasshopper Warbler **** | Marsh Tit **** | Siskin **** |
| Blue Tit **** | Great Black-b Gull **** | Meadow Pipit **** | Skylark * |
| Bullfinch **** | Great Spotted W'pecker **** | Merlin ** | Snipe **** |
| Canada Goose *** | Great Tit **** | Mistle Thrush *** | Song Thrush **** |
| Cetti's Warbler **** | Green Woodpecker **** | Moorhen **** | Sparrowhawk ** |
| Chaffinch * | Greenfinch **** | Mute Swan **** | Spotted Flycatcher *** |
| Chiffchaff **** | Grey Heron ** | Nightjar *** | Starling **** |
| Cirl Bunting **** | Herring Gull **** | Oystercatcher **** | Stock Dove **** |
| Collared Dove **** | Hobby ** | Peregrine **** | Stonechat **** |
| Common Crossbill **** | House Martin **** | Pheasant **** | Swallow ** |
| Coot ** | House Sparrow **** | Pied Flycatcher **** | Swift **** |
| Cormorant **** | Jackdaw **** | Raven ** | Tawny Owl * |
| Cuckoo **** | Jay *** | Red Grouse **** | Teal **** |
| Curlew ** | Kestrel **** | Red-backed Shrike * | Tree Pipit **** |
| Dartford Warbler **** | Kingfisher **** | Red-b Merganser * | Treecreeper **** |
| Dipper *** | Lesser Black-b Gull **** | Reed Bunting **** | Tufted Duck ** |
| Dunlin **** | Lesser Redpoll **** | Reed Warbler **** | Water Rail **** |
| Egyptian Goose ** | Lesser Whitethroat **** | Ring Ouzel **** | Whinchat **** |
| Feral Pigeon **** | Linnet *** | Robin *** | Willow Tit *** |
| Fulmar **** | Little Egret **** | Rock Pipit **** | Willow Warbler **** |
| Gadwall **** | Long-eared Owl ** | Rook **** | Wood Warbler **** |
| Garden Warbler **** | Long-tailed Tit **** | Sand Martin ** | Woodpigeon **** |
| Goldcrest *** | Magpie **** | Sedge Warbler **** | Yellowhammer **** |

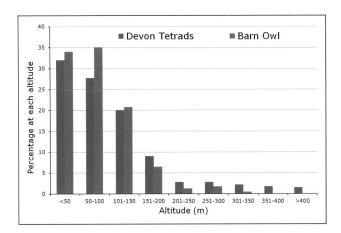

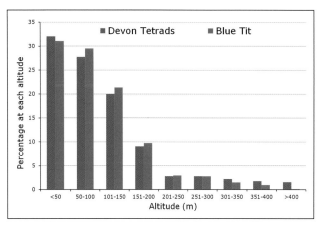

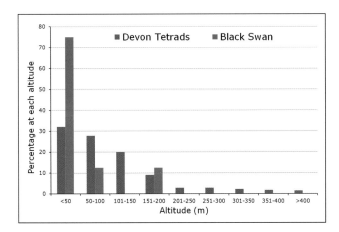

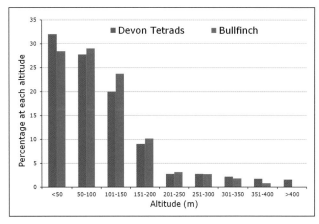

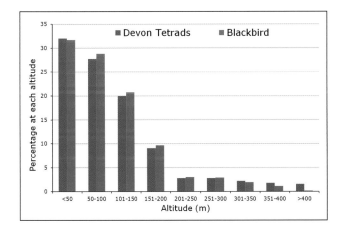

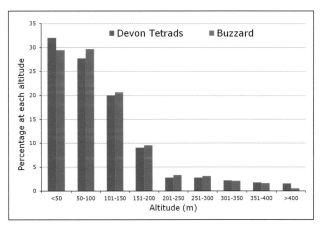

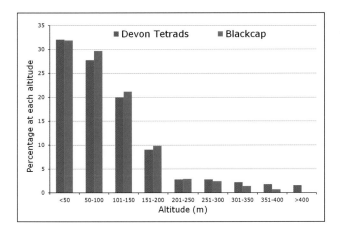

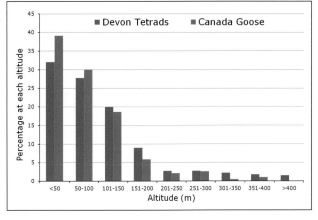

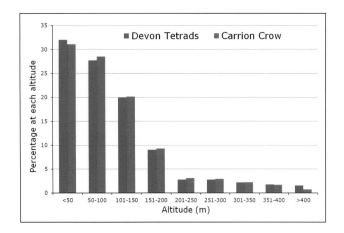

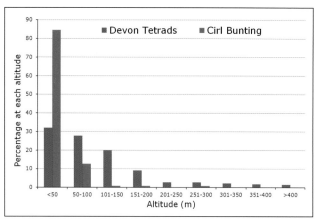

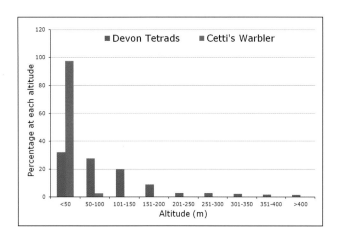

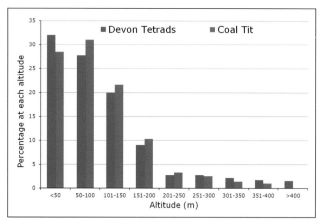

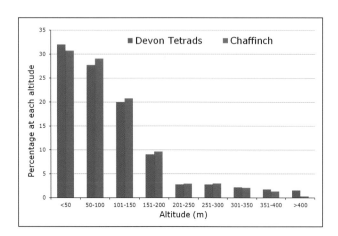

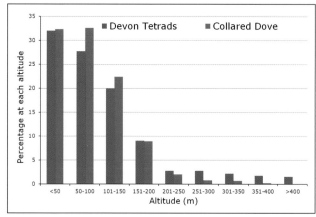

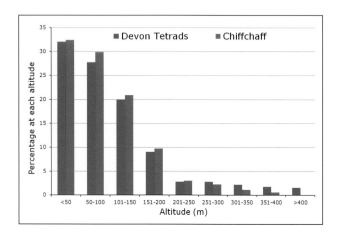

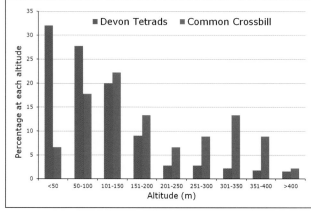

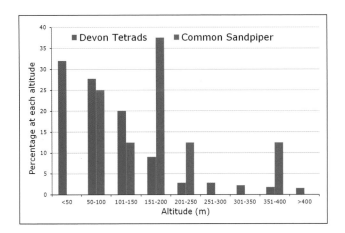

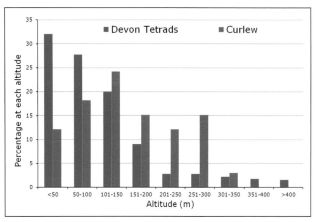

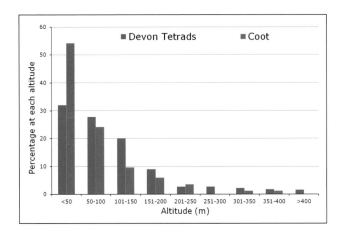

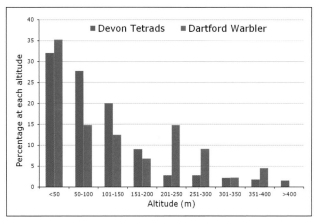

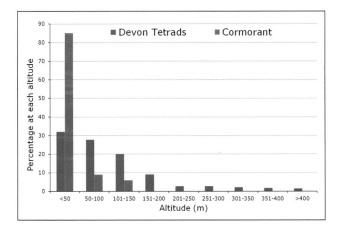

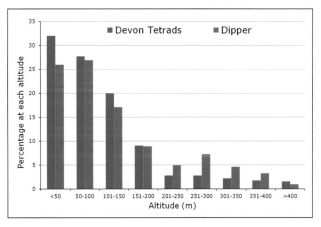

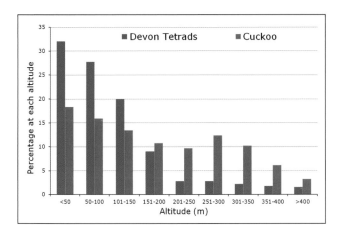

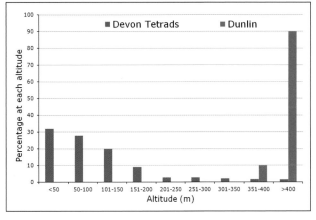

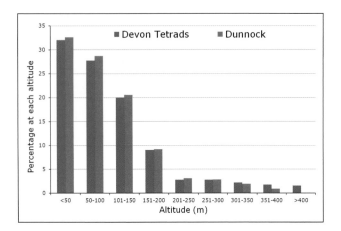

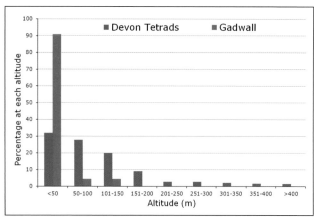

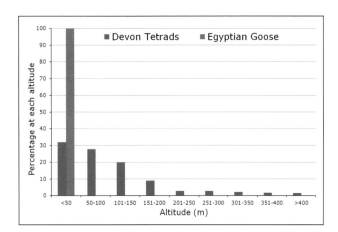

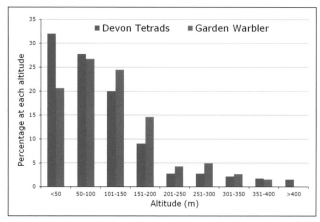

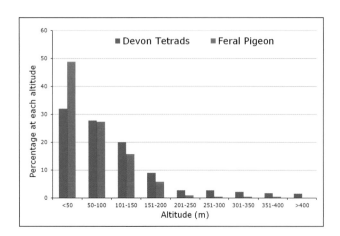

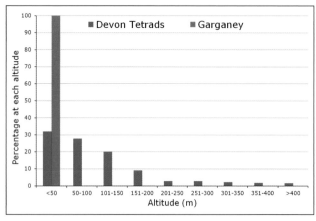

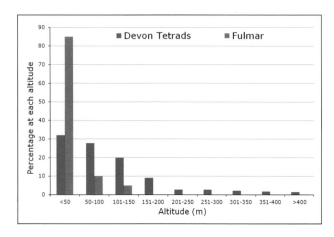

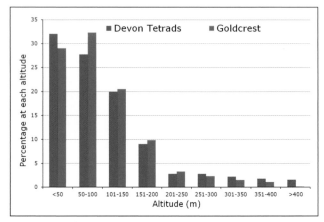

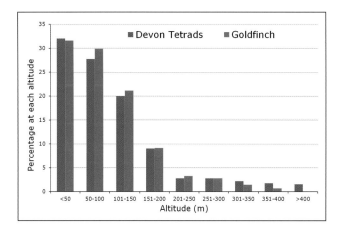

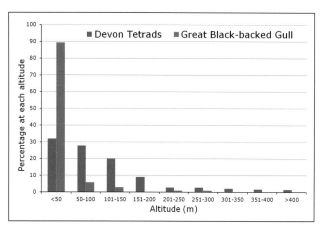

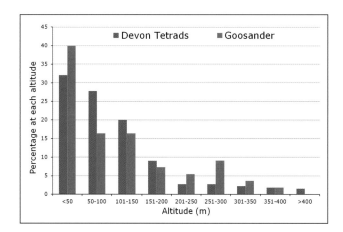

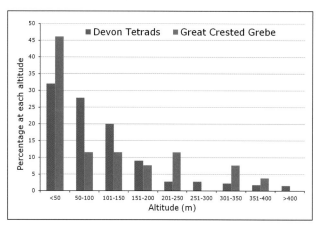

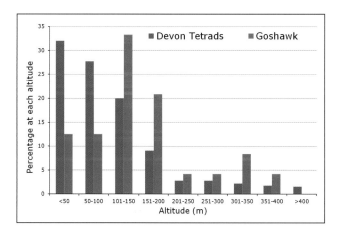

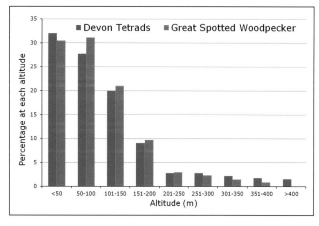

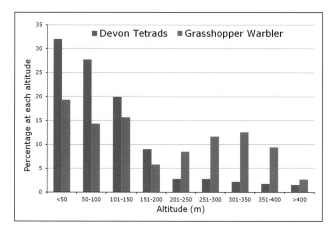

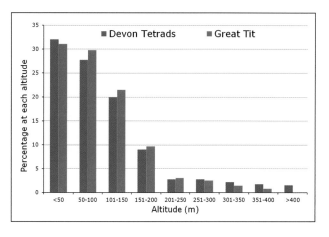

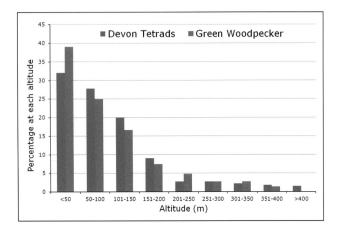

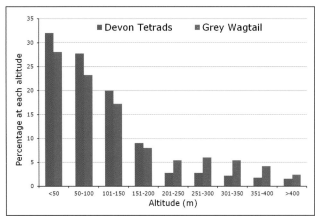

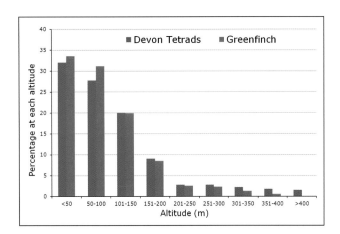

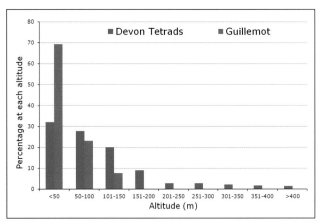

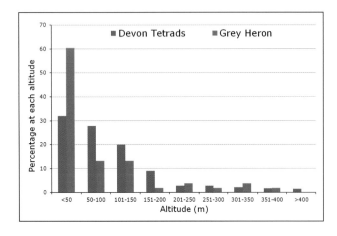

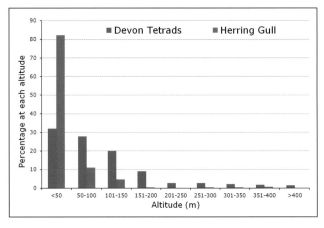

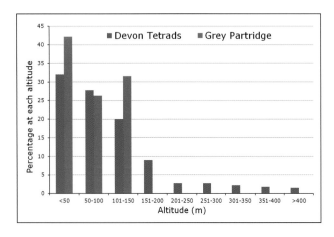

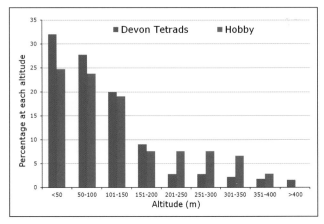

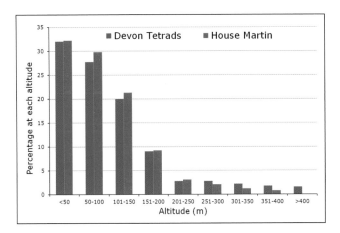

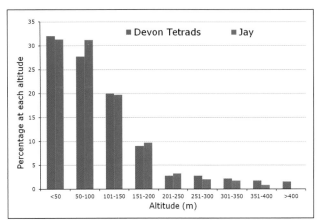

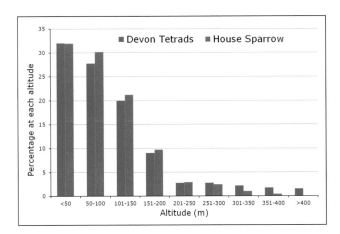

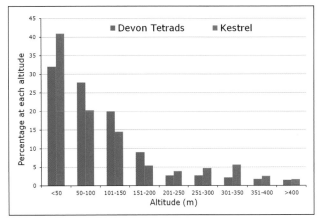

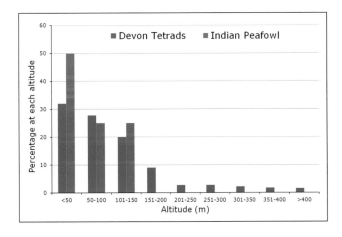

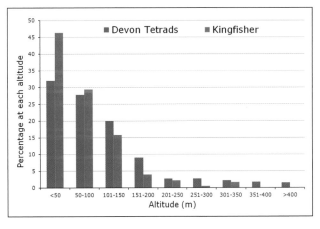

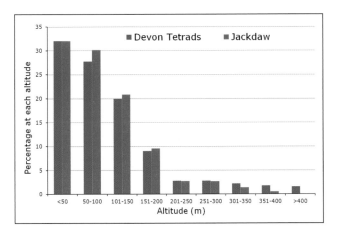

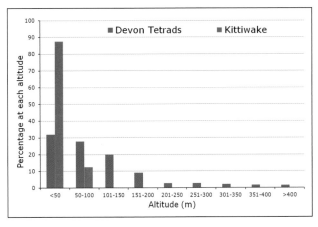

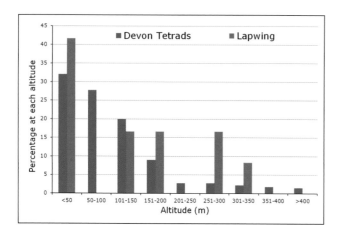

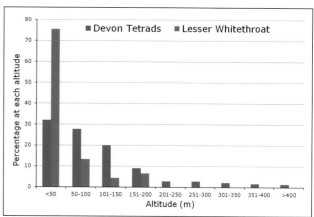

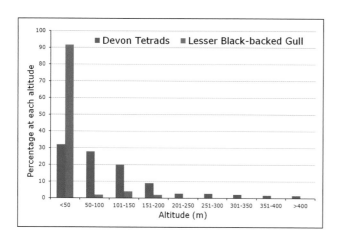

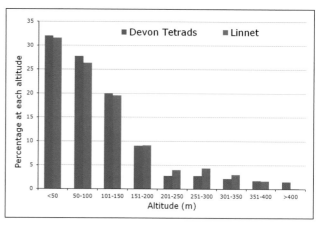

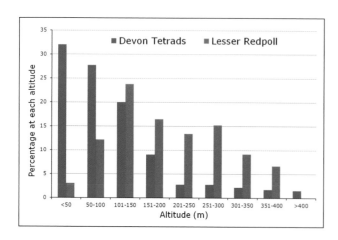

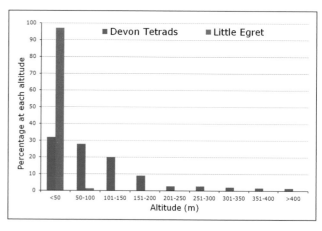

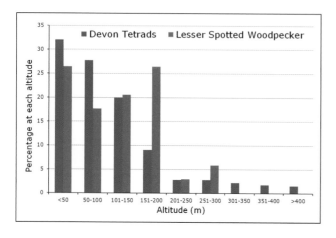

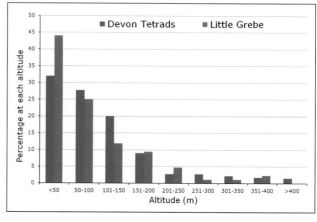

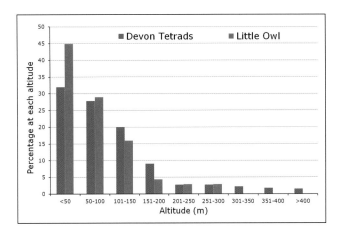

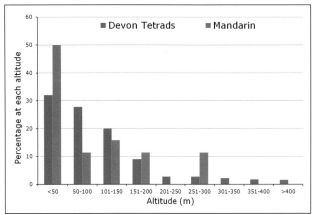

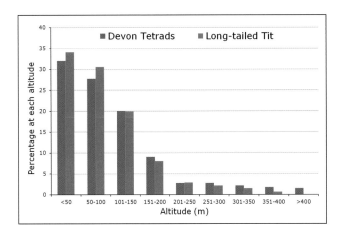

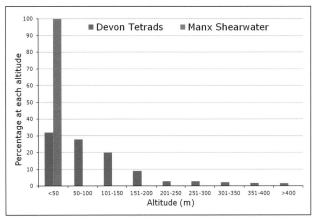

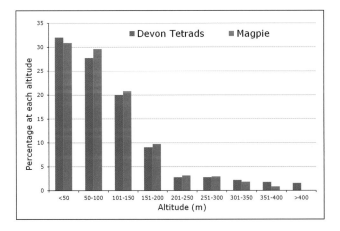

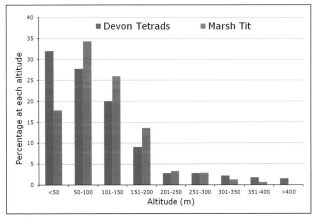

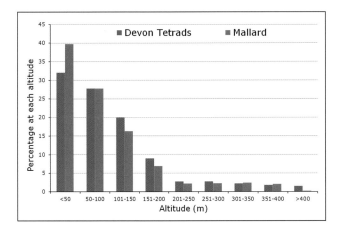

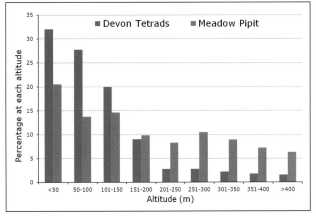

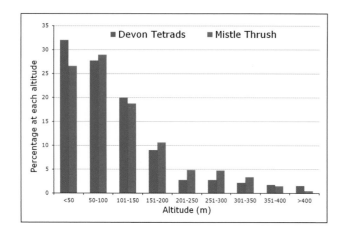

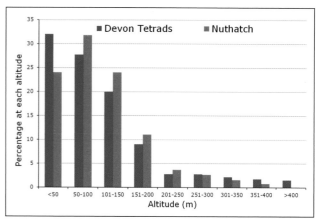

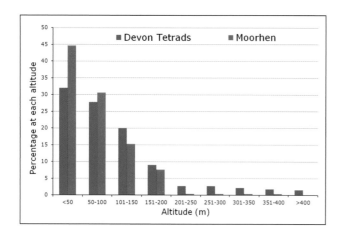

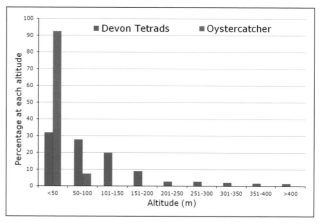

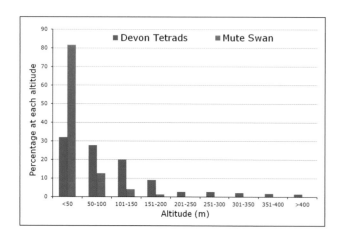

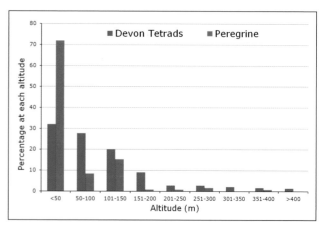

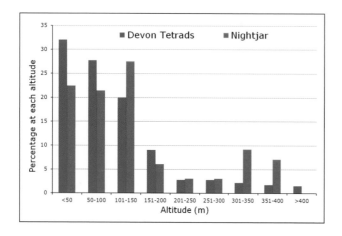

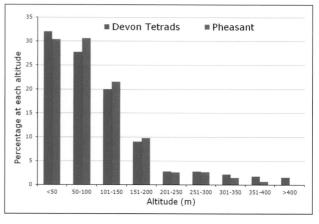

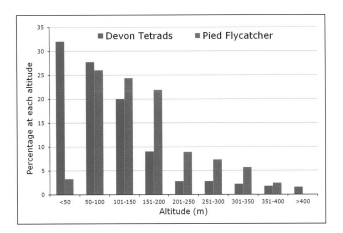

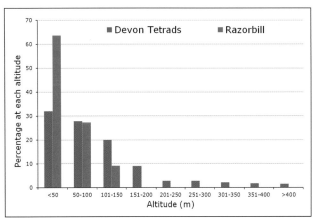

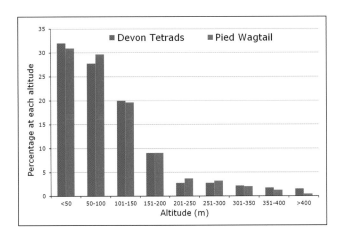

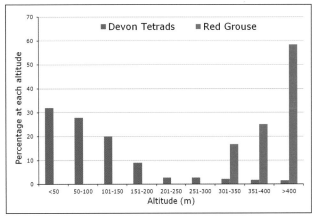

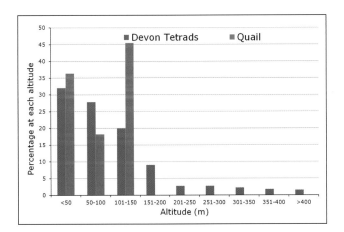

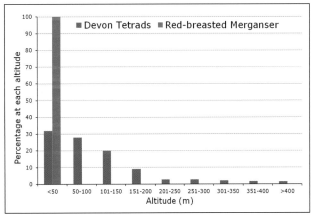

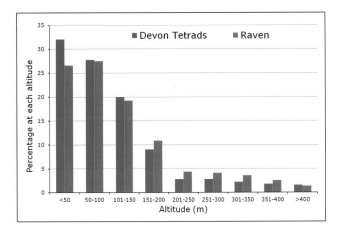

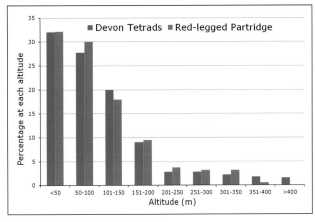

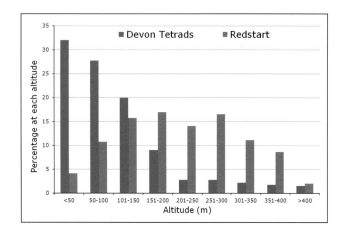

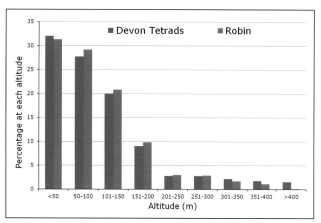

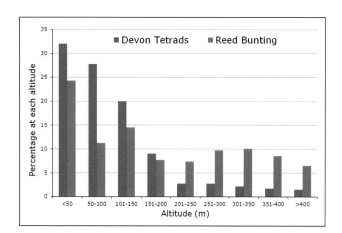

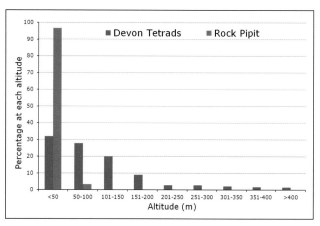

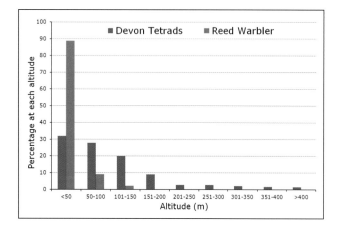

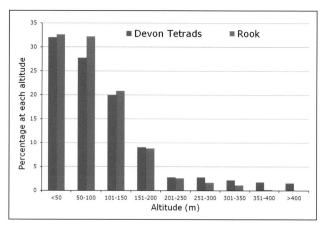

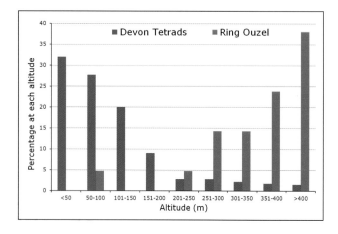

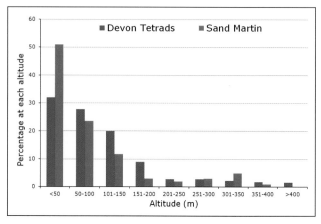

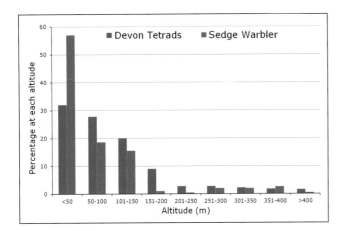

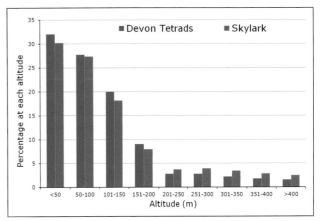

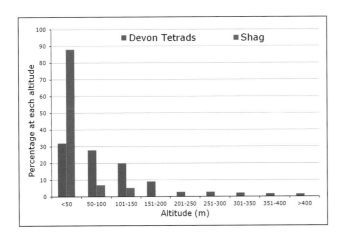

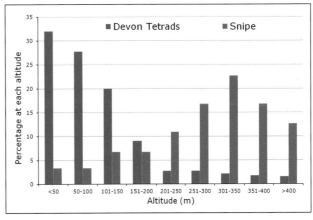

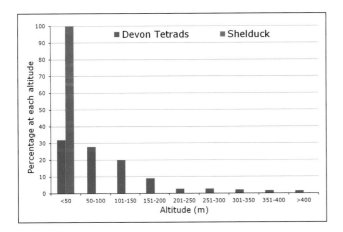

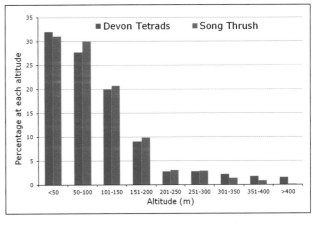

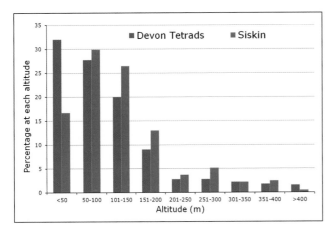

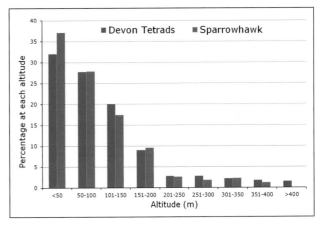

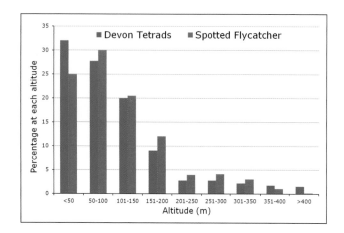

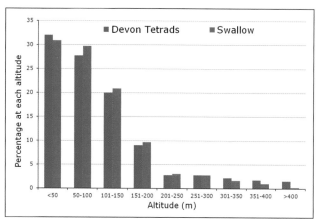

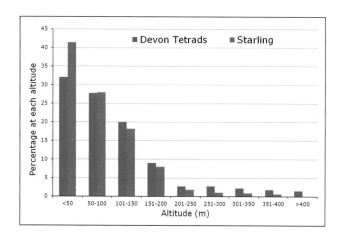

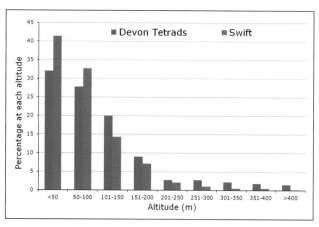

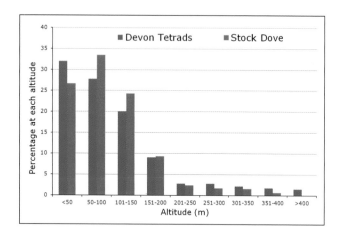

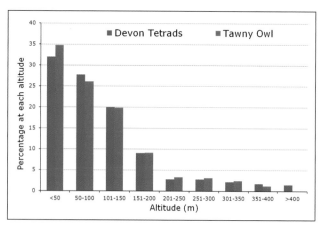

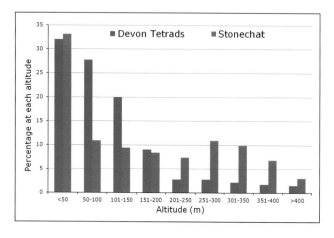

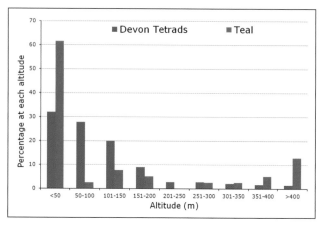

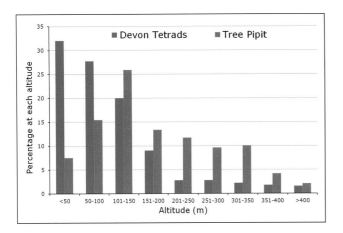

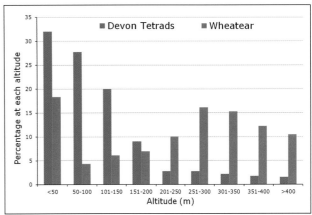

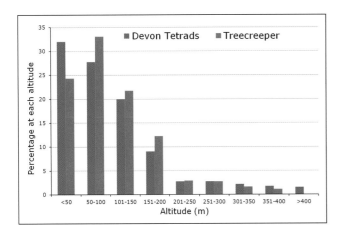

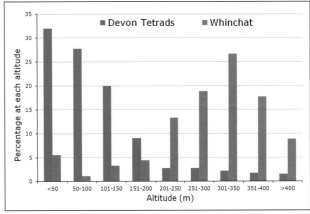

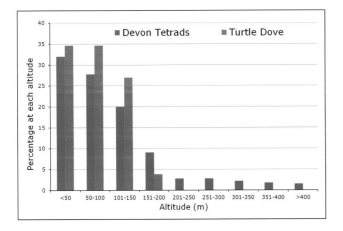

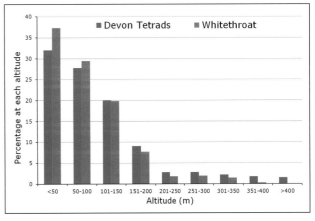

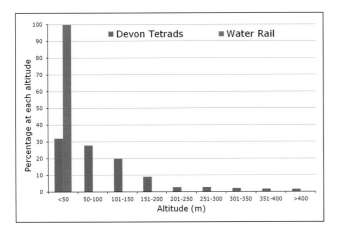

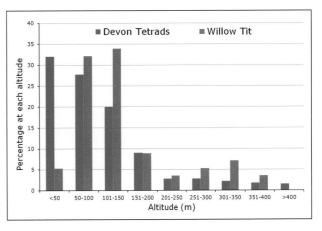

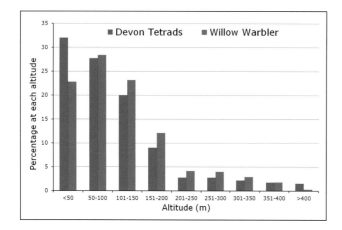

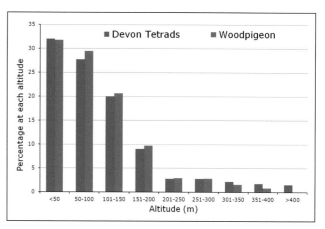

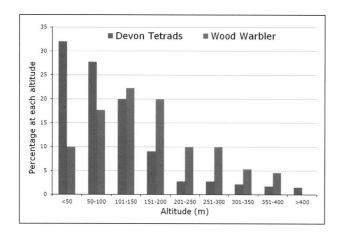

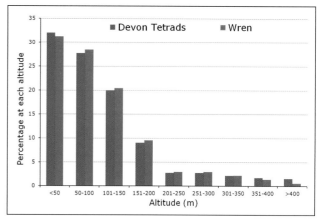

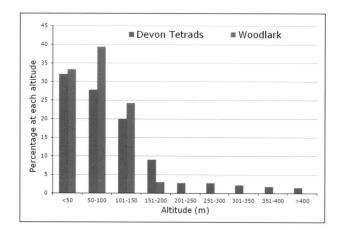

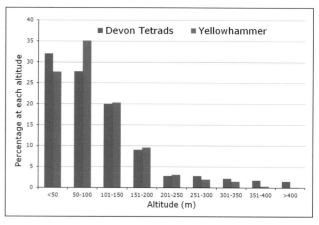

Photo: (Yellowhammer) Gary Thoburn

# Appendix 5

# Climate data 2007–2013

The data in Tables A–C were extracted from the Meteorological Office website (www.metoffice.gov.uk) and show the monthly mean values for **temperature** (Table A), **sunshine** and **air frost** (Table B) and **rainfall** (Table C) for the years 2007 to 2013 in the 'England SW and S Wales Region'. The deviations from the 1961–1990 averages are shown in the 'deviation' columns, thus positive figures mean results that are higher than that 30-year average and negative lower. *Photo: (Woodcock) Ernie Janes/NPL*

| Table A. Temperature | | | | | | | |
|---|---|---|---|---|---|---|---|
| **Year** | **Month** | **Maximum temp °C** | | **Minimum temp °C** | | **Mean temp °C** | |
| | | **Actual** | **Deviation** | **Actual** | **Deviation** | **Actual** | **Deviation** |
| 2007 | January | 9.6 | 2.8 | 4.5 | 3.0 | 7.0 | 2.9 |
| | February | 9.3 | 2.4 | 3.6 | 2.3 | 6.4 | 2.4 |
| | March | 10.9 | 2.0 | 3.3 | 1.0 | 7.1 | 1.5 |
| | April | 16.5 | 5.0 | 5.9 | 2.3 | 11.2 | 3.6 |
| | May | 15.9 | 1.2 | 7.7 | 1.3 | 11.8 | 1.3 |
| | June | 18.5 | 0.9 | 11.0 | 1.7 | 14.7 | 1.3 |
| | July | 18.1 | -1.3 | 11.2 | 0.0 | 14.6 | -0.7 |
| | August | 19.4 | 0.3 | 10.8 | -0.2 | 15.1 | 0.0 |
| | September | 17.7 | 0.7 | 9.7 | 0.3 | 13.7 | 0.5 |
| | October | 14.5 | 0.8 | 7.7 | 0.4 | 11.1 | 0.6 |
| | November | 11.0 | 1.2 | 4.7 | 0.8 | 7.8 | 1.0 |
| | December | 8.6 | 0.7 | 2.9 | 0.5 | 5.7 | 0.6 |
| 2008 | January | 9.5 | 2.7 | 4.0 | 2.5 | 6.7 | 2.6 |
| | February | 9.7 | 2.8 | 2.1 | 0.8 | 5.9 | 1.8 |
| | March | 9.5 | 0.6 | 3.1 | 0.8 | 6.3 | 0.7 |
| | April | 11.9 | 0.4 | 3.9 | 0.2 | 7.8 | 0.3 |
| | May | 17.5 | 2.8 | 8.9 | 2.5 | 13.2 | 2.7 |
| | June | 17.8 | 0.2 | 9.4 | 0.2 | 13.6 | 0.2 |
| | July | 19.3 | -0.2 | 11.7 | 0.5 | 15.5 | 0.2 |
| | August | 18.4 | -0.7 | 12.4 | 1.4 | 15.4 | 0.3 |
| | September | 16.9 | 0.0 | 9.2 | -0.2 | 13.1 | -0.1 |
| | October | 13.3 | -0.4 | 6.5 | -0.8 | 9.9 | -0.6 |
| | November | 10.1 | 0.3 | 5.0 | 1.0 | 7.5 | 0.6 |
| | December | 7.0 | -0.8 | 1.1 | -1.3 | 4.0 | -1.1 |

| Table A. Temperature, continued | | | | | | | |
|---|---|---|---|---|---|---|---|
| Year | Month | Maximum temp ºC | | Minimum temp ºC | | Mean temp ºC | |
| | | Actual | Deviation | Actual | Deviation | Actual | Deviation |
| 2009 | January | 6.4 | -0.4 | 0.4 | -1.1 | 3.4 | -0.8 |
| | February | 7.1 | 0.3 | 1.6 | 0.4 | 4.3 | 0.3 |
| | March | 10.6 | 1.7 | 2.9 | 0.5 | 6.8 | 1.1 |
| | April | 13.3 | 1.9 | 4.9 | 1.3 | 9.1 | 1.6 |
| | May | 15.5 | 0.8 | 7.3 | 0.9 | 11.4 | 0.8 |
| | June | 19.3 | 1.7 | 10.1 | 0.8 | 14.7 | 1.3 |
| | July | 18.9 | -0.6 | 12.1 | 0.9 | 15.5 | 0.2 |
| | August | 19.3 | 0.1 | 12.1 | 1.1 | 15.7 | 0.6 |
| | September | 17.6 | 0.7 | 9.7 | 0.3 | 13.7 | 0.5 |
| | October | 15.1 | 1.3 | 8.3 | 1.0 | 11.7 | 1.2 |
| | November | 11.4 | 1.6 | 6.3 | 2.4 | 8.8 | 2.0 |
| | December | 6.6 | -1.2 | 0.8 | -1.6 | 3.7 | -1.4 |
| 2010 | January | 4.8 | -2.1 | -1.2 | -2.7 | 1.8 | -2.4 |
| | February | 6.4 | -0.4 | 0.6 | -0.7 | 3.5 | -0.6 |
| | March | 9.5 | 0.5 | 1.8 | -0.5 | 5.7 | 0.0 |
| | April | 13.4 | 2.0 | 3.8 | 0.1 | 8.6 | 1.0 |
| | May | 15.3 | 0.6 | 6.1 | -0.3 | 10.7 | 0.2 |
| | June | 19.9 | 2.3 | 9.7 | 0.5 | 14.8 | 1.4 |
| | July | 20.0 | 0.6 | 12.5 | 1.3 | 16.2 | 0.9 |
| | August | 18.9 | -0.2 | 11.1 | 0.0 | 15.0 | -0.1 |
| | September | 17.4 | 0.5 | 9.8 | 0.4 | 13.6 | 0.4 |
| | October | 14.1 | 0.4 | 6.8 | -0.5 | 10.4 | -0.1 |
| | November | 8.7 | -1.1 | 2.7 | -1.3 | 5.7 | -1.2 |
| | December | 3.7 | -4.1 | -3.0 | -5.4 | 0.3 | -4.8 |
| 2011 | January | 6.6 | -0.2 | 1.1 | -0.4 | 3.9 | -0.3 |
| | February | 9.4 | 2.6 | 4.0 | 2.7 | 6.7 | 2.6 |
| | March | 11.0 | 2.1 | 2.6 | 0.3 | 6.8 | 1.2 |
| | April | 16.5 | 5.0 | 6.6 | 3.0 | 11.5 | 4.0 |
| | May | 15.5 | 0.9 | 7.8 | 1.4 | 11.6 | 1.1 |
| | June | 17.5 | -0.1 | 9.2 | 0.0 | 13.3 | -0.1 |
| | July | 19.1 | -0.3 | 10.6 | -0.5 | 14.9 | -0.4 |
| | August | 18.6 | -0.6 | 11.0 | -0.1 | 14.8 | -0.3 |
| | September | 18.0 | 1.1 | 11.2 | 1.8 | 14.6 | 1.5 |
| | October | 15.6 | 1.9 | 9.1 | 1.9 | 12.4 | 1.9 |
| | November | 12.6 | 2.8 | 7.3 | 3.3 | 9.9 | 3.1 |
| | December | 9.3 | 1.4 | 4.1 | 1.6 | 6.7 | 1.5 |

| Year | Month | Maximum temp ºC | | Minimum temp ºC | | Mean temp ºC | |
|------|-------|--------|-----------|--------|-----------|--------|-----------|
| | | Actual | Deviation | Actual | Deviation | Actual | Deviation |
| 2012 | January | 8.8 | 1.9 | 3.5 | 2.0 | 6.1 | 2.0 |
| | February | 7.5 | 0.7 | 1.4 | 0.1 | 4.4 | 0.4 |
| | March | 12.5 | 3.6 | 4.2 | 1.8 | 8.3 | 2.7 |
| | April | 11.1 | -0.4 | 3.3 | -0.3 | 7.2 | -0.4 |
| | May | 16.0 | 1.3 | 7.2 | 0.8 | 11.6 | 1.0 |
| | June | 16.6 | -1.0 | 10.2 | 1.0 | 13.4 | 0.0 |
| | July | 18.5 | -0.9 | 11.0 | -0.1 | 14.8 | -0.5 |
| | August | 19.5 | 0.3 | 12.7 | 1.7 | 16.1 | 1.0 |
| | September | 16.7 | -0.3 | 8.9 | -0.5 | 12.8 | -0.4 |
| | October | 13.1 | -0.6 | 6.8 | -0.4 | 10.0 | -0.5 |
| | November | 9.9 | 0.1 | 3.8 | -0.1 | 6.8 | 0.0 |
| | December | 8.7 | 0.8 | 2.8 | 0.4 | 5.7 | 0.6 |
| 2013 | January | 6.9 | 0.0 | 2.3 | 0.7 | 4.6 | 0.4 |
| | February | 6.3 | -0.5 | 0.9 | -0.4 | 3.6 | -0.5 |
| | March | 6.4 | -2.5 | 0.2 | -2.1 | 3.3 | -2.3 |
| | April | 10.8 | -0.7 | 3.1 | -0.5 | 6.9 | -0.6 |
| | May | 14.1 | -0.6 | 5.6 | -0.8 | 9.8 | -0.7 |
| | June | 17.6 | -0.1 | 9.4 | 0.2 | 13.5 | 0.0 |
| | July | 23.0 | 3.6 | 12.6 | 1.4 | 17.8 | 2.5 |
| | August | 20.4 | 1.2 | 12.2 | 1.1 | 16.3 | 1.2 |
| | September | 17.7 | 0.8 | 10.2 | 0.8 | 13.9 | 0.8 |
| | October | 15.4 | 1.6 | 9.7 | 2.5 | 12.6 | 2.1 |
| | November | 9.9 | 0.1 | 3.7 | -0.2 | 6.8 | 0.0 |
| | December | 9.7 | 1.9 | 3.6 | 1.1 | 6.6 | 1.5 |

Table A. Temperature, continued

Photo: (Black-winged Stilts) Steve Hatch

| Table B. Sunshine hours and Air frost | | | | | |
|---|---|---|---|---|---|
| Year | Month | Sunshine hours | | Air frost | |
| | | Actual | Deviation | Actual | Deviation |
| 2007 | January | 51.6 | 2.5 | 3.9 | -6.2 |
| | February | 69.8 | 2.0 | 4.8 | -5.3 |
| | March | 161.1 | 51.5 | 3.2 | -4.0 |
| | April | 221.0 | 62.0 | 0.9 | -2.9 |
| | May | 189.5 | -1.9 | 0.4 | -0.5 |
| | June | 143.2 | -45.2 | 0.0 | 0.0 |
| | July | 180.3 | -13.6 | 0.0 | 0.0 |
| | August | 210.8 | 33.7 | 0.0 | 0.0 |
| | September | 150.4 | 13.7 | 0.0 | 0.0 |
| | October | 111.2 | 17.0 | 0.7 | -0.2 |
| | November | 68.3 | 2.6 | 4.2 | -0.7 |
| | December | 54.3 | 7.9 | 8.3 | 0.0 |
| 2008 | January | 41.7 | -7.4 | 2.6 | -7.5 |
| | February | 113.2 | 45.4 | 7.9 | -2.2 |
| | March | 122.6 | 13.1 | 3.8 | -3.4 |
| | April | 185.7 | 27.0 | 5.0 | 1.3 |
| | May | 184.2 | -7.7 | 0.1 | -0.7 |
| | June | 219.6 | 30.3 | 0.0 | 0.0 |
| | July | 169.3 | -25.3 | 0.0 | 0.0 |
| | August | 101.2 | -76.3 | 0.0 | 0.0 |
| | September | 132.5 | -4.1 | 0.0 | 0.0 |
| | October | 113.5 | 19.7 | 1.4 | 0.6 |
| | November | 57.0 | -9.3 | 2.7 | -2.2 |
| | December | 73.9 | 27.7 | 13.0 | 4.7 |
| 2009 | January | 61.7 | 12.7 | 13.8 | 3.7 |
| | February | 54.1 | -13.5 | 9.4 | -0.7 |
| | March | 155.9 | 46.1 | 5.2 | -2.1 |
| | April | 172.2 | 12.8 | 1.3 | -2.5 |
| | May | 204.5 | 13.4 | 0.1 | -0.7 |
| | June | 215.7 | 26.5 | 0.0 | 0.0 |
| | July | 157.7 | -37.0 | 0.0 | 0.0 |
| | August | 153.4 | -22.9 | 0.0 | 0.0 |
| | September | 156.3 | 20.4 | 0.0 | 0.0 |
| | October | 91.1 | -2.8 | 0.5 | -0.3 |
| | November | 60.0 | -5.9 | 0.4 | -4.5 |
| | December | 62.7 | 16.6 | 11.3 | 3.1 |
| 2010 | January | 72.7 | 23.6 | 18.2 | 8.1 |
| | February | 75.1 | 6.8 | 11.3 | 1.2 |
| | March | 132.4 | 22.1 | 10.4 | 3.2 |
| | April | 217.2 | 57.5 | 2.9 | -0.9 |
| | May | 207.0 | 15.3 | 1.5 | 0.6 |
| | June | 262.1 | 73.5 | 0.0 | 0.0 |

| | | Sunshine hours | | Air frost | |
|---|---|---|---|---|---|
| Year | Month | Actual | Deviation | Actual | Deviation |
| 2010 | July | 145.7 | -48.6 | 0.0 | 0.0 |
| | August | 150.5 | -26.6 | 0.0 | 0.0 |
| | September | 144.4 | 8.2 | 0.0 | 0.0 |
| | October | 128.8 | 34.8 | 2.2 | 1.4 |
| | November | 75.7 | 9.9 | 8.5 | 3.6 |
| | December | 60.3 | 13.9 | 22.8 | 14.5 |
| 2011 | January | 58.3 | 9.3 | 13.2 | 3.2 |
| | February | 52.9 | -14.9 | 3.3 | -6.8 |
| | March | 154.9 | 45.0 | 7.9 | 0.7 |
| | April | 219.1 | 60.3 | 0.3 | -3.5 |
| | May | 178.9 | -13.5 | 0.2 | -0.7 |
| | June | 197.3 | 9.4 | 0.1 | 0.0 |
| | July | 174.8 | -19.4 | 0.0 | 0.0 |
| | August | 140.8 | -37.4 | 0.0 | 0.0 |
| | September | 130.5 | -5.4 | 0.0 | -0.1 |
| | October | 96.7 | 2.8 | 0.3 | -0.6 |
| | November | 63.3 | -2.6 | 0.7 | -4.2 |
| | December | 35.9 | -10.1 | 3.1 | -5.2 |
| 2012 | January | 59.1 | 9.9 | 5.8 | -4.3 |
| | February | 69.1 | 1.4 | 11.6 | 1.5 |
| | March | 167.9 | 58.2 | 2.1 | -5.2 |
| | April | 140.2 | -19.1 | 3.8 | 0.0 |
| | May | 210.0 | 19.1 | 0.5 | -0.3 |
| | June | 110.8 | -77.0 | 0.0 | 0.0 |
| | July | 167.4 | -25.0 | 0.0 | 0.0 |
| | August | 145.7 | -32.0 | 0.0 | 0.0 |
| | September | 145.2 | 8.2 | 0.1 | -0.1 |
| | October | 92.1 | -1.9 | 1.3 | 0.5 |
| | November | 64.7 | -1.3 | 3.9 | -1.0 |
| | December | 54.0 | 7.8 | 7.7 | -0.6 |
| 2013 | January | 45.7 | -3.4 | 10.3 | 0.2 |
| | February | 68.9 | 0.7 | 10.3 | 0.2 |
| | March | 95.0 | -15.5 | 15.7 | 8.4 |
| | April | 163.3 | 4.8 | 6.9 | 3.1 |
| | May | 209.2 | 17.3 | 0.9 | 0.0 |
| | June | 199.0 | 9.5 | 0.0 | -0.1 |
| | July | 302.9 | 110.0 | 0.0 | 0.0 |
| | August | 178.6 | 1.8 | 0.0 | 0.0 |
| | September | 111.2 | -24.4 | 0.0 | -0.1 |
| | October | 91.7 | -1.9 | 0.1 | -0.7 |
| | November | 72.8 | 6.6 | 4.6 | -0.3 |
| | December | 46.2 | 0.0 | 3.3 | -5.0 |

Table B. Sunshine hours and Air frost, continued

| | | Rainfall mm | | Days rain >=1 mm | |
|---|---|---|---|---|---|
| **Year** | **Month** | **Actual** | **Deviation** | **Actual** | **Deviation** |
| 2007 | January | 151.3 | 15.0 | 3.9 | -6.2 |
| | February | 167.6 | 70.2 | 4.8 | -5.3 |
| | March | 97.0 | -3.0 | 3.2 | -4.0 |
| | April | 19.0 | -54.1 | 0.9 | -2.9 |
| | May | 138.1 | 61.4 | 0.4 | -0.5 |
| | June | 146.7 | 74.1 | 0.0 | 0.0 |
| | July | 165.1 | 93.3 | 0.0 | 0.0 |
| | August | 77.0 | -14.7 | 0.0 | 0.0 |
| | September | 60.0 | -41.7 | 0.0 | 0.0 |
| | October | 54.4 | -69.2 | 0.7 | -0.2 |
| | November | 90.4 | -36.9 | 4.2 | -0.7 |
| | December | 153.6 | 11.4 | 8.3 | 0.0 |
| 2008 | January | 181.3 | 45.0 | 2.6 | -7.5 |
| | February | 60.4 | -37.0 | 7.9 | -2.2 |
| | March | 132.9 | 33.0 | 3.8 | -3.4 |
| | April | 72.2 | -0.7 | 5.0 | 1.3 |
| | May | 93.2 | 16.8 | 0.1 | -0.7 |
| | June | 61.4 | -10.8 | 0.0 | 0.0 |
| | July | 158.3 | 86.7 | 0.0 | 0.0 |
| | August | 167.1 | 75.3 | 0.0 | 0.0 |
| | September | 125.4 | 24.3 | 0.0 | 0.0 |
| | October | 155.4 | 33.0 | 1.4 | 0.6 |
| | November | 107.4 | -20.5 | 2.7 | -2.2 |
| | December | 86.2 | -55.1 | 13.0 | 4.7 |
| 2009 | January | 154.9 | 19.0 | 13.8 | 3.7 |
| | February | 61.1 | -35.9 | 9.4 | -0.7 |
| | March | 62.7 | -36.8 | 5.2 | -2.1 |
| | April | 74.1 | 1.5 | 1.3 | -2.5 |
| | May | 71.8 | -4.6 | 0.1 | -0.7 |
| | June | 63.4 | -9.5 | 0.0 | 0.0 |
| | July | 219.8 | 148.2 | 0.0 | 0.0 |
| | August | 76.8 | -14.6 | 0.0 | 0.0 |
| | September | 42.1 | -60.6 | 0.0 | 0.0 |
| | October | 117.3 | -4.9 | 0.5 | -0.3 |
| | November | 260.4 | 132.1 | 0.4 | -4.5 |
| | December | 137.5 | -4.3 | 11.3 | 3.1 |
| 2010 | January | 97.9 | -38.1 | 18.2 | 8.1 |
| | February | 78.4 | -19.6 | 11.3 | 1.2 |
| | March | 91.1 | -9.0 | 10.4 | 3.2 |
| | April | 39.6 | -33.7 | 2.9 | -0.9 |
| | May | 45.5 | -31.6 | 1.5 | 0.6 |
| | June | 34.5 | -37.4 | 0.0 | 0.0 |

Table C. Rainfall and Days rain

| | | Rainfall mm | | Days rain >=1 mm | |
|---|---|---|---|---|---|
| Year | Month | Actual | Deviation | Actual | Deviation |
| 2010 | July | 145.7 | -48.6 | 0.0 | 0.0 |
| | August | 150.5 | -26.6 | 0.0 | 0.0 |
| | September | 144.4 | 8.2 | 0.0 | 0.0 |
| | October | 128.8 | 34.8 | 2.2 | 1.4 |
| | November | 75.7 | 9.9 | 8.5 | 3.6 |
| | December | 60.3 | 13.9 | 22.8 | 14.5 |
| 2011 | January | 58.3 | 9.3 | 13.2 | 3.2 |
| | February | 52.9 | -14.9 | 3.3 | -6.8 |
| | March | 154.9 | 45.0 | 7.9 | 0.7 |
| | April | 219.1 | 60.3 | 0.3 | -3.5 |
| | May | 178.9 | -13.5 | 0.2 | -0.7 |
| | June | 197.3 | 9.4 | 0.1 | 0.0 |
| | July | 174.8 | -19.4 | 0.0 | 0.0 |
| | August | 140.8 | -37.4 | 0.0 | 0.0 |
| | September | 130.5 | -5.4 | 0.0 | -0.1 |
| | October | 96.7 | 2.8 | 0.3 | -0.6 |
| | November | 63.3 | -2.6 | 0.7 | -4.2 |
| | December | 35.9 | -10.1 | 3.1 | -5.2 |
| 2012 | January | 59.1 | 9.9 | 5.8 | -4.3 |
| | February | 69.1 | 1.4 | 11.6 | 1.5 |
| | March | 167.9 | 58.2 | 2.1 | -5.2 |
| | April | 140.2 | -19.1 | 3.8 | 0.0 |
| | May | 210.0 | 19.1 | 0.5 | -0.3 |
| | June | 110.8 | -77.0 | 0.0 | 0.0 |
| | July | 167.4 | -25.0 | 0.0 | 0.0 |
| | August | 145.7 | -32.0 | 0.0 | 0.0 |
| | September | 145.2 | 8.2 | 0.1 | -0.1 |
| | October | 92.1 | -1.9 | 1.3 | 0.5 |
| | November | 64.7 | -1.3 | 3.9 | -1.0 |
| | December | 54.0 | 7.8 | 7.7 | -0.6 |
| 2013 | January | 45.7 | -3.4 | 10.3 | 0.2 |
| | February | 68.9 | 0.7 | 10.3 | 0.2 |
| | March | 95.0 | -15.5 | 15.7 | 8.4 |
| | April | 163.3 | 4.8 | 6.9 | 3.1 |
| | May | 209.2 | 17.3 | 0.9 | 0.0 |
| | June | 199.0 | 9.5 | 0.0 | -0.1 |
| | July | 302.9 | 110.0 | 0.0 | 0.0 |
| | August | 178.6 | 1.8 | 0.0 | 0.0 |
| | September | 111.2 | -24.4 | 0.0 | -0.1 |
| | October | 91.7 | -1.9 | 0.1 | -0.7 |
| | November | 72.8 | 6.6 | 4.6 | -0.3 |
| | December | 46.2 | 0.0 | 3.3 | -5.0 |

Table C. Rainfall and Days rain, continued

# Devon List as at October 2015

The following lists all the accepted Category A, B & C species on the British List that have occurred in the county of Devon as at 31 October 2015. Subspecies recorded in the county are indented and italicised and appear under the relevant species name.

Photo: (Cormorant) Neil Bygrave

Mute Swan
Bewick's Swan
Whooper Swan
Bean Goose
   *Taiga Bean Goose* fabalis
   *Tundra Bean Goose* rossicus
Pink-footed Goose
White-fronted Goose
   *European W-f Goose* albifrons
   *Greenland W-f Goose* flavirostris
Lesser White-fronted Goose
Greylag Goose
Snow Goose
Canada Goose
Barnacle Goose
Brent Goose
   *Dark-bellied Brent Goose* bernicla
   *Pale-bellied Brent Goose* hrota
   *Black Brant* nigricans
Red-breasted Goose
Egyptian Goose
Ruddy Shelduck
Shelduck
Mandarin Duck
Wigeon
American Wigeon
Gadwall
Teal
Green-winged Teal
Mallard
Black Duck
Pintail
Garganey
Blue-winged Teal
Shoveler
Red-crested Pochard
Pochard
Ring-necked Duck
Ferruginous Duck
Tufted Duck
Scaup
Lesser Scaup
Eider

King Eider
Long-tailed Duck
Common Scoter
Surf Scoter
Velvet Scoter
Bufflehead
Goldeneye
Smew
Red-breasted Merganser
Goosander
Ruddy Duck
Quail
Red-legged Partridge
Red Grouse
Black Grouse
Grey Partridge
Pheasant
Golden Pheasant
Red-throated Diver
Black-throated Diver
Great Northern Diver
White-billed Diver
Black-browed Albatross
Fulmar
Fea's/Zino's Petrel
Cory's Shearwater
Great Shearwater
Sooty Shearwater
Manx Shearwater
Balearic Shearwater
Macaronesian Shearwater
Wilson's Petrel
Storm Petrel
Leach's Petrel
Gannet
Cormorant
   *Cormorant* carbo
   *Continental Cormorant* sinensis
Shag
Bittern
American Bittern
Little Bittern
Night-heron

Squacco Heron
Cattle Egret
Little Egret
Great White Egret
Grey Heron
Purple Heron
Black Stork
White Stork
Glossy Ibis
Spoonbill
Pied-billed Grebe
Little Grebe
Great Crested Grebe
Red-necked Grebe
Slavonian Grebe
Black-necked Grebe
Honey-buzzard
Black Kite
Red Kite
White-tailed Eagle
Short-toed Eagle
Marsh Harrier
Hen Harrier
Montagu's Harrier
Goshawk
Sparrowhawk
Buzzard
Rough-legged Buzzard
Osprey
Water Rail
Spotted Crake
Sora Rail
Little Crake
Baillon's Crake
Corncrake
Moorhen
Purple Gallinule
Coot
Crane
Little Bustard
Great Bustard
Stone-curlew
Black-winged Stilt

Avocet
Oystercatcher
American Golden Plover
Pacific Golden Plover
Golden Plover
Grey Plover
Sociable Plover
Lapwing
Little Ringed Plover
Ringed Plover
Semipalmated Plover
Killdeer
Kentish Plover
Greater Sand Plover
Dotterel
Whimbrel
Curlew
Black-tailed Godwit
Hudsonian Godwit
Bar-tailed Godwit
Turnstone
Knot
Ruff
Broad-billed Sandpiper
Curlew Sandpiper
Temminck's Stint
Sanderling
Dunlin
Purple Sandpiper
Baird's Sandpiper
Little Stint
White-rumped Sandpiper
Least Sandpiper
Buff-breasted Sandpiper
Pectoral Sandpiper
Western Sandpiper
Semipalmated Sandpiper
Wilson's Phalarope
Red-necked Phalarope
Grey Phalarope
Terek Sandpiper
Common Sandpiper
Spotted Sandpiper
Green Sandpiper
Solitary Sandpiper
Spotted Redshank
Greater Yellowlegs
Greenshank
Lesser Yellowlegs
Marsh Sandpiper
Wood Sandpiper
Redshank
Jack Snipe
Long-billed Dowitcher
Woodcock
Snipe
Great Snipe
Collared Pratincole
Cream-coloured Courser
Pomarine Skua
Arctic Skua
Long-tailed Skua

Great Skua
Puffin
Long-billed Murrelet
Black Guillemot
Ancient Murrelet
Razorbill
Little Auk
Guillemot
Sooty Tern
Bridled Tern
Little Tern
Gull-billed Tern
Caspian Tern
Whiskered Tern
Black Tern
White-winged Black Tern
Sandwich Tern
Lesser Crested Tern
Common Tern
Roseate Tern
Arctic Tern
Ivory Gull
Sabine's Gull
Kittiwake
Bonaparte's Gull
Black-headed Gull
Little Gull
Ross's Gull
Laughing Gull
Franklin's Gull
Mediterranean Gull
Audouin's Gull
Great Black-headed Gull
Common Gull
Ring-billed Gull
Lesser Black-backed Gull
    *Lesser B-b Gull* graellsii
    *Scandinavian Lesser B-b Gull*
        intermedius
Herring Gull
    *Herring Gull* argenteus
    *Scandinavian H Gull* argentatus
Yellow-legged Gull
Caspian Gull
American Herring Gull
Iceland Gull
    *Iceland Gull* glaucoides
    *Kumlien's Gull* kumlieni
Glaucous Gull
Great Black-backed Gull
Pallas's Sandgrouse
Rock Dove/Feral Pigeon
Stock Dove
Woodpigeon
Collared Dove
Turtle Dove
Great Spotted Cuckoo
Cuckoo
Black-billed Cuckoo
Yellow-billed Cuckoo
Barn Owl
Scops Owl

Snowy Owl
Little Owl
Tawny Owl
Long-eared Owl
Short-eared Owl
Nightjar
Chimney Swift
Swift
Alpine Swift
Little Swift
Hoopoe
Blue-cheeked Bee-eater
Bee-eater
Roller
Kingfisher
Wryneck
Green Woodpecker
Great Spotted Woodpecker
Lesser Spotted Woodpecker
Lesser Kestrel
Kestrel
Red-footed Falcon
Merlin
Hobby
Gyr Falcon
Peregrine
Ring-necked Parakeet
Eastern Phoebe
Red-eyed Vireo
Golden Oriole
Isabelline Shrike
Red-backed Shrike
Lesser Grey Shrike
Great Grey Shrike
Woodchat Shrike
Chough
Magpie
Jay
Nutcracker
Jackdaw
Rook
Carrion Crow
Hooded Crow
Raven
Goldcrest
Firecrest
Penduline Tit
Blue Tit
Great Tit
Crested Tit
Coal Tit
    *Coal Tit* britannicus
    *Continental Coal Tit* ater
Willow Tit
Marsh Tit
Bearded Tit
Woodlark
Skylark
Crested Lark
Shore Lark
Short-toed Lark
Bimaculated Lark

Sand Martin
Swallow
House Martin
Red-rumped Swallow
Cetti's Warbler
Long-tailed Tit
Greenish Warbler
Arctic Warbler
Pallas's Warbler
Yellow-browed Warbler
Hume's Warbler
Radde's Warbler
Dusky Warbler
Western Bonelli's Warbler
Eastern Bonelli's Warbler
Wood Warbler
Chiffchaff
 *Chiffchaff* collybita
 *'Grey Chiffchaff'* abietinus/tristis
 *Scandinavian Chiffchaff* abietinus
 *Siberian Chiffchaff* tristis
Iberian Chiffchaff
Willow Warbler
Blackcap
Garden Warbler
Barred Warbler
Lesser Whitethroat
 *Lesser Whitethroat* curruca
 *Siberian L. Whitethroat*
  halimodendri
Desert Warbler
Whitethroat
Spectacled Warbler
Dartford Warbler
Rüppell's Warbler
Subalpine Warbler
Sardinian Warbler
Grasshopper Warbler
Savi's Warbler
Booted Warbler
Icterine Warbler
Melodious Warbler
Aquatic Warbler
Sedge Warbler
Paddyfield Warbler
Blyth's Reed Warbler
Marsh Warbler
Reed Warbler
Great Reed Warbler
Waxwing
Nuthatch
Treecreeper
Wren
Starling
Rose-coloured Starling

Dipper
 *Dipper* gularis
 *Black-bellied Dipper* cinclus
White's Thrush
Swainson's Thrush
Grey-cheeked Thrush
Veery
Ring Ouzel
Blackbird
Dusky Thrush
Black-throated Thrush
Fieldfare
Song Thrush
Redwing
Mistle Thrush
American Robin
Rufous Bush Chat
Spotted Flycatcher
Robin
Thrush Nightingale
Nightingale
Bluethroat
 *Red-spotted Bluethroat* svecica
 *White-spotted Bluethroat* cyanecula
Red-flanked Bluetail
Red-breasted Flycatcher
Pied Flycatcher
Black Redstart
Redstart
Rock Thrush
Whinchat
Siberian Stonechat
Stonechat
Wheatear
 *Wheatear* oenanthe
 *Greenland Wheatear* leucorhoa
Desert Wheatear
Black-eared Wheatear
Pied Wheatear
Alpine Accentor
Dunnock
House Sparrow
Spanish Sparrow
Tree Sparrow
Yellow Wagtail
 *Yellow Wagtail* flavissima
 *Blue-headed Wagtail* flava
 *Ashy-headed Wagtail* cinereocapilla
 *Grey-headed Wagtail* thunbergii
 *Black-headed Wagtail* feldegg
Citrine Wagtail
Grey Wagtail
Pied Wagtail
 *Pied Wagtail* yarrellii
 *White Wagtail* alba

Richard's Pipit
Tawny Pipit
Olive-backed Pipit
Tree Pipit
Meadow Pipit
Red-throated Pipit
Rock Pipit
 *Rock Pipit* petrosus
 *Scandinavian Rock Pipit* littoralis
Water Pipit
Brambling
Chaffinch
Hawfinch
Common Rosefinch
Bullfinch
Trumpeter Finch
Greenfinch
Linnet
Twite
Lesser Redpoll
Common Redpoll
 *Mealy Redpoll* flammea
 *Greenland/Iceland Redpoll*
  rostrata/islandica
Two-barred Crossbill
Crossbill
Parrot Crossbill
Goldfinch
Serin
Siskin
Snow Bunting
Lapland Bunting
Rose-breasted Grosbeak
Eastern Towhee
Black-faced Bunting
Pine Bunting
Yellowhammer
Cirl Bunting
Ortolan Bunting
Rustic Bunting
Little Bunting
Yellow-breasted Bunting
Reed Bunting
Corn Bunting
Bobolink
Baltimore Oriole
Ovenbird
Black-and-white Warbler
Common Yellowthroat
Chestnut-sided Warbler
Blackpoll Warbler
Yellow-rumped Warbler

# Appendix 7

# Abbreviations and Glossary of Terms

Photo: (Swift) Paul Sterry/NPL

| | |
|---|---|
| **AHVLA** | Animal Health and Veterinary Laboratories Agency |
| **Amber listed** | Birds fulfilling at least one of the Amber-listed criteria which are: |
| | SPEC European Conservation status. Categorized as a Species of European Conservation Concern (SPEC 1, 2 or 3). |
| | Historical Decline – Recovery. Red listed for Historical Decline in a previous review but with substantial recent recovery (more than doubled in the last 25 years). |
| | Breeding Population Decline. As for red list criteria, but with moderate decline (by more than 25% but less than 50%). |
| | Non-breeding Population Decline. As for red list criteria, but with moderate decline (by more than 25% but less than 50%). |
| | Breeding Range Decline. As for red list criteria, but with moderate decline (by more than 25% but less than 50%). |
| | Rarity. UK breeding population of less than 300 pairs, or non-breeding population of less than 900 individuals. |
| | Localization. At least 50% of the UK breeding or non-breeding population found in 10 or fewer sites. |
| | International Importance. At least 20% of the European breeding or non-breeding population found in the UK. |
| **asl** | above sea level |
| **BBRC** | British Birds Rarities Committee |
| **BBS** | Breeding Bird Survey |
| **BoCC** | Birds of Conservation Concern |
| **BOU** | British Ornithologists' Union |

**British List (BOU) Categories:**

**A:** Species which have been recorded in an apparently natural state at least once since 1 January 1950.

**B:** Species which have been recorded in an apparently natural state at least once between 1 January 1800 and 31 December 1949, but have not been recorded subsequently.

**C:** Species which although introduced now derive from the resulting self-sustaining populations.

**D:** Species that would otherwise appear in Category A except that there is reasonable doubt that they have ever occurred in a natural state.

**E:** Species recorded as introductions, human-assisted transportees or escapees from captivity, and whose breeding populations (if any) are thought not to be self-sustaining.

| | |
|---|---|
| **BTO** | British Trust for Ornithology |

| | |
|---|---|
| **BWP** | Birds of the Western Palaearctic |
| **CCW** | Countryside Council for Wales (now NRW) |
| **DB** | Devon Birds |
| *DBR* | *Devon Bird Report* |
| **DBWPS** | Devon Bird Watching & Preservation Society (now Devon Birds) |
| **df** | Degrees of freedom (statistical term) |
| **G** | Test statistic for a contingency table |
| **ha** | hectare |
| **IUCN** | International Union for Conservation of Nature |
| **JNCC** | Joint Nature Conservation Committee |
| **kg** | kilogram |
| **km** | kilometre |
| **LNR** | Local Nature Reserve |
| **m** | metre |
| **masl** | metres above sea level |
| **mya** | million years ago |
| **NE** | Natural England |
| **NIEA** | Northern Ireland Environment Agency |
| **NNR** | National Nature Reserve |
| **NRW** | Natural Resources Wales |
| **P** | Probability (statistical term) |
| **PECBMS** | Pan-European Common Bird Monitoring Scheme |
| **Red listed** | Birds fulfilling at least one of the Red-listed criteria which are: |
| | IUCN Global Conservation Status. Species listed by BirdLife International as being Globally Threatened using IUCN criteria. |
| | Historical Decline. A severe decline in the UK between 1800 and 1995, without substantial recent recovery. |
| | Breeding Population Decline. Severe decline in the UK breeding population size, of more than 50%, over 25 years or the entire period used for assessments since the first BoCC review, starting in 1969 ("longer-term"). |
| | Non-breeding Population Decline. Severe decline in the UK non-breeding population size, of more than 50%, over 25 years or the longer-term. |
| | Breeding Range Decline. Severe decline in the UK range, of more than 50%, as measured by number of 10-km squares occupied by breeding birds, over 25 years or the longer term. |
| **RR** | Roving Record |
| **RSPB** | Royal Society for the Protection of Birds |
| **sq km** | square kilometre |
| **SNH** | Scottish Natural Heritage |
| **TTV** | Timed Tetrad Visit |
| **WeBS** | Wetland Bird Survey |
| **WWT** | Wildfowl & Wetlands Trust |

# Index